Indian Medicinal Plants Volume 1

a compendium of 500 species

Editors (Arya Vaidya Sala, Kottakkal)

P K WARRIER Managing Trustee

V P K NAMBIAR Consultant, Medicinal Plants

C RAMANKUTTY Assistant Physician

Illustrations

R VASUDEVAN NAIR
formerly Head, Department of Botany
Government Victoria College
Palakkad

Subject Experts

K Rajagopalan Chief Physician, Susrutha Bhavan, Kollam

V V Sivarajan Professor of Botany, University of Calicut

P R Varier formerly Chief Physician,
Kottakkal Arya Vaidya Sala, Thiruvananthapuram

S Varier formerly Chief Medical Advisor
Arya Vaidya Sala, Kottakkal

P S Varier Chief Medical Advisor
Arya Vaidya Sala, Kottakkal

Indira Balachandran Research Officer
Arya Vaidya Sala, Kottakkal

*N V K Varie*r Chief Editor 'Aryavaidyan'
Arya Vaidya Sala, Kottakkal

P Madhavikutty Chief Physician
Arya Vaidya Pharmacy, Shoranur

Indian Medicinal Plants

a compendium of 500 species

Volume 1

Vaidyaratnam P S Varier's
Arya Vaidya Sala
Kottakkal

Orient Longman

Indian Medicinal Plants Volume 1

First Published 1994

Reprinted 1994

ISBN 81 250 0301 0

Orient Longman Limited

Registered Office

3-6-272 Himayatnagar, Hyderabad 500 029 (A.P.) INDIA.

Other Offices:

Kamani Marg, Ballard Estate, Bombay 400 038
17 Chittaranjan Avenue, Calcutta 700 072
160 Anna Salai, Madras 600 002
1/24 Asaf Ali Road, New Delhi 110 002

80/1 Mahatma Gandhi Road, Bangalore 560 001
Plot No. 365, Saheed Nagar, Bhubaneswar 751 007
41/316 Gour Mohan, Ambady Lane, Chitoor Road, Cochin 682 011
S.C. Goswami Road, Panbazar, Guwahati 781 001
3-6-272 Himayatnagar, Hyderabad 500 029 (A.P.)
House No. 28/31, 15 Ashok Marg, Lucknow 226 001
City Centre Ashok, Govind Mitra Road, Patna 800 004

Phototypeset by

Venture Graphics
Chetpet, Madras 600 031.

Printed in India by offset at

Indcom Press
West Mambalam, Madras 600 033.

Published by

Orient Longman Ltd.
160 Anna Salai, Madras 600 002

Dedicated to

S. RAGHUNATHA IYER

whose research treatise forms the nucleus of this compendium

Foreword

In recent years interest in medicinal plants has increased considerably. Apart from the reliance on therapeutic values described in ancient texts and current interpretations by specialists in the field of ayurveda, laboratories in several countries have initiated analytical studies to scientifically determine the efficacy of better known medicinal plants in the treatment of diseases.

While descriptions of such plants have been available, sometimes in meticulous detail, it has not always been possible to authentically establish the identity of certain species. Some confusion has therefore prevailed and has led to a situation where the same plant might be known by different names, or where widely differing species share the same names. This has serious implications, and physicians and manufacturers of ayurvedic medicine have therefore had a critical interest in obtaining authentic descriptions of medicinal plants in currently valid taxonomic terms. They have likewise been interested in documenting the local-common names, the properties of specific parts which have medicinal value, and botanically accurate illustrations. As such a task would require the combined effort of Sanskrit scholars, systematic botanists and artists, attempts in that direction have been few and incomplete.

The late S Raghunatha Iyer, scion of a family known for its erudition in the old texts, a scholar in Sanskrit and disciple of the great Kottakkal school of ayurveda, undertook the above task, undaunted by the magnitude of the work involved. His treatise on 500 medicinal plants chosen by him perhaps at random, forms the nucleus of the present compendium.

P K Warrier, Managing Trustee of the Arya Vaidya Sala, Kottakkal, a renowned physician and scholar, together with V P K Nambiar, formerly systematic botanist at the Kerala Forest Research Institute and a specialist in the flora of the Western Ghats with a hereditary interest in herbal cures, and C Ramankutty, a learned physician of the Kottakkal Arya Vaidya Sala, undertook a thorough review of the work of Raghunatha Iyer. The result of their painstaking effort is this treatise in five volumes, the last of which includes the bibliography and index. They have taken the assistance of reputed subject specialists to supplement their authoritative knowledge of the subject.

The result of these endeavours is the presentation of this authoritative account of 500 medicinal plants, some of which are of common occurrence, some cultivated as vegetables and a few exotics. The treatise is interesting particularly for its contemporary understanding of therapeutic properties collected from various sources and more importantly from the Arya Vaidya Sala, Kottakkal, the treasure house of ayurvedic knowledge.

I have no doubt therefore that this scholarly work will prove interesting and useful, serve as a reference manual of authoritative information to physicians, and hopefully capture the attention of foresters and farmers to reverse the trend of shrinkage of our valuable plant resources.

P M GANAPATHY
Director
Indian Plywood Industries
Research and Training Institute

Bangalore
1993

Acknowledgements

I would like to express my grateful thanks to

Dr A N Henry, Botanical Survey of India, Southern Circle, Coimbatore, for updating the names of the medicinal species; Professor R Vasudevan Nair, Palghat, for the invaluable contribution of scientifically accurate illustrations; Dr P M Ganapathy, Director, Indian Plywood Industries Research Institute, Bangalore, for his detailed scrutiny of the manuscript and for writing the foreword; Mr N Sasidharan, Kerala Forest Research Institute, Peechi, for his assistance in establishing the accurate identity of some raw drugs; Professor A N Nambudiri, formerly Director, Tropical Botanic Garden and Research Institute, Palode, who helped us with excerpts from some rare books; the Director, National Botanical Research Institute, Lucknow and Mr P J Mathew, Tropical Botanic Garden and Research Institute, who provided us with photographs of some rare medicinal species; Mr K Ravindran, formerly Librarian, Kerala Forest Research Institute, for his generous advice, whenever we sought it, related to the publishing of this book; Mr C V Sukumaran for the pains taken in preparing the photographs, and Mr K G Warrier, Madras, for his comments on the typescript of the first volume.

I would also like to thank the subject experts for their infinite patience in scrutinising the material at many stages, and for their valuable suggestions. My thanks are also due to my colleagues Mr P.V.S. Variar, former General Manager, Dr P Madhavankutty, formerly Factory Manager and Mr K Balakrishna Kurup, General Manager, who participated in several discussions and offered their comments.

I am happy to record my sincere thanks to Orient Longman Ltd. Madras for undertaking the printing and publishing of this treatise.

P K WARRIER
Managing Trustee
Arya Vaidya Sala

Kottakkal
1993

Editor's Note

S Raghunatha Iyer (born 13 December 1911) was educated at Cheranellur in Kerala and later at the Arya Vaidya Pathasala in Kottakkal founded by Vaidyaratnam P S Varier where he obtained the Aryavaidyan diploma with a distinction. He joined the Pathasala as tutor in 1937 and became factory manager in 1942. He was in charge of various research projects undertaken by the Arya Vaidya Sala and continued to serve the institution as special officer, even after retirement, until his demise.

P S Varier, the founder of the Arya Vaidya Sala, in his declaration at the time of the inception of the institution, had laid down one of the aims of his new venture as being the manufacture of genuine ayurvedic medicines for distribution to the public and for helping ayurvedic physicians in their practice. With this in view, he undertook to promote research for the identification of genuine herbs and other materials used at the time, and also to improve the manufacturing process with new techniques, while staying with the fundamentals. Thus the endeavour to collect and establish the identity of such ingredients used traditionally in Kerala was undertaken by the manufacturing department.

When Raghunatha Iyer was factory manager he used the opportunity and scope to gather all genuine ayurvedic ingredients in use. He conducted practical tests to establish their identity with the help of ayurvedic nighantus, related texts and recent botanical studies. It is in this way that he was prompted to compile a treatise on medicinal plants.

Of the five hundred plants chosen by him some were vegetables in common use possessing medicinal properties. In compiling the profile for each plant he drew on verse texts from various Sanskrit treatises and was able to provide additional information on properties, uses and on alternative names in use. He made extensive notes to support the arguments advanced by him. Unfortunately he could not complete the treatise as he died in December 1983. The work was taken up afresh by V P K Nambiar who was assisted in the project by C Ramankutty.

In determining the accurate identity of controversial drugs, the panel of editors and subject experts have found it necessary to draw on various published sources before arriving at a consensus. Wherever a solution has been tentative, the lines for further research have been indicated.

Illustrations have been provided for all species except Commiphora myrrha (Nees) Engl. in Volume 2, and for *Plectranthus vettiveroides* (Jacob) Singh & Sharma and *Quercus infectoria* Olivier in Volume 4.

Key To Transliteration

Hindi	Kannada	Malayalam	Sanskrit	Tamil	Telugu	Transliteration Key
अ	ಅ	അ	अ	அ	అ	A, a
आ	ಆ	ആ	आ	ஆ	ఆ	Ā, ā
इ	ಇ	ഇ	इ	இ	ఇ	I, i
ई	ಈ	ഈ	ई	ஈ	ఈ	Ī, ī
उ	ಉ	ഉ	उ	உ	ఉ	U, u
ऊ	ಊ	ഊ	ऊ	ஊ	ఊ	Ū, ū
ऋ	ಋ	ഋ	ऋ	–	ఋ	Ṛ, ṛ
–	ೠ	–	–	–	ౠ	Ṝ, ṝ
ए	ಎ	എ	ए	எ	ఎ	E, e
–	ಏ	ഏ	–	ஏ	ఏ	Ē, ē
ऐ	ಐ	ഐ	ऐ	ஐ	ఐ	Ai, ai
ओ	ಒ	ഒ	ओ	ஒ	ఒ	O, o
–	ಓ	ഓ	–	ஓ	ఓ	Ō, ō
औ	ಔ	ഔ	औ	ஔ	ఔ	Ou/ou
अं	ಅಂ	അം	अं	–	అం	aṃ/aṁ
–	ಅಃ	അഃ	अः	–	అః	aḥ
क	ಕ	ക	क	க	క	ka
ख	ಖ	ഖ	ख	–	ఖ	kha
ग	ಗ	ഗ	ग	–	గ	ga
घ	ಘ	ഘ	घ	–	ఘ	gha
ङ	ಙ	ങ	ङ	ங	ఙ	ṅa
च	ಚ	ച	च	ச	చ	ca
छ	ಛ	ഛ	छ	–	ఛ	cha
ज	ಜ	ജ	ज	ஜ	జ	ja
झ	ಝ	ഝ	झ	–	ఝ	jha
ञ	ಞ	ഞ	ञ	ஞ	ఞ	ña

Hindi	Kannada	Malayalam	Sanskrit	Tamil	Telugu	Transliteration Key
ट	ಟ	ട	ट	ட	ట	ṭa
ठ	ಠ	ഠ	ठ	–	ఠ	ṭha
ड	ಡ	ഡ	ड	–	డ	ḍa
ढ	ಢ	ഢ	ढ	–	ఢ	ḍha
ण	ಣ	ണ	ण	ண	ణ	ṇa
त	ತ	ത	त	த	త	ta
थ	ಥ	ഥ	थ	–	థ	tha
द	ದ	ദ	द	–	ద	da
ध	ಧ	ധ	ध	–	ధ	dha
न	ನ	ന	न	ந/ன	న	na
प	ಪ	പ	प	ப	ప	pa
फ	ಫ	ഫ	फ	–	ఫ	pha
ब	ಬ	ബ	ब	–	బ	ba
भ	ಭ	ഭ	भ	–	భ	bha
म	ಮ	മ	म	ம	మ	ma
य	ಯ	യ	य	ய	య	ya
र	ರ	ര	र	ர	ర	ra
ल	ಲ	ല	ल	ல	ల	la
व	ವ	വ	व	வ	వ	va
श	ಶ	ശ	श	–	శ	śa
ष	ಷ	ഷ	ष	ஷ	ష	ṣa
स	ಸ	സ	स	ஸ	స	sa
ह	ಹ	ഹ	ह	ஹ	హ	ha
–	ಳ	ള	ळ	ள	ళ	ḷa
क्ष	ಕ್ಷ	ക്ഷ	क्ष	க்ஷ	క్ష	kṣa
–	–	ഴ	–	ழ	–	ḻa
–	ಱ	റ	–	ற	ఱ	Ṛa, ṛa
–	–	റ്റ	–	ற்ற	–	ṯṯ

Abbreviations used in the book

A.hṛ.	:	Aṣṭāṅgahṛdayaṃ
A.hṛ.Ci	:	Aṣṭāṅgahṛdayaṃ Cikitsāsthānaṃ
A.hṛ.Sū.	:	Aṣṭāṅgahṛydayaṃ Sūtṛasthānaṃ
A.hṛ.U.	:	Aṣṭāṅgahṛdayaṃ Uttarasthānaṃ
A.ma	:	Abhidhānamañjarī
A.saṁ.	:	Aṣṭāṅgasaṁgrahaṃ
A.saṁ.Sū.	:	Aṣṭāṅgasaṁgrahaṃ Sūtṛasthānaṃ
A.saṁ.U.	:	Aṣṭāṅgasaṁgrahaṃ Uttarasthānaṃ
Ā.saṁ.	:	Ātaṅgasaṁgrahaṃ
Ā.śi.	:	Āyuṛvēdaśikṣā
Ā.vi.	:	Āyuṛvēdavijñān
Bhā.pṛa	:	Bhāvapṛakāśaṃ
Bhā.pṛa.ni.	:	Bhāvapṛakāśanighaṇṭu
Bhai.ra.	:	Bhaiṣajyaratnāvali
Ca.Ci.	:	Carakasaṁhitā Cikitsāsthānaṃ
Ca.saṁ.	:	Carakasaṁhitā
Ca.saṁ.Sū., Ca.Sū.	:	Carakasaṁhitā Sūtṛasthānaṃ
Ca.Ka., Ca.saṃ.Ka.	:	Carakasaṁhitā Kalpasthānaṃ
Ca.da.	:	Cakṛadattaṃ
Dha.ni.	:	Dhanvantarinighaṇṭu
Dra.gu.saṁ	:	Dravyaguṇasaṁgrahaṃ
Dra.gu.vi., Dra.vi.	:	Dravyaguṇavijñān
Ga.ni.	:	Gadanigrahaṃ
Gu.pā.	:	Guṇapāṭhaṃ
Hā.saṁ.	:	Hārītasaṁhitā
Hṛ.pṛi.	:	Hṛdayapṛiyā
Kai.ni.	:	Kaiyadēvanighaṇṭu
Ma.ni.	:	Madanādinighaṇṭu

Ma.pā.ni.	:	Madanapālanighaṇṭu
Ma.vi.	:	Madanavinōdaṃ
Ni.ā.	:	Nighaṇṭu ādarś
Ni.ra.	:	Nighaṇṭuratnākaraṃ
Ni.saṁ.	:	Nighaṇṭusaṁgrahaṃ
Rā.ni.	:	Rājanighaṇṭu
Rā.va.	:	Rājavallabhaṃ
Śā.ni.	:	Śāligrāmanighaṇṭu
Śā.ni.bhū.	:	Śāligrāmanighaṇṭubhūṣaṇaṃ
Śi.ni., Śiva.	:	Śivadattanighaṇṭu
Si.bhē.ma.	:	Sidhabhēṣajamaṇimāla
Sō.ni.	:	Sōḍhalanighaṇṭu
Su.Ci.	:	Suśṛutasaṁhitā Cikitsāsthānaṃ
Su.saṁ., Su.	:	Suśṛutasaṁhitā
Su.saṃ. Sū., Su.Sū.	:	Suśṛutasaṁahitā Sūṭrasthānaṃ
Su.U.	:	Suśṛutasaṁhitā Uttarasthānaṃ
Sva.	:	Svayaṁkṛti
Vai.jī.	:	Vaidyajīvanaṃ
Vai.ni.	:	Vaidyakanighaṇṭu
Yō.ra.	:	Yōgaratnākaraṃ
Yō.ra.sa.	:	Yōgaratnasamuccayaṃ

AVS	:	Arya Vaidya Sala
Eng.	:	English
Coll.No.	:	Collection Number
Hin.	:	Hindi
Mal.	:	Malayalam
San.	:	Sanskrit
Tam.	:	Tamil
t.s.	:	transverse section
v.s.	:	vertical section

Contents

1. Abelmoschus esculentus **1**
2. Abelmoschus moschatus **4**
3. Abies spectabilis **7**
4. Abrus precatorius **10**
5. Acacia caesia **17**
6. Acacia catechu **19**
7. Acacia leucophloea **23**
8. Acacia nilotica **26**
9. Acacia polyantha **30**
10. Acacia sinuata **33**
11. Acalypha indica **36**
12. Achyranthes aspera **39**
13. Aconitum heterophyllum **42**
14. Aconitum napellus **47**
15. Acorus calamus **51**
16. Actiniopteris dichotoma **55**
17. Adenanthera pavonina **58**
18. Aegle marmelos **62**
19. Aerva lanata **67**
20. Agaricus campestris **70**
21. Ageratum conyzoides **74**
22. Alangium salvifolium **77**
23. Albizia lebbeck **81**
24. Albizia odoratissima **85**
25. Allium cepa **88**
26. Allium sativum **93**
27. Allophylus serratus **99**
28. Aloe barbadensis **103**
29. Alpina galanga **106**
30. Alstonia scholaris **111**
31. Alstonia venenata **115**
32. Alternanthera sessilis **118**

33. Amaranthus spinosus **121**
34. Ammania baccifera ssp. baccifera **125**
35. Amomum subulatum **128**
36. Amorphophallus paeoniifolius var. companulatus **132**
37. Anacardium occidentale **137**
38. Anacyclus pyrethrum **140**
39. Anamirta cocculus **143**
40. Ananas comosus **146**
41. Andrographis paniculata **149**
42. Anethum graveolens **153**
43. Anisomeles malabarica **157**
44. Annona squamosa **160**
45. Anogeissus latifolia **163**
46. Aphanamixis polystachya **167**
47. Aquilaria agallocha **171**
48. Arachis hypogaea **176**
49. Areca catechu **180**
50. Argemone mexicana **187**
51. Argyreia nervosa **191**
52. Aristolochia bracteolata **196**
53. Aristolochia indica **199**
54. Artemisia nilagirica **202**
55. Artocarpus communis **207**
56. Artocarpus heterophyllus **208**
57. Artocarpus hirsutus **215**
58. Asparagus racemosus **218**
59. Averrhoa carambola **224**
60. Azadirachta indica **227**
61. Bacopa monnieri **235**
62. Baliospermum montanum **240**
63. Bambusa arundinacea **244**
64. Barringtonia acutangula **250**
65. Basella alba var. rubra **253**
66. Bauhinia variegata **256**
67. Benincasa hispida **261**
68. Beta vulgaris **265**
69. Betula utilis **268**
70. Biophytum sensitivum **271**
71. Bixa orellana **274**
72. Blumea lacera **278**

73.Boerhaavia diffusa **281**
74. Bombax ceiba **289**
75. Borassus flabellifer **293**
76. Boswellia serrata **297**
77. Brassica juncea **301**
78. Brassica oleracea var. capitata **306**
79. Buchanania lanzan **309**
80. Butea monosperma **314**
81. Caesalpinia bonduc **320**
82. Caesalpinia sappan **323**
83. Cajanus cajan **326**
84. Calamus rotang **330**
85. Callicarpa macrophylla **334**
86. Calophyllum inophyllum **338**
87. Calotropis gigantea **341**
88. Calycopteris floribunda **346**
89. Camellia sinensis **349**
90. Canavalia gladiata **352**
91. Cannabis sativa **356**
92. Canscora decussata **361**
93. Canthium parviflorum **366**
94. Capparis decidua **368**
95. Capsicum annuum **375**
96. Cardiospermum halicacabum **377**
97. Careya arborea **380**
98. Carica papaya **383**
99. Carissa carandas **386**
100. Carthamus tinctorus **390**
Appendix A **394**
Appendix B **403**
Index to Sanskrit terms **419**

List of colour plates

		Page No
Plate 1	Abrus precatorius	**11**
Plate 2	Abrus precatorius	**15**
Plate 3	Aconitum heterophyllum	**43**
Plate 4	Adenanthera pavonina	**59**
Plate 5	Agarius campestris	**71**
Plate 6	Allium cepa	**89**
Plate 7	Aloe barbadensis	**102**
Plate 8	Arachis hypogaea	**177**
Plate 9	Argemone mexicana	**186**
Plate 10	Artocarpus communis	**206**
Plate 11	Artocarpus heterophyllus	**209**
Plate 12	Asparagus racemosus	**219**
Plate 13	Bacopa monneri	**234**
Plate 14	Bixa orellana	**275**
Plate 15	Bombax ceiba	**288**
Plate 16	Butea monosperma	**315**
Plate 17	Canavalia gladiata	**353**
Plate 18	Capsicum annuum	**374**
Plate 19	Carthamus tinctorius	**391**

Coll. No. AVS 2426

Abelmoschus esculentus **(Linn.) Moench**

(Hibiscus esculentus *Linn.*)

Malvaceae : (कार्पास–कुलम्)

Eng	:	Lady's finger, Okra
Hin	:	Bhiṇḍī, Bhiṇḍī-tōrī (भिण्डी, भिण्डी–तोरी)
Kan	:	Beṇḍekāyi, (ಬೆಂಡೆಕಾಯಿ)
Mal	:	Veṇṭa (വെണ്ട)
San	:	Bhēṇḍā (भेण्डा)
Tam	:	Veṇṭai (வெண்டை)
Tel	:	Beṇḍakāya (బెండకాయ)

Distribution : Throughout India, cultivated in areas upto 1,200 m

The plant : An annual erect herb, 0.9 – 2.1 m in height, covered with hair throughout; leaves simple, alternate, palmately 3–5 lobed, coarsely toothed, scabrous; flowers large, yellow with a purple centre, staminal tube antheriferous throughout; fruits long, 6 – 8 ribbed, capsular; seeds many, rounded, striate.

Parts used : fruits

Properties and uses: The fruits are sweet, mucilaginous, emollient, cooling, aphrodisiac, stomachic, haematinic, demulcent, diuretic, constipating and tonic. They are useful in vitiated conditions of *pitta,* gonorrhoea, urethrorrhea, abdominal disorders, anaemia, pruritus, strangury, diarrhoca and general debility.

भेण्डा भिण्डातिका भिण्डो भिण्डकः क्षेत्रसंभवः ।
चतुष्पदश्चतुष्पुण्ड्रः सुशाकश्चाम्ळपत्रकः ॥
करपर्णो वृत्तबीजो भवेदेकादशाह्वयः । (रा.नि.)
["Bhēṇḍā bhiṇḍātikā bhiṇḍō bhiṇḍakaḥ kṣētrasambhavaḥ
Catuṣpadaścatuṣpuṇḍraḥ suśākaścāmḷ apatrakaḥ
Karapaṃō vṛttabījō bhavēdēkādaśāhvayaḥ" (Rā.ni.)]

"करपर्णफलं रुच्यं पिच्छिलं गुरु वातळम्
वृष्यं श्ळेष्मकरं बल्यं शुक्ळवृद्धिकरं परम् ।
कासे मन्दानले वाते पीनसेषु विनिन्दितम्" (शा.नि.)

Abelmoschus esculentus

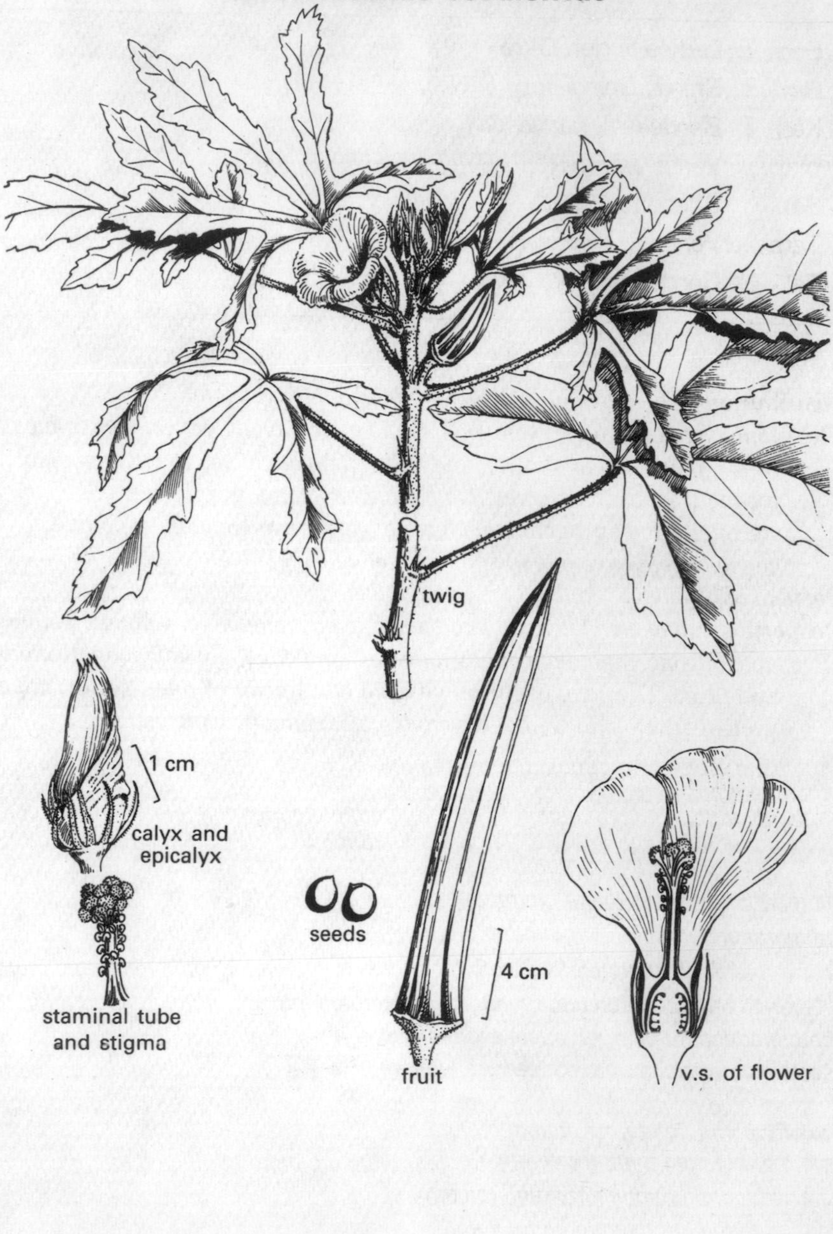

["Karaparṇaphalaṃ rucyaṃ picchilaṃ guru vātaḷaṃ
Vṛṣyaṃ śḷēṣmakaraṃ balyaṃ śukḷavṛddhikaraṃ paraṃ
Kāsē mandānalē vātē pīnasēṣu vininditaṃ" (Sā.ni.)]

"भेण्डा त्वम्ळरसा सोष्णा ग्राहिका रुचिकारिका । " (रा.नि.)
["Bhēṇḍā tvamḷarasā sōṣṇā grāhikā rucikārikā (Rā.ni)]

"भेण्डा त्वम्ळरसा चोष्णा ग्राही च रुचिकारका ।
राजनामानि घण्टे च द्रव्यं वृष्या परा स्मृता ॥ " (नि.र.)
["Bhēṇḍā tvamḷarasā cōṣṇā grāhī ca rucikārakā
Rājanāmāni ghaṇṭē ca dravyaṃ vṛṣyā parā smṛtā (Ni.ra)]

Coll.No. AVS 1444

***Abelmoschus moschatus* Medikus**

(Hibiscus abelmoschus *Linn.*)

Malvaceae (कार्पास–कुलम्)

Eng	:	Musk mallow, Ambrette seed plant
Hin	:	Latākastūri, Maskdānā (लताकस्तूरि, मस्कदाना)
Kan	:	Kaḍukastūri (ಕಾಡುಕಸ್ತೂರಿ)
Mal	:	Latākastūri, Kāṭṭukastūri, Kastūriveṇṭa (ലതാകസ്തൂരി, കാട്ടുകസ്തൂരി, കസ്തൂരിവെണ്ട)
San	:	Latākastūrikā (लताकस्तूरिका)
Tam	:	Veṟṟilaikkastūri, Kāṭṭukkastūri (வெற்றிலைக் கஸ்தூரி, காட்டுக் கஸ்தூரி)
Tel	:	Kastūribenḍavittu (కస్తూరిబెండవిత్తు)

Distribution : Cultivated throughout India

The plant : An erect hirsute or hispid annual herb, 60 – 180 cm in height; leaves simple, of varying shapes, usually palmately 3–7 lobed, lobes narrow-acute or oblong-ovate, crenate, serrate or irregularly toothed, hairy on both surfaces; flowers large, yellow with purple centre; fruits fulvous-hairy, capsular; seeds many, subreniform, black or greyish brown, scented.

Parts used: seeds

Properties and uses: The seeds are bitter, sweet, acrid, aromatic, cooling, aphrodisiac, ophthalmic, cardiotonic, digestive, stomachic, constipating, carminative, pectoral, diuretic, stimulant, antispasmodic, deodorant, insecticidal and tonic. They are useful in ophthalmopathy, cardiac debility, cough, asthma, bronchitis, hyperdipsia, burning sensation, vitiated conditions of *kapha* and *pitta,* nausea, dyspepsia, flatulent colic, diarrhoea, strangury, gonorrhoea, spermatorrhoea, calculi, halitosis, pectoral diseases, ptyalism, vomiting, hysteria and other neural disorders, pruritus, leucoderma and general debility.

"लताकस्तूरिका प्रोक्ता भेण्डा कस्तूरिपूर्वका ।
सुगन्धभेण्डा भेण्डी च गन्धपूर्वाऽपि च स्मृता ॥ " (स्व.)
["Latākastūrikā proktā bhēṇḍā kastūripūrvakā
Sugandhabhēṇḍā bhēṇḍī ca gandhapūrvaऽpi ca smṛtā" (Sva.)]

"कटुतिक्तरसं बीजं शीतवीर्यं च बृंहणम् ।

Abelmoschus moschatus

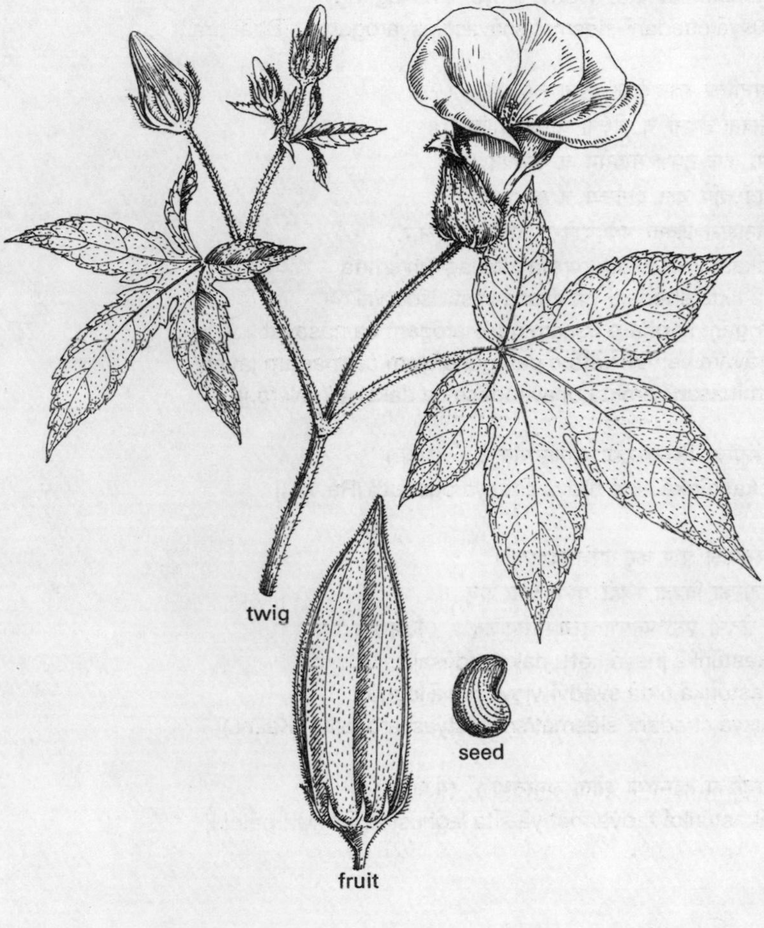

दीपनं पाचनं वृष्यं कफवातहरं स्मृतम् ॥
स्मृतिभ्रंशहरं हृद्यं तृष्णावान्तिश्रमापहम् ।
कोष्ठशूलहरं चैतत् जठरामयनाशनम् ॥ (स्व.)
[`Kaṭutiktarasaṃ bījaṃ śītavīryaṃ ca bṛṁhaṇaṃ
Dīpanaṃ pācanaṃ vṛṣyaṃ kaphavātaharaṃ smṛtaṃ
Smṛtibhraṃśaharaṃ hṛdyaṃ tṛṣṇāvāntiśṛamāpahaṃ
Kōṣṭhaśūlaharaṃ caitat jaṭharāmayanāśanaṃ'' (Sva.)]

"लताकस्तूरिका तिक्ता स्वाद्वी वृष्या हिमा लघुः ।
चक्षुष्या छेदनी श्ळेष्मतृष्णावस्त्यास्यरोगहृत् ॥" (भा.प्र.)
[`Latākastūrikā tiktā svādvī vṛṣyā himā laghuḥ
Cakṣuṣyā chēdanī śḷēṣmatṛṣṇāvastyāsyarōgahṛt'' (Bhā. pṛa.)]

"लताकस्तूरिका स्वादुर्वृष्या शीता लघुः स्मृता ।
नेत्र्या तिक्ता छेदनी च तीक्ष्णा वस्तिविशोधिनी ॥
वस्तिरोगं कफं तृष्णां मुखरोगं च नाशयेत् ।
लालास्रावं वमिं वातं दौर्गन्ध्यं च मदं जयेद् ॥
अलक्ष्मीनाशनी प्रोक्ता भवेद्देशे च दक्षिणे ।" (नि.र.)
[`Latākastūrikā svāduṛvṛṣyā śītā laghuḥ smṛtā
Nētṛyā tiktā chēdanī ca tīkṣṇā vastiviśōdhinī
Vastirōgaṃ kaphaṃ tṛṣṇāṃ mukharōgaṃ ca nāśayēt
Lālāsṛāvaṃ vamiṃ vātaṃ dauṛgandhyaṃ ca madaṃ jayēt
Alakṣmīnāśanī pṛōktā bhavēddēśē ca dakṣiṇē'' (Ni.ra.)]

"लताकस्तूरिका तिक्ता हृद्या शीतास्यरोगनुत् ।" (रा.व.)
[`Latākastūrikā tiktā hṛdyā śītāsyarōganut'' (Rā.va.)]

"लताकस्तूरिका ज्ञेया कटु दक्षिणदेशजा ।
लताकस्तूरिका तिक्ता स्वद्वी वृष्या हिमा लघुः ॥
चक्षुष्या छेदनी श्ळेष्मतृष्णावस्त्यास्यरोगजित् ।" (कै.नि.)
[Latākastūrikā jñeyā kaṭu dakṣiṇadēśajā
Latākastūrikā tiktā svādvī vṛṣyā himā laghuḥ
Cakṣuṣyā chēdanī śḷēṣmatṛṣṇāvastyāsyarōgajit'' (Kai.ni.)]

"लताकस्तूरिका तद्वन्नेत्र्या शीता लघुस्तथा ।" (म.पा.नि.)
[`Latākastūrikā tadvannētṛyā śītā laghustathā'' (Ma.pā.ni.)]

Coll. No. B.S.I. (N.C.) 46274

Abies spectabilis **(D.Don) Mirb.**

(=A.webbiana *Lindl.*)

Pinaceae (देवदारु–कुलम्)

Eng	:	East Himalayan silver fir
Hin	:	Tālīspatra, Tālīspatri (तालीसपत्र, तालीसपत्रि)
Kan	:	Taḷisapatri (ತಾಳಿಸಪತ್ರಿ)
Mal	:	Tālīsapatṛaṃ (താലീസപത്രം)
San	:	Tālīsaṃ, Tālīsapatṛaṃ (तालीसं, तालीसपत्रं)
Tam	:	Tālīsapatṛi (தாலீசபத்ரி)
Tel	:	Taḷīsapatri (తాళీసపత్రి)

Distribution : Upper Himalayan tracts

The plant : A very tall evergreen tree attaining a height of 60 m with strong horizontally spreading branches, young shoots covered with short brown hair; leaves simple, densely covering the twigs spreading in all directions, but more or less distichous when the twigs are viewed from below, each leaf 1.5–2.3 cm long; the cones are bluish in colour, seeds winged.

Parts used : leaves

Properties and uses : The leaves are bitter, sweet, acrid, thermogenic, aromatic, anodyne, expectorant, digestive, carminative, stomachic, antispasmodic, diuretic, febrifuge and tonic. They are useful in vitiated conditions of *kapha* and *vāta,* cough, asthma, bronchitis, dyspepsia, flatulence, colic, diarrhoea, epilepsy, phthisis, vomiting, ureteritis, strangury, hoarseness, hiccough, fever and emaciation.

"तालीसपत्रं तालीसं कासघ्नं च शुकोदरम् ।
प्रोक्तं तामलकीपत्रं पर्यायैः पर्णमञ्जरी ॥" (अ.म.)
['Tālīsapatṛaṃ tālīsaṃ kāsaghnaṃ ca śukōdaraṃ
Pṛōktaṃ tāmalakīpatṛaṃ paryāyaiḥ parṇamañjarī'' (A.ma.)]

"तालीसपत्रं तालीसं पत्राख्यं च शुकोदरं ।
धात्रीपत्रं चार्कबेधं करीपत्रं घनच्छदम् ॥
नीलं नीलाम्बरं तालं तालीपत्रं तलाह्वयम् ।
तालीसपत्रकस्येति नामान्याहुस्त्रयोदश ॥" (रा. नि.)
['Tālīsapatṛaṃ tālīsaṃ patṛākhyaṃ ca śukōdaraṃ

Abies spectabilis

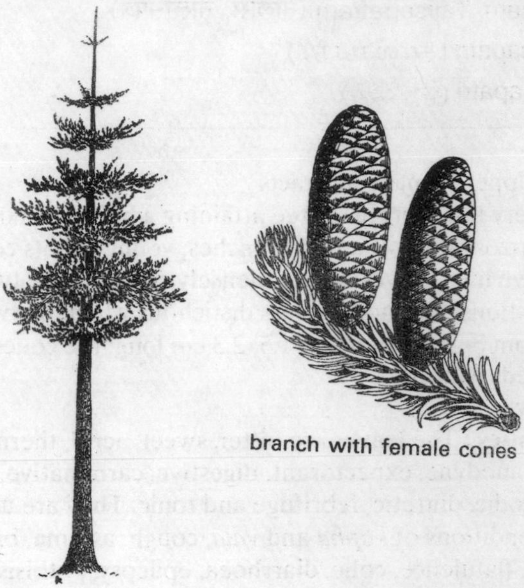

Dhātṛīpatṛaṃ cāṛkabēdhaṃ karīpaṭṛaṃ ghanacchadaṃ
Nīlaṃ nīlāmbaraṃ tālaṃ tālīpatṛaṃ talāhvayaṃ
Tālīsapatṛakasyēti nāmānyāhustṛayōdaśa'' (Rā.ni.)]

"तालीसं लघु तीक्ष्णोष्णं श्वासकासकफानिलान् ।
निहन्त्यरुचिगुल्मामवह्निमान्द्यक्षयामयान् ॥" (भा.प्र.)
["Tālīsaṃ laghu tīkṣṇōṣṇaṃ śvāsakāsakaphānilān
Nihantyarucigulmāmavahnimāndyakṣayāmayān" (Bhā.pṛa)]

"तालीसं श्वासकासघ्नं दीपनं श्ळेष्मपित्तजित् ।
मुखरोगहरं हृद्यं सुपत्रं पत्रसंवृतम् ॥ (ध.नि.)
["Tālīsaṃ śvāsakāsaghnaṃ dīpanaṃ śḷēṣmapittajit
Mukharōgaharaṃ hṛdyaṃ supatṛaṃ patṛasaṃvṛtaṃ" (Dha.ni.)]

"तालीसपत्रं तिक्तोष्णं मधुरं कफवातनुत् ।
कासहिक्काक्षयश्वासच्छर्दिदोषविनाशकृत् ॥" (रा.नि.)
["Tālīspatṛaṃ tiktōṣṇaṃ madhuraṃ kaphavātanut
Kāsahikkākṣayaśvāsacchaṛdidōṣavināśakṛt" (Rā.ni.)]

"तालीसपत्रं मधुरं तिक्तं चोष्णं लघु स्मृतम् ।
तीक्ष्णं स्वर्यं च हृद्यञ्च अग्निदीप्तिकरं मतम् ॥
श्वासं कासं कफं वातं क्षयगुल्मारुचिस्तथा ।
रक्तदोषं वामिंचाममग्निमान्द्यञ्च नाशयेत् ॥
मुखरोगं च पित्तं च नाशयेदिति कीर्तितम् ।" (नि.र.)
["Tālīsapatraṃ madhuraṃ tiktaṃ cōṣṇaṃ laghu smṛtaṃ
Tīkṣṇaṃ svaryaṃ ca hṛdyañca agnidīptikaraṃ mataṃ
Śvāsaṃ kāsaṃ kaphaṃ vātaṃ kṣayagulmārucistathā
Raktadōṣaṃ vamiṃcārnamagnimāndyañca nāśayēt
Mukharōgaṃ ca pittaṃ ca nāśayēditi kīṛtitaṃ" (Ni.ra.)]

Remarks: Very often the *tālīsapatṛa* bought from the market contains in addition to the leaves a lot of twigs as well as leaves of *Taxus baccata.* It is reported that in Maharashtra, Gujarat and Rajasthan leaves of *T. baccata* are in use as *tālīsapatṛa.*

Coll. No. AVS 1773

***Abrus precatorius* Linn.**

Fabaceae (अपराजिता–कुलम्)

Eng	:	Jequirity, Indian liquorice, Wild liquorice
Kan	:	Gurugunji (ಗುರುಗುಂಜಿ)
Hin	:	Guñcī, Ratti, Guñcācī (गुञ्ची, रत्ति, गुञ्चाची)
Mal	:	Kunni (കുന്നി)
San	:	Guñjā (गुञ्जा)
Tam	:	Kuntumaṇi (குந்துமணி)
Tel	:	Guruginja (గురుగింజ)

Distribution: Throughout India, on hedges and bushes in exposed areas

The plant: A deciduous, wiry climber with tough branches; leaves abruptly pinnate with many pairs of leaflets, the rachis ending in a spine; the leaflets oblong, rounded at both ends, thinly membranous; flowers pink, clustered on tubercles arranged along the rachis of one-sided pedunculate raceme; fruits pods, turgid with a sharp deflexed beak; seeds usually scarlet with a black spot or sometimes pure white.

Parts used: roots, leaves, seeds

Properties and uses: The roots and leaves are astringent, sweet, emetic,diuretic and alexeteric. They are useful in cough, pharyngodynia, pectoralgia, inflammation, strangury and in vitiated conditions of *vāta.*

The seeds are acrid, bitter, astringent, purgative, toxic, abortifacient, aphrodisiac and trichogenous. They are useful in vitiated conditions of *pitta* and *vāta,* ophthalmopathy, leucoderma, skin diseases, wounds, alopecia, asthma, tubercular glands, stomatitis, hyperdipsia and fever.

"गुञ्जावल्ली तु मधुरा चिञ्चापत्री स शिम्बिका ।
बीजं कृष्णारुणं तस्य जायते सर्वभूमिषु ॥" (शिवदासः)
["Guñjāvallī tu madhurā ciñcāpatrī sa śimbikā
Bījaṃ kṛṣṇāruṇaṃ tasya jāyatē sarvabhūmiṣu" (Śivadāsaḥ)]

"कृष्णकाम्बोजिका गुञ्जा रक्तिका काकणन्दिका ।
चूडामणिः शीतपाकी शिखण्डी कृष्णळा लता ॥

Abrus precatorius

Plate 1

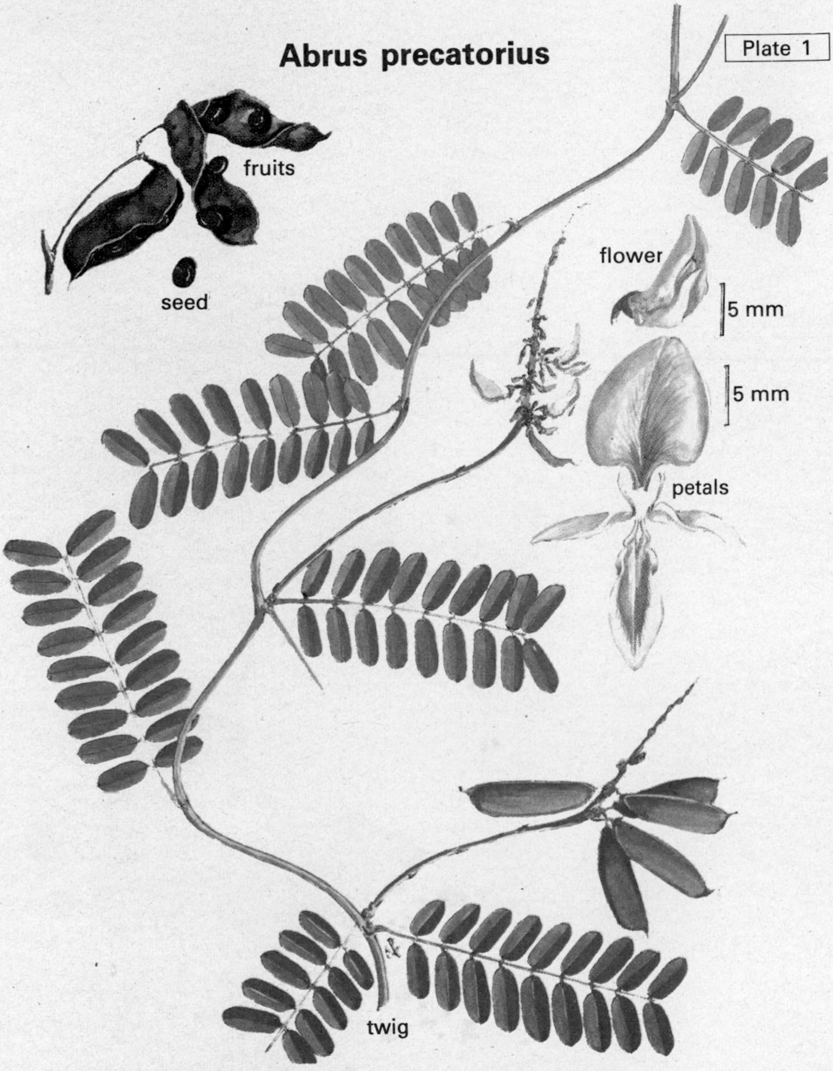

द्वितीया श्वेतकाम्बोजी दुर्मुखा काकपीलुका ।
काकादनी काकभिण्डी वक्रशल्या किरीटिका ॥" (म.नि.)
["Kṛṣṇakāmbōjikā guñjā raktikā kākaṇandikā
Cūḍāmaṇiḥ śītapākī śikhaṇḍī kṛṣṇaḷā latā
Dvitīyā śvētakāmbōjī duṛmukhā kākapīlukā
Kākādanī kākabhiṇḍī vakṛaśalyā kirīṭikā" (Ma.ni.)]

गुञ्जा चूडामणिः सौम्यः शिखण्डी कृष्णळारुणा ।
ताम्रिका शीतपाकी स्यादुच्चटा कृष्णचूडिका ॥
रक्ता च रक्तिका चैव काम्बोजी भिल्लिभूषणा ।
वन्यास्या मानचूडा च विज्ञेया षोडशाह्वया ॥
द्वितीया श्वेतकाम्बोजी श्वेतगुञ्जा भिरिण्टिका ।
काकादनी काकपीलुर्वक्रशल्या षडाह्वया ॥ (रा. नि.)
["Guñjā cūḍāmaṇiḥ saumyā śikhaṇḍī kṛṣṇaḷāruṇā
Tāmṛikā śītapākī syāduccaṭā kṛṣṇacūḍikā
Raktā ca raktikā caiva kāmbōjī bhillibhūṣaṇā
Vanyāsyā mānacūḍā ca vijñēyā ṣōḍaśāhvayā
Dvitīyā śvētakāmbōjī śvētaguñjā bhiriṇṭikā
Kākādanī kākapīluṛvaktṛaśalyā ṣaḍāhvayā" (Rā.ni.)]

"गुञ्जाद्वयं तु केश्यं स्यात् वातपित्तज्वरापहम् ।
मुखशोषभ्रमश्वासतृष्णामदविनाशनं ॥
नेत्रामयहरं वृष्यं बल्यं कण्डूव्रणापहम् ।
कृमीन् प्रलुप्तकुष्ठानि रक्ता च धवळाऽपि च ॥" (भा.प्र.)
["Guñjādvayaṃ tu kēśyaṃ syāt vātapittajvarāpahaṃ
Mukhaśōṣabhṛamaśvāsatṛṣṇāmadavināśanaṃ
Nēṭrāmayaharaṃ vṛṣyaṃ balyaṃ kaṇḍūvṛaṇāpahaṃ
Kṛmīnpṛaluptakuṣṭhāni raktā ca dhavaḷāऽpi ca" (Bhā.pṛa.)]

"गुञ्जा रूक्षा तथा तिक्ता वीर्योष्णा च प्रकीर्तीता ।
विषवैषम्यजन्तुघ्नी रोगग्रामभयापहा ॥
गुञ्जाद्वयं तु शीतोष्णं बीजं वान्तिकरं शिफा ।
शूलघ्नी विषहृत्पत्रं वश्ये श्वेता प्रशस्यते ॥" (ध.नि.)
["Guñjā rūkṣā tathā tiktā vīryōṣṇā ca pṛakīṛttitā
Viṣavaiṣamyajantughnī rōgagrāmabhayāpahā
Guñjādvayaṃ tu śītōṣṇaṃ bījaṃ vāntikaraṃ śiphā
Sūlaghnī viṣahṛtpatṛaṃ vaśyē śvētā pṛaśasyatē" (Dha.ni.)]

"गुञ्जाऽनुष्णा रसे तिक्ता कषाया कफपित्तहा ।
चक्षुष्या शुक्ळळा केश्या त्वच्या रुच्या बलप्रदा ॥
इन्द्रलुप्तहरा तीव्रा सविषा मदमोहकृत् ।
हन्ति रक्षोग्रहविषं कण्डूकुष्ठविषकृमीन् ॥" (कै.नि.)
["Guñjāऽnuṣṇā rasē tiktā kaṣāyā kaphapittahā
Cakṣuṣyā śukḷaḷā kēśyā tvacyā rucyā balapṛadā
Indraluptaharā tīvṛā saviṣā madamōhakṛt

Hanti rakṣōgrahaviṣaṃ kaṇḍūkuṣṭhaviṣakṛmīn" (Kai.ni.)]

"गुञ्जाद्वयं स्वादुतिक्तं बल्यं चोष्णं कषायकम् ।
त्वच्यं केश्यञ्च रुच्यञ्च शीतं वृष्यं मतं बुधैः ॥
नेत्ररोगं विषं पित्तमिन्द्रलुप्तं व्रणं कृमीन् ।
राक्षसग्रहपीडां च कण्डूं कुष्ठं कफं ज्वरम् ॥
मुखशीर्षरुजं वातं भ्रमं श्वासं तृषां तथा ।
मोहं मदं नाशयति बीजं वान्तिकरं मतम् ॥
शूलनाशकरं मूलं पर्णं च विषनाशकम् ।
श्वेतगुञ्जा विशेषेण वशीकरणकृन्मता ॥" (शा.नि.)
["Guñjādvayaṃ svādutiktaṃ balyaṃ cōṣṇaṃ kaṣāyakaṃ
Tvacyaṃ kēśyañca rucyañca śītaṃ vṛṣyaṃ mataṃ budhaiḥ
Nētrarōgaṃ viṣaṃ pittamindraluptaṃ vraṇaṃ kṛmīn
Rākṣasagraphapīḍāṃ ca kaṇḍūṃ kuṣṭhaṃ kaphaṃ jvaraṃ
Mukhaśīṛṣarujaṃ vātaṃ bhramaṃ śvāsaṃ tṛṣāṃ tathā
Mōhaṃ madaṃ nāśayati bījaṃ vāntikaraṃ mataṃ
Śūlanāśakaraṃ mūlaṃ parṇaṃ ca viṣanāśakaṃ
Śvētaguñjā viśēṣēṇa vaśīkaraṇakṛnmatā" (Śā.ni.)]

"क्रियातिवृत्ते जठरे त्रिदोषे तु विशेषतः ॥
दद्यादापृच्छ्य तज्ज्ञातीन् पातुं मद्येन कल्कितम् ।
मूलं काकादनी गुञ्जा करवीरकसंभवम् ॥" (अ.हृ.चि. १५)
["Kriyātivṛttē jaṭharē tridōṣē tu viśēṣatah
Dadyādāpṛcchya tajñātīn pātuṃ madyēna kalkitaṃ
Mūlaṃ kākādanī guñjā karavīrakasambhavaṃ" (A.hṛ.Ci.15.)]

Remarks : In appearance and structure, the roots of both varieties (red and white) are identical, but in Kerala the physicians usually prefer the white-seeded variety.

Abrus precatorius

Plate 2

Cyan

Coll. No. AVS 2448

Acacia caesia (Linn.) Willd.

(A.intsia *Willd.*)

Mimosaceae (बब्बुल–कुलम्)

Hin	:	Ailā, Nikuñcaṃ (ऐला, निकुञ्चं)
Kan	:	Antarike (ಅಂತರಿಕೆ)
Mal	:	Īñca, Iñca (ഈഞ്ച, ഇഞ്ച)
San	:	Nikuñjikā (निकुञ्जिका)
Tam	:	Iñcakkāi, Śīṅkkāi (இஞ் சக்காய், சீங்காய்)
Tel	:	Nallsandra (నల్లసంద్ర)

Distribution : Throughout India, in dry forests

The plant: A large climbing prickly shrub with 5-angled stem; leaves compound, rachis 10 – 20 cm long with a large oblong swollen gland at the base and below 3 – 4 of the uppermost pinnae; leaflets 8–15 pairs, glabrous; flowers white in axillary and terminal panicles; fruits thin pods, dark brown with thickened sutures.

Parts used: bark, flowers

Properties and uses: The soft beaten bark of the plant has cleansing properties and protects the skin against microorganisms. The flowers are reported to be used by Santal women to treat menstrual disorders.

"निकुञ्जिका कुञ्जिका स्यात् प्रोक्ता सा कुञ्जवल्लरी ।
बृहद्वल्ली .... (स्व.)
[Nikuñjikā kuñjikā syāt prōktā sā kuñjavallarī
Bṛhadvallī ...." (Sva.)]

" .... त्वगस्यास्तु घर्षणेनाङ्गसौख्यदा ।
त्वच्या केश्या देहशुद्धिकान्तिपुष्टिकरी परा ॥ " (स्व.)
["................. tvagasyāstu gharṣaṇēnāngasaukhyadā
Tvacyā kēśyā dēhaśuddhikāntipuṣṭikarī parā" (Sva.)]

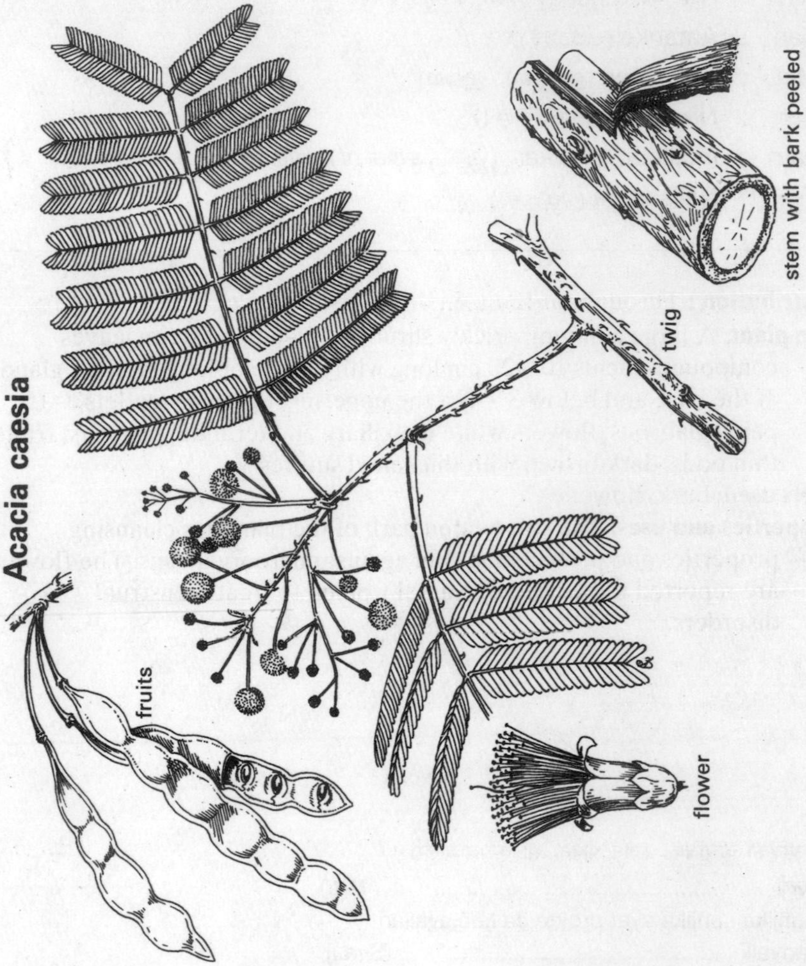
Acacia caesia
fruits
twig
flower
stem with bark peeled

Coll. No. AVS 2402

Acacia catechu (Linn.f.) Willd.

Mimosaceae (बब्बुल–कुलम्)

Eng	:	Cutch tree
Hin	:	Khair, Khairā (खैर, खैरा)
Kan	:	Kaḷu (ಕಳು)
Mal	:	Karinnāli (കരിങ്ങാലി)
San	:	Khadiraḥ (खदिरः)
Tam	:	Karunkāli (கருங்காலி)
Tel	:	Podalimānu (పొడలిమాను)

Distribution : Eastern slopes of Western Ghats, Andhra Pradesh, Bihar, Punjab and Himalayas upto an elevation of 1,500 m

The plant : A moderate sized deciduous tree, 9–12 m in height with dark greyish or brown rough bark and hooked short spines, leaves bipinnately compound, leaflets 30 – 50 pairs, main rachis pubescent with a large conspicuous gland near the middle of the rachis; flowers pale yellow, sessile in peduncled axillary spikes; fruits flat brown pods, shiny and with a triangular beak at the apex and narrowed at the base; seeds 3–10 per pod.

The gummy extract of the wood is commercially known as `kath' or `cutch'. The cutch available in the market is brittle of different shapes and dark brown in colour. On breaking, it is found to be shiny and forms crystal-like pieces.

Parts used: bark, heartwood, kath

Properties and uses: The bark is useful in melancholia, conjunctivitis and haemoptysis. The heartwood is bitter, astringent, acrid, cooling, depurative, anthelmintic, antiseptic, antidysenteric, antipyretic, appetiser, haemostatic, haematinic, anti-inflammatory and tonic. It is useful in vitiated conditions of *kapha* and *pitta,* catarrh, cough, pruritus, leprosy, leucoderma, skin diseases, helminthiasis, anorexia, diarrhoea, dysentery, foul ulcers and wounds, haemoptysis, haematemesis, haemorrhages, intermittent fever, inflammations, odontopathy, anaemia, diabetes, splenomegaly and pharyngodynia.

The kath is acrid, bitter, thermogenic, digestive, appetiser, aphrodisiac, vulnerary, anthelmintic, depurative and tonic.It is useful in vitiated conditions of *kapha* and *vāta,* laryngopathy, flatulence,

Acacia catechu

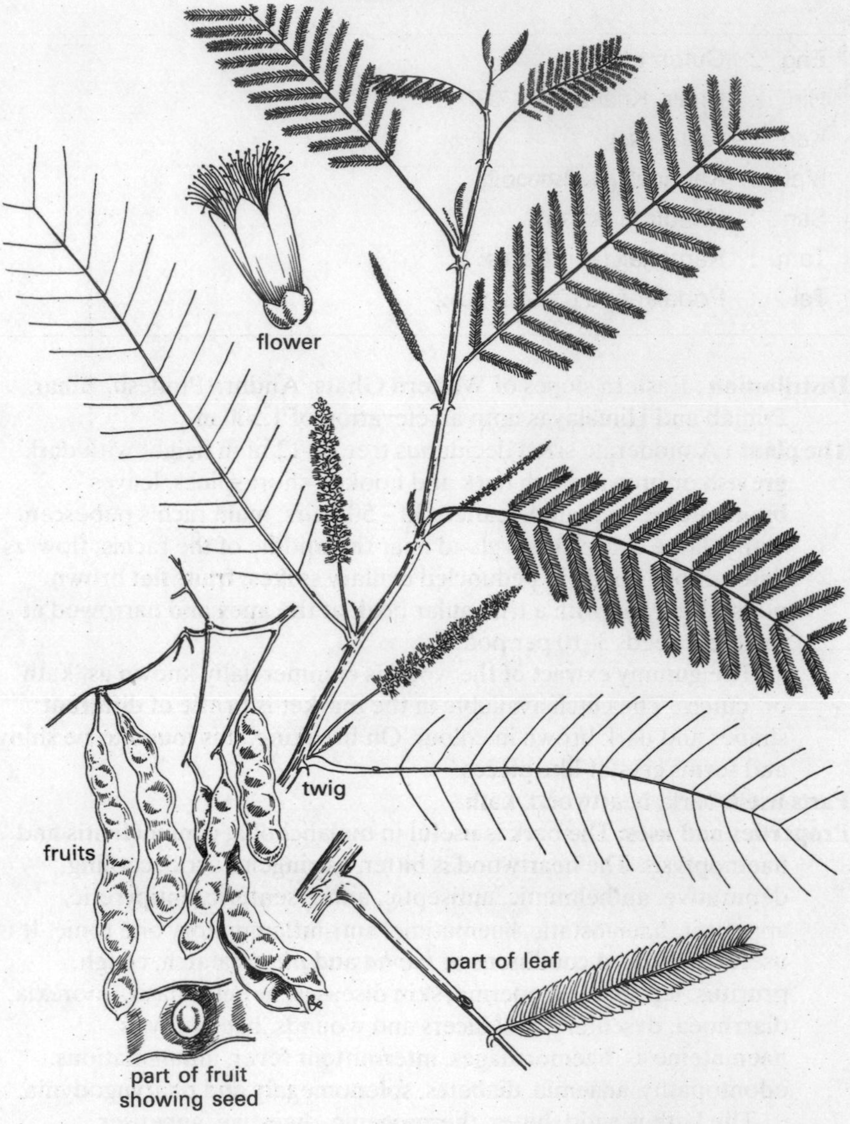

anorexia, ulcers, wounds, helminthiasis, leucoderma, leprosy, skin diseases, urorrhea, colporrhagia, erysipelas and odontopathy.

खदिरो गायत्र्याह्व क्षिति क्षमी दन्तधावनः शल्यः ।
कुष्ठघ्नो होमतरुः सकण्टको रक्तसारश्च ॥
प्रोच्यते बालपत्रोऽज्झो बालः कुटिलकण्टकः ।
जिह्मशल्यो होमवृक्षः शब्दैः पर्यायवाचकैः ॥ " (अ.म.)
["Khadirō gāyatryāhvaḥ kṣiti kṣamī dantadhāvanaḥ śalyaḥ
Kuṣṭhagnō hōmataruḥ sakaṇṭakō raktasāraśca
Prōcyatē bālapatrōjjhō bālaḥ kuṭilakaṇṭakaḥ
Jihmaśalyō hōmavṛkṣaḥ śabdaiḥ paryāyavācakaiḥ" (A.ma.)]

"खदिरो बालपत्रश्च खाद्यः पत्री क्षिति क्षमा ।
सुशल्यो वक्रकण्टश्च यज्ञांगो दन्तधावनः ॥
गायत्री जिह्मशल्यश्च कण्टी सारद्रुमस्तथा ।
कुष्ठारिर्बहुसारश्च मेध्यः सप्तदशाह्वयः ॥" (रा. नि.)
["Khadirō bālapatraśca khādyaḥ patrī kṣiti kṣamā
Suśalyō vakrakaṇṭaśca yajñāmgō dantadhāvanaḥ
Gāyatrī jihmaśalyaśca kaṇṭī sāradrumastathā
Kuṣṭhārirbahusāraśca mēdhyaḥ saptadaśāhvayaḥ" (Rā.ni.)]

"खदिरः शतिळो दन्त्यः कण्डूकासारुचिप्रणुत् ।
तिक्तः कषायो मेदोघ्नः कृमिमेहज्वरव्रणान् ॥
श्वित्रशोफामपित्तास्रपाण्डुकुष्ठकफान् हरेत् । " (भा.प्र.)
[Khadiraḥ śītaḷō dantyaḥ kaṇḍūkāsārucipraṇut
Tiktaḥ kaṣāyō mēdōghnaḥ kṛmimēhajvaravraṇān
Śvitraśōphāmapittāsrapāṇḍukuṣṭhakaphān harēt" (Bhā.pra.)]

"खदिरः स्याद् रसे तिक्तो हिमः पित्तकफास्रनुत् ।
कुष्ठामकासकण्डूतिकृमिदोषहरः स्मृतः ॥ " (ध.नि.)
["Khadiraḥ syād rasē tiktō himaḥ pittakaphāsranut
Kuṣṭhāmakāsakaṇḍūtikṛmidōṣaharaḥ smṛtaḥ" (Dha.ni.)]

"खदिर कुष्ठघ्नानाम् " (च.सू.२५)
[Khadiraḥ kuṣṭhaghnānāṃ" (Ca.Sū.25.)]

"शनैर्मेहिनं खदिरकषायम् " (सु.चि. २२)
["Śanaiṛmēhinaṃ khadirakaṣāyaṃ" (Su.Ci.22.)]

"ചവർത്തുമധുരിച്ചുള്ളു കരിങ്ങാലിയുടെ രസം
സർവ്വകുഷ്ഠപ്രമേഹഞ്ച മേദസ്സും പിത്തവും കഫം
ഇവ വർദ്ധിക്കിലന്നേരം ശമിപ്പാനുമിതുത്തമം" (ഗു.പാ)

["Cavarttumadhuriccu!!u karinnāliyuṭe rasaṃ
Sarvakuṣṭhapramēhañca mēdassuṃ pittavuṃ kaphaṃ
Iva varddhikkilannēraṃ śamippānumituttamaṃ" (Gu.pā.)]

Remarks: The gummy extract of the wood is known as cutch.

Eng	:	Cutch,Catechu
Hin	:	Katthā (कत्था)
Kan	:	Kaḷusāra (ಕಳುಸಾರ)
Mal	:	Kāttu (കാത്ത്)
San	:	Khadirasāraḥ (खदिरसारः)
Tam	:	Kācukkaṭṭi (காசுக்கட்டி)
Tel	:	Kodiramu (తెల్లతుమ్మ)

"खादिरः खदिरोद्भूतः तत्सारो रंगतः स्मृतः ।
ज्ञेयः खदिरसारश्च तथा रंगः षडाह्वयः ॥" (रा.नि.)

["Khādiraḥ khadirōdbhutaḥ tatsārō ramgadaḥ smṛtaḥ
Jñēyaḥ khadirasāraśca tathā ramgaḥ ṣaḍāhvayaḥ" (Ra.ni.)]

"कटुकः खदिरसारः तिक्तोष्णः कफवातहृत् ।
व्रणकण्ठामयघ्नश्च रुचिकृद्दीपनः परः ॥" (रा. नि.)

["Kaṭukaḥ khadirasāraḥ tiktōṣṇaḥ kaphavātahṛt
Vraṇakaṇṭhāmayaghnaśca rucikṛddīpanaḥ paraḥ" (Rā.ni.)]

"निर्यासस्तस्य मधुरो बल्यः शुक्लविवर्द्धनः ।
सारस्तु विशदो व्रण्यो मुखरोगकफास्रजित् ॥" (म.वि.)

["Niryāsastasya madhurō balyaḥ śukḷavivarddhanaḥ
Sārastu viśadō vraṇyō mukharōgakaphāsrajit." (Ma.vi.)]

Coll. No. B.S.I.(A.C.)2340

Acacia leucophloea **(Roxb.) Willd.**

Mimosaceae (बब्बुल–कुलम्)

Eng	:	White babool, Distiller's acacia
Hin	:	Safēd bābul, Śarāb ki kikār (सफेद बाबुल, शराब कि किकार)
Kan	:	Biḷijāli (ಬಿಳಿಜಾಲಿ)
Mal	:	Veḷvēlaṃ, Veḷvēlakaṃ (വെൾവേലം, വെൾവേലകം)
San	:	Arimēdaḥ (अरिमेदः)
Tam	:	Veḷvēlaṃ, Paṭṭaiccārāyamaraṃ (வெள்வேலம், பட்டைச்சாராயமரம்)
Tel	:	Tellatumma (తెల్లతుమ్మ)

Distribution: Throughout India, in dry deciduous forests

The plant: A moderate sized tree upto 30 m in height with spreading branches, crooked and gnarled stems, white spines and pale yellowish grey to nearly white bark with pale red inside: leaves bipinnate, 2.5–5 cm long, main rachis pubescent with a cup-shaped gland between each pair of pinnae, 5–15 pairs of pinnae of 12–30 pairs linear-oblong, obtuse; flowers in large terminal tomentose panicles, heads numerous, globose; fruits sessile, thin, flat, slightly curved pods, covered with pale brown tomentum; seeds 10 – 20 per pod.

Parts used: bark

Properties and uses: The bark is astringent, bitter, thermogenic, styptic, alexeteric, anthelmintic, vulnerary, demulcent, constipating, expectorant and antipyretic. It is useful in vitiated conditions of *kapha,* bronchitis, cough, inflammation, skin diseases, leucoderma, leprosy, pruritus, erysipelas, vomiting, wounds, ulcers, diarrhoea, dysentery, internal and external haemorrhages, dental caries, oral ulcers, proctoptosis, stomatitis and intermittent fevers.

"अरिमेदो भवेद्वेलो मुखरोगरिपुर्हिमः ।
गोधास्कन्धश्च सर्पारिस्त्वक्सारः कट्फलेति च ॥ " (अ.म.)
["Arimēdō bhavēdvēlō mukharōgaripuṛhimaḥ
Gōdhāskandhaśca saṛpāristvaksarāḥ kaṭphalēti ca" (A.ma.)]

"इरिमेदोऽरिमेदश्च गोधास्कन्धोऽरिमेदकः ।
अहिमेदोऽहिमारश्च पूतिमेदोऽहिमेदकः ॥ " (रा.नि.)

Acacia leucophloea

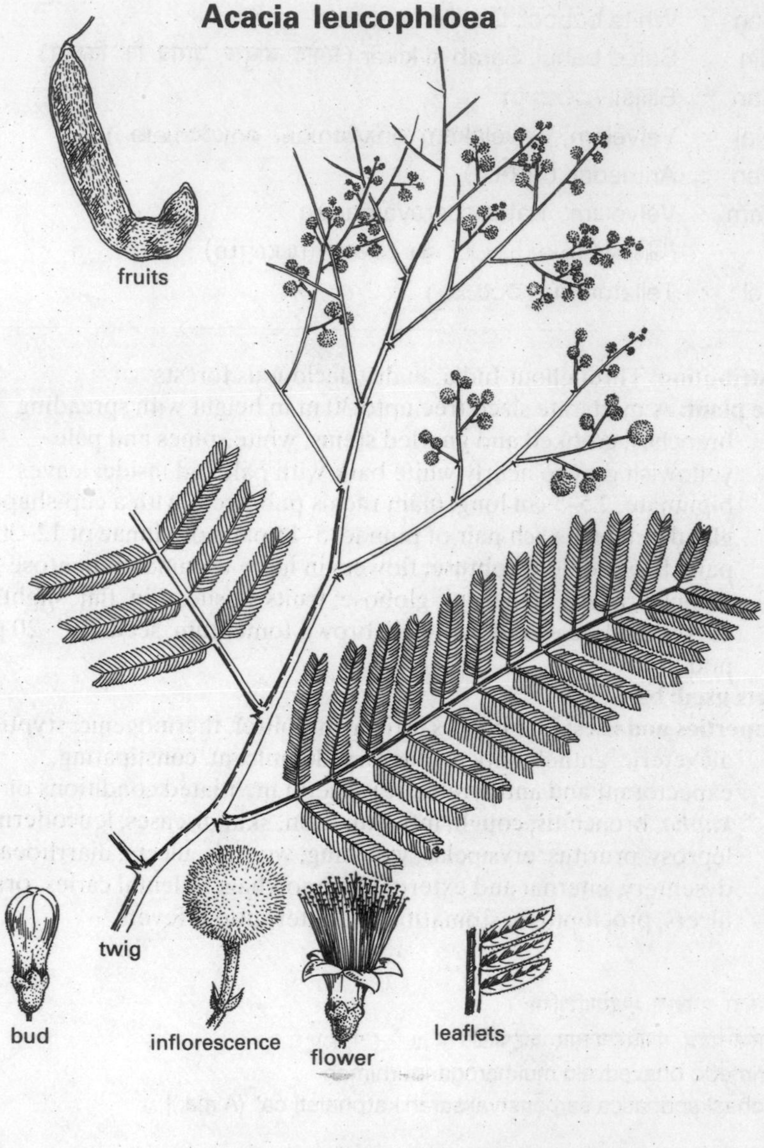

["Irimēdōʃrimēdaśca gōdhāskandhōʃrimēdakaḥ
Ahimēdōʃhimāraśca pūtimēdōʃhimēdakaḥ" (Rā.ni.)]

"अरिमेदः कषायोष्णो मुखदन्तगदास्रजित् ।
हन्ति कण्डूविषश्ळेष्मकृमिकुष्ठविषव्रणान् ॥ " (भा.प्र.)
["Arimēdaḥ kaṣāyōṣṇō mukhadantagadāsṛajit
Hanti kaṇḍūviṣaśḷēṣmakṛmikuṣṭhaviṣavraṇān" (Bhā.pṛa.)]

"अरिमेदः कषायोष्णस्तिक्तो भूतविनाशकः ।
शोफातिसारकासघ्नो विषवीसर्पनाशनः ॥ " (रा.नि.)
["Arimēdaḥ kaṣāyōṣṇastiktō bhūtavināśakaḥ
Śōphātisārakāsaghnō viṣavīsaṛpanāśanaḥ" (Rā.ni.)]

"अरिमेदस्य निर्यासो मधुरस्तु बलप्रदः ।
धातुवृद्धिकरश्चैव मुनिभिः संप्रभाषितः ॥ " (नि.र.)
["Arimēdasya niryāsō madhurastu balapṛadaḥ
Dhātuvṛddhikaraścaiva munibhiḥ sampṛabhāṣitaḥ" (Ni.ra.)]

"रिमः कटुः कषायोष्णस्तीक्ष्णो हन्ति कफं कृमीन् ।
कण्डूरक्तग्रहान् वस्तिमुखदन्तगदानपि ॥
तत्फलं तिक्तमधुरं स्निग्धोष्णं कफवातनुत् । " (कै. नि.)
["Rimaḥ kaṭuḥ kaṣāyōṣnastīkṣṇō hanti kaphaṃ kṛmīn
Kaṇḍūraktagrahān vastimukhadantagadānapi
Tatphalaṃ tiktamadhuraṃ snigdhōṣnaṃ kaphavātanut" (Kai.ni.)]

"इरिमेदो व्रणे पथ्यो मुखदन्तामयापहः ॥ " (सो.नि.)
["Irimēdō vṛaṇē pathyō mukhadantāmayāpahaḥ" (Sō.ni.)]

Remarks : According to some reports, the bark of *Acacia ferruginea* DC. is also used as *arimēdaḥ* in some parts of India.

Coll. No. B.S.I.(A.Z.C.) 9736

Acacia nilotica (Linn.) Willd.ex Del. ssp. indica (Benth.) Brenan

(A.arabica *auct.non(Lam.) Willd.*)

Mimosaceae (बब्बुल–कुलम्)

Eng	:	Babul, Black babool, Indian gum arabic tree
Hin	:	Babūl, Bābur (बबूल, बाबुर)
Kan	:	Karijāli, Baunijali (ಕರಿಜಾಲಿ. ಬೌನಿಜಲಿ)
Mal	:	Karivēlaṃ (കരിവേലം)
San	:	Baṛburaḥ, Vāvarī (बर्बुरः, वावरी)
Tam	:	Karuvēlaṃ, Karuvēl (கருவேலம், கருவேல்)
Tel	:	Nallatumma (నల్లతుమ్మ)

Distribution: Throughout India, in deciduous forests, also cultivated

The plant: A moderate sized tree upto 10 m in height with dark brown or black longitudinally fissured rough bark and reddish brown heart-wood, branchlets slender, pubescent when young; leaves bipinnately compound, main rachis downy, often with glands, stipular spines highly variable, often whitish, straight and sharp, pinnae 4 – 9 pairs, leaflets subsessile, 10 – 25 pairs, nearly glabrous; flowers golden yellow in globose heads, peduncles axillary in fascicles of 2 – 6; fruits stalked, compressed, moniliform pods with constrictions between the seeds; seeds 8–12 per pod.

The 'gum' (gum Arabic) exudes from cuts in the bark in the form of rounded or ovoid 'tears', each drop about 1.25 cm in size. Its colour varies from pale yellow to black.

Parts used: bark, gum

Properties and uses: The bark is astringent, acrid, cooling, styptic, emollient, vulnerary, anthelmintic, constipating, depurative, aphrodisiac, diuretic, expectorant, alexeteric, emetic and nutritive. It is useful in vitiated conditions of *kapha* and *pitta,* haemorrhages, wounds, ulcers, helminthiasis, ascites, chronic dysentery, diarrhoea, leprosy, leucoderma, skin diseases, burning sensation, strangury, cough, bronchitis, leucorrhoea, haemorrhoids, proctoptosis, seminal weakness, pharyngodynia, uterovesical disorders, oral ulcers and odontopathy.

The gum is sweet, astringent, cooling, emollient, expectorant, constipating, liver tonic, aphrodisiac, haemostatic, antipyretic and tonic. It is useful in vitiated conditions of *vāta* and *pitta*, cough, asthma, diarrhoea, dysentery, seminal weakness, haemorrhages,

Acacia nilotica ssp. indica

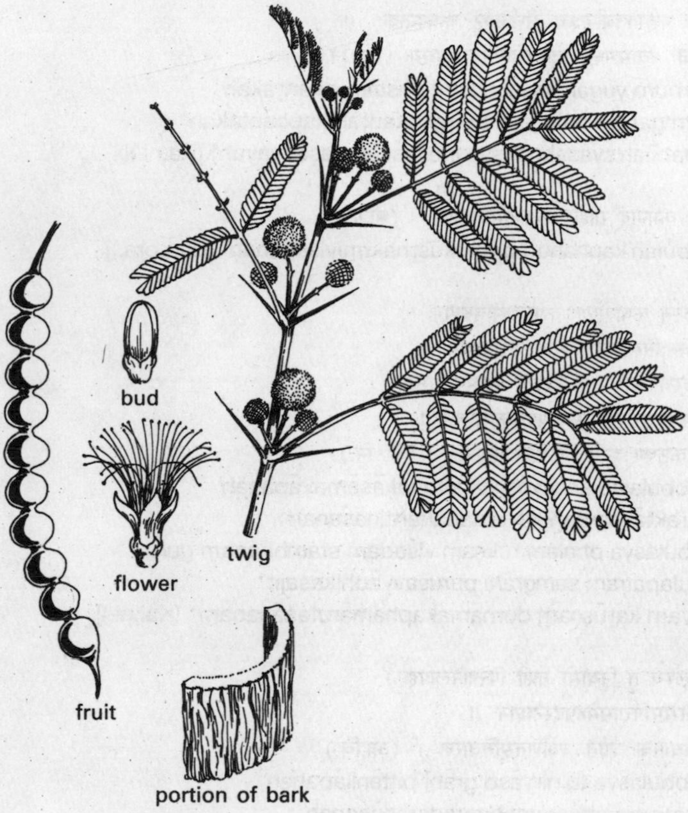

leprosy, pharyngodynia, pneumonosis, haemorrhoids, urinogenital discharges, burns, colic, intermittent fevers and general debility.

"बबूलः किङ्किरातः स्यात् किङ्कराटः सपीतकः ।
स एव कथितस्तज्ञैराभा षड्पदमोदिनी ॥" (भा. प्र.)
["Babūlaḥ kiṅkirātaḥ syāt kiṅkarāṭaḥ sapītakaḥ
Sa ēva kathitastajñairābhā ṣaṭpadamōdinī" (Bhā.pṛa.)]

बर्बुरो युगळाक्षश्च कण्टालुस्तीक्ष्णकण्टकः ।
गोश्रृंगः पङ्क्तिबीजश्च दीर्घकण्टः कफान्तकः ॥
दृढबीजः श्वासभक्ष्यो ज्ञेयश्चेति दशाह्वयः । (रा.नि.)
["Baṛburō yugaḷākṣaśca kaṇṭālustīkṣṇakaṇṭakaḥ
Gōśṛmgaḥ panktibījaśca dīṛghakaṇṭaḥ kaphāntakaḥ
Dṛḍhabījaḥ śvāsabhakṣyō jñēyaśceti daśāhvayaḥ" (Rā.ni.)]

बबूलः कफनुद् ग्राही कुष्ठकृमिविषापहः । (भा.प्र.)
["Babūlaḥ kaphanud grāhī kuṣṭhakṛmiviṣāpahaḥ" (Bhā.pṛa.)]

बब्बुलस्तु कषायोष्णः कफकासामयापहः ।
आमरक्तातिसारघ्नः पित्तदाहार्त्तिनाशनः ॥
बब्बुलस्य फलं रूक्षं विशदं स्तंभनं गुरु ।
बबूलपत्रं संग्राहि पुरुषव्याधिकासजित् ॥
रुच्यं कटूष्णं दुर्नामकफमारुतनाशनम् । (कै. नि.)
["Babbulastu kaṣāyōṣṇaḥ kaphakāsāmayāpahaḥ
Amaraktātisāraghnaḥ pittadāhāṛttināśanaḥ
Babbulasya phalaṃ rūkṣaṃ viśadaṃ stambhanaṃ guru
Babūlapaṭraṃ samgrāhi puruṣavyādhikāsajit
Rucyaṃ kaṭūṣṇaṃ duṛnāmakaphamārutanāśanaṃ" (Kai.ni.)]

"बब्बुलस्य तु निर्यासो ग्राही पित्तानिलापहः ।
रक्तातिसारपित्तास्रमेहप्रदरनाशनः ॥
भग्नसंधानकः शीतः शोणितस्रुतिवारणः ।" (आ.वि.)
["Babbulasya tu niryāsō grāhī pittānilāpahaḥ
Raktātisārapittāsṛamēhapṛadaranāśanaḥ
Bhagnasamdhānakaḥ śītaḥ śōṇitasṛutivāraṇaḥ" (Ā.vi.)]

"बर्बुरस्तु कषायोष्णः कफकासामयापहः ।
आमरक्तातिसारघ्नः पित्तदाहार्त्तिनाशनः ॥" (रा.नि.)
["Baṛburastu kaṣāyōṣṇaḥ kaphakāsāmayāpahaḥ
Amaraktātisāraghnaḥ pittadāhāṛtināśanaḥ" (Rā.ni.)]

"बब्बूलो व्रणकर्णास्यनाडीघ्नः कफहृत् सरः ।

कुष्ठघ्नश्च फलं तस्य भेदनं कृमिनाशनम् ॥ " (सो.नि.)
["Babbūlō vraṇakarṇāsyanāḍīghnaḥ kaphahṛt saraḥ
Kuṣṭhaghnaśca phalaṃ tasya bhēdanaṃ kṛmināśanaṃ" (Sō.ni.)]

"बब्बूलस्तिक्तमधुरः स्निग्धः शीतोष्णतूवरः ।
आमरक्तातिसाराणां नाशनो ग्राहको मतः ॥
कफं कासं च पित्तं च दाहं रक्तातिसारकम् ।
वातं प्रमेहं शमयेत् पर्णन्तु ग्राहकं मतम् ॥
रुच्यं कटूष्णकासघ्नं वातपुंस्त्वकफार्शनुत् ।
बब्बूलस्य फलं रूक्षं विशदं स्तंभनं गुरु ॥
कषायं मधुरं शीतं लेखनं कफपितत्तहृत् ।" (नि.र.)
["Babbūlastiktamadhuraḥ snigdhaḥ śītōṣṇatūvaraḥ
Āmaraktātisārāṇāṃ nāśanō grāhakō mataḥ
Kaphaṃ kāsaṃ ca pittaṃ ca dāhaṃ raktātisārakaṃ
Vātaṃ pramēhaṃ śamayēt parṇantu grāhakaṃ mataṃ
Rucyaṃ kaṭūṣṇakāsaghnaṃ vātapuṃstvakaphārśanut
Babbūlasya phalaṃ rūkṣaṃ viśadaṃ stambhanaṃ guru
Kaṣāyaṃ madhuraṃ śītaṃ lēkhanaṃ kaphapittahṛt" (Ni.ra.)]

Acacia polyantha Willd.

(A. suma *(Roxb.) Buch.-Ham.*)

Mimosaceae (बब्बुल–कुलम्)

Eng	:	White cutch tree, White catechu
Hin	:	Śvētakhair (श्वेतखैर)
Kan	:	Kandaraha, Mūgali, (ಕಂದರಹ, ಮೂಗಲಿ)
Mal	:	Veṇkarinnāli, Sōmarāyattoli (വെൺകരിങ്ങാലി, സോമരായത്തൊലി)
San	:	Kadaraḥ, Sōmavalkaḥ (कदरः, सोमवल्कः)
Tam	:	Kōvil, Śilaiyuñcai (கோவில், சிலையுஞ்சை)
Tel	:	Tellatumma, Sōmavalkamu, Tellasundra (తెల్లతుమ్మ, సోమవల్కము, తెల్లసుంద్ర)

Distribution: Bengal, Bihar, Karnataka and Tamil Nadu, in moist localities

The plant: A medium sized tree with white bark exfoliating in papery flakes with horizontal patches of darker colour, young shoots downy; leaves bipinnate, leaflets 30 – 50 pairs, linear-oblong, pubescent, nerves obscure, glands between many of the pairs of pinnae, stipular spines short, straight or slightly hooked; flowers sessile, white, in spikes; fruits flat pods, 7–12 cm long with a triangular beak at the apex; seeds many.

Parts used: heartwood

Properties and uses: The heartwood is bitter, astringent, acrid, thermogenic, depurative, anthelmintic and revulsive. It is useful in leprosy, leucoderma, pruritus, skin diseases, vitiated conditions of *kapha*, diabetes, helminthiasis, ulcers, epilepsy, insanity, rheumatism and obesity.

"कदरः खदिराकारः काळस्कन्धश्च कामुकः कामी ।
नेमी च सोमवल्कः पथिद्रुमः श्यामसारश्च ॥
नेमीवृक्षो महाकाळः काळकः क्षुद्रकण्टकः ।
चक्रवृक्ष इति ज्ञेयः शब्दैः पर्यायवाचकैः ॥" (अ.म.)
["Kadaraḥ khadirākāraḥ kāḷaskandhaśca kāmukaḥ kāmī
Nēmī ca sōmavalkaḥ pathidrumaḥ śyāmasāraśca
Nēmivṛkṣō mahākāḷaḥ kāḷakaḥ kṣudrakaṇṭakaḥ
Cakṛavṛkṣa iti jñēyaḥ śabdaiḥ paryāyavācakaiḥ" (A.ma.)]

"कदर : सोमवल्कश्च श्यामसारोऽथ कार्मुकः ।

Acacia polyantha

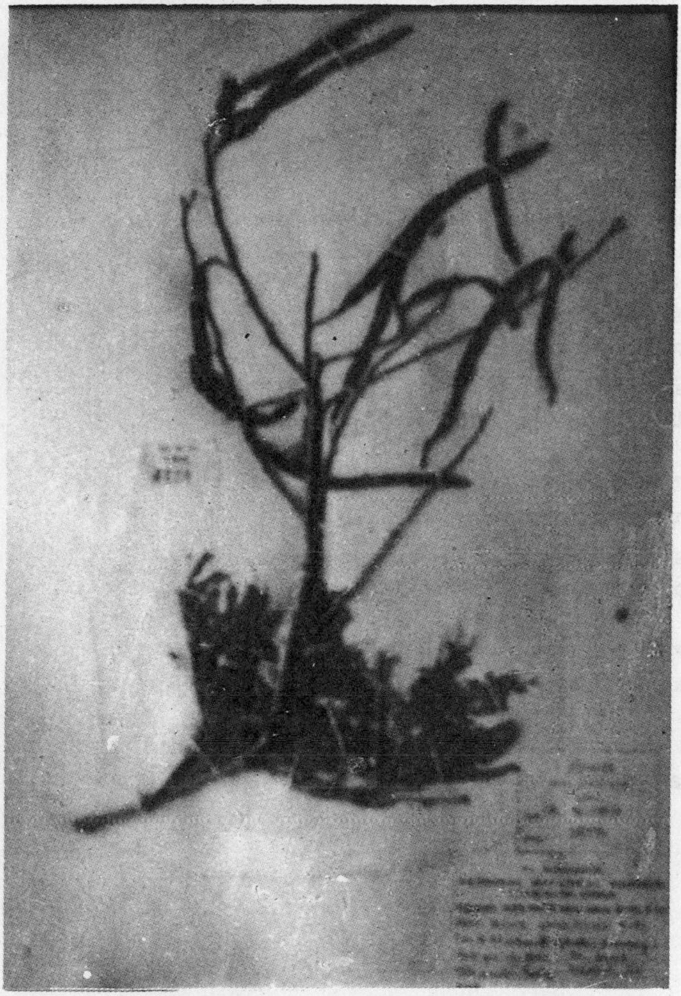

Courtesy: NBRI, Lucknow.

कण्टाद्यो गोरडो वक्रो महावृक्षो द्विजप्रियः ॥
महावल्कः संवरणो मार्गवृक्षः सुकण्टकी ।
काम्बोजीपत्रकः सोमो नेमिवृक्षो मरुद्भव : ॥ (सो.नि.)
["Kadaraḥ sōmavalkaśca śyāmasārō|tha kārmukaḥ
Kaṇṭādyō gōraḍō vakrō mahāvṛkṣō dvijapriyaḥ
Mahāvalkaḥ saṁvaraṇō mārgavṛkṣaḥ sukaṇṭakī
Kāmbōjīpatrakaḥ sōmō nēmivṛkṣō marudbhavaḥ" (Sō.ni.)]

"कदरो विशदो वर्ण्यो मुखरोगकफास्रजित् ।" (भा. प्र. & कै.नि.)
["Kadarō viśadō varṇyō mukharōgakaphāsrajit "(Bhā.pra.& Kai.ni.)]

"प्रमेहमेदोदोषघ्नः कफपित्तव्रणापहः ।
पाण्डुकुष्ठप्रशमनः कदरः श्वित्रनाशनः ॥ (म.नि.)
["Pramēhamēdōdōṣaghnaḥ kaphapittavraṇāpahaḥ
Pāṇḍukuṣṭhapraśamanaḥ kadaraḥ śvitranāśanaḥ" (Ma.ni.)]

"श्वेतस्तु खदिरस्तिक्तः कषायः कटुरुष्णकः ।
कण्डूतिभूतकुष्ठघ्नः कफवातव्रणापहः ॥ (रा.नि.)
["Śvētastu khadirastiktaḥ kaṣāyaḥ kaṭuruṣṇakaḥ
Kaṇḍūtibhūtakuṣṭhaghnaḥ kaphavātavraṇāpahaḥ" (Rā.ni.)]

"श्वेतस्तु खदिरस्तिक्तः शीतः पित्तकफापहः ।
रक्तदोषहरश्चैव कण्डूकुष्ठविनाशनः ॥ (ध.नि.)
["Svētastu khadirastiktaḥ śītaḥ pittakaphāpahaḥ
Raktadōṣaharaścaiva kaṇḍūkuṣṭhavināśanaḥ" (Dha.ni.)]

"सारस्तु विशदो वर्ण्यो मुखरोगकफास्रनुत् ॥ (म.वि.)
["Sārastu viśadō varṇyō mukharōgakaphāsranut" (Ma.vi.)]

"गोरडाख्यो गुणैरेभिर्युक्तो न्यूनः स बृंहणः ॥ (सो.नि.)
["Gōraḍākhyō guṇairēbhiryuktō nyūnaḥ sa bṛmhaṇaḥ" (Sō.ni.)]

Acacia sinuata (Lour.) Merr.

(A. concinna *(Willd.) DC.*)

Mimosaceae (बब्बुल – कुलम्)

Eng	:	Soapnut-acacia
Hin	:	Sātalā, Kōcī (सातला, कोची)
Kan	:	Śēge (ಶೀಗೆ)
Mal	:	Caṛmalanta, Caṛmantala, Cīkkākkā, Cīnikkā, Cīvikkā (ചർമലന്ത, ചർമന്തല, ചീക്കാക്കാ, ചീനിക്കാ, ചീവിക്കാ)
San	:	Saptalā, Caṛmasāhvā (सप्तला, चर्मसाह्वा)
Tam	:	Cikaikkāi, Cīyakkāi, Cīkkāi (சிகைக்காய், சீயக்காய், சீக்காய்)
Tel	:	Śikāya (శికాయ)

Distribution: Throughout India, in forests

The plant: A stout prickly climbing shrub with brown branches dotted with white; leaves bipinnate, main rachis bearing sharp hooked prickles and a large gland on the petiole, pinnae 8 pairs or more, leaflets subsessile, sensitive, unequal sided, glabrous; flowers small in globose heads, polygamous; fruits short-stalked thin pods, flat, coriaceous, the sutures straight; seeds 6 – 10 per pod.

Parts used: pods

Properties and uses: The pods are bitter, astringent, cooling, diuretic, emetic, deobstruant, detergent, depurative and anthelmintic. They are useful in vitiated conditions of *pitta,* burning sensation, constipation, renal and vesical calculi, strangury, haemorrhoids, erysipelas, leucoderma, leprosy, prurigo, abscesses and eczema.

The powdered pods (known as *cikkikkai* powder) are the best alternatives to soaps in all cases of skin diseases.

"सातला सप्तला सारी विदुळा विमलाऽमला ।
बहुफेना चर्मकषा फेना दीप्ता मराळिका ॥ (ध.नि.)
["Sātalā saptalā sārī viduḷā vimalāʃmalā
Behuphēnā caṛmakaṣā phēnā dīptā marāḷikā" (Dha.ni.)]

"सातला शोधनी तिक्ता कफपित्तास्रदोषनुत् ।
शोफोदराध्मानहरा किञ्चिन्मारुतकृद्भवेत् ॥" (ध.नि.)
["Sātalā śōdhanī tiktā kaphapittāsṛadōṣanut
Śōphōdarādhmānaharā kiñcinmārutakṛdbhavēt" (Dha.ni.)]

Acacia sinuata

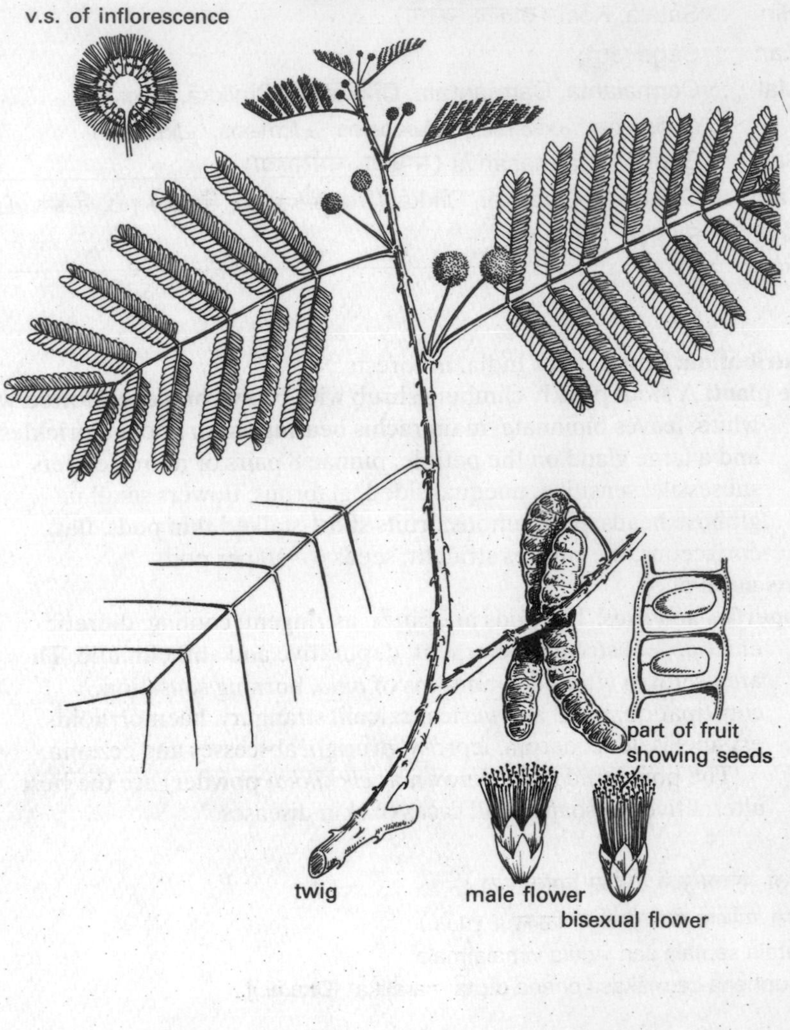

"सातला कफपित्तघ्नी लघु तिक्ता कषायिका ।
विसर्पकुष्ठविस्फोटव्रणशोफनिकृन्तनी ॥" (रा.नि.)
["Sātalā kaphapittaghnī laghu tiktā kaṣāyikā
Visarpakuṣṭhavisphōṭavraṇaśōphanikṛntanī" (Rā.ni.)]

"मूलत्वगादिकं ग्राह्यं"
["Mūlatvagādikaṃ grāhyaṃ"]

Remarks: In 'Amarakōśa', *vimalā, sātalā, bhūriphēnā* and *carmakaṣā* are given as synonyms for *saptalā.* In the same text *saptalā* is mentioned as a synonym for *navamallika (tūśimulla)* also. This has led to lot of confusion.

The Sanskrit Commentary `Vākyapṛadīpikā' (Trikkovil Uzhutra Varier) on 'Aṣṭāṅgahṛdayaṃ' gives the term *bṛahmi* in Malayalam for *saptalā* included under the vegetable group of drugs *Paṭōlasaptalāriṣṭādi* as mentioned in 'Aṣṭāṅgahṛdayaṃ- Sūṭrasthānaṃ' Chapter -6. But `Pāṭhyakāra' interprets it to mean *caṛmantara* and gives it another Sanskrit term *brāhmī viśēṣaḥ.* Since *saptalā* and *caṛmasāhvā* are the synonyms for the same drug, it may not be proper to regard them as two different ones. In the text 'Sahasṛayogaṃ' in the formulation of *Nārācakacūṛṇaṃ* the Malayalam term *brahmi* is used for *sātalā.* In 'Abhidhānamañjarī' both *sātalā* and *caṛmasāhvā,* the two synonyms of *saptalā,* have been used as *sātala brahmi* in Malayalam.

It would not be proper to identify *caṛmasāhvā, (Acacia sinuata)* as *brahṃi* or *brahmīv iśēṣaṃ* as the former is a terrestrial prickly climber seen in forests while the latter is a hydrophyte growing along the water courses. Besides, the words *saptalā, sātalā* and *caṛmasāhvā* are synonyms of the same drug *caṛmakaṣā* which is always identified in Malayalam as *caṛmalanta (Acacia sinuata).* The word *caṛmakaṣā,* which means that which rubs away skin eruptions, is also appropriate for *cīnikkā (caṛmalanta).*

Coll. No. AVS 1181

Acalypha indica **Linn.**

Euphorbiaceae (एरण्ड–कुलम्)

Eng	:	Indian acalypha
Hin	:	Kuppīkhōklī (कुप्पीखोकली)
Kan	:	Kuppigiḍa (ಕುಪ್ಪಿಗಿಡ)
Mal	:	Kuppamēni (കുപ്പമേനി)
San	:	Haritamañjarī (हरितमञ्जरी)
Tam	:	Kuppaimēṇi, Kuppavēṇi (குப்பைமேனி, குப்பவேணி)
Tel	:	Kuppiceṭṭu, Kuppinṭa, Muripinḍi (కుప్పిచెట్టు, కుప్పింట, మురిపిండి)

Distribution: A weed found throughout the plains of India

The plant: An erect, annual herb with numerous ascending branches; leaves long-petioled, ovate or rhombic-ovate, acute, cuneate at base, crenate-serrate, glabrous, thin; both male and female flowers in axillary spikes, male flowers minute, followed by a tuft of sterile flowers, the females scattered, 3 – 5 surrounded by a many-nerved bract; fruits capsules, small, concealed by the bract; seeds ovoid, smooth, pale brown.

Parts used: whole plant

Properties and uses: The plant is bitter, acrid, expectorant, purgative, emetic, gastrointestinal irritant and diuretic. The roots and leaves are used to treat skin diseases, constipation, ulcers, bronchitis, vitiated conditions of *vāta,* otalgia and croup.

"कोकिला काकळी मुण्डा कुत्स्यपर्णी वृषोदरी ।
श्वेतशुण्ठी मुराकान्ता प्रोक्ता हरितमञ्जरी ॥" (स्व.)
["Kōkilā kākaḷī muṇḍā kutsyaparṇī vṛṣōdarī
Śvētaśuṇṭhī murākāntā prōktā haritamañjarī" (Sva.)]

"कासश्वासहरी तिक्ता कफघ्नी कटुका तथा ।
रेचनी मूत्रळा चैव ज्वरवातहरा स्मृता ॥
तत्पत्रस्वरसं प्रोक्तं कर्णशूलहरं परम् ।
पत्रकल्कस्य वर्त्तिस्तु बालानां मलबन्धहृत् ॥" (स्व.)

Acalypha indica

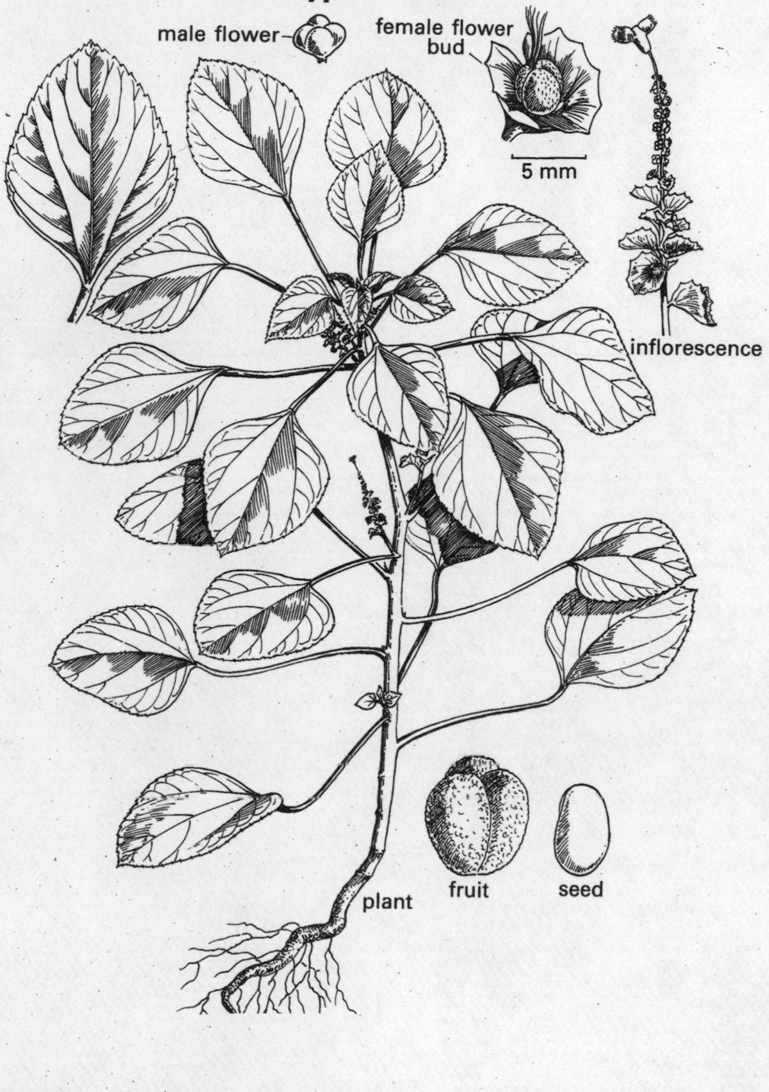

["Kāsaśvāsaharī tiktā kaphaghnī kaṭukā tathā
Rēcanī mūtraḷā caiva jvaravātaharā smṛtā
Tatpatṛasvarasaṃ pṛōktaṃ karṇaśūlaharaṃ paraṃ
Patṛakalkasya vaṛttistu bālānāṃ malabandhahṛt" (Sva.)]

Coll. No. AVS 1422

Achyranthes aspera **Linn.**

Amaranthaceae (तण्डुलीय–कुलम्)

Eng	:	Prickly chaff-flower plant
Hin	:	Circiṭā, Cicīṃḍā (चिरचिटा, चिचींडा)
Kan	:	Uttarani (ಉತ್ತರಣಿ)
Mal	:	Kaṭalāṭi, Vankaṭalāṭi, Valiyakaṭalāṭi (കടലാടി, വൻകടലാടി, വലിയ കടലാടി)
San	:	Apāmārgaḥ (अपामार्गः)
Tam	:	Kaṭalāṭi, Nāyuruvi (கடலாடி, நாயுருவி)
Tel	:	Apāmargāmu (అపామార్గము)

Distribution: Throughout India, along roadsides and waste places as well as on hills upto 900 m

The plant: An erect, much branched suffruticose or diffuse shrub upto one metre in height with quadrangular striate pubescent branches, thickened just above the nodes; leaves simple, opposite, exstipulate, velvety tomentose, orbicular, obovate or elliptic, 10 cm long and 7.5 cm broad; flowers bracteate and bracteolate, greenish, deflexed, in slender spikes often 45 cm long; fruits easily disarticulating oblong urticle; seeds single, inverse.

Parts used: whole plant

Properties and uses: The plant is acrid, bitter, thermogenic, expectorant, revulsive, carminative, digestive, stomachic, laxative, anodyne, depurative, anthelmintic, diuretic, linthontriptic, sudorific, demulcent, haematinic and anti-inflamatory. It is useful in cough, asthma, bronchitis, dyspepsia, flatulence, colic, painful inflammations, dropsy, ophthalmopathy, vomiting, leprosy, skin diseases, pruritus, helminthiasis, strangury, renal and vesical calculi, cardiac disorders, anaemia, vitiated conditions of *kapha* and *vāta* and general debility.

"अपामार्गस्तु शिखरी किणिही खरमञ्जरी ।
दुर्ग्रहश्चाप्यधःशल्यः प्रत्यक्पुष्पी मयूरकः ॥
काण्डकण्टः शैखरिको मर्कटी दुरभिग्रहः ।
वशिरश्च पराक्पुष्पी कण्टी मर्कटपिप्पली ॥
कटुर्मञ्जरिको नन्दी क्षवकः पङ्क्तिकण्टकः ।

Achyranthes aspera

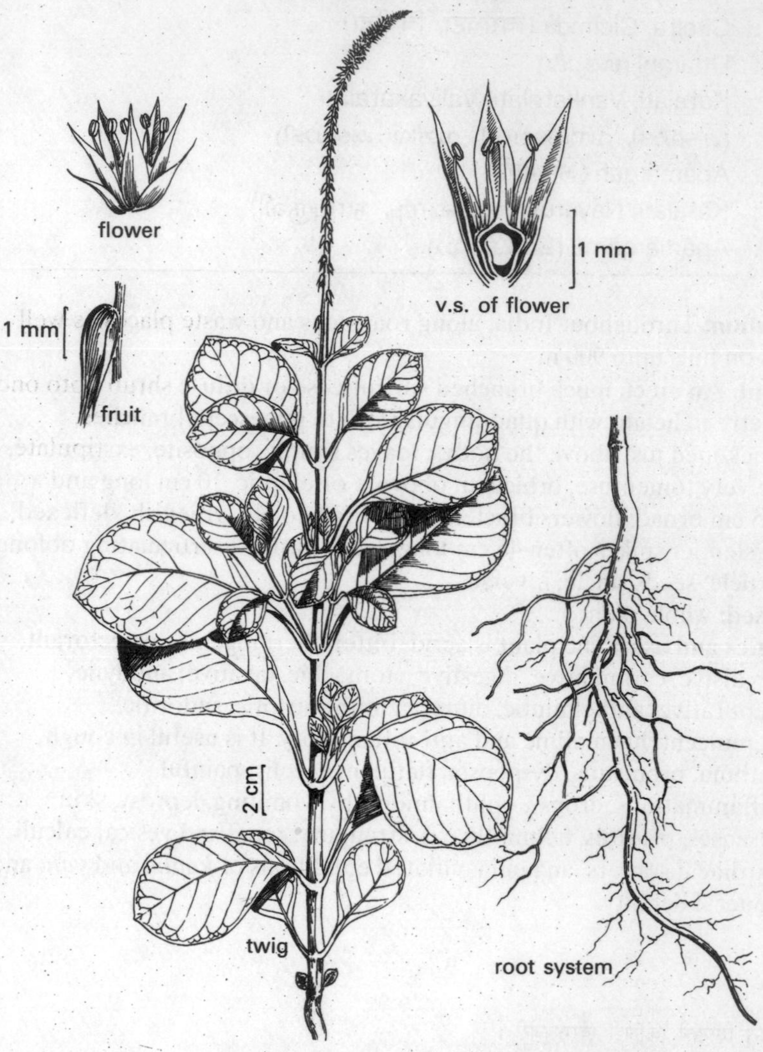

मालाकण्टश्च कुब्जश्च त्रयोविंशतिनामकः ॥" (रा.नि.)
["Apāmārgastu śikharī kiṇihī kharamañjarī
Durgrahaścāpyadhaḥśalyaḥ pratyakpuṣpī mayūrakaḥ
Kāṇḍakaṇṭaḥ śaikharikō markaṭī durabhigrahaḥ
Vaśiraśca parākpuṣpī kaṇṭī markaṭapippalī
Kaṭurmañjarikō nandī kṣavakaḥ panktikaṇṭakaḥ
Mālākaṇṭaśca kubjaśca trayōviṁśatināmakaḥ" (Rā.ni.)]

"अपामार्गः सरस्तीक्ष्णो दीपनस्तिक्तकः कटुः ।
पाचनो नावनश्छर्दिकफमेदोऽनिलापहा ॥
निहन्ति हृद्रुजाध्मानार्शःकण्डूशूलोदरापची ।" (भा.प्र.)
["Apāmārgaḥ sarastīkṣṇō dīpanastiktakaḥ kaṭuḥ
Pācanō nāvanaśchardikaphamēdō'nilāpahā
Nihanti hydrujādhmānārśaḥkaṇḍūśulōdarāpacī" (Bhā.pra.)]

"अपामार्गोऽग्निकृत् तीक्ष्णो नस्यात् शीर्षकृमीन् जयेत् ।
वामको रक्तसंग्राही रक्तातीसारहृन्मतः ॥" (सो.नि.)
["Apāmārgō'gnikrt tīkṣṇō nasyāt śīrṣakrmīn jayēt
Vāmakō raktasaṁgrāhī raktatīsārahṛnmataḥ" (Sō.ni.)]

"कफमेदोऽनिलहरा छेदनी स्रंसनी तथा ।
रसे पाके च कटुका वीर्योष्णा खरमञ्जरी ॥" (म.नि.)
["Kaphamēdō'nilaharā chēdanī sraṁsanī tathā
Rasē pākē ca kaṭukā vīryōṣṇā kharamañjarī" (Ma.ni.)]

"अपामार्गस्तु तिक्तोष्णः कटुश्च कफनाशनः ।
अर्शकण्डूदराध्मानो रक्तहृद् ग्राहि वान्तिकृत् ॥" (ध.नि., रा.नि.)
["Apāmārgastu tiktōṣṇaḥ kaṭuśca kaphanāśanaḥ
Arśakaṇḍūdarādhmānō raktahrd grāhi vāntikrt" (Dha.ni., Rā.ni.)]

"नस्ये वान्ते प्रशस्तः स्यात् दद्रुकण्डूकफापहः ।
अपामार्गाग्निकृत् तीक्ष्णः क्लेदनः स्रंसनः परः ॥" (रा.व.)
["Nasyē vāntē praśastaḥ syāt dadrukaṇḍūkaphāpahaḥ
Apāmārgāgnikrt tīkṣṇaḥ klēdanaḥ sraṁsanaḥ paraḥ" (Rā.va.)]

കടലാടി ശമിപ്പിക്കും വാതത്തേയും കഫത്തെയും
പിന്നെ വസ്തിയിലുണ്ടാകും രോഗങ്ങൾക്കൊക്കെയും ഗുണം (ഗു.പാ.)
["Kaṭalāṭi śamippikkuṃ vātattēyuṃ kaphatteyuṃ
Pinne vastiyiluṇṭākuṃ rōgannaḷkkokkeyuṃ guṇaṃ". (Gu.pā.)]

Coll. No. B.S.I. (N.C.) 66957

Aconitum heterophyllum **Wall. ex Royle**

Ranunculaceae (वत्सनाभ–कुलम्)

Eng	:	Atis root
Hin	:	Atīs (अतीस)
Kan	:	Ativiṣa (ಅತಿವಿಷ)
Mal	:	Ativiṭayaṃ (അതിവിടയം)
San	:	Ativiṣā (अतिविषा)
Tam	:	Ativaḍayaṃ (அதிவடையம்)
Tel	:	Ativasa (అతివస)

Distributrion: Sub-Alpine and Alpine zones of the Himalayas

The plant: A herb, stem erect, simple, at times branched; leaves more or less heteromorphous, lowest leaves with long petioles, usually 5-lobed to the middle, uppermost leaves amplexicaul; flowers in leafy panicle, blue or violet; fruits follicles, 16 – 18 mm long; seeds obpyramidal, blackish brown, angles more or less winged.

Roots tuberous, whitish or grey, smooth, cross-section pure white in which 2 – 6 blackish vascular supplies are seen arranged in a discontinuous ring, cylindric-oblong or conic, upto 2.5 cm long and 0.5 – 1.5 cm thick; breaks very easily and tastes very bitter.

Parts used: roots

Properties and uses: The roots are acrid, bitter, thermogenic, expectorant, alexeteric, stomachic, digestive, antiperiodic and tonic. They are useful in dysentery, diarrhoea, stomach disorders, fever, malarial fever, vomiting, helminthiasis, haemorrhoids, haemorrhages, internal inflammatory conditions and general debility. They are highly recommended for diseases in children.

"घुणवल्लभा घुणेष्टा घुणप्रिया शृङ्गिका च शुककन्दा ।
विषमोपविषा|तिविषा विषा च विश्वेति मादी स्यात् ।।" (अ.म.)
["Ghuṇavallabhā ghuṇeṣṭā ghuṇapriya śṛṅgikā ca śukakandā
Viṣamōpaviṣā|tiviṣā viṣā ca viśveti madrī syat" (A.ma.)]
अतिविषा श्वेतकन्दा विश्वा शृङगी च भङ्गुरा ।
विरूपा श्यामकन्दा च विश्वरूपा महौषधी ।।
वीरा प्रतिविषा चार्दा विषा श्वेतवचा स्मृता ।
अरुणोपविषा चैव ज्ञेया षोडशसम्मिता ।।

Aconitum heterophyllum

Plate 3

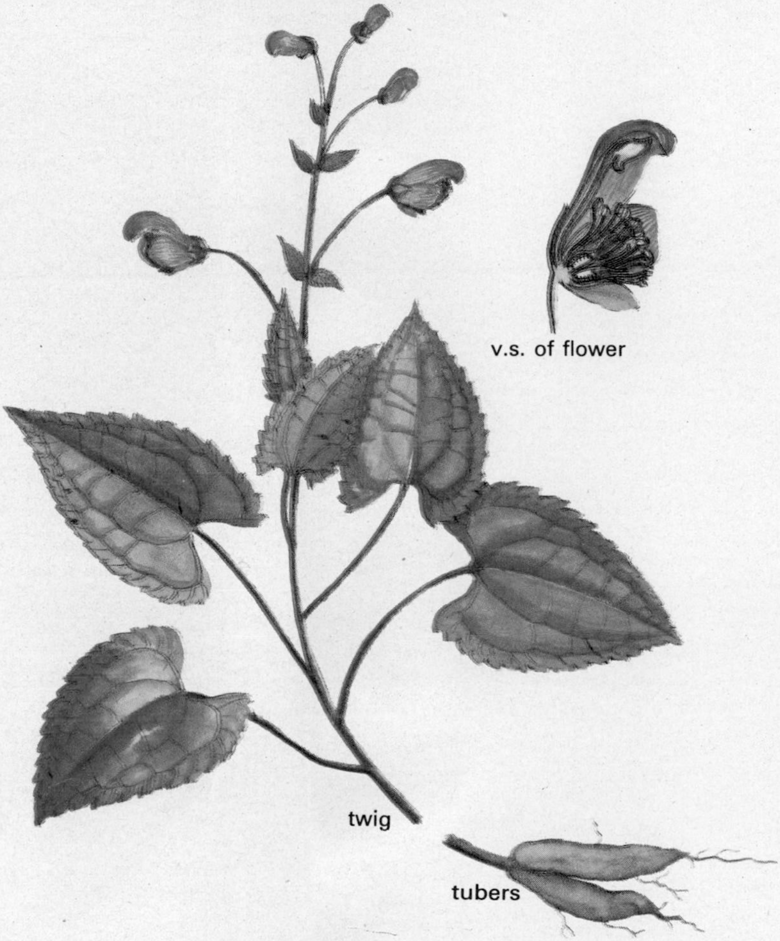

["Ativiṣā śvētakandā viśvā śṛṅgī ca bhaṅgurā
Virūpā syāmakandā ca viśvarūpā mahauṣadhī
Vīrā prativiṣā cārdrā viṣā śvētavacā smṛtā
Aruṇōpaviṣā caiva jñēyā ṣōḍaśasaṁmitā" (Rā.ni.)]

विषा सोष्णा कटुस्तिक्ता दीपनी पाचनी हरेत् ।
कफपित्तातिसारामविषकासवमिकृमीन् ॥"
["Viṣā sōṣṇā kaṭustiktā pacanī dīpanī harēt
Kaphapittātisārāmaviṣakāsavamikṛmīn" (Bhā.pra.)]

"कटूष्णाऽतिविषा तिक्ता कफपित्तज्वरापहा ।
आमातिसारकासघ्नी विषच्छर्दिविनाशिनी ॥" (ध.नि. & रा.नि.)
["Kaṭūṣṇāऽtiviṣā tiktā kaphapittajvarāpahā
Āmātisārakāsaghnī viṣacchardivināsinī" (Dha.ni. & Rā.ni.)]

"त्रिप्रकारं चातिविषं किञ्चिदुष्णं च तिक्तकम् ।
अग्निदीप्तिकरं ग्राहि त्रिदोषाणां च पाचकम् ॥
रक्तपित्तज्वरामातिसारकासविषापहम् ।
यकृद्वान्तितृषां चैव कृमीनर्शांश्च पीनसम् ॥
पित्तोदरं चातिसारं हर्षव्याधिहरं मतम् ।" (नि.र.)
["Triprakāraṃ cātiviṣaṃ kiñciduṣṇāṃ ca tiktakaṃ
Agnidīptikaraṃ grāhi tridōṣāṇāṃ ca pācakaṃ
Raktapittajvarāmātisārakāsaviṣāpahaṃ
Yakṛdvāntitṛṣāṃ caiva kṛmīnarśāṃśca pīnasaṃ
Pittōdaraṃ cātisāraṃ harṣavyādhiharaṃ mataṃ" (Ni.ra.)]

विषा सोष्णा लघुस्तिक्ता दीपनी पाचनी जयेत् ।
कफपित्तातिसारामविषकासवमिकृमीन् ॥" (कै.नि.)
["Viṣā sōṣṇā laghustikatā dīpanī pācanī jayēt
Kaphapittātisārāmaviṣakāsavamikṛmīn (Kai.ni.)]

"അതിവിടയമെരിച്ചിട്ടും കച്ചിട്ടും രസമായ് വരും
സരണഹരം ജ്വരകഫപിത്താപഹരം
കാസഘ്നം ദീപനഞ്ച ദ്രുതഹരം." (ഗു.പാ.)
["Ativiṭayamericciṭṭuṃ kacciṭṭuṃ rasamāyvaruṃ
Saraṇaharaṃ jvarakaphapittāpaharaṃ
Kāsaghnaṃ dīpanañca drutaharaṃ" (Gu.pā.)]

Remarks:
"त्रविधाऽतिविषा ज्ञेया शुक्ळा कृष्णा तथाऽरुणा ।" (नि.र.)
["Trividhāऽtiviṣā jñēyā śukḷā kṛṣṇā tathāऽruṇā" (Ni.ra.)]

"श्यामकन्दो चोपविषा सा विज्ञेया चतुर्विधा ।
रक्ता श्वेता भृशं कृष्णा पीतवर्णा तथैव सा ॥" (म.नि.)

[Śyāmakandō cōpaviṣā sā vijñēyā caturvidhā
Raktā śvētā bṛśaṃ kṛṣṇā pītavaṛṇā tathaiva sā" (Ma.ni.)]

'Indian Medicinal Plants' also mentions four varieties: 'The root is exhibited as white, yellow, red and black varieties, the white variety is the best.' Therefore, it is the white variety *Aconitum heterophyllum* which is used in the formulations.

The root of *Cryptocoryne spiralis* (Retz.) Fischer ex Wydler which is called *nāṭṭativiṭayaṃ* in Malayalam, is inexpensive and freely available in the market. Though it is said to have tonic and antiperiodic properties, it has none of the other properties enumerated for *ativiṭayaṃ (A. heterophyllum)*. Hence, it should not be used as a substitute for *ativiṣā (ativiṭayaṃ)*.

Coll. No. AVS 2405

Aconitum napellus **Linn.**

(=A.ferox *Wall.*)

Ranunculaceae (वत्सनाभ–कुलम्)

Eng	:	Indian aconite, Monk's hood
Hin	:	Bachnāg, Mīṭhāviṣ (बछनाग, मीठाविष)
Kan	:	Vatsanābhi (ವತ್ಸನಾಭಿ)
Mal	:	Vatsanābhi (വത്സനാഭി)
San	:	Vatsanābhaḥ (वत्सानाभः)
Tam	:	Vasanāvi (வசநாவி)
Tel	:	Vatsanābhi (వత్సనాభి)

Distribution: Northern Himalayas of Nepal and Kashmir

The plant: A biennial herb with tuberous roots, 60 – 90 cm in height with an erect stem, slender to rather robust, finely pubescent in the upper part; leaves scattered, basal 5 – 6, upper leaves upto 10, petioles slender, blades somewhat fleshy, reniform, rarely cordate-orbicular with a wide and shallow sinus, 5-pedatipartite almost to the base, lobes narrow, inciso-dentate, or laciniate, ultimate segments or teeth acute, uppermost blades sessile or subsessile, much smaller and less dissected; flowers blue, in loose racemes, floral leaves much reduced and passing into trifid or entire and linear-lanceolate bracts; sepals blue, hairy, uppermost helmet shaped, laterals oblique, orbicular-obovate, broadly clawed; fruits oblong, conspicuously reticulate follicles; seeds obovoid to obpyramidal.

Roots are dark brown externally and the fracture is scarcely farinaceous and yellowish; on tasting, it produces a strong tingling sensation. The innovation bud is conic and the scales are persistent and prominently and finely nerved.

Parts used: roots

Properties and uses: The roots are sweet, thermogenic, narcotic, anodyne, anti-inflammatory, diaphoretic, diuretic, expectorant, nervine tonic, stomachic, appetiser, carminative, digestive, stimulant, sialagogue, cardiotonic, emmenagogue, anaphrodisiac, depurative, sedative and febrifuge. They are useful in vitiated conditions of *vāta, pitta* and *kapha,* cephalalgia, neuralgia, painful inflammations, strangury, cough, asthma, bronchitis, hypotension, dyspepsia, flatulence, colic, cardiac debility, dysmenorrhoea, amenorrhoea, spermatorrhoea, leprosy, skin diseases, sciatica, gout, paralysis, hepatopathy,

Aconitum napellus

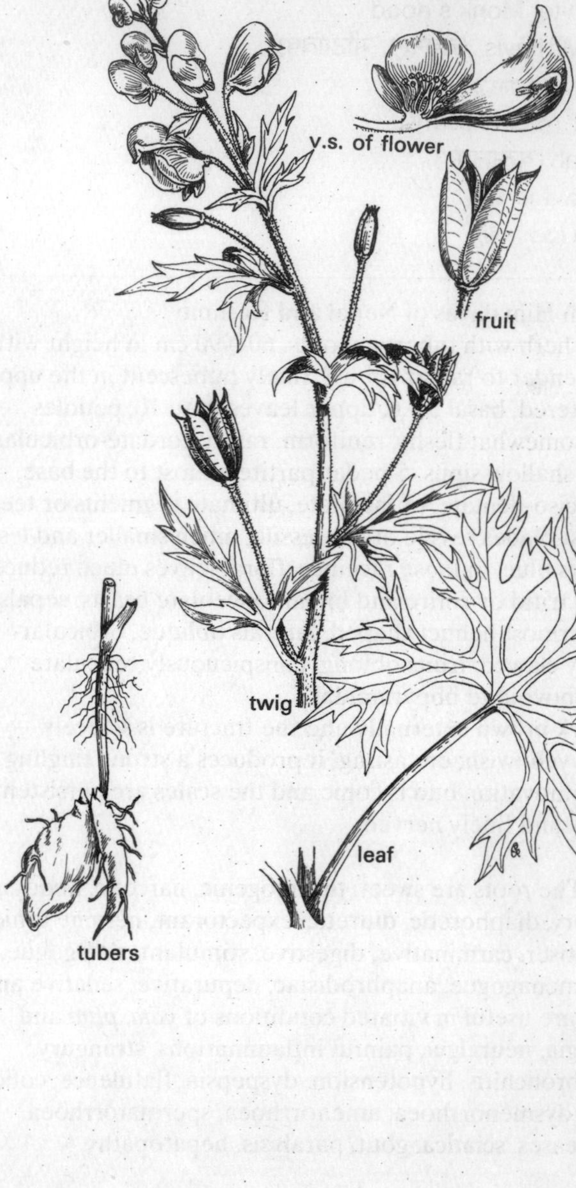

splenopathy, pharyngodynia, diabetes, nasal discharges, fever, inflammatory fevers and debility.

"सिन्दुवारसदृक्पत्रो वत्सनाभ्याकृतिस्तथा ।
यत्पार्श्वेन तरोर्वृद्धिर्वत्सनाभः स भाषितः ॥" (भा.प्र.)
["Sinduvārasadṛkpatrō vatsanābhyākṛtistathā
Yatpārśvēna tarōrvṛddhirvatsanābhaḥ sa bhāṣitaḥ" (Bhā.pra.)]

"अमृतं स्यात् वत्सनाभो विषमुग्रं महौषधम् ।
गरळं मरणं नागं स्तोककं प्राणहारकम् ॥
गरळं स्थावराद्यं स्यात् प्रोक्तं चैकादशाह्वयम् ।" (रा.नि.)
["Amṛtaṃ syāt vatsanābhō viṣamugraṃ mahauṣadhaṃ
Garaḷaṃ maraṇaṃ nāgaṃ stōkakaṃ prāṇahārakaṃ
Garaḷaṃ sthāvarādyaṃ syāt prōktaṃ caikādaśāhvayaṃ" (Rā.ni.)]

"विषं प्राणहरं प्रोक्तं व्यवायि च विकाषि च ।
आग्नेयं वातकफहृत् योगवाहि मदावहम् ॥
तदेव युक्तियुक्तं तु प्राणदायि रसायनम् ।
योगवाहि त्रिदोषघ्नं बृंहणं वीर्यवर्द्धनम् ॥" (भा.प्र.)
["Viṣaṃ prāṇaharaṃ prōktaṃ vyavāyi ca vikāṣi ca
Āgnēyaṃ vātakaphahṛt yōgavāhi madāvahaṃ
Tadēva yuktiyuktaṃ tu prāṇadāyi rasāyanaṃ
Yōgavāhi tridōṣaghnaṃ bṛmhaṇaṃ vīryavarddhanaṃ" (Bhā.pra.)]

"रूक्षमुष्णं तथा तीक्ष्णं सूक्ष्ममाशु व्यवायि च ।
विकाषि विशदं चैव लघ्वपाकी च ते दश ॥
तद्रौक्ष्यात् कोपयेद् वायुमौष्ण्यात् पित्तं सशोणितम् ।
तैक्ष्ण्यात् मतिं मोहयति मर्मबन्धान् भिनत्ति च ॥
शरीरावयवान् सौक्ष्म्यात् प्रविशेद्धि करोति च ।
आशुत्वादाशुवत् प्रोक्तं व्यवायात् प्रकृतिं हरेत् ॥
विकाषित्वाद्दीपयति दोषान् धातून् मलानपि ।
अतिरिच्येत वैशद्याद् दुश्चिकित्स्यञ्च लाघवात् ॥
दुर्जरं चाविपाकित्वात् तस्मात् क्ळेशयते चिरम् ।
विषं रसायनं बल्यं वातश्ळेष्मविकारनुत् ॥
कटुतिक्तं कषायं च मदकारि सुखप्रदम् ।
व्यवायि च शिरोद्वाहि कुष्ठवातास्रनाशनम् ॥
अग्निमान्द्यश्वासकासप्ळीहोदरभगन्दरम् ।
गुल्मपाण्डुव्रणार्शांसि नाशयेद्विधिसेवितम् ॥" (शा.नि.)
["Rūkṣamuṣṇaṃ tathā tīkṣṇaṃ sūkṣmamāśu vyavāyi ca
Vikāṣi viśadaṃ caiva laghvāpākī ca tē daśa
Tadraukṣyāt kōpayēd vāyumauṣṇyāt pittaṃ sa śōṇitaṃ

Taikṣṇyāt matiṃ mōhayati marmabandhān bhinatti ca
Śarīrāvayavān saukṣmyāt praviśēddhi karōti ca
Āśutvādāśuvatprōktaṃ vyavāyāt prakṛtiṃ harēt
Vikāṣitvāddīpayati dōṣān dhātūn malānapi
Atiricyēta vaiśadyād duścikitsyañaca lāghavāt
Durjaraṃ cāvipākitvāt tasmātkḷēśayatē ciraṃ
Viṣaṃ rasāyanaṃ balyaṃ vātaśḷēṣmavikāranut
Kaṭutiktaṃ kaṣāyaṃ ca madakāri sukhapradaṃ
Vyavāyi ca śirōdvāhi kuṣṭhavātāsṛanāśanaṃ
Agnimāndyaśvāsakāsapḷīhōdarabhagandaraṃ
Gulmapāṇḍuvṛaṇārśāṃsi nāśayēdvidhisēvitaṃ" (Śā.ni.)]

"वत्सनाभोऽतिमधुरः सोष्णो वातकफापहः ।
कण्ठरुक्सन्निपातघ्नः पित्तसंशोधनोऽपि च ॥" (ध.नि.)
["Vatsanābhōऽtimadhuraḥ sōṣṇō vātakaphāpahaḥ
Kaṇṭharuksannipātaghnaḥ pittasaṃśōdhanōऽpi ca" (Dha.ni.)]

"वत्सनाभोऽतिमधुरः सोष्णो वातकफापहः ।
कण्ठरुक्सन्निपातघ्नः पित्तसन्तापकारकाः ॥" (रा.नि.)
["Vatsanābhōऽtimadhuraḥ sōṣṇō vātakaphāpahaḥ
Kaṇṭharuksannipātaghnaḥ pittasantāpakārakāḥ" (Rā.ni.)]

Remarks: Indian aconite or Monk's hood is a virulent poison and hence purification is needed before using.The roots are purified either in cow's urine or milk. The purification with milk is more effective.

Coll. No. AVS 2406

Acorus Calamus **Linn.**

Araceae (सूरण–कुलम्)

Eng	:	Sweet flag
Hin	:	Bacc, Gōrbācc (बाच्च, गोरबाच्च)
Kan	:	Bāji (ಬಾಜಿ)
Mal	:	Vayampụ (വയമ്പ്)
San	:	Vacā, Ugragandhā (वचा, उग्रगन्धा)
Tam	:	Vaśampu (வசம்பு)
Tel	:	Vasa (వస)

Distribution: Throughout India in areas elevated upto 1,800 m, in marshes, also cultivated

The plant: A semi-aquatic rhizomatous perennial herb, rhizome creeping, much branched, as thick as the middle finger, cylindrical or slightly compressed, light brown or pinkish brown externally, white and spongy within; leaves bright green, distichous, ensiform, base equitant, thickened in the middle, margins wavy; flowers light brown densely packed in sessile cylindric spadix; fruits oblong turbinate berries with a pyramidal top; seeds few, pendant from the apex of the cells.

Parts used: rhizomes

Properties and uses: The rhizome is acrid, bitter, thermogenic, aromatic, intellect promoting, emetic, laxative, carminative, stomachic, anthelmintic, emmenagogue, diuretic, alexeteric, expectorant, anodyne, antispasmodic, aphrodisiac, anticonvulsant, resuscitative, anti-inflammatory, sudorific, antipyretic, sialagogue, insecticidal, tranquillising, nervine tonic, sedative and tonic. It is useful in vitiated conditions of *vāta* and *kapha,* stomatopathy, hoarseness, colic, flatulence, dyspepsia, helminthiasis, amenorrhoea, dysmenorrhoea, nephropathy, calculi, strangury, cough, bronchitis, odontalgia, pectoralgia, hepatodynia, otalgia, inflammations, gout, epilepsy, delirium, amentia, convulsions, depression and other mental disorders, tumours, dysentery, hyperdipsia, haemorrhoids, intermittent fevers, skin diseases, numbness and general debility.

Acorus calamus

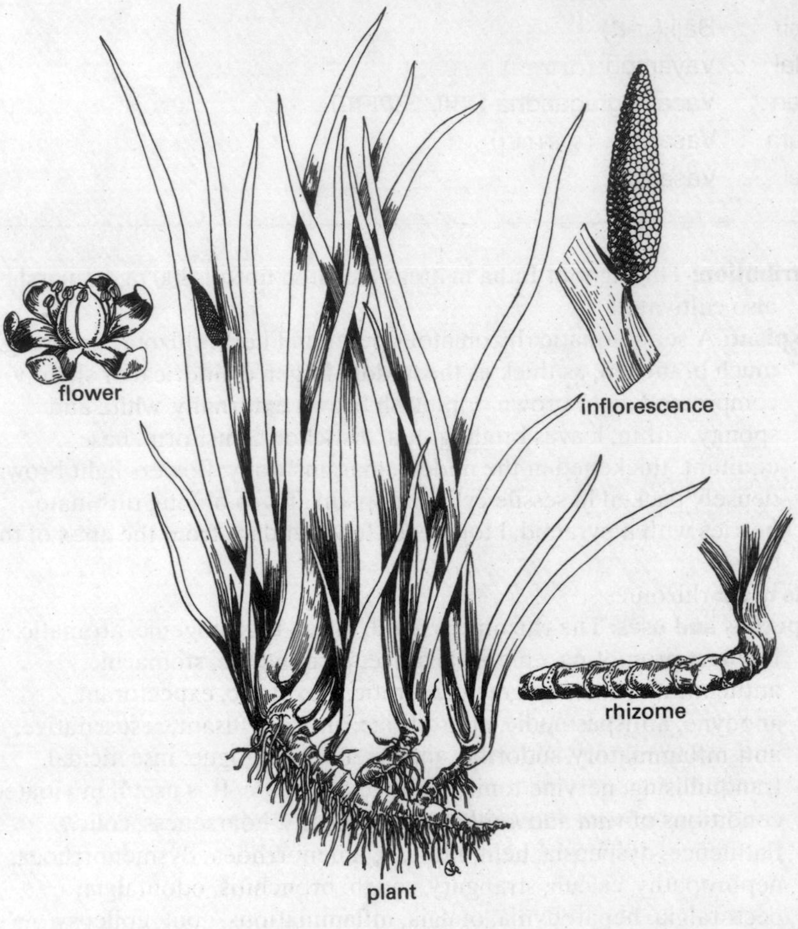

"वचोग्रगन्धा षड्ग्रन्धा गोलोमी शतपर्विका ।
क्षुद्रपत्री च मङ्गल्या जटिलोग्रा च लोमशा ॥" (भा.प्र.)
["Vacōgragandhā ṣaḍgrandhā gōlōmī śataparvikā
Kṣudrapatrī ca mangalyā jaṭilōgrā ca lōmaśā" (Bha.pra.)]

"वचोग्रगन्धा गोलोमी जटिलोग्रा च लोमशा ।
अन्या श्वेतवचा मेध्या षड्ग्रन्धा हैमवत्यपि ॥" (ध.नि.)
["Vacōgragandhā gōlōmī jaṭilōgrā ca lōmaśā
Anyā śvētavaca mēdhyā ṣaḍgrandhā haimavatyapi" (Dha.ni.)]

वचोग्रगन्धा गोलोमी जटिलोग्रा च लोमशा ।
रक्षोघ्नी विजया भद्रा मङ्गल्येति दशाह्वया ॥
मेध्या श्वेतवचा त्वन्या षड्ग्रन्धा दीर्घपत्रिका ।
तीक्ष्णगन्धा हैमवती मङ्गल्या विजया च सा ॥ (रा.नि.)
["Vacōgragandhā gōlōmī jaṭilōgrā ca lōmaśā
Rakśōghnī vijayā bhadrā mangalyēti daśāhvayā
Mēdhyā śvētavacā tvanyā ṣaḍgrandhā dīrghapatrikā
Tīkṣṇagandhā haimavatī mangalyā vijayā ca sā (Rā.ni.)]

"वचोग्रगन्धा कटुका तिक्तोष्णा वान्तिवह्निकृत् ।
विबन्धाध्मानशूलघ्नी शकृन्मूत्रविशोधिनी ॥
अपस्मारकफोन्मादभूतजन्त्वनिलान् हरेत् ।" (भा.प्र.)
["Vacōgragandhā kaṭukā tiktōṣṇā vāntivahnikṛt
Vibandhādhmānaśūlaghnī śakṛnmūtraviśōdhinī
Apasmārakaphōnmādabhūtajantvanilān harēt" (Bhā.pra.)]

"वामिनी कटुतिक्तोष्णा वातश्ळेष्मरुजापहा ।
कण्ठ्या मेध्या च कृमिहृद्विबन्धाध्मानशूलनुत् ॥
वचाद्वयं तु कटुकं रूक्षोष्णं मलमूत्रळम् ।
दीपनं कफवातघ्नं मेध्यायुष्यं च पाचनम् ॥
जन्तुघ्नं चोग्रगन्धं स्याल्लघु कण्ठास्यरोगजित् ।" (ध.नि.)
["Vāminī kaṭutiktōṣṇā vātaślēṣmarujāpahā
Kaṇṭhyā mēdhyā ca kṛmihṛdvibandhādhmānaśūlanut
Vacādvayaṃ tu kaṭukaṃ rūkṣōṣṇaṃ malamūtraḷaṃ
Dīpanaṃ kaphavātaghnaṃ mēdhyāyuṣyaṃ ca pācanaṃ
Jantughnaṃ cōgragandhaṃ syāllaghu kaṇṭhāsyarōgajit" (Dha.ni.)]

"मेध्या कफहरा चैव तिक्ता कट्वी विपाकतः ।
उन्मादापस्मृतिहरा रक्षोघ्नी चे वचा मता ॥" (म.नि.)
["Mēdhyā kaphaharā caiva tiktā kaṭvī vipākataḥ
Unmādāpasmṛtiharā rakṣōghnī ca vacā matā" (Ma.ni.)]

"वचा तीक्ष्णा कटूष्णा च कफामग्रन्थिशोफनुत् ।
वातज्वरातिसारघ्नी वान्तिकृन्मदभूतनुत् ॥

श्वेतवचा]तिगुणाढ्या मतिमेधायुः समृद्धिदा कफनुत् ।
वृष्या च वातभूतकृमिदोषघ्नी च दीपनी च वचा ॥" (रा.नि.)
["Vacā tīkṣṇā kaṭūṣṇa ca kaphāmagranthiśōphanut
Vātajvarātisāraghnī vāntikṛnmadabhūtanut
Śvētavacā]tiguṇāḍhyā matimēdhāyuḥ samṛddhidā kaphanut
Vṛṣyā ca vātabhūtakṛmidōṣaghnī ca dīpanī ca vacā" (Rā.ni.)]

"वचा तिक्ता कटुः पाके कटुरुष्णामपाचनी ।
दीपनी वामनी मेध्या जीवनी वाक्स्वरप्रदा ॥
हन्त्युन्मादमपस्मारं रक्षोजन्तुकफानिलान् ।
शूलं विबन्धमाध्मानं शकृन्मूत्रविशोधनी ॥" (कै.नि.)
["Vacā tiktā kaṭuḥ pākē kaṭuruṣṇāmapācanī
Dīpanī vāmanī mēdhyā jīvanī vāksvarapradā
Hantyunmādamapasmāraṃ rakṣōjantukaphānilān
Śūlaṃ vibandhamādhmānaṃ śakṛnmūtraviśōdhanī" (Kai.ni.)]

"वचायुर्बुद्धिस्मृतिदा कफवातामभूतहृत् । (सो.नि.)
["Vacāyuṛbuddhismṛtidā kaphavātāmabhūtahṛt" (Sō.ni.)]

"वचोष्णा कटुका तिक्ता वामनी स्वरवह्निकृत् ।
अपस्मारकफोन्मादभूतशूलानिलाञ्जयेत् ॥" (म.पा.नि.)
["Vacōṣṇā kaṭuka tiktā vāmanī svaravahnikṛt
Apasmārakaphōnmādabhūtaśūḷānilāñjayēt" (Ma.pā.ni.)]

"वचायुष्या वातकफतृष्णाघ्नी स्मृतिवर्द्धिनी ।" (रा.व.)
["Vacāyuṣyā vātakaphatṛṣṇāghnī smṛtivaṛddhinī" (Rā.va.)]

വയമ്പു നന്നു ബുദ്ധിക്കും കാർഷ്ണ്യം ദീപനപാചനം
നന്നേറ്റം ദന്തശൂലക്കും കുഷ്ഠവാതവലാസജിത്. (ഗു.പാ.)
["Vayampu nannu buddhikkuṃ kāṛṣṇyaṃ dīpānapācanaṃ
Nannēṟṟaṃ dantaśūlakkuṃ kuṣṭhavātavalāsajit". (Gu.pā.)]

Remarks: The Materia Medicas like 'Bhāvapṛakāśaṃ', 'Rājanighaṇṭu' etc., mention another variety of *vacā, śvētavacā* or *hymavatī (veḷvayampu)*, which 'Dravyaguṇavijñān' identifies as *Iris germanica.*

It is reported that there is another variety of *vacā (Acorus gramineus* Soland.) found growing abundantly in the Himalayas. The *śvetavacā* mentioned in ancient textbooks might perhaps be this plant.

Coll. No. AVS 2532

Actiniopteris dichotoma **Bedd.**

Polypodiaceae (अश्वकत्री–कुलम्)

Eng	:	Peacock's tail
Hin	:	Mayūrśikhā, Mōrpaṁkhī (मयूरशिखा, मोरपंखी)
Kan	:	Mayūraśikha (ಮಯೂರಶಿಖ)
Mal	:	Mayūraśikha, Mayilāṭuṁśikha, Nānmukappullụ (മയൂരശിഖ, മയിലാടുംശിഖ, നാന്മുകപ്പുല്ല്)
San	:	Mayūraśikhā (मयूरशिखा)
Tam	:	Mayilāṭumśikhai (மயிலாடும்சிகை)
Tel	:	Mayūraśikha (మయూరశిఖ)

Distribution: Throughout India, very common in the lower hills of Attappady, upto 600 m in Nilgiris.

The plant: A herbaceous miniature palm-like fern upto 25 cm high with densely tufted stipe. Fronds fan-like with numerous dichotomous segments which are rush-like in texture, veins few, subparallel with distinct midrib, segments of fertile frond longer than those of the barren one, sori linear, elongate, submarginal.

Parts used: whole plant

Properties and uses: The plant is bitter, astringent, sweet, cooling, acrid, constipating, anthelmintic, haemostatic, antileprotic and febrifuge. It is useful in vitiated conditions of *kapha* and *pitta,* diarrhoea, dysentery, helminthiasis, haemoptysis, haematemesis, leprosy, skin diseases, diabetes and fever.

"मयूराह्वशिखा प्रोक्ता सहस्राङ्घ्रिर्मधुच्छदा।" (भा.प्र.)
["Mayūrāhvaśikhā prōktā sahasrāṅghrirmadhucchadā" (Bhā.pra.)]

"मयूराह्वशिखा ज्ञेया साहस्री मधुकच्छदा।" (म.पा.नि.)
["Mayūrāhvaśikhā jñēyā sāhasrī madhukacchadā"(Ma.pā.ni.)]

"मधूकपर्णी साहस्री मयूराह्वशिखा स्मृता ।" (कै.नि.)
["Madhūkaparṇī sāhasrī mayūrāhvaśikhā smṛtā" (Kai.ni.)]

"नीलकण्ठशिखा लघ्वी पित्तश्लेष्मातिसारजित् ।" (भा.प्र.)
["Nīlakaṇṭhaśikhā laghvī pittaśḷeṣmātisārajit" (Bhā.pra.)]

Actiniopteris dichotoma

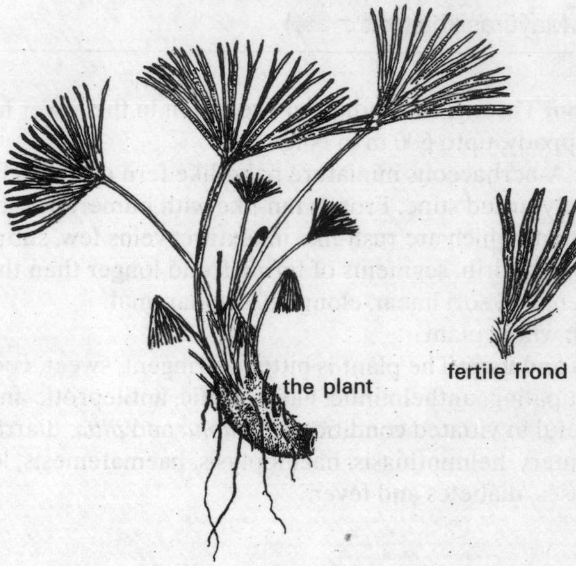

"मयूराह्वशिखा लघ्वी पित्तश्ळेष्मातिसारजित् ।" (म.पा.नि.)
["Mayūrāhvaśikhā laghvī pittaśḷēṣmātisārajit" (Ma.pā.ni.)]

"मयूराह्वशिखा शीता कषायाऽम्ळाऽम्ळपाकिनी* ।
लघ्वी पित्तकफौ पक्वमतीसारं विनाशयेत् ॥" (कै.नि.)
(*"कषाया कटुपाकिनी" इति केचित्)
["Mayūrāhvaśikha śītā kaṣāyāʃmḷāʃmḷapākinī*
Laghvī pittakaphau pakvamatīsāraṃ vināśayēt (Kai.ni.)]
(* "kaṣāyā kaṭupākinī" iti kēcit.)

"साज्या मयूरचूडा तु पीता तण्डुलवारिणा ।
सर्व–सर्पविषं हन्यात् काकजंघाऽथवा ध्रुवम् ॥" (सोढलः)
["Sājyā mayūracūḍā tu pītā taṇḍulavāriṇā
Sarva-sarpaviṣaṃ hanyat kākajaṁghāʃthavā dhṛuvaṃ" (Sōḍhalaḥ)]

Remarks: In 'Dravyaguṇavijñān' P.V. Sharma regards *Adiantum caudatum* as *mayūraśikhā,* whereas in 'Bhāvapṛakāśanighaṇṭu' and 'Sāligrāmanighaṇṭubhūṣaṇaṃ' *Celosia cristata* is described as *mayūraśikhā.*

Coll. No. AVS 1772

Adenanthera pavonina **Linn.**

Mimosaceae (बब्बुल–कुलम्)

Eng	:	Coralwood tree, Redwood tree
Hin	:	Bārāguñcī (बारागुञ्ची)
Kan	:	Manjaṭṭi (ಮಂಜಟ್ಟಿ)
Mal	:	Mañcāṭi (മഞ്ചാടി)
San	:	Kucandanaḥ, Tāmrakaḥ (कुचन्दनः, ताम्रकः)
Tam	:	Yānai kunṭumaṇi (யானை குண்டுமணி)
Tel	:	Banḍigurvina, Mansēnikotta (బండిగుర్విన, మంసేనికొట్ట)

Distribution: Throughout India, in deciduous forests, also cultivated as avenue trees

The plant: A medium sized, handsome unarmed deciduous tree about 20m in height with a clear bole of 6.0 m having greyish brown bark with longitudinal fissures; leaves bipinnate, the pinnae 3 – 6 pairs, opposite, leaflets many, alternate, ovate - oblong, obtuse, glabrous, unequal sided, dark green above; flowers pale yellow, in short peduncled racemes; fruits falcately curved pointed pods, the valves spirally twisted after dehiscence; seeds shining brilliant scarlet, lenticular - globose.

Parts used: bark, leaves, seeds, heartwood

Properties and uses: The bark and leaves are astringent, vulnerary and aphrodisiac, and are useful in colonorrhea, haematuria, ulcers, pharyngopathy, vitiated conditions of *vāta* and gout. The seeds are bitter, astringent, sweet, cooling, aphrodisiac, suppurative, antiemetic and febrifuge. They are useful in vitiated conditions of *vāta* and *pitta,* gout, burning sensation, hyperdipsia, vomiting, fever and giddiness. The heart wood is astringent, aphrodisiac, haemostatic, and is useful in dysentery, haemorrhages and vitiated conditions of *vāta.*

"आरक्ततुवरी बीजः ताम्रकश्च सुवर्त्तुळः ।
बर्बरः शम्बरश्चैव प्रवाळस्तैस्तु चन्दनः ॥
रक्तचन्दनसादृश्यात् रञ्जको रक्तकाण्डकः ।
शोणवृक्षः ताम्रकाण्डः शोणसारः कुचन्दनः ॥" (स्व.)

Adenanthera pavonina

Plate 4

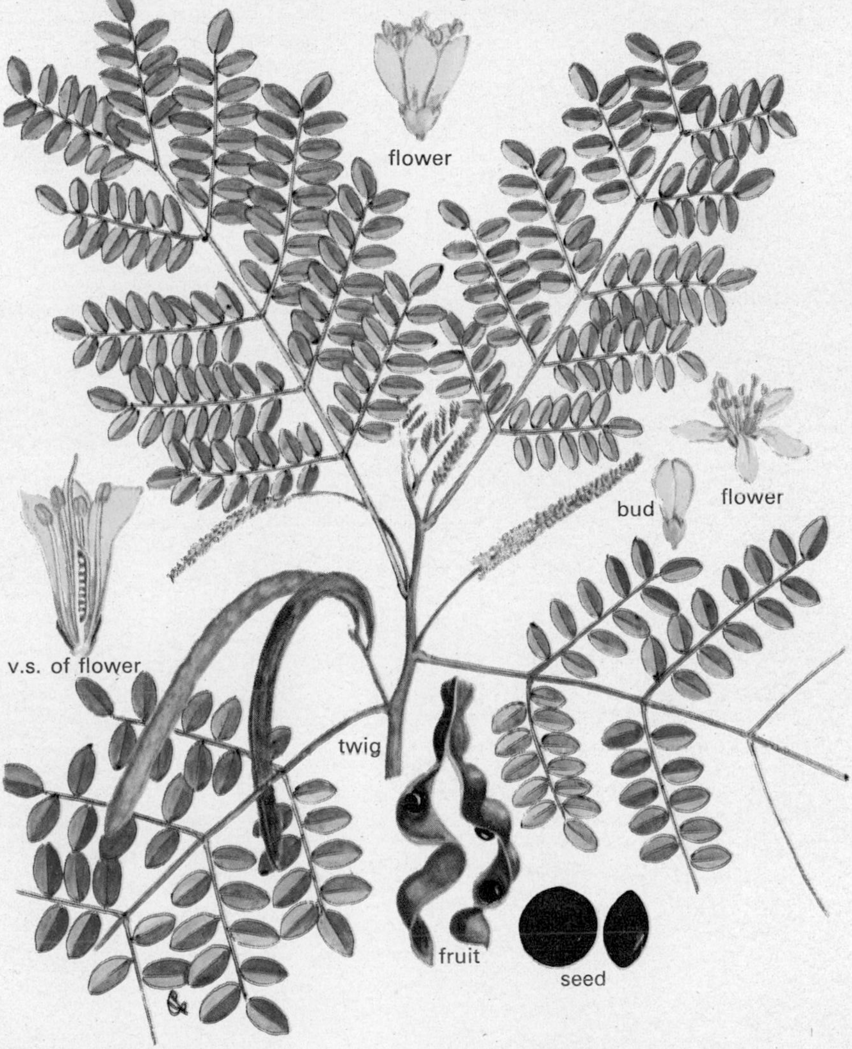

["Āraktatuvarībījaḥ tāmṛakaśca suvaṛttuḷaḥ
Baṛbaraḥ śaṁbaraścaiva pṛavāḷastaistu candanaḥ
Raktacandanasādṛśyāt ranjakō raktakāṇḍakaḥ
Śoṇavṛksaḥ tāmṛakāṇḍaḥ śōṇasāraḥ kucandanaḥ" (Sva.)]

स्वादुतिक्तकषायोऽसौ पित्तभ्रान्तिवमिज्वरान् ।
रक्तवातं च शमयेत् वृष्यस्तृष्णाहरश्च सः ॥
वक्त्रकण्ठामयेष्वस्य पत्रत्वक्क्वाथ इष्यते ।
काष्ठसारकषायस्तु वृष्यो रक्तातिसारजित् ॥
रक्तचन्दनवत् चास्य प्रयोगः शस्यते सदा ।" (स्व.)
["Svādutiktakaṣāyōऽsau pittabhṛāntivamijvarān
Raktavātaṃ ca śamayēt vṛṣyastṛṣṇāharaśca saḥ
Vaktṛakaṇṭhāmayēṣvasya patṛatvakkvātha iṣyatē
Kāṣṭhasārakaṣāyastu vṛṣyō raktātisārajit
Raktacandanavat cāsya pṛayōgaḥ śasyatē sadā" (Sva.)]

Coll. No. AVS 2223

***Aegle marmelos* (Linn.) Corr.**

Rutaceae (जम्बीर–कुलम्)

Eng	:	Bael tree, Holy fruit tree
Hin	:	Bēl, Sirphal (बेल, सिरफल)
Kan	:	Belapatri (ಬೇಲಪತ್ರೆ)
Mal	:	Kūvvaḷaṃ, Kūḷakaṃ (കൂവ്വളം, കൂളകം)
San	:	Vilvaḥ, Śivadrumaḥ, Śrīphalaḥ (विल्वः, शिवद्रुमः, श्रीफलः)
Tam	:	Kūviḷaṃ, Vilvaṃ (கூவிளம், வில்வம்)
Tel	:	Bilvamu, Mārēdu (బిల్వము, మారేడు)

Distribution: Throughout India,in dry forests, also cultivated

The plant: A medium sized armed deciduous tree upto 8.0 m high with straight,sharp,axillary thorns and yellowish brown shallowly furrowed corky bark; leaves trifoliate, aromatic, alternate, leaflets ovate or ovate-lanceolate, crenate, pellucid-punctate, the laterals subsessile and the terminal long-petioled; flowers greenish white, e, sweet scented, in axillary panicles; fruits globose, woody berry with yellowish rind; seeds numerous oblong, compressed, embedded in orange brown sweet gummy pulp.

Parts used: roots, leaves, fruits

Properties and uses: The roots are sweet, astringent, bitter and febrifuge. They are useful in diarrhoea, dysentery, dyspepsia, stomachalgia, cardiopalmus, vitiated conditions of *vāta,* seminal weakness, uropathy, vomiting, intermittent fever, swellings and gastric irritability in infants. The leaves are astringent, laxative, febrifuge and expectorant, and are useful in ophthalmia, deafness, inflammations, catarrh, diabetes and asthmatic complaints. The unripe fruits are bitter, acrid, sour, astringent, digestive and stomachic, and are useful in diarrhoea, dysentery and stomachalgia. The ripe fruits are astringent, sweet, aromatic, cooling, febrifuge, laxative and tonic, and are good for the heart and brain and in dyspepsia.

"विल्वस्तु पूतिपातः शाण्डिल्यः श्रीफलश्च माणूरः ।
मुष्टिफलश्च शलाटः शैलूषः कर्कटः श्रियाह्वश्च ॥

Aegle marmelos

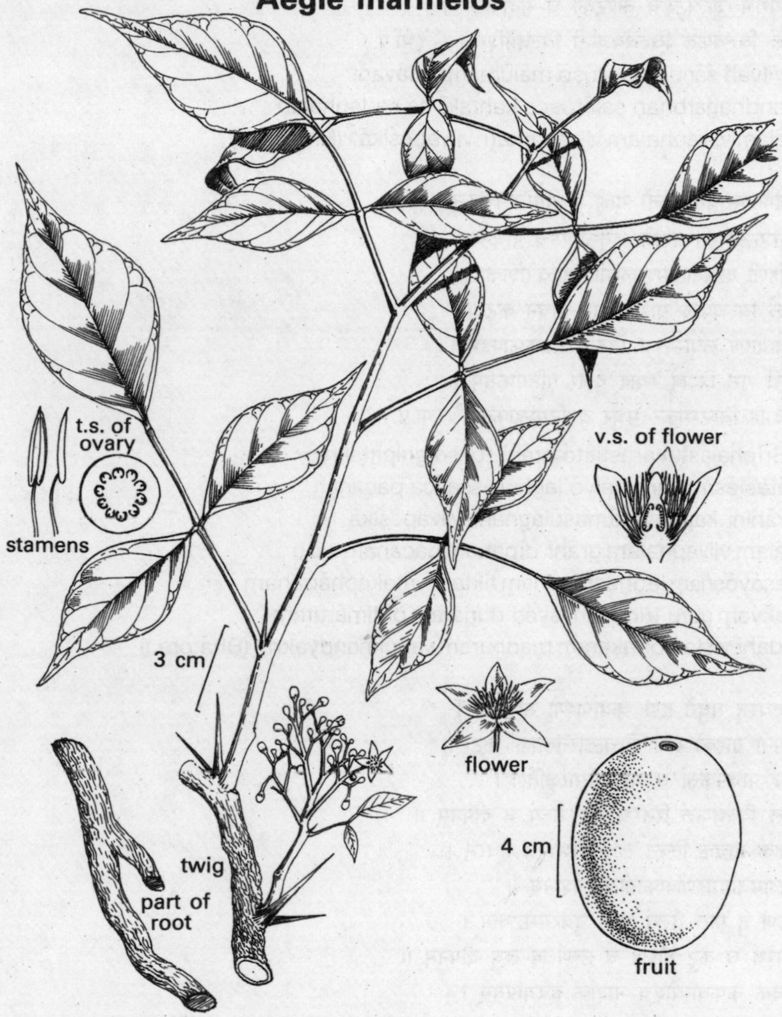

सदाफलः पीलुफलो हृद्यगन्धः शलाटिकः ।
शलाटुद्रुम इत्युक्तो शब्दैः पर्यायवाचकैः ॥" (अ.म.)
["Vilvastu pūtipātaḥ śāṇḍilyaḥ śṛiphalaśca māṇūraḥ
Muṣṭiphalaśca śalāṭaḥ śailūṣaḥ kaṛkaṭaḥ śṛiyāhvaśca
Ṣadāphalaḥ pīluphalō hṛdyagandhaḥ śalāṭikaḥ
Śalāṭudruma ityuktō śabdaiḥ paryāyavācakaiḥ" (A.ma.)]

"विल्वः शाण्डिल्यशैलूषो मालूरश्रीफलावपि ।
गन्धगर्भः शलाटुश्च कण्टकी च सदाफलः ॥
बालं विल्वफलं विल्वकर्कटी विल्वपेशिका ।" (भा.प्र.)
["Vilvaḥ śāṇḍilyaśailūṣō mālūraśṛīphalāvapi
Gandhagaṛbhaḥ śalāṭuśca kaṇṭakī ca sadāphalaḥ
Bālaṃ vilvaphalaṃ vilvakaṛkaṭī vilvapēśikā" (Bhā.pra.)]

"श्रीफलस्तुवरस्तिक्तो ग्राही रूक्षोऽग्निपित्तकृत् ।
वातश्ळेष्महरो बल्यो लघुरुष्णश्च पाचनः ॥
ग्राहिणी कफवातामशूलघ्नी विल्वपेशिका ।
बालं विल्वफलं ग्राही दीपनं पाचनं कटु ॥
कषायोष्णं लघुस्निग्धं तिक्तं वातकफापहम् ।
पक्वं गुरु त्रिदोषं स्याद् दुर्जरं पूतिमारुतम् ॥
विदाहि विष्टम्भकरं मधुरं वह्निमान्द्यकृत् ।" (भा.प्र.)
["Śṛīphalastuvarastiktō grāhī rūkṣōऽgnipittakṛt
Vātaśḷēṣmaharō balyō laghuruṣṇaśca pācanaḥ
Grāhiṇī kaphavātāmaśūlaghanī vilvapēśikā
Bālaṃ vilvaphalaṃ grāhī dīpanaṃ pācanaṃ kaṭu
Kaṣāyōṣṇaṃ laghusnigdhaṃ tiktaṃ vātakaphāpahaṃ
Pakvaṃ guru tṛidōṣaṃ syād duṛjaraṃ pūtimārutaṃ
Vidāhi viṣṭambhakaraṃ madhuraṃ vahnimāndyakṛt" (Bhā.pṛa.)]

विल्वस्तु मधुरो हृद्यः कषायोष्णो रुचिप्रदः ।
दीपनो ग्राहको रूक्षः पित्तळस्तिक्तकः कटुः ॥
गुरुः पाचनकर्त्ता च वातातीसारजूर्तिहा ।
बालं विल्वफलं स्निग्धं गुरु रुच्यं च दीपनम् ॥
ग्राहकं पाचकं तिक्तं लघु चोष्णं च तूवरम् ।
शूलामवातग्रहणीकफातीसारनाशनम् ॥
तरुणं तु फलं वैल्वं ग्राही तुवरमम्ळकम् ।
स्निग्धं च कटु तीक्ष्णं च उष्णं च लघु दीपनम् ॥
पाचकं कफवाय्वोश्च नाशकं हृदयप्रियम् ।
पक्वं वैल्वं दाहकरं मधुरं गुरु तूवरम् ॥
विष्टम्भकारी तिक्तोष्णं ग्राहकं कटु दोषळम् ।
दुर्जरं वातळं चाग्निमान्द्यकृत् ऋषिभिर्मतम् ॥
विल्वमूलं तु मधुरं त्रिदोषच्छर्दिशूलनुत् ।
लघु कृच्छहरं वातकफपित्तस्य नाशकम् ॥

पर्णानि ग्राहकाणि स्युर्वातनाशकराणि च ।" (नि.र.)
["Vilvastu madhurō hṛdyaḥ kaṣāyōṣṇō rucipradaḥ
Dīpanō grāhakō rūkṣaḥ pittaḷastiktakaḥ kaṭuḥ
Guruḥ pācanakaṛttā ca vātātīsārajūṛtihā
Bālaṃ vilvaphalaṃ snigdhaṃ guru rucyaṃ ca dīpanaṃ
Grāhakaṃ pācakaṃ tiktaṃ laghu cōṣṇaṃ ca tūvaraṃ
Śūlāmavātagrahaṇīkaphātīsāranāśanaṃ
Taruṇaṃ tu phalaṃ vailvaṃ grāhī tuvaramamḷakaṃ
Snigdhaṃ ca kaṭu tīkṣṇaṃ ca uṣṇaṃ ca laghu dīpanaṃ
Pācakaṃ kaphavāyvōsca naśakaṃ hṛdayapriyaṃ
Pakvaṃ vailvaṃ dāhakaraṃ madhuraṃ guru tūvaraṃ
Viṣṭambhakārī tiktōṣṇaṃ grāhkaṃ kaṭu dōṣaḷaṃ
Duṛjaraṃ vātaḷaṃ cāgnimāndyakṛt ṛṣibhiṛmataṃ
Vilvamūlaṃ tu madhuraṃ tṛidōṣacchaṛdiśūlanut
Laghu kṛcchṛaharaṃ vātakaphapittasya nāśakaṃ
Paṛṇāni grāhakāṇi syuṛvātanāśakarāṇi ca" (Ni.ra.)]

विल्वमूलं त्रिदोषघ्नं छर्दिघ्नं मधुरं लघु ।
विशल्या तु फलं बालं स्निग्धं संग्राहि दीपनम् ॥
कटुतिक्तकषायोष्णं तीक्ष्णं वातकफापहम् ।
विद्यात्तदेव संपक्वं मधुरानुरसं गुरु ॥
विदाहि विष्टम्भकरं दोषहृत् पूतिमारुतम् (ध.नि.)
["Vilvamūlaṃ tṛidōṣaghnaṃ chaṛdighnaṃ madhuraṃ laghu
Viśalyā tu phalaṃ bālaṃ snigdhaṃ saṃgrāhi dīpanaṃ
Kaṭutiktakaṣāyōṣṇaṃ tīkṣṇaṃ vātakaphāpahaṃ
Vidyāttadēva sampakvaṃ madhurānurasaṃ guru
Vidāhi viṣṭambhakaraṃ dōṣahṛt pūtimārutaṃ" (Dha.ni.)]

विल्वस्तु मधुरो हृद्यः कषायः पित्तजिद् गुरुः ।
कफज्वरातिसारघ्नी रुचिकृद्दीपनः परः ॥
विल्वमूलं त्रिदोषघ्नं मधुरं लघु वातनुत् ।
फलं तु कोमळं स्निग्धं गुरु संग्राहि दीपनम् ॥
तदेव पक्वं विज्ञेयं मधुरं सरसं गुरु ।
कटुतिक्तकषायोष्णं संग्राही च त्रिदोषजित् ॥" (रा.नि.)
["Vilvastu madhurō hṛdyaḥ kaṣāyaḥ pittajid guruḥ
Kaphajvarātisāraghnī rucikṛddīpanaḥ paraḥ
Vilvamūlaṃ tṛidōṣaghnaṃ madhuraṃ laghu vātanut
Phalaṃ tu kōmaḷaṃ snigdhaṃ guru saṃgrāhi dīpanaṃ
Tadēva pakvaṃ vijñēyaṃ madhuraṃ sarasaṃ guru
Kaṭutiktakaṣāyōṣṇaṃ saṃgrāhī ca tṛidōṣajit" (Rā.ni.)]

"मूलत्वक्पत्रबालफलादिकं ग्राह्यं, मूलकाष्टं ग्राह्यमित्येके,
मूलत्वग्ग्राह्यमित्यपरे, मूलं समग्रं ग्राह्यमिति बहवः।"
[Mūlatvakpaṭrabālaphalādikaṃ grāhyaṃ, mūlakāṣṭaṃ grāhyamityēkē,

mūlatvaggrāhyamityaparē, mūlaṃ samagraṃ grāhyamiti bahavaḥ")

"കൂവ്വളത്തിന്നുടെവേരിൻ രസം കച്ചുചവർത്തതു
കഫവാതപ്രശമനമുഷ്ണം ഛർദ്ദിക്കുമുത്തമം
ഇക്കിളും ശ്വാസകാസങ്ങൾ ക്ഷയരോഗത്തിനും ഗുണം." (ഗു.പാ.)
["Kūvvaḷattinnuṭevērin rasaṃ kaccucavarttatu
Kaphavātapraśamanamuṣṇaṃ charddikkumuttamaṃ
Ikkiḷuṃ śvāsakāsaṅṅaḷkṣayarōgattinuṃ guṇaṃ". (Gu.pā.)]

Remarks : It is worth mentioning here that it is the pulp of the tender bael fruit that is to be used wherever the terms *bālavilvaṃ*, *vilvakarkaṭī*, *vilvapēśikā*, *vilvamaddhyaṃ*, *vilvamajjā* and *vilvaśalāṭu* are mentioned in the formulations.

Coll. No. AVS 1062

Aerva lanata (Linn.) Juss. ex Schultes

Amaranthaceae (तण्डुलीय–कुलम्)

Hin	:	Chāyā, Gōrakhgāñjā (छाया, गोरखगाञ्जा)
Kan	:	Biḷihindisōppu (ಬಿಳಿಹಿಂಡಿಸೊಪ್ಪು)
Mal	:	Ceṟūḷa, Ceṟuvūḷa, Ceṟupūḷa (ചെറൂള, ചെറുവൂള, ചെറുപൂള)
San	:	Bhadrā (भद्रा)
Tam	:	Ceṟupūḷai (செறுபூளை)
Tel	:	Pinḍiceṭṭu (పిండిచెట్టు)

Distribution : Throughout India, in waste lands

The plant : An erect or prostrate, many branched undershrub, 30 – 60 cm in height, woolly, tomentose throughout; leaves simple, alternate, short-petioled, densely tomentose, usually smaller in the flowering branches; flowers very small, sessile, bisexual, greenish or hoary-white, often clustered in spikes, perianth calycine membranous, five free, filaments of the five stamens connate at the base with alternating linear staminodes; fruits greenish, roundish, compressed utricle; seeds kidney shaped with shining black, coriaceous testa.

Parts used : whole plant

Properties and uses : The plant is astringent, bitter, cooling, emollient, vermifuge, suppurative, diuretic and lithontriptic. It is useful to treat boils, cephalalgia, cough, strangury and lithiasis.

"भद्रा गोरक्षगञ्जा च श्वेतपुष्पी च भद्रिका ।" (स्व.)
[`Bhadrā gōrakṣagañjā ca śvētapuṣpī ca bhadrikā'' (Sva.)]

रक्तपित्तहरी शीता भद्रा कृच्छ्रप्रमेहजित् ।" (हृ.प्रि.)
[`Raktapittaharī śītā bhadrā kṛcchraprамēhajit'' (Hṛ.pri.)]

"गोरक्षगञ्जा तुवरा सतिक्ता
लघ्वी च तीक्ष्णा परमुष्णवीर्या ।
कफपित्तहृन्मूत्रविरेचनीया
प्रभावतोऽप्यश्मरिनाशनी स्यात् ॥" (द्र.गु.वि.)
[Gōrakṣagañjā tuvarā satiktā

Aerva lanata

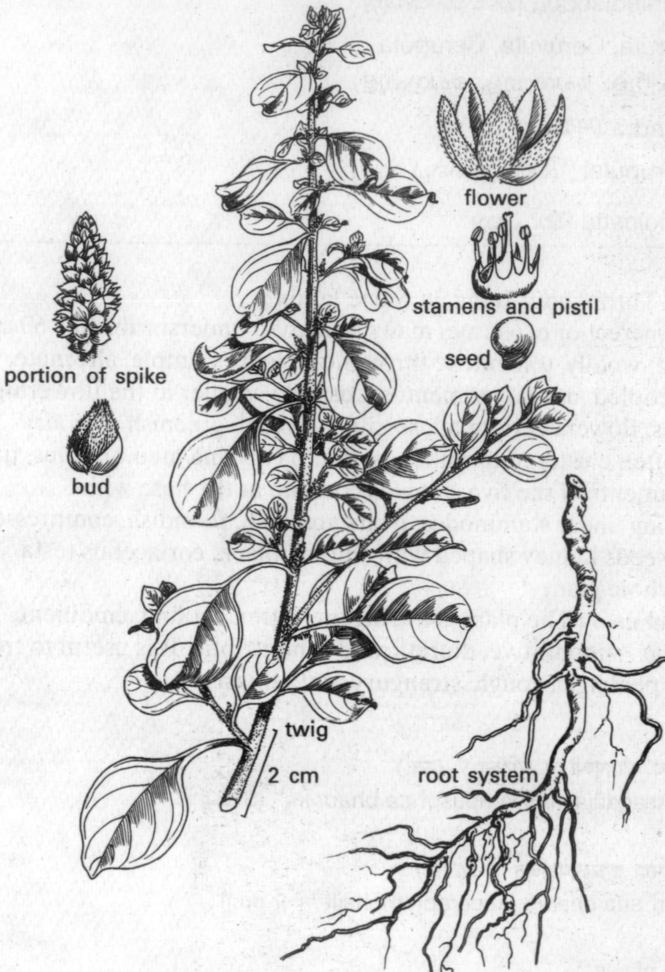

laghvī ca tīkṣṇā paramuṣṇavīryā
Kaphapittahṛnmūtravirēcanīyā
prabhāvatōʃpyaśmarināśanī syāt'' (Dra.gu.vi.)]

Remarks : Both 'Indian Medicinal Plants' and Nadkarni's 'Materia Medica' give the Sanskrit name *aśmabhēdā* to *Aerva lanata.* But in Kerala *aśmabhēdā* is identified as *Rotula aquatica (kallūṛvañci)* and *bhadra* and *bhadrikā* as *Aerva lanata.* The practice of using this by some as one of the drugs of *bṛhatīdvayaṃ* (*Solanum indicum* and *S. surattense*) should not be encouraged pending further investigations.

Coll. No. AVS 2449

Agaricus campestris Linn. ex Fries

(Psalliota campestris *(Linn.) Fr.*)

Agaricaceae (छत्रक—कुलम्)

Eng	:	Mushroom, Common mushroom
Hin	:	Kumbī, Kumī, Sampakichatṛī (कुम्बी, कुमी, सम्पकिछत्री)
Mal	:	Kūṇ (കൂൺ)
San	:	Chatṛakaḥ, Bhūchatṛā (छत्रकः, भूछत्रा)
Tam	:	Nāikkuṭai (நாய்க்குடை)
Tel	:	Kukkagoḍugu (కుక్క గొడుగు)

Distribution : Throughout India, on dead organic matter

The plant : The fungus appears as buttons on the surface of the ground when young; when mature it has underground rhizomorphs, a cylindrical aerial stipe bearing an annulus and an umbrella-shaped fleshy pileus. On the undersurface of the pileus, there are many radiating plate-like gills.

Parts used : whole plant.

Properties and uses : The fungus is sweet, cooling, indigestible, laxative, aphrodisiac and tonic. It is useful in ophthalmopathy, nasitis, hydrocele, paralysis, hepatodynia, constipation, seminal weakness and general debility.

"उक्तं संस्वेदजं शाकं भूमिच्छन्नं शिलीन्ध्रकम् ।
क्षितिगोमयकाष्ठेषु वृक्षादिषु च तद् भवेत् ॥" (भा.प्र.)
["Uktaṃ samsvēdajaṃ śākaṃ bhūmicchannaṃ śilīndhṛakaṃ
Kṣitigōmayakāṣṭhēṣu vṛkṣādiṣu ca tad bhavēt'' (Bhā.pṛa.)]

"सर्पच्छत्रं भूमिकन्दो भूमिस्फोटश्च छत्रकः ।
भूकन्दः पृथिवीस्फोटः शिलीन्ध्रं कवकं स्मृतम् ॥" (कै.नि.)
["Saṛpacchatṛaṃ bhūmikandō bhūmisphōṭaśca chatṛakaḥ
Bhūkandaḥ pṛthivīsphōṭaḥ śilīndhṛaṃ kavakaṃ smṛtaṃ'' (Kai.ni.)]

"सर्वे संस्वेदजाः शीताः दोषळाः पिच्छिलाश्च ते ।
गुरवश्छर्द्यतीसारज्वरश्ळेष्मामयप्रदाः ॥
श्वेताः शुभ्रस्थलीकाष्ठवंशगोव्रजसम्भवाः ।

Agaricus campestris

Plate 5

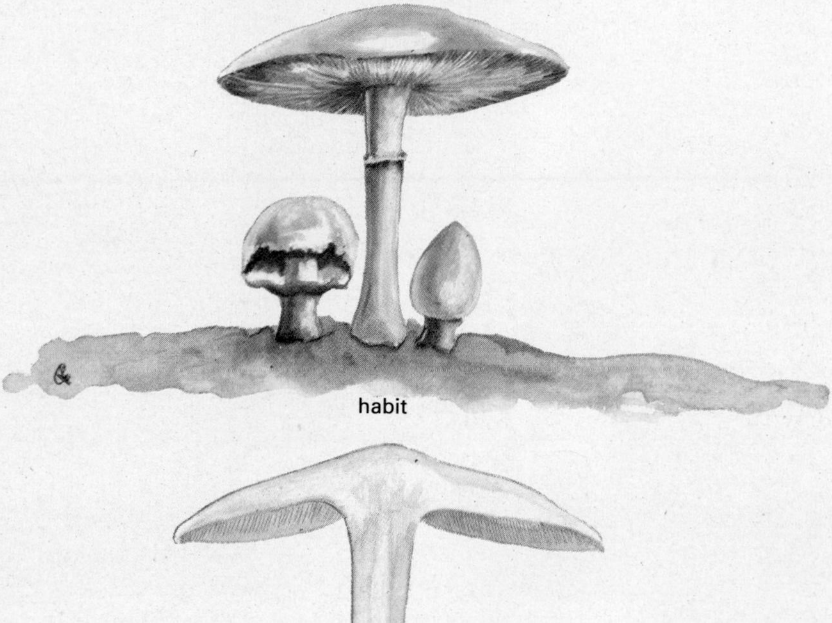

habit

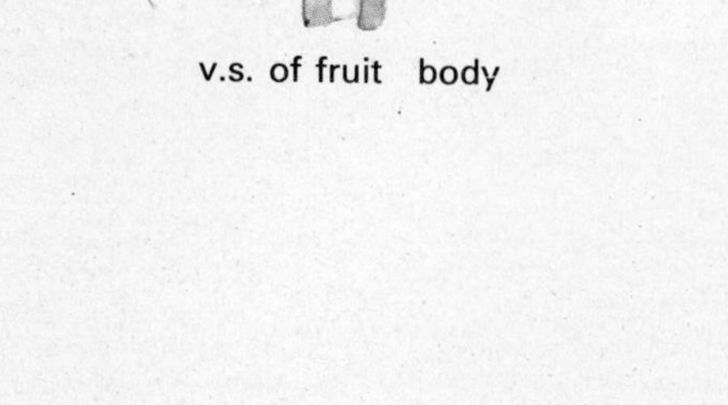

v.s. of fruit body

नातिदोषकरास्ते स्युः शेषास्तेभ्यो विगर्हिताः ॥" (भा.प्र.)
[`Saṛvē samsvēdajāḥ śītāḥ dōṣaḷāḥ picchilāśca tē
Guravaścharḍyatīsārajvaraśḷēṣmāmayapṛadāḥ
Svētāḥ śubhṛasthalīkāṣṭhavamśagōvṛajasambhavāḥ
Nātidōṣakarāstē syuḥ śēṣāstēbhyō vigaṛhitāḥ'' (Bhā. pṛa.)]

"भूकन्दो मधुरो वृष्यो बल्यो रूक्षो हिमो गुरुः ।
दुर्जरो भेदनो मृत्स्नो रोचनोऽतित्रिदोषळः ॥
क्षुद्रजं तुवरं पाके कटु तद्वत् पुरीषजम् ।
सर्पछत्रकवर्ज्यास्तु बह्व्योन्याश्छत्रजातयः ॥
गुर्व्यः पीनसकत्र्यस्तु सर्वदोषप्रकोपनाः ।
कफकृच्छीतवीर्यं तु सर्वदोषविवर्द्धनम् ॥
रसे पाके च मधुरं गुरुष्णं कृष्णछत्रकम् ।
श्वेतं गुरुं विपाके तु रक्तं स्यात् स्वल्पदोषकृत् ॥" (कै.नि.)
[`Bhūkandō madhurō vṛṣyō balyō rūkṣō himō guruḥ
Duṛjarō bhēdanō mṛtsnō rōcanōʃtitṛidōṣaḷaḥ
Kṣudrajaṃ tuvaraṃ pākē kaṭu tadvat purīṣajaṃ
Saṛpachatṛakavaṛjyāstu bahvyōnyāśchatṛajātayaḥ
Guṛvyaḥ pīnasakatṛyastu saṛvadōṣapṛakōpanāḥ
Kaphakṛcchītavīryaṃ tu saṛvadōṣavivaṛddhanaṃ
Ṛasē pākē ca madhuraṃ gurūṣṇaṃ kṛṣṇachatṛakaṃ
Śvētaṃ guruṃ vipākē tu raktaṃ syāt svalpadōṣakṛt'' (Kai.ni.)]

"भूच्छत्रं शीतळं बल्यं गुरु भेदी त्रिदोषजित् ।" (म.पा.नि.)
[`Bhūcchatṛaṃ śītaḷaṃ balyaṃ guru bhēdi tṛidōṣajit'' (Ma.pā.ni.)]

"शीता बल्या सुनेशानी गुरुर्भेदकरा मधुः ।
त्रिदोषकारिणी वृष्या कफदा च मता बुधैः ॥
भेदास्त्रयः समाख्याताः कृष्णो रक्तश्च पाण्डुरः ।
कृष्णा रसे च पाके च मधुरोष्णा गुरुः स्मृता ॥
श्वेता तु पाककाले च गुर्वी रक्ताल्पदोषदा ।" (नि.र.)
[`Sītā balyā sunēśāni guruṛbhēdakarā madhuḥ
Tṛidōṣakāriṇī vṛṣyā kaphadā ca matā budhaiḥ
Bhēdāstṛayaḥ samākhyātāḥ kṛṣṇō raktaśca pāṇḍuraḥ
Kṛṣṇā rasē ca pākē ca madhurōṣṇā guruḥ smṛtā
Svētā tu pākakālē ca guṛvī raktālpadōṣadā'' (Ni.ra.)]

Coll. No. AVS 2269

Ageratum conyzoides Linn.

Asteraceae (भृङ्गराज–कुलम्)

Eng	:	Goat weed, Appa grass
Hin	:	Viṣadōḍī (विषदोडी)
Kan	:	Nayituḷasi (ನಾಯಿತುಳಸಿ)
Mal	:	Kāṭṭappa, Appa, Muṙiyan pacca (കാട്ടപ്പ, അപ്പ, മുറിയൻ പച്ച)
San	:	Viṣamuṣṭiḥ (विषमुष्टिः)
Tam	:	Pūmpullu (பூம்புல்லு)

Distribution : Throughout India, in plains and hills and in forests as undergrowth

The plants : A softly hairy annual weed upto 90 cm in height; leaves opposite or the upper ones alternate, more or less hairy on both sides, margins ciliate; flowers pale in heads, pappus of 5-scales, dilated at the base almost equalling the corolla; fruits achenes, black in colour, 5-angled and attenuated at the base.

Parts used : roots, leaves

Properties and uses : The roots are bitter, acrid, thermogenic, digestive, lithontriptic, appetiser and ophthalmic. They are useful in vitiated conditions of *kapha* and *vāta,* dyspepsia, anorexia, purulent ophthalmia, renal and vesical calculi and pharyngopathy. The leaves are styptic and antidysenteric, and are commonly used for haemorrhoids, wounds and sores. A poultice of the leaves is good for boils and the juice is used as a lotion for eyes. The tribals make use of the juice for treating fresh cuts and wounds.

"विषमुष्टिः केशमुष्टिः सुमुष्टिरणुमुष्टिकः ।
क्षुपडोडिसमायुक्तो मुष्टिः पञ्चभिधः स्मृतः ॥" (रा.नि.)
["Viṣamuṣṭiḥ kēśamuṣṭiḥ sumuṣṭiraṇumuṣṭikaḥ
Kṣupaḍōḍisamāyuktō muṣṭiḥ pañcabhidhaḥ smṛtaḥ" (Rā.ni.)]

"विषमुष्टिः कटुस्तिक्तो दीपनः कफवातहृत् ।
कण्ठामयहरो रुच्यो रक्तपित्तार्त्तिदाहकृत् ॥" (रा.नि.)

Ageratum conyzoides

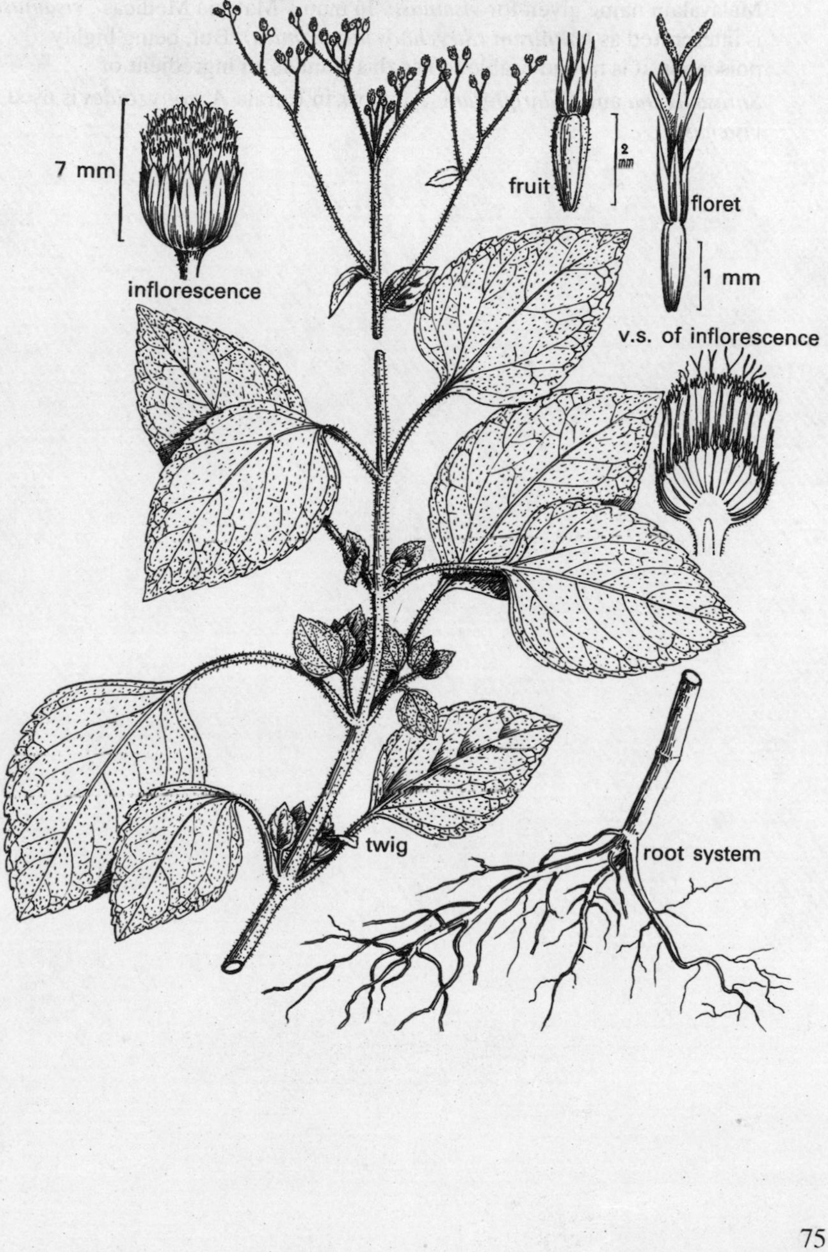

["Viṣamuṣṭiḥ kaṭustiktō dīpanaḥ kaphavātahṛt
K'aṇṭhāmayaharō rucyō raktapittāṛttidāhakṛt" (Rā.ni.)]

"കാട്ടപ്പയരിശസ്സിന്നും നന്നു ദുർദ്ദേവതാഹരം." (ഗു.പാ.)
["Kāṭṭappayariśassinnuṃ nannu duṛddēvatāharaṃ" (Gu.pā.)]

Remarks : In treatises like `Sahasṛayōgaṃ', *kāṭṭappa(Ageratum conyzoides)* is the Malayalam name given for *viṣamuṣṭi.* In many `Materia Medicas', *viṣamuṣṭi* is interpreted as *kāññiraṃ (Strychnos nux-vomica).* But, being highly poisonous, it is not advisable to use this plant as an ingredient of *Surasādigaṇa* and *Śūlārighṛtaṃ*. Anyhow, in Kerala *A. conyzoides* is used as *viṣamuṣṭi.*

Coll. No. AVS 1964

Alangium salvifolium **(Linn. f.) Wang.**

Alangiaceae (अङ्कोल–कुलम्)

Eng	:	Sage-leaved alangium
Hin	:	Angōl, Ḍhērā, Ḍhēlā (अङ्कोल, ढेरा, ढेला)
Kan	:	Ankōlamara (ಅಂಕೋಲಮರ)
Mal	:	Ankōlaṃ, Vēlittoṇḍi, Aḻiññil (അങ്കോലം, വേലിത്തൊണ്ടി, അഴിഞ്ഞിൽ)
San	:	Ankōlaḥ, Ankōḍaḥ (अङ्कोलः, अङ्कोडः)
Tam	:	Alāngi (அலாங்கி)
Tel	:	Ankolamu, Ūḍugucettu (అంకోలము. ఊడుగుచెట్టు)

Distribution : In the forests of south India

The plant : A small deciduous tree or shrub, armed or not; leaves alternate, usually unequal at the base; flowers white or yellowish-white, fragrant, in axillary fascicles; fruits 1–2 seeded berries crowned by the calyx lobes, yellowish or red when ripe.

Parts used: roots, fruits

Properties and uses : The roots are acrid, astringent, emollient, anthelmintic, thermogenic, diuretic and purgative. Root bark is an antidote for several poisons. The roots are useful for external application in acute case of rheumatism, leprosy and inflammation and for external and internal application in case of bites of rabid dogs. Fruits are sweet, cooling and purgative, and are useful in treating burning sensation and haemorrhages.

"अङ्कोलः कोलको रेची रेचिको दीर्घकीलकः ।
पीतसारस्ताम्रफलो विषजित् सेचनो भवेत् ॥ (अ.म.)
["Ankōlaḥ kōlakō rēcī rēcikō dīrghakīlakaḥ
Pītasārastāmṛaphalō viṣajit sēcanō bhavēt" (A.ma.)]

"अङ्कोलः कोठरो रेची गूढपत्रो निकोचकः ।
गुप्तस्नेहो पीतसारो मदनो गूढमल्लिका ॥
पीतस्ताम्रफलो ज्ञेयो दीर्घकालो गुणाढ्यकः ।
कोलः कोलम्बकर्णश्च गन्धपुष्पश्च रोचनः ॥
विज्ञानतैलगर्भश्च स्मृतिसंख्याभिधा स्मृतः ।" (रा.नि.)
["Ankōlaḥ kōṭharō rēcī gūḍhapatrō nikōcakaḥ
Guptasnēhō pītasārō madanō gūḍhamallikā
Pītastāmṛaphalō jñēyō dīrghakālō guṇāḍhyakaḥ

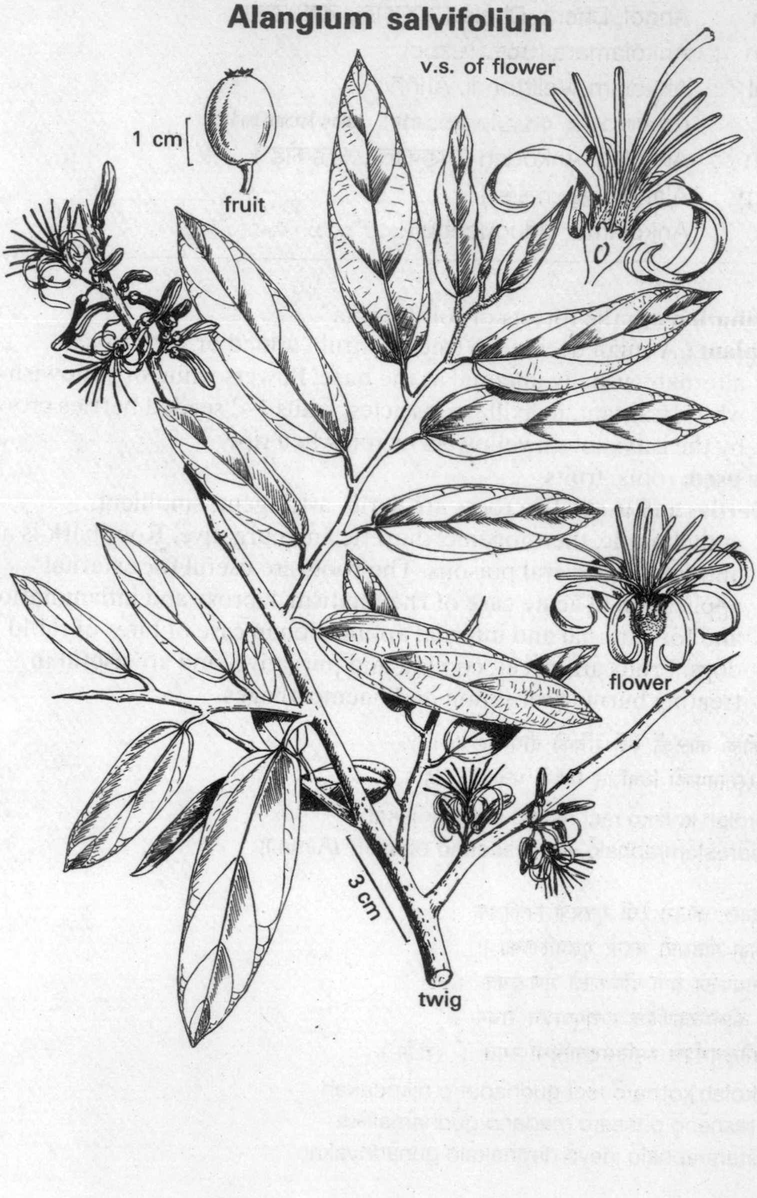
Alangium salvifolium
v.s. of flower
1 cm
fruit
flower
3 cm
twig

Kōlaḥ kōlambakarṇaśca gandhapuṣpaśca rōcanaḥ
Vijñānatailagarbhaśca smṛtisaṁkhyābhidhā smṛtaḥ" (Rā.ni.)]

अङ्कोडकः कटुस्तीक्ष्णः स्निग्धोष्णस्तुवरो लघुः ।
रेचनः कृमिशूलामशोफग्रहविषापहा ॥
विसर्पकफपित्तास्रमूषिकाहिविषापहा ।
तत्फलं शीतळं स्वादु श्ळेष्मघ्नं बृंहणं गुरु ॥
बल्यं विरेचनं वातपित्तदाहक्षयास्रजित् ।
["Aṅkoḍākaḥ kāṭustīkṣṇaḥ snigdhōṣṇastuvarō laghuḥ
Rēcanaḥ kṛmiśūlāmaśōphagrahaviṣāpahā
Visarpakaphapittāsṛamūṣikāhiviṣāpahā
Tatphalaṃ śītaḷaṃ svāduḥ śḷēṣmaghnaṃ bṛṁhaṇaṃ guru
Balyaṃ virēcanaṃ vātapittadāhakṣayāsṛajit" (Bhā.pra.)]

"अङ्कोलः स्निग्धतीक्ष्णोष्णः कटुको वातनाशनः ।
कुक्कुराखुविषं हन्ति ग्रहजन्तुविषापहः ॥
भूतहृत् विषहृत् चैव कण्ठ्या सूतस्य शोधनः ।" (ध.नि.)
["Aṅkōlaḥ snigdhatīkṣṇōṣṇaḥ kaṭukō vātanāśanaḥ
Kukkurākhuviṣaṃ hanti grahajantuviṣāpahaḥ
Bhūtahṛt viṣahṛt caiva kaṇṭhyā sūtasya śōdhanaḥ" (Dha.ni.)]

"श्ळेष्मळं गुरुविष्टम्भि चाङ्कोडफलमग्निजित् ।" (च.सं.)
["Śḷēṣmaḷaṃ guruviṣṭambhi cāṅkōḍaphalamagnijit" (Ca.saṁ.)]

अङ्कोलमूलकल्को वा बस्तमूत्रेण कल्कितः ।
पानलेपनयोर्युक्तः सर्वाखुविषनाशनः ॥ (अ.हृ.)
["Aṅkōlamūlakalkō vā bastamūtṛēṇa kalkitaḥ
Pānalēpanayōṛyuktaḥ saṛvākhuviṣanāśanaḥ" (A.hṛ.)]

अङ्कोलः कटुकः स्निग्धो विषलूतादिदोषनुत् ।
कफानिलहरः सूतशुध्दिकृत् रेचनीयकः ॥ (रा.नि.)
["Aṅkōlaḥ kaṭukaḥ snigdhō viṣalutadidoṣanut
Kaphānilaharaḥ sūtaśuddhikṛt rēcanīyakaḥ" (Rā.ni.)]

रसो वान्तिकरश्यास्य विषदोषकफापहः ।
वातशूलशोफकृमिग्रहपीडामपित्तहा ॥
रक्तदोषविसर्पघ्नः श्वानाखुविषनाशनः ।
ओतोर्विषकटीशूलमतिसारं च नाशयेत् ॥
पिशाचपीडाशमनो बीजं चास्य तु शीतळम् ।
धातुवृध्दिकरं स्वादु चाग्निमान्द्यकरं गुरु ॥
रसे पाके च मधुरं बलकृत् कफकृत् सरम् ।
स्निग्धं वृष्यं च दाहध्नं वातपित्तक्षयापहम् ॥
रक्तदोषं कफं पित्तं विसर्पं चैव नाशयेत् । (नि.र.)
["Rasō vāntikaraścāsya viṣadōṣakaphāpahaḥ
Vātaśūlaśōphakṛmigrapīḍāmapittahā
Raktadōṣavisaṛpaghnaḥ śvānākhuviṣanāśanaḥ

Ōtōrviṣakaṭīśūlamatisāraṃ ca nāśayēt
Piśācapīḍāśamanō bījaṃ cāsya tu śītaḷaṃ
Dhātuvṛddhikaraṃ svādu cāgnimāndyakaraṃ guru
Rasē pākē tu madhuraṃ balakṛtkaphakṛtsaraṃ
Snigdhaṃ vṛṣyaṃ ca dāhaghnaṃ vātapittakṣayāpahaṃ
Raktadōṣaṃ kaphaṃ pittaṃ visaṛpaṃ caiva nāśayēt" (Ni.ra.)]

Albizia lebbeck **(Linn.) Benth.**

Mimosaceae (बब्बुल–कुलम्)

Eng	:	Siris tree
Hin	:	Śirīs, Sirīs (शिरीस, सिरीस)
Kan	:	Bēgemara (ಬೇಗೆಮರ)
Mal	:	Nenmēnivāka, Vāka (നെന്മേനിവാക, വാക)
San	:	Śirīṣaḥ, Bhaṇḍī (शिरीषः, भण्डी)
Tam	:	Vākai, Śirīdaṃ (வாகை, சிரீதம்)
Tel	:	Dirisana (దిరిసన)

Distribution : Throughout India, in moist, teak-bearing forests, also cultivated

The plant : A medium to large sized unarmed deciduous tree about 20 m in height with an umbrella-shaped crown and grey to dark brown rough irregularly cracked bark; leaves abruptly bipinnate, main rachis with a large gland above the base and one below the uppermost pair of pinnae, pinnae 2 – 4 pairs, leaflets 5 – 9 pairs with glands between their bases, the lateral ones elliptic-oblong, the two terminal ovate-oblong, all unequal sided; flowers white, fragrant, in globose umbellate heads; fruits long, characteristic pods, bluntly pointed, thin, pale yellow, smooth, shiny, reticulately veined above the seed; seeds 4 – 12, pale brown, ellipsoid, oblong, compressed.

Parts used : bark, flowers, seeds

Properties and uses : The bark is astringent, bitter, acrid, sweet, mildly thermogenic, expectorant, aphrodisiac, anti-inflammatory, anodyne, cephalic, ophthalmic, depurative, restorative and tonic. It is useful in vitiated conditions of *pitta* and *kapha,* cough and catarrh, asthma, enlarged cervical glands, ophthalmopathy, nyctalopia, strengthening gums, scrofula, skin eruptions, leprosy, leucoderma, sprains, wounds, ulcers, neuralgia, inflammations, erysipelas, diarrhoea and all types of poisoning. It is also used as a dentifrice in odontopathy. The flowers are useful in chronic cough and bronchitis. The seeds are useful in inflammations, scrofula, skin diseases, leprosy, leucoderma, chronic catarrh, seminal weakness, ophthalmopathy and poisoning.

Albizia lebbeck

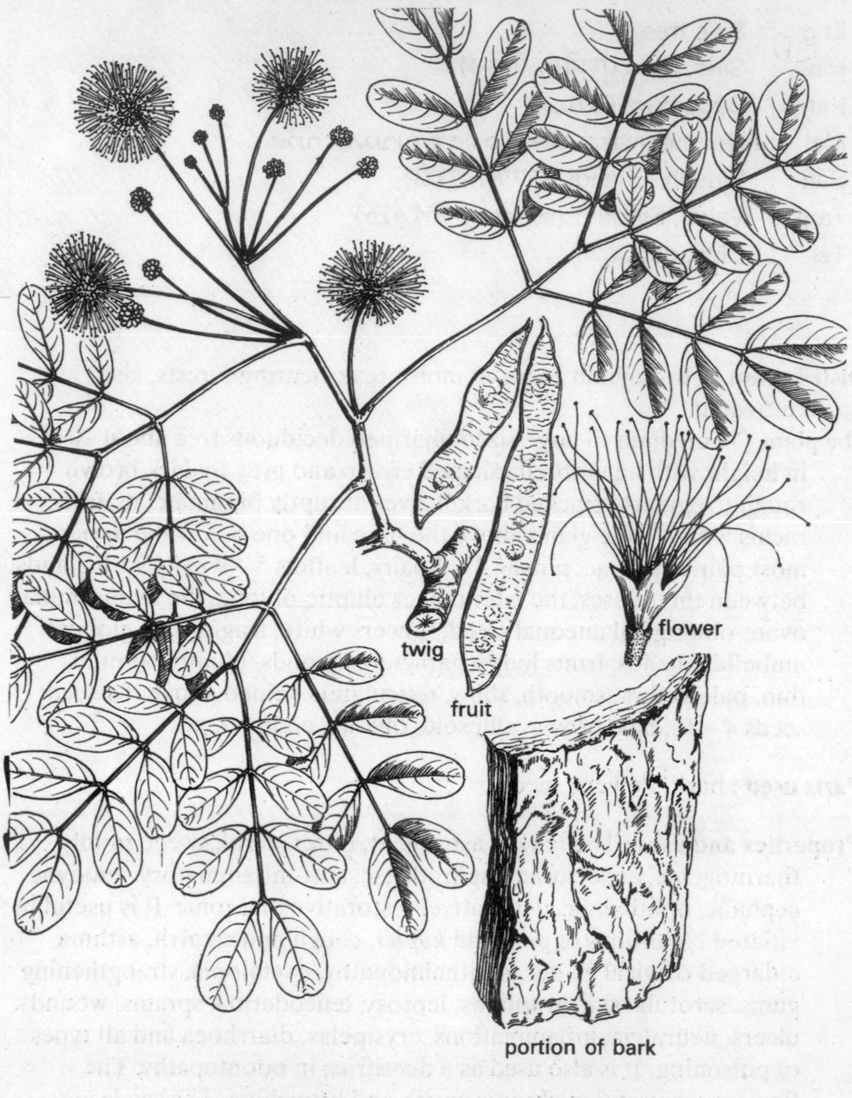

"शिरीषो मधुपुष्पश्च वृत्तपुष्पो शुकप्रियः ।
भण्डी शुकाभपुष्पश्च चक्षुपुष्पो विषापहः ॥" (म.नि.)
["Sirīṣō madhupuṣpaśca vṛttapuṣpō śukapriyaḥ
Bhaṇḍī śukābhapuṣpaśca cakṣupuṣpō viṣāpahaḥ" (Ma.ni.)]

"शिरीषः सितपुष्पश्च भण्डिको मृदुपुष्पकः ।
शुकेष्टो बर्हिपुष्पश्च विषहन्ता सुपुष्पकः ॥
उद्दानकः शुकतरुर्ज्ञेयो लोमशपुष्पकः ।
कपीतनः कलिङ्गश्च श्यामळः शङ्खिनीफलः ॥
मधुपुष्पस्तथा वृत्तपुष्पः सप्तदशाह्वयः ।" (रा.नि.)
["Śirīṣaḥ sitapuṣpaśca bhaṇḍikō mṛdupuṣpakaḥ
Śukēṣṭō barhipuṣpaśca viṣahantā supuṣpakaḥ
Uddānakaḥ śukatarurjñēyō lōmaśapuṣpakaḥ
Kapītanaḥ kalingaśca śyāmaḷaḥ śankhinīphalaḥ
Madhupuṣpastathā vṛttapuṣpaḥ saptadaśāhvayaḥ" (Rā.ni.)]

"कफपित्तहरश्चैव विषव्रणविशोधनः ।
शीतवीर्यो विसर्पघ्नो शिरीषो मधुरो रसः ॥" (म.नि.)
["Kaphapittaharaścaiva viṣavraṇaviśōdhanaḥ
Śītavīryō visarpaghnō śirīṣō madhurō rasaḥ" (Ma.ni.)]

"शिरीषो मधुरोऽनुष्णस्तिक्तश्च तुवरो लघुः ।
दोषशोषविसर्पघ्नः कासव्रणविषापहः ॥" (भा.प्र.)
["Śirīṣō madhurōऽnuṣṇastiktaśca tuvarō laghuḥ
Dōṣaśōṣavisarpaghnaḥ kāsavraṇaviṣāpahaḥ" (Bhā.pra.)]

"तिक्तोष्णो विषहा वर्ण्यस्त्रिदोषशमनो लघुः ।
शिरीषः कुष्ठकण्डूघ्नस्त्वग्दोषश्वासकासहा ॥ (ध.नि.)
["Tiktōṣṇō viṣahā varṇyastridōṣaśamanō laghuḥ
Śirīṣaḥ kuṣṭhakaṇḍūghnastvagdōṣaśvāsakāsahā" (Dha.ni.)]

"शिरीषो कटुकः शीतो विषवातहरः परः ।
पामासृक्कुष्ठकण्डूतित्वग्दोषाणां विनाशकः ॥" (रा.नि.)
["Śirīṣō kaṭukaḥ śītō viṣavātaharaḥ paraḥ
Pāmāsṛkkuṣṭhakaṇḍūtitvagdōṣāṇāṃ vināśakaḥ" (Rā.ni.)]

"शिरीषो मधुरोऽनुष्णः सतिक्तस्तुवरो लघुः ।
निहन्ति दोषवीसर्पशोफकासविषव्रणान् ॥" (कै.नि.)
["Śirīṣō madhurōऽnuṣṇaḥ satiktastuvarō laghuḥ
Nihanti dōṣavīsarpaśōphakāsaviṣavraṇān" (Kai.ni.)]

"शिरीषोऽर्शोविषस्वेदत्वग्रुक्च्छोफविसर्पनुत् । (शा.नि.)
["Śirīṣōऽrśōviṣasvēdatvagrukcchōphavisarpanut" (Śā.ni.)]

"शिरीषो विषघ्नानां" (च.सं.सू.२५)
["Śirīṣō viṣaghnānāṃ" (Ca.saṁ.Sū.25.)]

".........നെന്മേനിയിവൾക്കുള്ള പൂക്കളും
മലത്തിനെ നിരോധിക്കും വിഷഘ്നം ശ്ലേഷ്മവർദ്ധനം" (ഗു.പാ.)
[".................nenmēniyivaḷkkuḷḷa pūkkaḷuṃ
Malattine nirōdhikkuṃ viṣaghanaṃ śḷēṣmavarddhanaṃ" (Gu.pā.)]

Remarks: 'The Pharmacognosy of Ayurvedic Drugs', a Kerala university publication, identifies this plant as *Albizia marginata* Merr. and says that this identification is based upon the fact that this plant is seen growing in plenty in south Kerala and being used as *nenmēnivāka* by the Ayurvedic practitioners. But most other Indian publications including `The Ayurvedic Formulary of India' identifies this as *A. lebbeck.* This species also is abundantly available throughout Kerala. Hence, it seems that *A.lebbeck* is more appropriate to be used as *śirīṣaṃ*.

Albizia odoratissima (Linn.f.) Benth.

Mimosaceae (बब्बुल–कुलम्)

Eng	:	Black siris, Kala siris
Hin	:	Kālā śirīs (काला शिरीस)
Kan	:	Bilvāra (ಬಿಲ್ವಾರ)
Mal	:	Puḷivāka, Nellivāka, Karivāka, Kunnivāka (പുളിവാക, നെല്ലിവാക, കരിവാക, കുന്നിവാക)
San	:	Bhūśirīṣaḥ (भूशिरीषः)
Tam	:	Karuvākai, Sittilavākai (கருவாகை, சித்திலவாகை)
Tel	:	Cinḍuga, Sirisi, Telsu (చిందుగ, సిరిసి, తెల్సు)

Distribution : Throughout India, in areas upto an elevation of 1,500 m

The plant : A medium sized unarmed tree about 20 m in height with dark coloured young shoots and grey, rough, irregularly cracked bark with dark patches; leaves abruptly pinnate, alternate, main rachis with a gland on the upper side near its basal part and often with similar glands at the bases of the first two pairs of pinnae, leaflets unequal sided, rounded, or semicordate at base, obtuse or rounded at the apex, dark green, slightly pubescent above; flowers white, fragrant, sessile, numerous, in small globose 5–10 or more flowered heads, in corymbiform spreading panicles; fruits shortly stalked pods, brown, slightly reticulately veined; seeds flat, yellow.

Parts used : bark

Properties and uses : The bark is astringent, acrid, cooling, depurative and expectorant, and is useful in ulcers, leprosy, skin diseases, erysipelas, cough, bronchitis, diabetes and burning sensation.

"श्रूषा तु भूशिरीषः शिरीषको ध्वांक्षिकः सफला ।
तरुधूमो दुरदरिकः कनीयशीर्षोऽतिदुर्बला ज्ञेया ॥" (अ.म.)
["Śṛūṣā tu bhūśirīṣaḥ śirīṣakō dhvāmkṣikaḥ saphalā
Tarudhūmō duradarikaḥ kanīyaśīrṣōऽtiduṛbalā jñēyā" (A.ma.)]

"कफपित्तहरः शीतः विषव्रणविशोधनः ।
भूशिरीषो विसर्पघ्नः नक्तान्ध्ये च प्रशस्यते ॥" (स्व.)
["Kaphapittaharaḥ śītaḥ viṣavraṇaviśōdhanaḥ
Bhūśirīṣō visaṛpaghnaḥ naktāndhyē ca praśasyatē" (Sva.)]

Albizia odoratissima

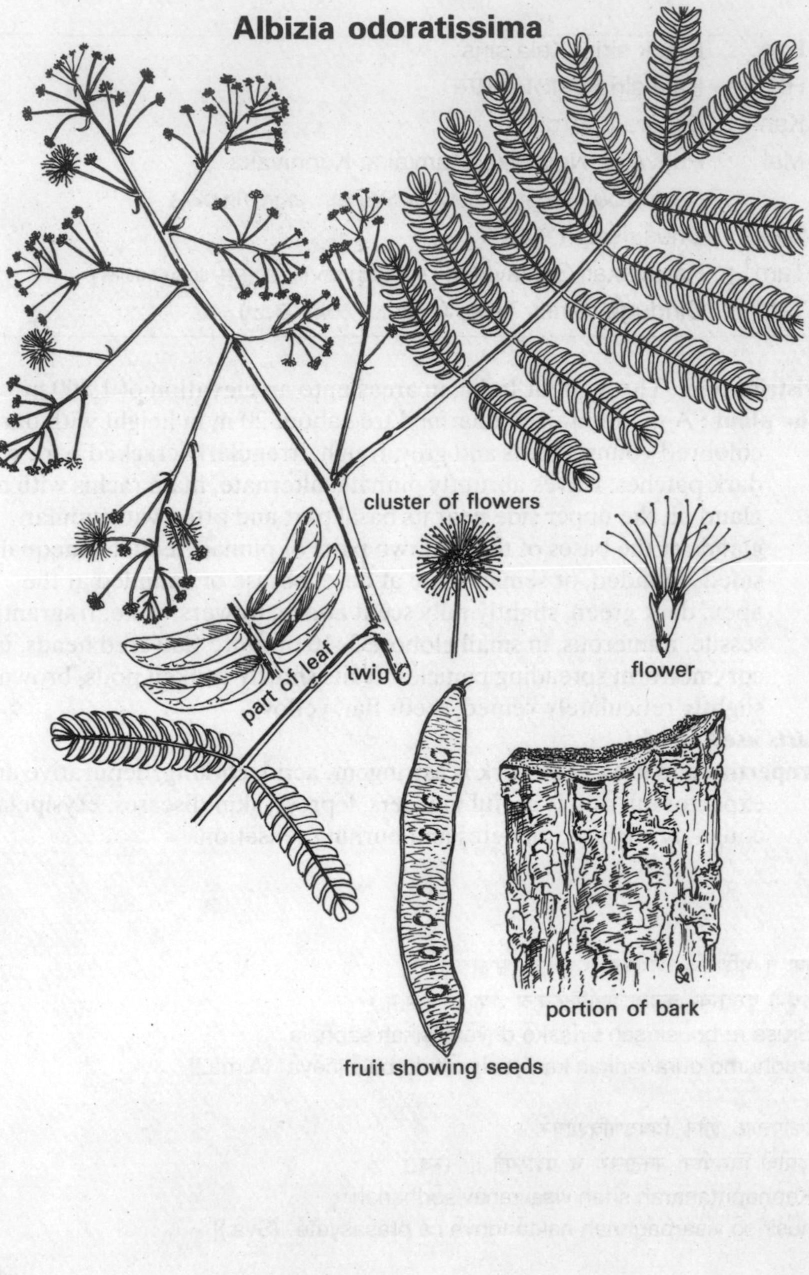

“നിലവാകരസം കയ്പു ദീപനം വിഷനാശനം
പിന്നെക്കോഷ്ഠത്തിലുണ്ടാകും ശ്ലേഷ്മത്തെ കളയും ദ്രുതം.” (ഗു.പാ.)
["Nilavākarasaṃ kaypu dīpanaṃ viṣanāśanaṃ
Pinnekkōṣṭhattiluṇṭākuṃ śḷēṣmatte kaḷayuṃ drutaṃ" (Gu.pā.)]

Coll. No. AVS 2407

Allium cepa **Linn.**

Liliaceae (रसोन–कुलम्)

Eng	:	Onion
Hin	:	Pyāj (प्याज)
Kan	:	Niruḷḷi (ನೀರುಳ್ಳಿ)
Mal	:	Cuvannuḷḷi, Ceṛiya uḷḷi (ചുവന്നുള്ളി, ചെറിയ ഉള്ളി)
San	:	Palāṇḍuḥ (पलाण्डुः)
Tam	:	Venkāyam, Īruḷḷi (வெங்காயம், ஈருள்ளி)
Tel	:	Ullipāya, Ulligaḍḍa, Erragaḍḍa (ఉల్లిపాయ, ఉల్లిగడ్డ, ఎఱ్ఱగడ్డ)

Distribution : Cultivated throughout India

The plant : A biennial or perennial herb with aromatic fleshy underground bulb; leaves linear, hollow, cylindric and fleshy; flowers many, white in globular umbels, spathe composed of 2–3 reflexed walls.
The underground bulbs which are medicinally used vary in size, colour, shape, firmness, strength of flavour and keeping quality.

Parts used : bulbs

Properties and uses : The bulbs are acrid, sweet, aromatic, thermogenic, antiperiodic, antibacterial, aphrodisiac, emmenagogue, emollient, expectorant, carminative, stomachic, diuretic, anodyne and tonic. They are useful in haemorrhoids, dysentery, flatulence, dyspepsia, colic, jaundice, splenopathy, hepatopathy, pneumonopathy, asthma, bronchitis, ophthalmia, vomiting, otalgia, pharyngodynia, malarial fever, lumbago, epilepsy, tumours, wounds, paralysis, arthralgia, leucoderma and skin diseases.

"चतुर्थो लशुनो रक्तः पलाण्डुश्च पलाण्डुकः ।
वारणो दुर्दनो दुर्दुर्नतार्कः परिकीर्त्तितः ॥" (अ.म.)
["Caturtthō laśunō raktaḥ palāṇḍuśca palāṇḍukaḥ
Vāraṇō durdanō durdurnatārkaḥ parikīrttitaḥ" (A.ma.)]

"पलाण्डुः तीक्ष्णकन्दश्च उळ्ळी च मुखदूषणः ।
शूद्रप्रियः कृमिघ्नश्च दीपनो मुखगन्धकः ॥
बहुपत्रो विश्वगन्धो रोचनो रुद्रसंज्ञकः ।" (रा.नि.)

Allium cepa

Plate 6

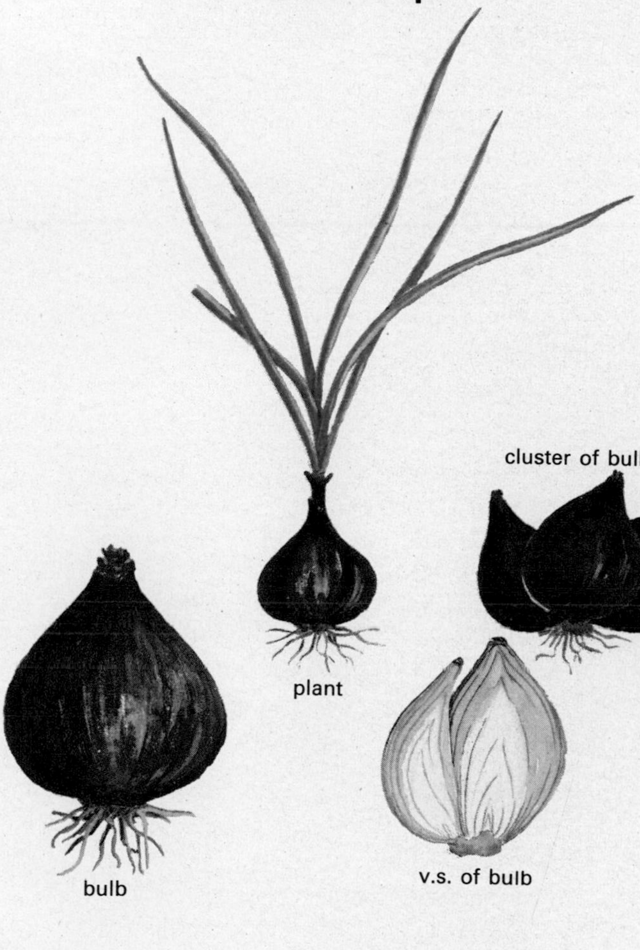

["Palāṇḍuḥ tīkṣṇakandaśca uḷḷī ca mukhadūṣaṇaḥ
Śūdrapṛiyaḥ kṛmighnaśca dīpanō mukhagandhakaḥ
Bahupatṛō viśvagandhō rōcanō rudrasaṁjñakaḥ" (Rā.ni.)]

"पलाण्डुस्तु गुणैर्ज्ञेयो रसोनसदृशो बुधैः ।
स्वादुः पाके रसेनोष्णः कफकृन्नातिपित्तळः ॥
हरते केवलं वातं बलवीर्यकरो गुरुः । (भा.प्र.)
["Palāṇḍustu guṇairjñēyō rasōnasadṛśō budhaiḥ
Svāduḥ pākē rasēnōṣṇaḥ kaphakṛnnātipittaḷaḥ
Haratē kēvalaṃ vātaṃ balavīryakarō guruḥ" (Bhā.pṛa.)]

"श्ळेष्मळो मारुतघ्नश्च पलाण्डुर्न च पित्तहृत् ।
आहारयोगी बल्यश्च गुरुर्वृष्योऽथ रोचनः ॥" (च.सं.सू. २७)
["Śḷēṣmaḷō mārutaghnaśca palāṇḍuṛna ca pittahṛt
Āhārayōgī balyaśca guruṛvṛṣyōऽtha rōcanaḥ" (Ca.saṁ. Sū.27)]

नात्युष्णवीर्योऽनिलहा कटुश्च
तीक्ष्णो गुरुर्नातिकफावहश्च ।
बलावहः पित्तकरोऽथ किञ्चित्
पलाण्डुरग्निं परिवर्धयेत्तु ॥
स्निग्धो रुचिष्यः स्थिरधातुकारी
बल्योऽथ मेधाकफपुष्टिदश्च ।" (सु.सं.सू. ४६)
["Nātyuṣṇavīryōऽnilahā kaṭuśca
tīkṣṇō guruṛnātikaphāvahaśca
Balāvahaḥ pittakarōऽtha kiñcit
palāṇḍuragniṃ parivaṛdhayēttu
Snigdhō ruciṣyaḥ sthiradhātukārī
balyōऽtha mēdhākaphapuṣṭidaśca" (Su.saṁ.Sū.46)]

"बीजं पलाण्डोर्वृष्यः स्याद्दन्तकीटप्रमेहजित् ।" (नि.र.)
["Bījaṃ palāṇḍōṛvṛṣyaḥ syāddantakīṭapṛamēhajit" (Ni.ra.)]

"पलाण्डुस्तद्गुणैर्न्यूनो विपाके मधुरस्तु सः ।
कफं करोति नो पित्तं केवलोऽनिलनाशनम् ॥" (ध.नि.)
["Palāṇḍustadguṇaiṛnyūnō vipākē madhurastu saḥ
Kaphaṃ karōti nō pittaṃ kēvalōऽnilanāśanaṃ" (Dha.ni.)]

"पलाण्डुः कटुको बल्यः कफपित्तहरो गुरुः ।
वृष्यश्च रोचनः स्निग्धो वान्ति दोषविनाशनः ॥" (रा.नि.)
["Palāṇḍuḥ kaṭukō balyaḥ kaphapittaharō guruḥ
Vṛṣyaśca rōcanaḥ snigdhō vāntidōṣavināśanaḥ" (Rā.ni.)]

"पलाण्डुर्वातकफहा शुक्ळळा शूलगुल्मनुत् ।" (हा.सं)
[Palāṇḍuṛvātakaphahā śukḷaḷā śūlagulmanut" (Hā.saṁ.)]

"पलाण्डुस्तद्गुणैर्न्यूनः श्ळेष्मळो नातिपित्तळः ।
स्वादुपाकरसोऽनुष्णः केवलानिलनाशनः ॥ (कै.नि.)
["Palāṇḍustadguṇairnyūnaḥ śḷēṣmaḷō nātipittaḷaḥ
Svādupākarasō∫nuṣṇaḥ kēvalānilanāśanaḥ" (Kai.ni.)]

Coll. No. AVS 2408

Allium sativum **Linn.**

Liliaceae (रसोन–कुलम्)

Eng	:	Garlic
Hin	:	Laśun, Lahasun (लशुन, लहसुन)
Kan	:	Beḷḷuḷḷi (ಬೆಳ್ಳುಳ್ಳಿ)
Mal	:	Veḷḷuḷḷi (വെള്ളുള്ളി)
San	:	Laśunaḥ, Rasōnaḥ (लशुनः, रसोनः)
Tam	:	Veḷḷai pūṇṭu (வெள்ளைப் பூண்டு)
Tel	:	Vellulli, Tellagaḍḍa (వెల్లుల్లి, తెల్లగడ్డ)

Distribution : Cultivated throughout India

The plant : A scapigerous foetid perennial herb with underground compound bulbs covered over by outer white thin scales and with simple, smooth, round stem, surrounded at the bottom by tubular leaf sheath; leaves simple, long, flat, linear; flowers small, white in rounded umbels mixed with small bulbils, the entire umbel enclosed in a teardrop-shaped membranous spathe, flowers usually sterile.

Parts used : bulbs

Properties and uses : The bulbs are acrid, bitter, sweet, astringent, salty, thermogenic, aperient, anodyne, oleagenous; aphrodisiac, anthelmintic, expectorant, febrifuge, diuretic, alexeteric, emmenagogue, rubefacient, stimulant, anticholesterol, antibacterial, antifungal and tonic. They are useful in vitiated conditions of *kapha* and *vāta,* cough, whooping cough, bronchitis, asthma, fever, facial paralysis, flatulence, colic, constipation, atonic dyspepsia, helminthiasis, duodenal ulcers, pulmonary and laryngeal tuberculosis, ophthalmopathy, cardiopathy, fatigue, leucoderma, leprosy, hysteria, haemorrhoids, sciatica, otalgia, lumbago, swellings, splenopathy, hepatopathy, pneumonopathy, arthralgia and dental caries.

"राहोरमृतचौर्येण लूनाद्ये पतिता गळात् ।
अमृतस्य कणा भूमौ ते रसोनत्वमागताः ॥
द्विजा नाश्नन्ति तमतो दैत्यदेहसमुद्भवम् ।
साक्षादमृतसम्भूतेर्ग्रामणिः स रसायनम् ॥" (अ.हृ.उ. ३९)

Allium sativum

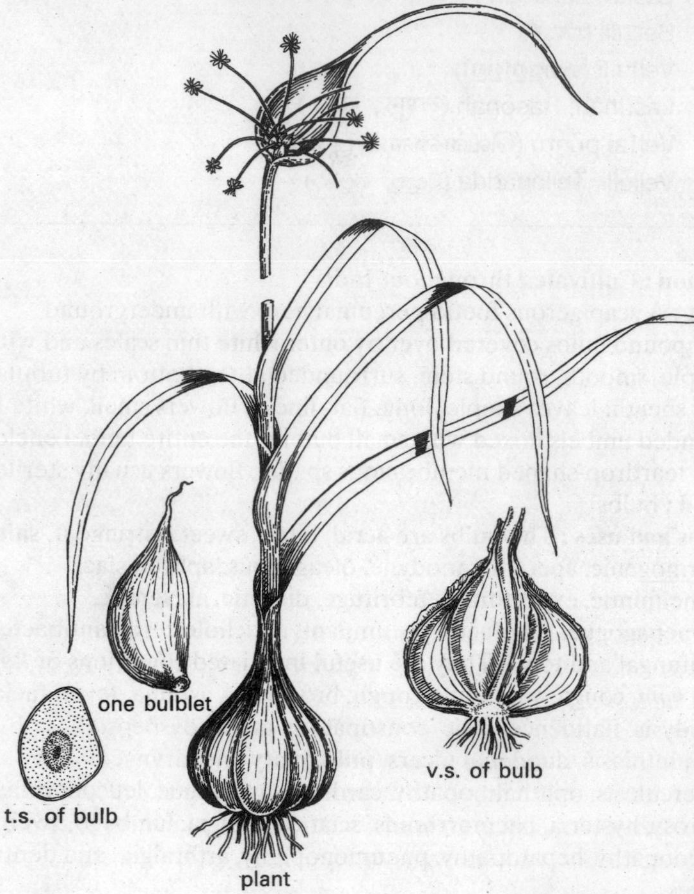

["Rāhōramṛtcauryēṇa lūnādyē patitā gaḷāt
Amṛtasya kaṇā bhūmau tē rasōnatvamāgatāḥ
Dvijā nāśnanti tamatō daityadēhasamudbhavaṃ
Sākṣādamṛtasambhūtērgrāmaṇiḥ sa rasāyanaṃ" (A.hṛ.U.39.)]

"यथामृतं वैनतेयो जहार सुरसत्तमात् ।
तदा ततोऽपतद्बिन्दुः स रसोनोऽभवत् भुवि ॥" (भा.प्र.)
["Yathāmṛtaṃ vainatēyō jahārā surasattamāt
Tadā tatōऽpatadbinduḥ sa rasōnōऽbhavat bhuvi" (Bhā.pṛa.)]

"पञ्चभिश्च रसैर्युक्तो रसेनाम्ळेन वर्जितः ।
तस्माद्रसोन इत्युक्तो द्रव्याणां गुणवेदिभिः ॥" (भा.प्र.)
["Pañcabhiśca rasaiṛyuktō rasēnāmḷēna vaṛjitaḥ
Tasmādrasōna ityuktō dravyāṇāṃ guṇavēdibhiḥ" (Bhā.pṛa.)]

"लशुनस्तु रसोनः स्यादुग्रगन्धो महौषधम् ।
अरिष्टो म्ळेच्छकन्दश्च यवनेष्टो रसोनकः ॥" (भा.प्र.)
["Laśunastu rasōnaḥ syādugragandhō mahauṣadhaṃ
Ariṣṭō mḷēcchakandaśca yavanēṣṭō rasōnakaḥ" (Bhā.pṛa.)]

कटुकश्चापि मूलेषु तिक्तः पत्रेषु संस्थितः ।
नाळे कषाय उद्दिष्टो नाळाग्रे लवणः स्मृतः ॥
बीजे तु मधुरः प्रोक्तो रसस्तद्गुणवेदिभिः ।
रसोनो बृंहणो वृष्यः स्निग्धोष्णः पाचनः सरः ॥
रसे पाके च कटुकस्तीक्ष्णो मधुरको मतः ।
बलवर्णकरो मेधाहितो नेत्र्यो रसायनः ॥
हृद्रोगजीर्णज्वरकुक्षिशूल
विबन्धगुल्मारुचिकासशोफान् ।
दुर्नामकुष्ठानलसादजन्तु
समीरणश्वासकफांश्च हन्ति ॥ (भा.प्र.)
["Kaṭukaścāpi mūlēṣu tiktaḥ patrēṣu samsthitaḥ
Nāḷē kaṣāya uddiṣṭō nāḷāgrē lavaṇaḥ smṛtaḥ
Bījē tu madhuraḥ prōktō rasastadguṇavēdibhiḥ
Rasōnō bṛmhanō vṛṣyaḥ snigdhōṣṇaḥ pācanaḥ saraḥ
Rasē pākē ca kaṭukastīṣṇō madhurakō mataḥ
Balavaṛṇakarō mēdhāhitō nētryō rasāyanaḥ
Hṛdrōgajīṛṇajvarakukṣiśūla
vibandhagulmārucikāsaśōphān
Duṛnāmakuṣṭhānalasādajantu
samīraṇaśvāsakaphāmśca hanti" (Bhā.pṛa.)]

"लशुनो भृशतीक्ष्णोष्णः कटुपाकरसः सरः
हृद्यः केश्यो गुरुर्वृष्यः स्निग्धो रोचनदीपनः ॥
भग्नसन्धानकृत् बल्यो रक्तपित्तप्रदूषणः ।

किलासकुष्ठगुल्मार्शोमेहकृमिकफानिलान् ॥
सहिध्मापीनसश्वासकासान् हन्ति रसायनम् ।" (अ.हृ.सू.६)
["Laśunō bhṛśatīkṣṇōṣṇaḥ kaṭupākarasaḥ saraḥ
Hṛdyaḥ kēśyō gururvṛsyaḥ snigdhō rōcanadīpanaḥ
Bhagnasandhānakṛt balyō raktapittapradūṣaṇaḥ
Kilāsakuṣṭhagulmārśōmēhakṛmikaphānilān
Sahidhmāpīnasaśvāsakāsān hanti rasāyanam" (A.hr.Sū.6)]

"स्निग्धोष्णतीक्ष्णः कटुपिच्छिलश्च
गुरुः सरः स्वादुरसश्च बल्यः ।
वृष्यश्च मेधास्वरवर्णचक्षु-
भग्नास्थिसन्धानकरो रसोनः ॥
हृद्रोगजीर्णज्वरकुक्षिशूल-
विबन्धगुल्मारुचिकासशोषान् ।
दुर्नामकुष्ठानलसादजन्तु-
समीरणश्वासकफांश्च हन्ति ॥" (सु.सूं.४६)
["Snigdhōṣṇatīkṣṇaḥ kaṭupicchilaśca
guruḥ saraḥ svādurasaśca balyaḥ
Vṛṣyaśca mēdhāsvaravarṇacakṣur-
bhagnāsthisandhānakarō rasōnaḥ
Hṛdrōgajīrṇajvarakukṣiśūla-
vibandhagulmārucikāsaśōṣān
Durnāmakuṣṭhānalasādajantu-
samīraṇasvāsakaphāmśca hanti" (Su.Sū.46)]

"कृमिकुष्ठकिलासघ्नो वातघ्नो गुल्मनाशनः ।
स्निग्धश्चोष्णश्च वृष्यश्च लशुनः कटुको गुरुः॥" (च.सू.२७)
["Kṛmikuṣṭhakilāsaghnō vātaghnō gulmanāśanaḥ
Snigdhaścōṣṇaśca vṛṣyaśca laśunaḥ kaṭukō guruḥ" (Ca.Sū.27)]

"पित्तरक्तविनिर्मुक्तसमस्तावरणाऽऽवृते ।
शुद्धे वा विद्यते वायौ न द्रव्यं लशुनात् परम् ॥" (अ.हृ.उ.३९)
["Pittaraktavinirmuktasamastāvaraṇāऽऽvṛtē
Śuddhē vā vidyatē vāyau na dravyam laśunāt param" (A.hṛ.U.39)]

रसोन उष्णः कटुपिच्छिलश्च
स्निग्धो गुरुः स्वादुरसोऽतिबल्यः ।
वृष्यश्च मेधास्वरवर्णचक्षु-
भग्नास्थिसन्धानकरः सुतीक्ष्णः ॥ (ध.नि.)
["Rasōna uṣṇaḥ kaṭupicchilaśca
snigdhō guruḥ svādurasōऽtibalyaḥ
Vṛṣyaśca mēdhāsvaravarṇacakṣur-
bhagnāsthisandhānkaraḥ sutīkṣṇaḥ" (Dha.ni.)]

"शीलयेल्लशुनं शीते, वसन्तेऽपि कफोल्बणः
घनोदयेऽपि वातार्तः सदा वा ग्रीष्मलीलया ॥" (अ.हृ.उ.३९)
["Śīlayēllaśunaṃ śītē, vasantēऽpi kaphōlbaṇaḥ
Ghanōdayēऽpi vātārtaḥ, sadā vā grīṣmalīlayā" (A.hr̥.U.39)]

"रसोनोऽम्ळरसो न स्यात् गुरूष्णः कफवातनुत् ।
अरुचिकृमिहृद्रोगशोफघ्नश्च रसायनः ॥" (रा.नि.)
["Rasōnōऽmḷarasō na syāt gurūṣṇaḥ kaphavātanut
Arucikr̥mihr̥drōgaśōphaghnaśca rasāyanaḥ" (Rā.ni.)]

"रसोनः सर्वांगं प्रसरति मरुन्नाशकरः सरो वृष्यः स्निग्धो
गुरुररुचिकासज्वरहरः । कफं कासं गुल्मं क्षयति च केश्यः कृमिहरः
प्रमेहार्शःकुष्ठश्वयथुहर उक्तस्त्वशिशिरः । प्रभग्ने सन्धानो रुधिर –
युतपित्तं प्रकुरुते ज्वरव्याधिध्वंसी पचयति च शूलप्रशमनः ।" (शा.नि.)
["Rasōnaḥ sarvāṃgaṃ prasarati marunnāśakaraḥ sarō vr̥ṣyaḥ snigdhō gururarucikāsajvaraharaḥ. Kaphaṃ kāsaṃ gulmaṃ kṣayati ca kēśyaḥ kr̥miharaḥ pramēhārśaḥkuṣṭhaśvayathuhara uktastva-śiśiraḥ. Prabhagnē sandhānō rudhirayutapittaṃ prakurutē jvara-vyādhidhvāṃsī pacayati ca śūlapraśamanaḥ" (Śā.ni.)]

"लशुनः क्षारमधुरः कण्ढ्यो वृष्यो गुरुः सरः ।
भग्नसन्धानकृद्बल्यो रक्तपित्तप्रदूषणः ॥" (रा.व.)
["Laśunaḥ kṣāramadhuraḥ kaṇḍhyō vr̥ṣyō guruḥ saraḥ
Bhagnasandhānakr̥dbalyō raktapittapradūṣaṇaḥ" (Rā.va.)]

लशुनः कटुकः पाके रसे स्निग्धो गुरुः सरः ।
तीक्ष्णोष्णो मधुरो वृष्यो हृद्यो बृंहणपाचनः ॥
पित्तास्रबलमेधाक्षिवर्णकेशस्वराग्निकृत् ।
भग्नसन्धानकृद् हन्यात् कफवातारुचिकृमीन् ॥
हिक्काकासज्वरश्वासकुष्ठमेहामपीनसान् ।
श्वित्रार्शोगुल्महृद्रोगशूलशोफान् रसायनम् ॥" (कै.नि.)
["Laśunaḥ kaṭukaḥ pākē rasē snigdhō guruḥ saraḥ
Tīkṣṇōṣṇō madhurō vr̥ṣyō hr̥dyō br̥ṃhaṇapācanaḥ
Pittāsṛabalamēdhākṣivarṇakēśasvarāgnikr̥t
Bhagnasandhānakr̥d hanyāt kaphavātārucikr̥mīn
Hikkākāsajvaraśvāsakuṣṭhamēhāmapīnasān
Śvitrārśōgulmahr̥drōgaśūlaśōphān rasāyanaṃ" (Kai.ni.)]

"ഉള്ളിക്കുള്ള ഗുണം ഹൃദ്യം തീക്ഷ്ണം പാകേ രസം കടു
വിരേചനകരം സ്നിഗ്ധം വൃഷ്യം കേശത്തിനും ഗുണം
ഭഗ്നസന്ധാനകൃദ് വൃഷ്യം ദീപനം ബലവർദ്ധനം
കിലാസം ഗുന്മവും വാതം കൃമികുഷ്ഠപ്രമേഹവും

പീനസം കഫമർശസ്സും കാസശ്വാസഞ്ചനാശയേത്
ഹിദ്ധ്മാവിനെ ശമിപ്പിക്കും രക്തപിത്തസ്യ വർദ്ധനം
ഓരോ ഗുണങ്ങളെക്കൊണ്ടുമിതുനല്ല രസായനം." (ഗു.പാ.)

["Uḷḷikkuḷḷa guṇaṃ hṛdyaṃ tīkṣṇaṃ pākē rasaṃ kaṭu
Virēcanakaraṃ snigdhaṃ vṛṣyaṃ kēśattinuṃ guṇaṃ
Bhagnasandhānakṛd vṛṣyaṃ dīpanaṃ balavarddhanaṃ
Kilāsaṃ gulmavuṃ vātaṃ kṛmikuṣṭ hapramēhavuṃ
Pīnasaṃ kaphamarśassuṃ kāsaśvāsañca nāśayēt
Hidhmāvine śamippikkuṃ raktapittasya varddhanaṃ
Ōrō guṇaṅṅaḷekkoṇṭumitunalla rasāyanaṃ" (Gu.pā.)]

Coll. No. AVS 1116

Allophylus serratus **(Roxb.) Kurz**

Sapindaceae (फेनिल–कुलम्)

Hin	:	Tippāni (तिप्पानि)
Kan	:	Tōgaraṭṭi (ತೊಗರಟ್ಟಿ)
Mal	:	Mukkaṇṇapperukụ, Mukkaṇṇanpēḷu, Mukkaṇṇanperēra (മുക്കണ്ണപ്പെരുക്, മുക്കണ്ണൻപേഴ്, മുക്കണ്ണൻ പെരേര)
San	:	Tṛipuṭaḥ (त्रिपुटः)
Tam	:	Amalai (அமலை)
Tel	:	Eravalu (ఎరవలు)

Distribution : Throughout south India and Assam hills

The plant : A small tree or a large shrub with whitish bark; leaves 3-foliate, alternate, crowded at the ends of branchlets, pubescent, leaflets 5–12.5 cm long, ovate or elliptic, acute or acuminate, serrate-dentate, more or less hairy on both surfaces; flowers small, white in fascicles, on spicate axillary racemes, stamens 8, inserted on the receptacle inside the disc; fruits smooth, globose, red when ripe.

Parts used : whole plant

Properties and uses : The plant is astringent, bitter, sweet, anti-inflammatory, vulnerary, digestive, carminative and constipating. It is useful in bone fractures, dislocations, inflammations, ulcers, wounds, dyspepsia, anorexia and diarrhoea. The fruits are sweet, cooling and nourishing tonic.

"त्रिपुटा त्र्यक्षिशाखोटा रक्तमुद्‌गा सुगोळका ।" (स्व.)
["Tṛipuṭā tryakṣiśākhōṭā raktamudgā sugōḷakā" (Sva.)]

"कषायतिक्तमधुरं समूलं शोफनाशनम् ॥
अस्थिभङ्गहरं प्रोक्तमङ्गमर्द्दव्रणापहम् ।
फलं स्वादु हिमं रुच्यं मूलं दीपनपाचनम् ॥" (स्व.)
["Kaṣāyatiktamadhuraṃ samūlaṃ śōphanāśanaṃ
Asthibhangaharaṃ prōktamangamarddavraṇāpahaṃ
Phalaṃ svādu himaṃ rucyaṃ mūlaṃ dīpanapācanaṃ" (Sva.)]

Allophylus serratus

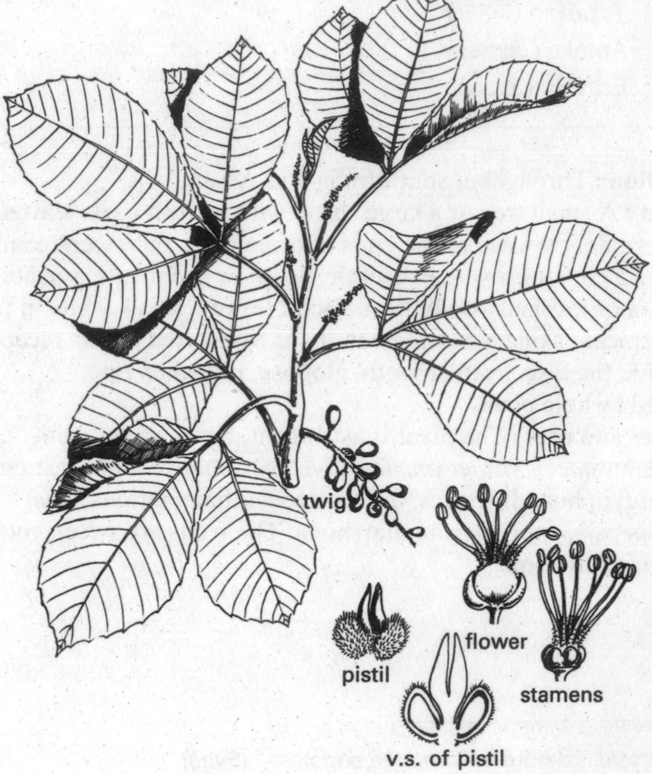

Plate 7

Aloe barbadensis

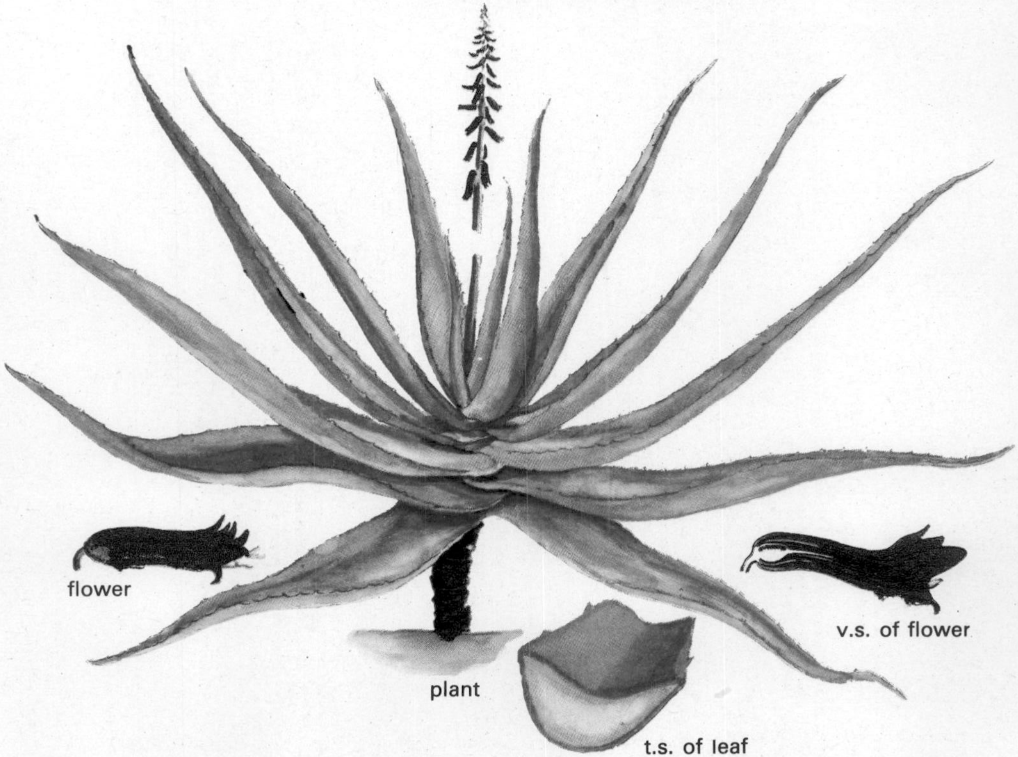

***Aloe barbadensis* Mill.**

(=A.vera *(Linn.) Burm.*)

Liliaceae (रसोन–कुलम्)

Eng	:	Indian aloe, Curacao aloe, Barbados aloe, Jaffarabad aloe
Hin	:	Ghīkuāṁr, Ghīkumārī (धीकुआँर, धीकुमारी)
Kan	:	Kathaligiḍa (ಕತ್ತಲಿಗಿಡ)
Mal	:	Kaṫṫuvāḻa, Kaṫṫāṟvāḻa (കറ്റുവാഴ, കറ്റാർവാഴ)
San	:	Kumārī, Ghṛtakumārī (कुमारी, घृतकुमारी)
Tam	:	Kattaḷai, Sirukattaḷai (கத்தளை, சிறுகத்தளை)
Tel	:	Kalabanda (కలబంద)

Distribution : Cultivated or seen wild in hedge-rows in the drier parts of India

The plant : A coarse perennial with short stem and shallow root system; leaves fleshy in rosettes, sessile, often crowded with horny prickles on thc margins, convex below, 45 – 60 cm long, tapering to a blunt point, surface pale green with irregular white blotches; flowers yellow or orange in racemes; fruits loculicidal capsule.

Parts used : leaf-juice, elio

Properties and uses : The plant is bitter, sweet, cooling, anthelmintic, aperient, carminative, deobstruent, depurative, diuretic, stomachic, emmenagogue, ophthalmic and alexeteric. The juice is used in dyspepsia, amenorrhoea, burns, colic, hyperadenosis, hepatopathy, splenopathy, skin diseases, constipation, spanomenorrhea, vitiated conditions of *vāta* and *pitta,* abdominal tumours, dropsy, carbuncles, sciatica, lumbago and flatulence.

The elio is used for helminthiasis in children and is a purgative, anthelmintic and emmenagogue. It is used for local application in painful inflammations, chronic ulcers and catarrhal and purulent ophthalmia.

"कुमारी गृहकन्या च कन्या घृतकुमारिका ।" (भा.प्र.)
["Kumārī gṛhakanyā ca kanyā ghṛtakumārikā" (Bhā.pṛa.)]

गृहकन्या कुमारी च कन्यका दीर्घपत्रिका ।
स्थलेरुहा मृदुः कन्या बहुपत्रा/मरा/जरा ॥

कण्टकप्रावृता वीरा भृङ्गेष्टा विपुलस्रवा ।
व्रणघ्नी तरुणी रामा कपिला चाम्बुधिस्रवा ॥
सुकण्टका स्थूलदळेत्येकविंशतिनामका । (रा.नि.)
["Gṛhakanyā kumārī ca kanyakā dīrghapatṛikā
Sthalēruhā mṛduḥ kanyā bahupatṛaʃmaraʃjarā
Kaṇṭakaprāvṛtā vīrā bhṛṅgēṣṭā vipulasṛavā
Vṛaṇaghnī taruṇī rāmā kapilā cāmbudhisṛavā
Sukaṇṭakā sthūladaḷētyēkaviṁśatināmakā" (Rā.ni.)]

"गृहकन्या हिमा तिक्ता मदगन्धी कफापहा ।
पित्तकासविषश्वासकुष्ठघ्नी च रसायनी ॥" (रा.नि.)
["Gṛhakanyā himā tiktā madagandhī kaphāpahā
Pittakāsaviṣaśvāsakuṣṭhaghnī ca rasāyanī" (Rā.ni.)]

"तन्मध्यदण्डो मधुरः कुमारीसदृशो गुणैः ।
विशेषात्कृमिपित्तघ्नः पुष्पमस्य गुरु स्मृतम् ॥
वातं पित्तं कृमींश्चैव नाशयेदिति कीर्तितम् ।" (शा.नि.)
["Tanmadhyadaṇḍō madhuraḥ kumārīsadṛśō guṇaiḥ
Viśēṣātkṛmipittaghnaḥ puṣpamasya guru smṛtam
Vātaṃ pittaṃ kṛmīmścaiva nāśayēditi kīrttitaṃ" (Śā.ni.)]

"कुमारी भेदनी शीता तिक्ता नेत्र्या रसायनी ।
मधुरा बृंहणी बल्या वृष्या वातविषप्रणुत् ॥
गुल्मप्लीहयकृद्वृद्धिकफज्वरहरी भवेत् ।
ग्रन्थ्यग्निदग्धविस्फोटपित्तरक्तत्वगामयान् ॥" (भा.प्र.)
["Kumārī bhēdanī śītā tiktā nētryā rasāyanī
Madhurā bṛmhaṇī balyā vṛṣyā vātaviṣapraṇut
Gulmaplīhayakṛdvṛddhikaphajvaraharī bhavēt
Granthyagnidagdhavisphōṭapittaraktatvagāmayān" (Bhā.pra.)]

"कुमारी शीतळा तिक्ता मधुरा भेदिनी जयेत् ।
गुल्मप्लीहयकृद्वृद्धिं कफज्वरहरी हरेत् ॥
ग्रन्थ्यग्निदग्धविस्फोटपित्तरक्तत्वगामयान् ।
चक्षुष्या विषवातघ्नी बल्या वृष्या रसायनी ॥
वातपित्तकृमिहरं कुमारीकुसुमं गुरु ।" (कै.नि.)
["Kumārī śītaḷā tiktā madhurā bhēdinī jayēt
Gulmaplīhayakṛdvṛddhiṃ kaphajvaraharī harēt
Granthyagnidagdhavisphōṭapittaraktatvagāmayān
Cakṣuṣyā viṣavātaghnī balyā vṛṣyā rasāyanī
Vātapittakṛmiharaṃ kumārīkusumaṃ guru" (Kai.ni.)]

Eng	:	Elio
Hin	:	Musabbar, Ēluā (मुसब्बर, एलुआ)
Kan	:	Lōḷisara (ಲೋಳಿಸರ)
Mal	:	Sannināyakaṃ, Cennināyakaṃ (സന്നിനായകം, ചെന്നിനായകം)
San	:	Kumārīsāra, Kṛṣṇabōḷaḥ (कुमारीसार, कृष्णबोळः)
Tam	:	Cennināyakaṃ (சென்னிநாயகம்)
Tel	:	Mūsāmbaramu (ముసాంబరము)

"ऐलेयकः कृष्णबोळः कुमारीसारतोद्भवा ।" (भा.प्र.)
["Ailēyakaḥ kṛṣṇabōḷaḥ kumārīsāratōdbhavā" (Bhā.pra.)]

"कृष्णबोळः कटुः शीतो भेदको रसशोधनः ।
शूलाध्मानकफान् वातं कृमिगुल्मौ च नाशयेत् ॥" (रा.नि.)
["Kṛṣṇabōḷaḥ kaṭuḥ śītō bhēdakō rasaśōdhanaḥ
Śūlādhmānakaphān vātaṃ kṛmigulmau ca nāśayēt" (Rā.ni.)]

കറ്റാർവാഴയുടെ വീര്യം ശീതമാകയുമുണ്ടത്
കൃമിരോഗങ്ങൾ ദുർന്നാമനേത്രരോഗഭഗന്ദരം
ശൂലഗുല്മോദരം കുഷ്ഠം വിഷകാസഞ്ച നാശയേത്.
കറ്റാർവാഴയുടെ നീരും തണുപ്പാകുന്നിതേറ്റവും
വാതപിത്തങ്ങളെത്തീർക്കും ഗുരുവാകയുമുണ്ടത്
കറ്റാർവാഴയുടെ പൂവു ശീതളം വാതപിത്തജിത്. (ഗു.പാ.)

["Kaṟṟāṟvāḻayuṭe vīryaṃ śītamākayumuṇṭatu
Kṛmirōgaṅṅaḷ duṟnāmanētrarōgabhagandaraṃ
Śūlagulmōdaraṃ kuṣṭhaṃ viṣakāsañca nāśayēt
Kaṟṟāṟvāḻayuṭe nīruṃ taṇuppākunnitēṟṟavuṃ
Vātapittaṅṅaḷettīṟkkuṃ guruvākayumuṇṭatu
Kaṟṟāṟvāḻayuṭe pūvu śītaḷaṃ vātapittajit" (Gu.pā.)]

Alpinia galanga (Linn.) Willd.

Zingiberaceae (आर्द्रक–कुलम्)

Eng	:	Greater galangal, Java galangal
Hin	:	Kulañajn, Kuliñjan (कलञ्जन, कुलिञ्जन)
Kan	:	Doḍḍarasagaḍḍe (ದೊಡ್ಡರಸಗಡ್ಡೆ)
Mal	:	Aratta, Ciṟṟaratta (അരത്ത, ചിറ്റരത്ത)
San	:	Rāsnā, Sugandhamūlā (रास्ना, सुगन्धमूला)
Tam	:	Arattai, Pērarattai (அரத்தை, பேரரத்தை)
Tel	:	Dumparāṣṭramu (దుంపరాష్ట్రము)

Distribution : Throughout the Western Ghats, also cultivated

The plant : A perennial, aromatic, rhizomatous herb, 1.8 – 2.1 m in height; leaves oblong-lanceolate, glabrous, acuminate, very shortly petioled, ligule short, rounded, ciliate; flowers fragrant, greenish white with red veined lips, in dense panicles; fruits capsules orange red when ripe.

Parts used: rhizomes

Properties and uses : The rhizomes are bitter, acrid, thermogenic, aromatic, nervine tonic, stimulant, revulsive, carminative, stomachic, disinfectant, aphrodisiac, expectorant, bronchodilator, febrifuge, anti-inflammatory and tonic. They are useful in vitiated conditions of *vāta* and *kapha,* rheumatoid arthritis, inflammations, stomatopathy, pharyngopathy, cough, asthma, bronchitis, hiccough, dyspepsia, stomachalgia, obesity, diabetes, cephalalgia, tubercular glands and intermittent fevers.

"रास्ना युक्तरसा स्याच्छ्रेयस्या श्रेयसी रसा युक्ता ।
सुवहा सुगन्धमूला रस्या सा गन्धनाकुली चेति ॥" (अ.म.)
["Rāsnā yuktarasā syācchṛēyasyā śṛēyasī rasā yuktā
Suvahā sugandhamūlā rasyā sā gandhanākulī cēti" (A.ma.)]

"रास्ना युक्तरसा रस्या सुवहा रसना रसा ।
एलापर्णी च सुरसा सुगन्धा श्रोयसी तथा ॥" (भा.प्र.)
["Rāsnā yuktarasā rasyā suvahā rasanā rasā
Elāparṇī ca surasā sugandhā śṛēyasī tathā " (Bhā.pra)]

Alpinia galanga

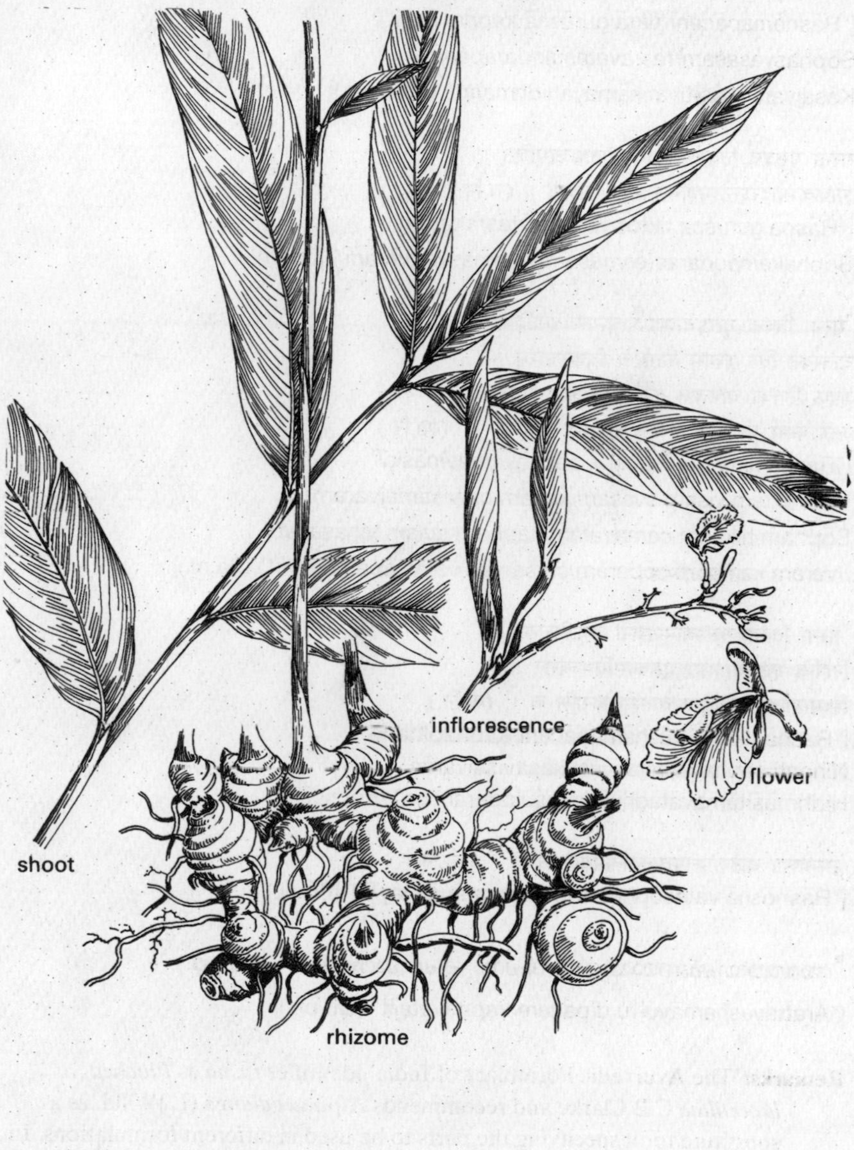

"विशेषाद्वातरोगघ्नी तैलादिषु नियोजिता ।
विषघ्नी श्वासकासघ्नी रास्ना हिक्कानिवारणी ॥" (म.नि.)
["Viśēṣādvātarōgaghnī tailādiṣu niyōjitā
Viṣaghnī śvāsakāsaghnī rāsnā hikkānivāraṇī" (Ma.ni.)]

"रास्नामपाचनी तिक्ता गुरूष्णा कफवातजित् ।
शोफश्वाससमीरास्रवातशूलोदरापहा ॥
कासज्वरविषाशीतिवातिकामयहिध्महृत् ।" (भा.प्र.)
["Rāsnāmapācanī tiktā gurūṣṇā kaphavātajit
Śōphaśvāsasamīrāsṛavātaśūlōdarāpahā
Kāsajvaraviṣāśītivātikāmayahidhmahṛt" (Bhā.pṛa.)]

रास्ना गुरुश्च तिक्तोष्णा विषवातास्रकासजित् ।
शोफकम्पोदरश्ळेष्मशमन्यामस्य पाचनी ॥ (ध.नि.)
["Rāsnā guruśca tiktōṣṇā viṣavātāsṛakāsajit
Śōphakampōdaraśḷēṣmaśamanyāmasya pācanī" (Dha.ni.)]

"रास्ना तिक्ता गुरुश्चोष्णा पाचन्यामविनाशिनी ।
वातरक्तं विषं श्वासं कासं च विषमज्वरम् ॥
शोफं हिक्कां चामवातं कफं शूलं विनाशयेत् ।
ज्वरं कम्पं चोदरं च सर्वान् वातांश्च नाशयेत् ॥" (शा.नि.)
["Rāsnā tiktā guruścōṣṇā pācanyāmavināśinī
Vātaraktaṃ viṣaṃ śvāsaṃ kāsaṃ ca viṣamajvaraṃ
Śōphaṃ hikkāṃ cāmavātaṃ kaphaṃ śūlaṃ vināśayēt
Jvaraṃ kampaṃ cōdaraṃ ca saṛvān vātāṃśca nāśayēt" (Śā.ni.)]

"रास्ना तिक्ता गुरूष्णामपाचनी कफपित्तहा ।
निहन्ति शोफवातास्रश्वासकासविषज्वरान् ॥
हिध्माशीतामवाताढ्या वातशूलोदराणि च ।" (कै.नि.)
["Rāsnā tiktā gurūṣṇāmapācanī kaphapittahā
Nihanti śōphavātāsṛaśvāsakāsaviṣajvarān
Hidhmāśītāmavātāḍhyā vātaśūlōdarāṇi ca" (Kai.ni.)]

"रास्नोष्णा वातशोफामवातवातामयान् जयेत् ।" (सो.नि.)
["Rāsnōṣṇā vātaśōphāmavātavātāmayān jayēt" (Sō.ni.)]

"അരത്തയുഷ്ണമായുള്ളു ദീപനം കഫവാതജിത്." (ഗു.പാ.)
["Arattayuṣṇamāyuḷḷu dīpanaṃ kaphavātajit" (Gu.pā.)]

Remarks: 'The Ayurvedic Formulary of India' identifies *rāsnā* as *Pluchea lanceolata* C.B.Clarke and recommends *Alpinia galanga* (L.)Willd. as a substitute for it specifying the parts to be used in different formulations. In 'Dravyaguṇavijñān' Prof.P.V.Sharma (1983) also uses the same identification. According to him it is the leaf which is to be used in different formulations.

'The Glossary of Vegetable Drugs in Bṛhattrayī', however, advises us to use the root and mentions that it is *A.galanga* which is being used as a substitute for this drug in south India. It also adds that the synonyms of *rāsnā* such as *ēlāparṇī, rāsnā, yuktarasā* and *gandhamūla* are appropriate for *Pluchea lanceolata* and warns us against using *Vanda roxburghii* and such other orchids.

On the contrary, `Wealth of India, and Indian Medicinal Plants' identify *rāsnā* and its synonyms as *Vanda tessellata (V.roxburghii).* For *Pluchea lanceolata* the former gives *rāsnā* as its Sanskrit name. Both these attribute to *Vanda tessellata* all the properties and uses mentioned in Ayurvedic texts for *rāsnā.* However, while `Wealth of India' recommends the whole plant of *Pluchea lanceolata* for medicinal purposes, `Indian Medicinal Plants used in Ayurvedic preparations' (A.C.Dey, 1980) also identifies *rāsnā* as *Vanda tessellata.*

While Dr A. Lakshmipathi (1946) in '100 useful Drugs' identifies *rāsnā* as another variety of *Alpinia* species, *Alpinia officinarum,* Dr A.Nesamani in his `Auṣadhasasyaṅṅaḷ' considers this as still another species i.e. *A.calcarata.* 'Bhāvapṛakāśanighaṇṭu' gives three Latin names for *rāsnā* viz. *Pluchea lanceolata, Inula racemosa* and *Vanda roxburghii.* Again 'Śāligrāmanighaṇṭu bhūṣaṇaṃ' identifies *rāsnā* as *Vanda roxburghii* or *Pluchea lanceolata.* Shri K.M.Vaidya in his `Aṣṭāṅgahṛdayakōśaṃ' uses *Vanda roxburghii* as its Latin name.

In recent publications it is seen reported that *Pluchea lanceolata, Vanda roxburghii* and *Alpinia galanga,* all have antirheumatic properties and that from experimental studies it has been proved that *Plauchea lanceolata* is more effective than the others as a drug for rheumatic complaints.

It has to be pointed out, however, that the descriptions of the plant *rāsnā* mentioned by the Ācaryās in the ancient texts have no similarities to *Vanda tessellata.*

Pluchea lanceolata which is abundantly available in north India is not at all seen in south India. Though the `Glossary of Vegetable Drugs in Bṛhattrayī' mentions that many of the synonyms given for *rāsnā* are appropriate for *P. lanceolata,* we have to point out that the words *sugandhamūlā* and *ēlāparṇī* which have certain particular connotations are more appropriate to *Alpinia galanga* than to *Pluchea lanceolata.*

`Indian Medicinal Plants', 'Materia Medica' (K.M. Nadkarni) and `Wealth of India' identify a plant with the Sanskrit name *kulañjana* as *Alpinia galanga.* But `Bhāvapṛakāśaṃ' `Rājanighaṇṭu' and `Nighaṇṭuratnākaraṃ' mention *rāsnā* and *kulañjana* as two different plants and give them different properties. The following quotations from them will make this clear :

"कुलञ्जो गन्धमूलश्च तीक्ष्णमूलः कुलञ्जनः ।
कुलञ्जः कटुतिक्तोष्णो दीपनो मुखदोषनुत् ॥" (रा.नि.)
["Kulañjō gandhamūlaśca tīkṣṇamūlaḥ kulañjanaḥ
Kulañjaḥ kaṭutiktōṣṇō dīpanō mukhadōṣanut" (Rā.ni.)]

"कुलिञ्जनं कटुस्तिक्तमुष्णं चाग्निप्रदीपनम् ।
रुच्यं स्वर्यं च हृद्यं च मुखकण्ठविशुद्धिकृत् ॥
मुखदोषं कफं श्वासं कासं वातं ध्रुवं जयेत् ।
बृहत्कुष्ठगुणैर्ज्ञेयं न्यूनमस्मादिति स्मृतम् ॥" (नि.र.)
["Kuliñjanaṃ kaṭustiktamuṣṇaṃ cāgnipradīpanaṃ
Rucyaṃ svaryaṃ ca hṛdyaṃ ca mukhakaṇṭhaviśuddhikṛt
Mukhadōṣaṃ kaphaṃ śvāsaṃ kāsaṃ vātaṃ dhṛuvaṃ jayēt
Bṛhatkuṣṭhaguṇairjñeyaṃ nyūnamasmāditi smṛtaṃ" (Ni.ra.)]

"सुगन्धाप्युग्रगन्धा च विशेषात्कफकासनुत् ।
सुस्वरत्वकरी रुच्या हृत्कण्ठमुखशोधनी ॥
स्थूलग्रन्थिः सुगन्धा स्यात् ततो हीनगुणा स्मृता ।" (भा.प्र.)
["Sugandhāpyugragandhā ca viśēṣātkaphakāsanut
Susvaratvakarī rucyā hṛtkaṇṭhamukhaśōdhanī
Sthūlagranthiḥ sugandhā syāt tatō hīnaguṇā smṛtā" (Bhā.pra.)]

The Kerala publications like 'Ōṣadhinighaṇṭu', 'Āyuṛvēdaviśvakōṣaṃ' and 'Sanskrit-Malayalam Dictionary' (Kanippayoor Sankaran Nambudirippad) give the Malayalam terms *citťaratta* and *pēraratta* for *nākulī* and *gandhanākulī*, respectively. Amarakōśa, of course, gives these two synonyms for *rāsnā.* On the other hand the Commentaries on 'Bhāvapṛakaśaṃ', Rājanighaṇṭu' etc., identify, *nākulī* as *Rauvolfia serpentina (cuvanna amalpori).* The author of 'Dravyaguṇavijñān', however, identifies, *nākulī* as *Aristolochia indica (karaḷayaṃ).*

Though there is such a lot of confusion in the identity of this plant, in Kerala the rhizome of *Alpinia galanga* is used as *rāsnā.* Besides, *A.galanga,* two other species of the plant *A.calcarata* and *A.malaccensis* are available in plenty in the market. They are known as *pēraratta* in Malayalam and their rhizomes are also used in the formulations.

Coll. No. AVS 2064

***Alstonia scholaris* (Linn.) R.Br.**

Apocynaceae (कुटज-कुलम्)

Eng	:	Devil tree, Shaitan wood
Hin	:	Chāttiyān, Śaittān kā jaṭ (छात्तियान, शैत्तान का जट)
Kan	:	Hāle (ಹಾಲೆ)
Mal	:	Ēḻilampāla, Yakṣippāla, Pāla, Daivappāla (ഏഴിലംപാല, യക്ഷിപ്പാല, പാല, ദൈവപ്പാല)
San	:	Saptaparṇaḥ, Saptachadaḥ (सप्तपर्णः, सप्तछदः)
Tam	:	Ēḻilappālai, Pālai (ஏழிலைப்பாலை, பாலை)
Tel	:	Phalagaruḍa, Ēḍākularaṭiceṭṭu, Ēdakulaphala (ఫలగరుడ, ఏడాకులరటిచెట్టు, ఏడాకులఫల)

Distribution: Throughout India,in deciduous and evergreen forests, also in plains

The plant: A large evergreen tree upto 3.0 m in height with a straight often fluted and buttressed bole, about 110 cm in diameter, bark greyish brown, rough, lenticellate abounding in bitter,milky latex; leaves 4 – 7 in a whorl, coriaceous, elliptic-oblong, pale beneath; flowers small, greenish white, numerous in umbellate panicles, corolla tube short, very strongly scented; fruits follicles, 30 – 60 cm long; seeds papillose with brownish hair at each end.

Parts used: bark, leaves, milky exudate

Properties and uses: The bark is bitter, astringent, acrid, thermogenic, digestive, laxative, anthelmintic, febrifuge, antipyretic, depurative, galactagogue, stomachic, cardiotonic and tonic. It is useful in fevers, malarial fevers, abdominal disorders, diarrhoea, dysentery, dyspepsia, leprosy, skin diseases, pruritus, tumours, chronic and foul ulcers, asthma, bronchitis, cardiopathy, helminthiasis, agalactia and debility. The tender leaves in the form of poultice are good for ulcers with foul discharges. The milky exudate is bitter and is good for ulcers, vitiated conditions of *vāta* and otalgia.

"सप्तच्छदो गुच्छपुष्पः शतपुष्पो बृहच्छविः ।
सप्तपर्णः सप्तपत्रः सप्ताह्वः सप्तसंज्ञकः ॥
श्रीपर्णः स्निग्धपर्णश्च सर्वक्षीरी सुवर्णकः ।
बृहत्त्वगिति विख्यातः शब्दैः पर्यायवाचकैः ॥" (अ.म.)

Alstonia scholaris

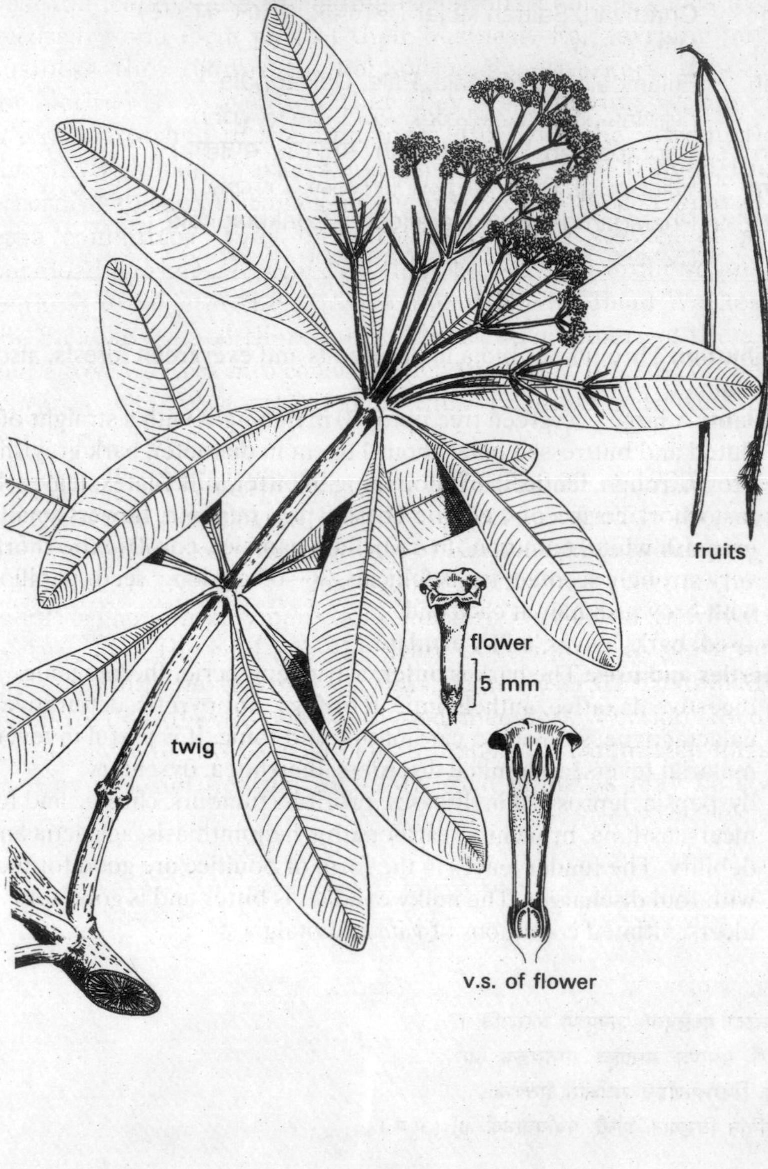

["Saptacchadō gucchapuṣpaḥ śatapuṣpō bṛhacchaviḥ
Saptaparṇaḥ saptapatṛaḥ saptāhvaḥ saptasamjñakaḥ
Śrīparṇaḥ snigdhaparṇaśca saṛvakṣīrī suvarṇakaḥ
Bṛhattvagiti vikhyātaḥ śabdaiḥ paryāyavācakaiḥ" (A.ma.)]

"सप्तपर्णो विशालत्वक् शारदो विषमच्छदः ।" (भा.प्र.)
["Saptaparṇō viśālatvak śāradō viṣamacchadaḥ " (Bhā. pṛa.)]

"सप्तपर्णः पत्रवर्णः शुक्तिपर्णः सुपर्णकः ।
सप्तच्छदो गुच्छपुष्पोऽयुग्मपर्णो मुनिच्छदः ॥
बृहत्त्वक् बहुपर्णश्च तथा शाल्मलिपत्रकः ।
मदगन्धो गन्धिपर्णो विज्ञेयो वङ्किभूमितः ॥ " (रा.नि.)
["Saptaparṇaḥ patṛavaṛṇaḥ śuktiparṇaḥ suparṇakaḥ
Saptacchadō gucchapuṣpoǀyugmaparṇō municchadaḥ
Bṛhattvak bahuparṇaśca tathā śālmalipatṛakaḥ
Madagandhō gandhiparṇō vijñēyō vaṅkibhūmitaḥ " (Rā.ni.)]

"कुष्ठज्वरप्रशमनो विशेषात् व्रणशोधनः ।
तिक्तः कषायानुरसः सप्ताह्वो रक्तशोधनः ॥" (म.नि.)
["Kuṣṭhajvarapṛaśamanō viśēṣāt vṛaṇaśōdhanaḥ
Tiktaḥ kaṣāyānurasaḥ saptāhvō raktaśōdhanaḥ" (Ma.ni.)]

"सप्तपर्णो व्रणश्ळेष्मवातकुष्ठास्रजन्तुजित् ।
दीपनः श्वासगुल्मघ्नः स्निग्धोष्णस्तुवरः सरः ॥ "(भा.प्र.)
["Saptaparṇō vṛaṇaśḷēṣmavātakuṣṭhāsṛajantujit
Dīpanaḥ śvāsagulmaghnaḥ snigdhōṣṇastuvaraḥ saraḥ" (Bhā.pṛa.)]

"सप्तपर्णः कषायोष्णस्तिक्तो दीप्तिकरः सरः ।
स्निग्धो हृद्यः कृमिश्वासकुष्ठगुल्मव्रणास्रजित् ॥
मदगन्धिः त्रिदोषघ्नः शूलरक्तरुजापहः।" (ग.नि.)
["Saptaparṇaḥ kaṣāyōṣṇastiktō dīptikaraḥ saraḥ
Snigdhō hṛdyaḥ kṛmiśvāsakuṣṭhagulmavṛaṇāsṛajit
Madagandhiḥ tṛidōṣaghnaḥ śūlaraktarujāpahaḥ" (Ga.ni.)]

"सान्द्रमेहिनं सप्तपर्णकषायम् " (सु.चि. ११)
["Sāndramēhinaṃ saptaparṇakaṣāyaṃ" (Su.Ci.11)]

"सप्तच्छदार्कक्षीराभ्यां पूरणं कृमिशूलनुत्" (अ.हृ.उ.२२)
["Saptacchadāṛkakṣīrābhyāṃ pūraṇaṃ kṛmiśūlanut" (A.hṛ.U.22)]

"त्वक्पत्रकुसुमक्षीरादिकं ग्राह्यं"
["Tvakpatṛakusumakṣīrādikaṃ grāhyaṃ"]

"सप्तपर्णस्तु तिक्तोष्णस्त्रिदोषघ्नश्च दीपनः ।

मदगन्धो निरुन्धेऽयं व्रणरक्तामयकृमीन् ॥ "(रा.नि.)
["Saptaparṇastu tiktōṣṇastridōṣaghnaśca dīpanaḥ
Madagandhō nirundhēऽyaṃ vraṇaraktāmayakṛmīn" (Rā.ni.)]

"त्रिदोषशमनो हृद्यः सुरभिर्दीपनः सरः ।
शूलगुल्मकृमीन् कुष्ठं हन्ति शाल्मलिपत्रकः ॥ (ध.नि.)
["Tridōṣaśamanō hṛdyaḥ surabhirdīpanaḥ saraḥ
Śūlagulmakṛmīn kuṣṭhaṃ hanti śālmalipatrakaḥ" (Dha.ni.)]

"सप्तपर्णः कषायोष्णः सुस्निग्धो दीपनः सरः
हृद्यो दोषकृमीश्वासकुष्ठगुल्मव्रणास्रजित् ॥ " (कै.नि.)
["Saptaparṇaḥ kaṣāyōṣṇaḥ susnigdhō dīpanaḥ saraḥ
Hṛdyō dōṣakṛmiśvāsakuṣṭhagulmavraṇāsrajit " (Kai.ni.)]

Coll. No. AVS 1286

***Alstonia venenata* R.Br.**

Apocynaceae (कुटज–कुलम्)

Mal	:	Aṇalivēgaṃ (അണലിവേഗം)
Kan	:	Addasoppu (ಅಡ್ಡಸೊಪ್ಪು)
San	:	Viṣaghnī, Anādanā (विषघ्नी, अनादना)
Tam	:	Śinnappālai (சின்னப்பாலை)

Distribution: Throughout India in deciduous forests in areas upto 1,800 m elevation

The plant: A large shrub or a small tree upto 6.0 m in height with greyish brown bark and bright yellow hard and woody root; leaves simple, in whorls of 3–6, membranous, lanceolate, margins wavy, finely acuminate, main nerves numerous, close, parallel, united by intramarginal nerve; flowers white, in terminal, subumbellate cymes or in racemes; fruits fusiform, stalked and beaked follicles, tapering at both ends, seeds many, flattened with a tuft of hair at each end.

Parts used: roots, fruits

Properties and uses: The roots are bitter, astringent, thermogenic, depurative, antitoxic, febrifuge and anodyne. They are useful in skin diseases, erysipelas, leprosy, cobra bite and other venomous bites, epilepsy, fatigue, fever and otalgia. The fruits are useful in syphilis, insanity and epilepsy.

"क्षुद्रश्च सप्तपर्णोऽन्यो विषघ्नश्चाप्यनादनः ।
क्षुद्रपूर्वश्च विज्ञेयः सप्तपर्णस्तु नामतः ॥
नातीवसुरभीनस्य सुमानीति विशिष्यते ।" (स्व.)
["Kṣudraśca saptaparṇōʃnyō viṣghnaścāpyanādanaḥ
Kṣudrapūrvaśca vijñēyaḥ saptaparṇastu nāmataḥ
Nātīvasurabhīnasya sumānīti viśiṣyatē" (Sva.)]

"सप्तच्छदसमानं स्याद्गुणे, त्वक्कुष्ठनाशिनी ॥
फिरङ्गविषवीसर्पभूतापस्मारपीडनम् ।

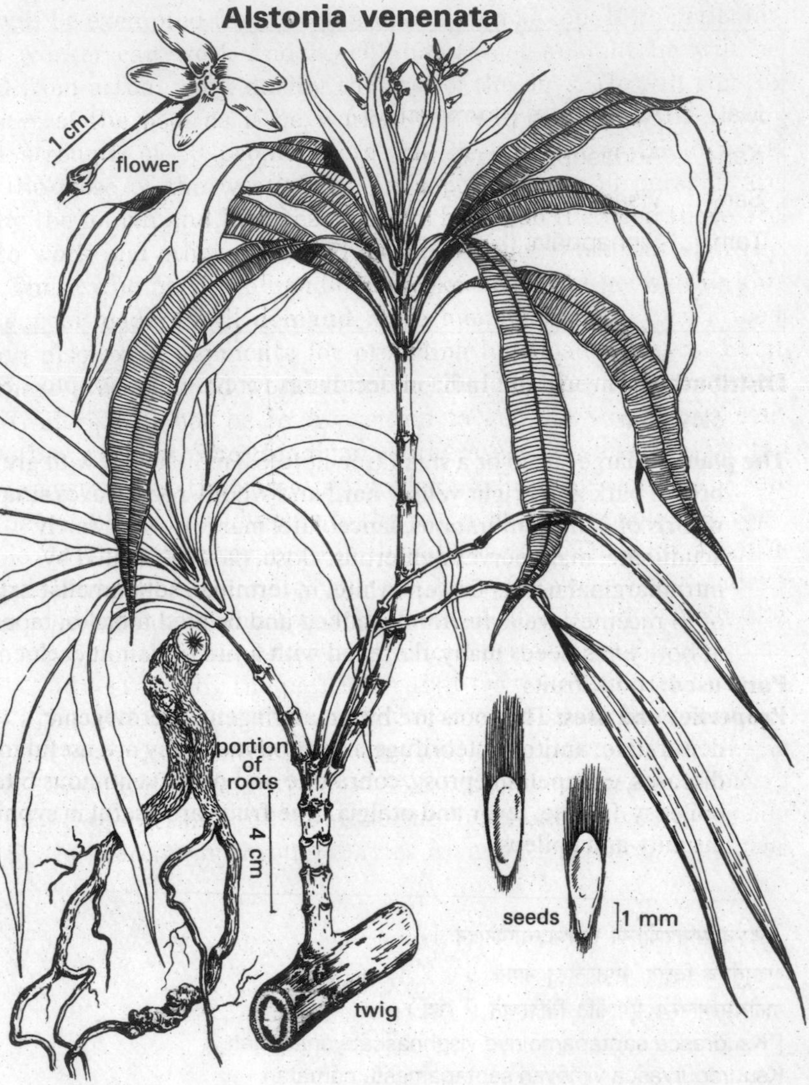
Alstonia venenata
1 cm
flower
portion
of
roots
4 cm
seeds
1 mm
twig

नाशयेत्, कर्णशूलघ्नी मूर्च्छाज्वरहरी च सा ॥ " (स्व.)
["Saptacchadasamānaṃ syādguṇē, tvakkuṣṭhanāśinī
Phiraṅgaviṣavīsarpabhūtāpasmārapīḍanaṃ
Nāśayēt, kaṛṇaśūlaghnī mūṛcchājvaraharī ca sā" (Sva.)]

Coll. No. AVS 2227

***Alternanthera sessilis* (Linn.) R.Br.ex DC.**

(A. triandra *Lam.*)

Amaranthaceae (तण्डुलीय–कुलम्)

Hin	:	Gudrisāg (गुद्रिसाग)
Kan	:	Hōnugonesoppu (ಹೊನಗೊನೆಸೊಪ್ಪು)
Mal	:	Mīnaṅṅāṇi, Ponnannani, Ponnankannikkira (മീനങ്ങാണി, പൊന്നങ്ങാണി, പൊന്നാങ്കണ്ണിക്കീര)
San	:	Matsyaksi, Patturah (मत्स्याक्षी , पत्तूर)
Tam	:	Ponnannkannikkirai (பொன்னாங்கண்ணிக்கீரை)
Tel	:	Ponnagantikūra (పొన్నగంటికూర)

Distribution : Throughout India,in moist places upto 2,100 m, often cultivated.

The plant: A much branched prostrate herb, branches often purplish, frequently rooting at the lower nodes; leaves simple, opposite, somewhat fleshy, lanceolate, oblanceolate or linear-oblong, obtuse or subacute, sometimes obscurely denticulate, glabrous, shortly petiolate; flowers small, white, in axillary clusters; fruits compressed obcordate utricles, seeds suborbicular.

Parts used: whole plant

Properties and uses: The plant is bitter, sweet, astringent, acrid, cooling, constipating, depurative, digestive, cholagogue, galactagogue and febrifuge and is useful in vitiated conditions of *kapha* and *pitta,* burning sensation, diarrhoea, leprosy, skin disease, dyspepsia, haemorrhoids, agalactia, splenomegaly and fever.

"पत्तूरः काण्डपुष्पश्च मत्स्याक्षो मीनलोचनः ।
जीमूतपत्रो विद्वद्भिर्मत्स्याक्षक उदाहृतः ॥
प्रोक्तो द्वितीयः पत्तूरः क्षेत्रजः क्षेत्रिकः क्षमः ।
हेमपुष्पी हेमकन्या भिषग्भिः परिपठ्यते ॥" (अ.म.)
["Pattūraḥ kāṇḍapuṣpaśca matsyākṣō mīnalōcanaḥ
Jīmūtapatṛō vidvadbhiṛmatsyākṣaka udāhṛtaḥ
Pṛōktō dvitīyaḥ pattūraḥ kṣētṛajaḥ kṣētṛikaḥ kṣamaḥ
Hēmapuṣpī hēmakanyā bhiṣagbhiḥ paripaṭhyatē" (A.ma.)]

Alternanthera sessilis

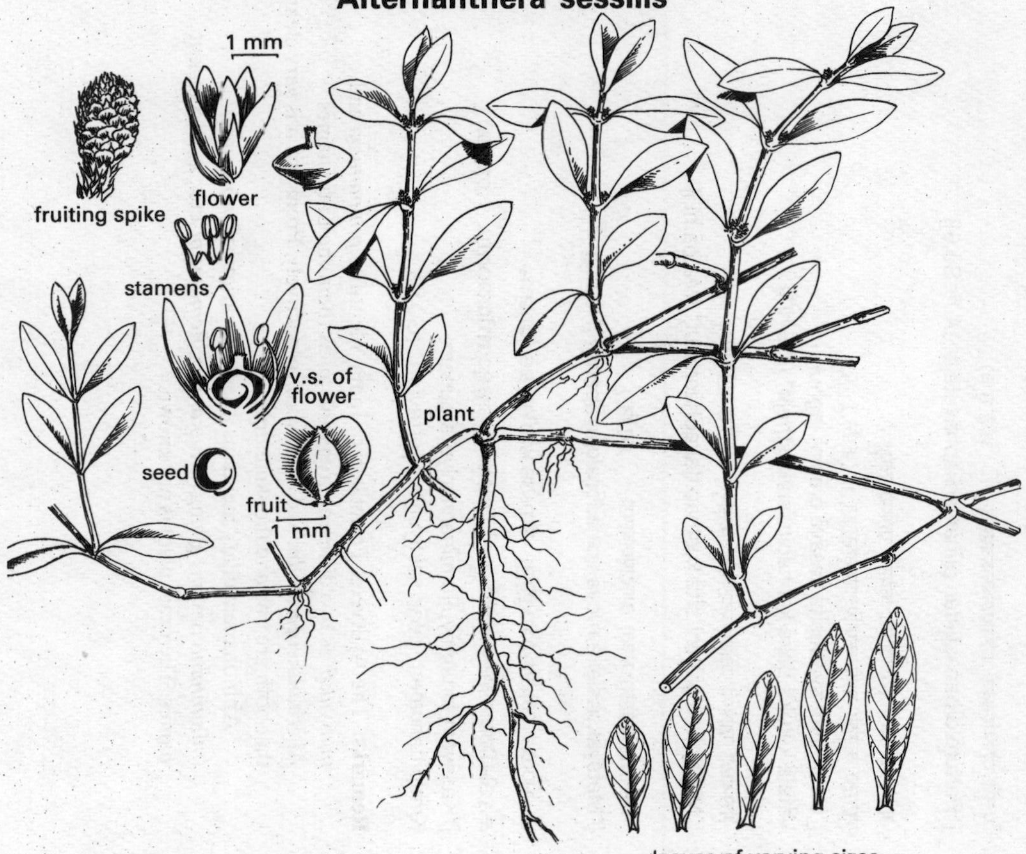

"मत्स्याक्षी बाह्‌ळिका मत्स्यगन्धा मत्स्यादनीति च । " (भा.प्र.)
["Matsyākṣī bāhḷikā matsyagandhā matsyādanīti ca" (Bhā.pṛa)]

"मत्स्याक्षी ग्राहिणी शीता कुष्ठपित्तकफास्रजित् ।
लघुस्तिक्ता कषाया च स्वाद्वी कटुविपाकिनी ॥ " (भा.प्र.)
["Matsyākṣī grāhiṇī śītā kuṣṭhapittakaphāṣrajit
Laghustiktā kaṣāyā ca svādvī kaṭuvipākinī" (Bhā.pṛa.)]

"पत्तूरो दीपनस्तिक्तः प्लीहार्शःकफवातजित् ।" (अ.हृ.सू.६)
["Pattūrō dīpanastiktaḥ plīhārśaḥkaphavātajit" (A.hṛ.Sū.6)]

"बाह्‌ळी तिक्ता स्वादुशीता कषाया ग्राहिणी लघुः ।
वातळा कटुका पाके कफपित्तास्रकुष्ठजित् ॥ (कै.नि.)
["Bāhḷī tiktā svāduśītā kaṣāyā grāhiṇī laghuḥ
Vātaḷā kaṭukā pākē kaphapittāṣrakuṣṭhajit" (Kai.ni.)]

"मत्स्याक्षी ग्राहिणी शीता कुष्ठपित्तकफास्रनुत् । " (म.पा.नि.)
["Matsyākṣī grāhiṇī śītā kuṣṭhapittakaphāṣranut" (Ma.pā.ni.)]

"मत्स्याक्षी शिशिरा रुच्या व्रणदोषक्षयापहा । " (रा.नि.)
["Matsyākṣī śiśirā rucyā vṛaṇadōṣakṣayāpahā" (Rā.ni.)]

കഷായം തിക്തമായുള്ളു മീനങ്ങാണിയുടെ ഗുണം
കൃമിപിത്തങ്ങളെത്തീർപ്പാൻ ശക്തിയുള്ളൊന്നിതേറ്റവും. (ഗു.പാ.)
["Kaṣāyaṃ tiktamāyuḷḷu mīnaṅṅāṇiyuṭe guṇaṃ
Kṛmipittaṅṅaḷettīṛppān saktiyuḷḷonnitēṟṟavuṃ" (Gu.pā.)]

Remarks: `The Ayurvedic Formulary of India' identifies *ponnaṅṅāṇi* and *matsyākṣī* as two different drugs and gives them the Latin names *Alternanthera triandra* and *A. sessilis,* respectively. From this it is very clear that both are one and the same drug.

`Abhidhānamañjari' mentions a second variety of *mīnaṅṅāṇi* *(mīnaṅṅāṇiviśēṣaṃ)* giving *hēmakannyā, hēmapuṣpī* etc., as its Sanskrit names. The exact plant is not known.

Coll. No. AVS 1115

***Amaranthus spinosus* Linn.**

Amaranthaceae (तण्डुलीय–कुलम्)

Eng	:	Prickly amaranth
Hin	:	Caulēyī, Kaṭēlī (चौलेयी, कटेली)
Kan	:	Mulluhalavesōppu (ಮುಲ್ಲುಹರಿವೆಸೋಪ್ಪು)
Mal	:	Muḷḷancīra, Ceṛucīra (മുള്ളൻചീര, ചെറുചീര)
San	:	Taṇḍulīyaḥ (तण्डुलीय)
Tam	:	Muḷḷukkīrai (முள்ளுக்கீரை)
Tel	:	Muḷḷutoṭakūra (ముళ్ళుతోటకూర)

Distribution: Throughout India,in waste lands

The plant: An erect, glabrous, spinous herb, varying in colour from green to red or purple, 30–60 cm in height with grooved branches and sharp divaricate spines in the leaf axils; leaves simple, alternate, ovate, lanceolate or oblong, entire, glabrous above, main nerves numerous, conspicuous below; flowers small, sessile, yellowish white or pale green, numerours, in dense axillary clusters and in terminal or interrupted spikes; fruits ovoid capsules, membranous, circumscissile about the middle.

Parts used: whole plant

Properties and uses: The plant is sweet, cooling, alexeteric, laxative, diuretic, stomachic, antipyretic, febrifuge, sudorific, galactagogue, haematinic, appetiser and tonic it is useful in vitiated onditions of *pitta,* hyperdipsia, burning sensation, hallucination, leprosy, eczema, bronchitis, leucorrhoea, menorrhagia, haemorrhoids, abscesses, boils, burns, strangury, nausea, flatulence, colic, anorexia, fever, intermittent fevers, agalactia, anaemia and general debility.

The roots are thermogenic and haemostatic. They are useful in vitiated conditions of *kapha,* menorrhagia, haemoptysis, haematemesis and leucorrhoea.

"कथयन्ति तण्डुलीयं माबीरं तण्डुलेयकं घोषम्
घननादं तण्डुलकं घनस्वनं त(ण्डु)लीवेगम् ॥
घनरोचिर्महानादं तण्डुलं तण्डुमित्यपि ।
तण्डुलीयकमित्यार्याः शब्दैः पर्यायवाचकैः ॥ " (अ.म.)

["Kathayanti taṇḍulīyaṃ mābīraṃ taṇḍulēyakaṃ ghōṣaṃ

Amaranthus spinosus

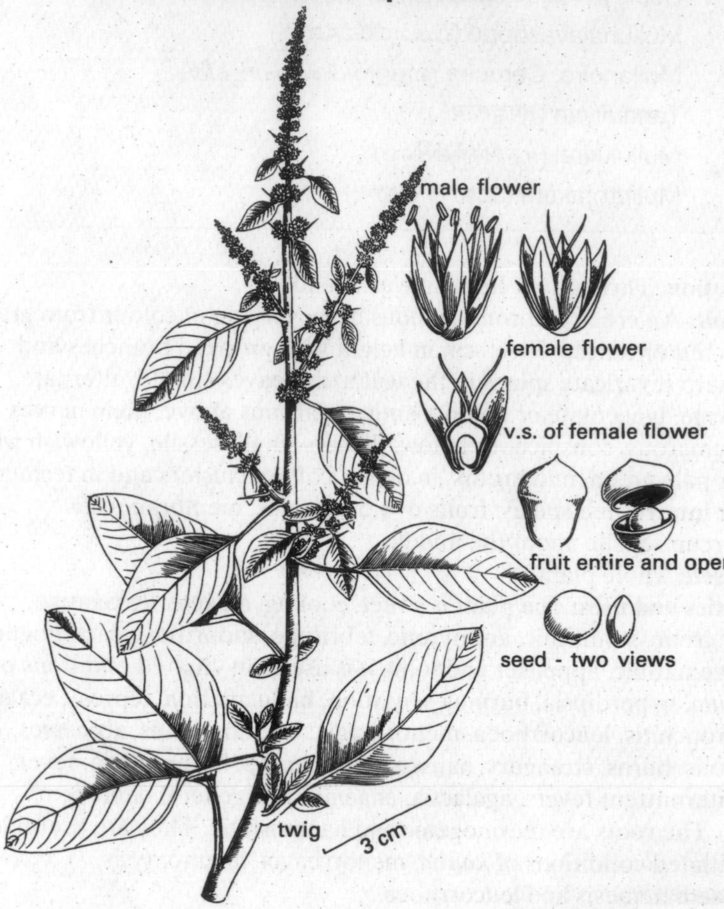

Ghananādaṃ taṇḍulakaṃ ghanasvanaṃ ta(ṇḍu)līvēgaṃ
Ghanarōciṃmahānādaṃ taṇḍulaṃ taṇḍumityapi
Taṇḍulīyakamityāryāḥ śabdaiḥ paryāyavācakaiḥ" (A.ma.)]

"तण्डुलीयो मेघनादः काण्डेरस्तण्डुलेरकः ।
भण्डीरस्तण्डुलीबीजो विषघ्नश्चाल्पमारिषः ॥" (भा.प्र.)
["Teṇḍulīyō mēghanādaḥ kāṇḍērastaṇḍulērakaḥ
Bhaṇḍīrastaṇḍulībījō viṣaghnaścālpamāriṣaḥ" (Bhā.pṛa.)]

"तण्डुलीयस्तु भण्डीरस्तण्डुली तण्डुलीयकः ।
ग्रान्थिली बहुवीर्यश्च मेघनादो घनस्वनः ॥
सुशाकः पथ्यशाकश्च स्फूर्जथुः स्वनिताह्वयः ।
वीरतण्डुलनामा च पर्यायाश्च चतुर्दश ॥" (रा.नि.)
["Taṇḍulīyastu bhaṇḍīrastaṇḍulī taṇḍulīyakaḥ
Granthilī bahuvīryaśca mēghanādō ghanasvanaḥ
Suśakaḥ pathyaśākaśca sphūṛjathuḥ svanitāhvayaḥ
Vīrataṇḍulanāmā ca paryāyāśca catuṛdaśa" (Rā.ni.)]

"तण्डुलीयो लघुः शीतो रूक्षः पित्तकफास्रजित् ।
सृष्टमूत्रमलो रुच्यो दीपनो विषहारकः ॥" (भा.प्र.)
["Taṇḍulīyo laghuḥ śītō rūkṣaḥ pittakaphāsṛajit
Sṛṣṭamūṭramalō rucyō dīpanō viṣahārakaḥ" (Bhā.pṛa.)]

"तण्डुलीयस्तु शिशिरो मधुरो विषनाशनः ।
रुचिकृद्दीपनः पथ्यः पित्तदाहभ्रमापहः ॥
तण्डुलीयकदळं हिमस्पर्शः पित्तरक्तविषकासविनाशी ।
ग्राहकं च मधुरं च विपाके दाहशोषशमनं रुचिदायि ॥ " (रा.नि.)
["Taṇḍulīyastu śiśirō madhurō viṣanāśanaḥ
Rucikṛddīpanaḥ pathyaḥ pittadāhabhṛamāpahaḥ
Taṇḍulīyakadaḷaṃ himaspaṛśaḥ pittaraktaviṣakāsavināśī
Grāhakaṃ ca madhuraṃ ca vipākē dāhaśōṣaśamanaṃ rucidāyi " (Rā. ni.)]

"तण्डुलीयकमूलं स्यादुष्णं श्ळेष्मविनाशनम् ।
रजोरोधकरं रक्तपित्तप्रदरसंहरम् ॥" (आ.सं.)
["Taṇḍulīyakamūlaṃ syāduṣṇaṃ śḷēṣmavināśanaṃ
Rajōrōdhakaraṃ raktapittapṛadarasamharaṃ" (Ā.saṃ.)]

"तण्डुलीयो विषघ्नश्च रूक्षः शीततरः शुचिः ।
मधुरो रसपाकाभ्यां रक्तपित्तापघातकः ॥ (ध.नि.)
["Taṇḍulīyō viṣaghnaśca rūkṣaḥ śītataraḥ śuciḥ
Madhurō rasapākābhyāṃ raktapittāpaghātakaḥ" (Dha.ni.)]

"तण्डुलीयो हिमो रूक्षः स्वादुपाकरसो लघुः ॥
मदपित्तविषास्रघ्नो दीपनः सृष्टमूत्रविट्॥ " (कै.नि.)
["Taṇḍulīyō himō rūkṣaḥ svādupākarasō laghuḥ

Madapittaviṣāsṛaghnō dīpanaḥ sṛṣṭamūtraviṭ" (Kai.ni.)]

"तण्डुलियो लघुः शीतो रूक्षः पित्तकफास्रजित् ।
सृष्टमूत्रमलो रुच्यो दीपनो रक्तपित्तहा ।" (म.पा.नि.)
["Taṇḍulīyō laghuḥ śītō rūkṣaḥ pittakaphāsṛajit
Sṛṣṭamūṭramalō rucyọ dīpanō raktapittahā" (Ma.pā.ni.)]

"तण्डुलीयो हिमो रूक्षः स्वादुपाकरसो लघुः
रक्तपित्तहरो हृद्यो विषघ्नो मदनाशनः ॥ (सो.नि.)
["Taṇḍulīyō himō rūkṣaḥ svādupākarasō laghuḥ
Raktapittaharō hṛdyō viṣaghnō madanāśanaḥ" (Sō.ni.)]

Coll. No. AVS 1427

Ammania baccifera Linn. ssp. *baccifera*

Lythraceae : (धातकी–कुलम्)

Eng	:	Blistering ammania
Hin	:	Dādamārī, Kuraṇṭā (दादामारी, कुरण्टा)
Mal	:	Nīrummēlneruppụ, Kalluruvi (നീരുമ്മേൽ നെരുപ്പ്, കല്ലുരുവി)
San	:	Kuraṇḍikā (कुरण्डिका)
Tam	:	Kalluruvi, Nīrummēl neruppu (கல்லுருவி, நீர்மேல் நெருப்பு)
Tel	:	Agnivendrapāku (అగ్నివెంద్రపాకు)

Distribution: Throughout India,in marshy localities

The plant: An erect glabrous reddish herb upto 60 cm in height, branches usually opposite; leaves lower opposite, upper sometimes alternate, oblong or narrow-elliptic, rounded or subcordate, usually obtuse or subacute; flowers reddish in dense axillary clusters, apetalous or with minute petals; fruits depressed globose capsules covered by calyx tube upto the middle.

Parts used: whole plant

Properties and uses: The plant is bitter, acrid, cooling, appetiser, rubifacient, laxative, stomachic, diuretic, aphrodisiac and lithontriptic. It is useful in vitiated conditions of *kapha* and *pitta,* burning sensation, anorexia, dyspepsia, flatulence, colic, strangury, seminal weakness, renal and vesical calculi, rheumatism, intermittent fevers and herpetic eruptions.

"कुरण्डिका क्षेत्रभूषा कुरण्टी क्षेत्रनाशिनी। " (शा.नि.)
["Kuraṇḍikā kṣētṛabhūṣā kuraṇṭī kṣētranāśinī" (Sā.ni.)]

"कुरण्डिका सरा रुच्या गुर्वी चाग्निप्रदीपनी ।
नाशनी कफवातानां वैद्यैस्तु परिकीर्त्तिता ॥
बृहत्कुरण्डिका शीता पाके माध्वी कटुः स्मृता ।
तिक्ता क्षारा च रूक्षा च सरा वृष्या जटा मता ॥
वातळा पित्तळा वस्तौवातकारी कफापहा ।
रक्तदोषं मूत्रकृच्छ्रं नाशयेदिति कीर्त्तिता ॥ (नि.र.)

Ammannia baccifera

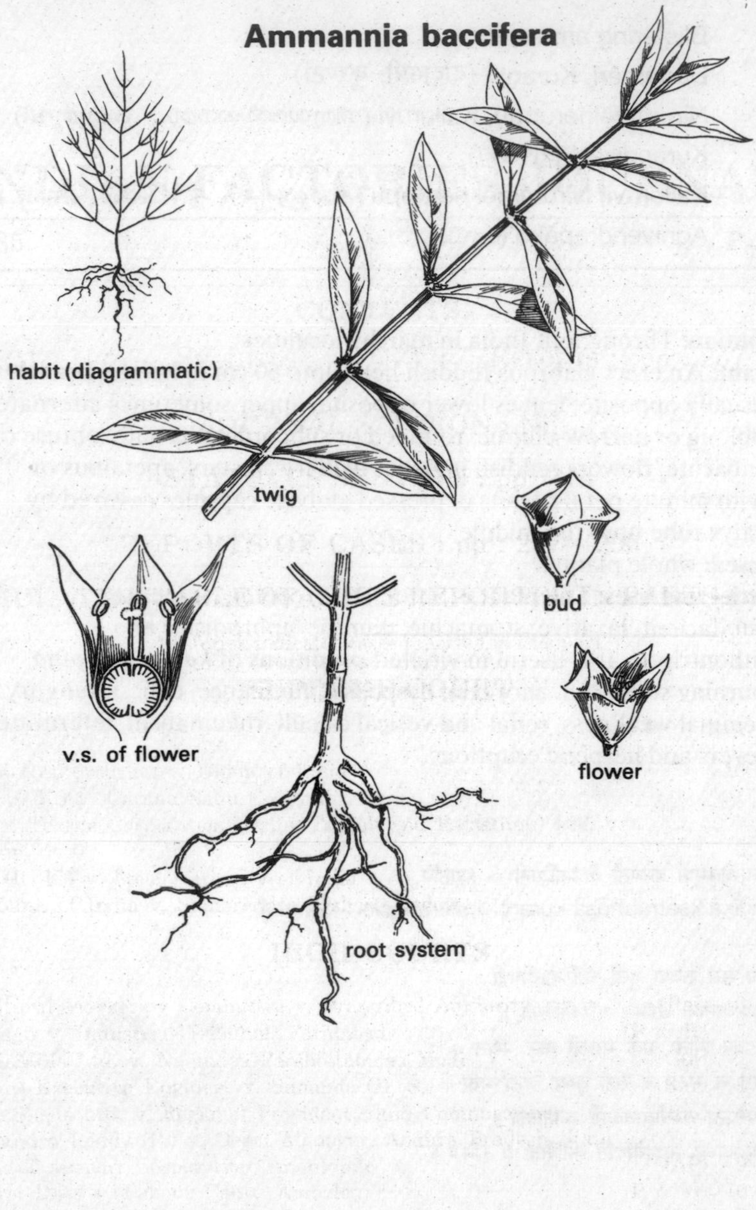

["Kuraṇḍikā sarā rucyā guṛvī cāgnipṛadīpanī
Nāśanī kaphavātānāṃ vaidyaistu parikīṛttitā
Bṛhatkuraṇḍikā śītā pākē mādhvī kaṭuḥ smṛtā
Tiktā kṣārā ca rūkṣā ca sarā vṛṣyā jaṭā matā
Vātaḷā pittaḷā vastauvātakārī kaphāpahā
Raktadōṣaṃ mūṭrakṛcchṛaṃ nāśayēditi kīṛttitā" (Ni.ra.)]

Remarks: The *bṛhatkuraṇḍikā* mentioned above is *Ammania multiflora* Roxb.

Coll. No. AVS 2409

***Amomum subulatum* Roxb.**

Zingiberaceae : (आर्द्रक–कुलम्)

Eng	:	Greater cardamom, Nepal cardamom
Hin	:	Baḍī Ilāyacī, Bārī Ilāyacā (बडी इलायची, बारी इलायची)
Kan	:	Doḍḍayelakki (ದೊಡ್ಡಯೆಲಕ್ಕಿ)
Mal	:	Pērēlaṃ (പേരേലം)
San	:	Sthūlailā, Bhadrailā (स्थूलैला, भद्रैला)
Tam	:	Periya ēlaṃ, Kāṭṭēlaṃ, Pērēlaṃ (பெரிய ஏலம், காட்டேலம், பேரேலம்)
Tel	:	Pedda ēlakkāya, Adaviēlakkāya (పెద్ద ఏలక్కాయ, అడవి ఏలక్కాయ)

Distribution: In the Eastern Himalayas

The plant: A herb with leafy stem upto 90–100 cm in height, leaves oblong-lanceolate, bright green, glabrous on both surfaces; flowers white in globose shortly peduncled spikes, bracts reddish brown, lip ovate-cuneate, emarginate, yellowish white, filaments very short, anther crest small, truncate, entire; fruits reddish brown, densely echinate globose capsules; seeds many, held together by a viscid sugary pulp.

Parts used: seeds

Properties and uses: The seeds are acrid, bitter, aromatic, thermogenic, deodorant, appetiser, carminative, digestive, stomachic, constipating, depurative, vulnerary, anodyne, cardiac and liver tonic, expectorant, diuretic, febrifuge, sudorific and hypnotic. They are useful in vitiated conditions of *kapha* and *vāta,* halitosis, anorexia, dyspepsia, colic, flatulence, hyperacidity, vomiting, diarrhoea, dysentery, skin diseases, pruritus, wounds, ulcers, cephalalgia, odontalgia, neuralgia, cardiac debility, liver congestion, splenomegaly, cough, bronchitis, strangury, fever, proctoptosis, hyperdipsia and gonorrhoea.

"भद्रैला बृहदेला तु स्थूलैला तु सुगन्धिका ।
त्रिदिवा त्रिदिवोद्भूता पृथ्वीका कन्यका पुटा ॥" (म.नि.)
["Bhadrailā bṛhadēlā tu sthūlailā tu sugandhikā
Tṛidivā tṛidivōdbhūtā pṛthvīkā kanyakā puṭā" (Ma.ni.)]

Amomum subulatum

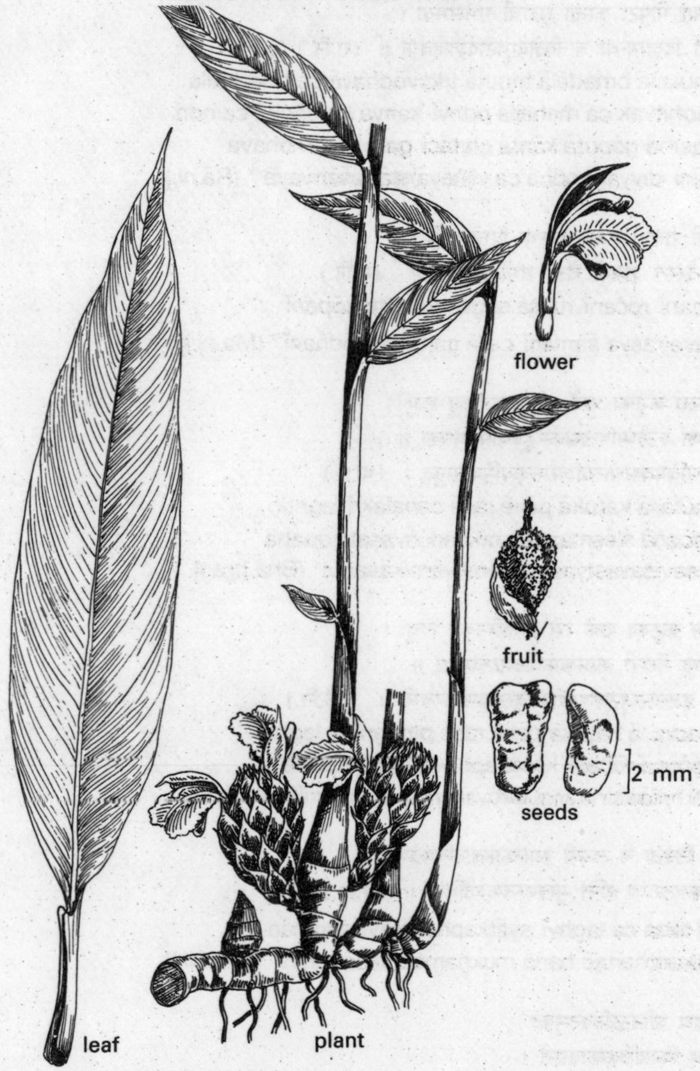

"एला स्थूला च बहुळा पृथ्वीका त्रिपुटाऽपिच ।
भद्रैला बृहदेला च चन्द्रबाला च निष्कुटिः ॥" (भा.प्र.)
["Elā sthūlā ca bahuḷā pṛthvīkā tripuṭāʃpi ca
Bhadrailā bṛhadēlā ca candrabālā ca niṣkuṭiḥ " (Bhā.pṛa.)]

"स्थूलैला बृहदेला त्रिपुटा त्रिदिवोद्भवा च भद्रैला ।
सुरभित्वक् च महैला पृथ्वी कन्या कुमारिका चैन्द्री ॥
कायस्था गोपुटा कान्ता घृताची गर्भसंभवा ।
इन्द्राणी दिव्यगन्धा च विज्ञेयाऽष्टादशाह्वया ॥" (रा.नि.)
["Sthūlailā bṛhadēlā tṛipuṭā tṛidivōdhavā ca bhadrailā
Surabhitvak ca mahailā pṛthvī kanyā kumārikā caindrī
Kāyasthā gōpuṭā kāntā ghṛtācī gaṛbhasambhavā
Indrāṇī divyagandhā ca vijñēyāʃṣṭādaśāhvayā " (Rā.ni.)]

"दीपनी रोचनी रूक्षा सुगन्धा पित्तकोपनी ।
आस्यवैरस्य शमनी चैला गर्भविशोधनी ॥ " (म.नि.)
["Dīpanī rōcanī rūkṣā sugandhī pittakōpanī
Āsyavairasya śamanī cailā gaṛbhaviśōdhanī " (Ma.ni.)]

"स्थूलैला कटुका पाके रसे चानलकृत् लघुः ।
रूक्षोष्णा श्ळेष्मपित्तास्रकण्डूश्वासतृषापहा ॥
हृल्लासविषवस्त्यास्यशिरोरुक्वमिकासनुत् ।" (भा.प्र.)
["Sthūlailā kaṭukā pākē rasē cānalakṛt laghuḥ
Rūkṣōṣṇā śḷēṣmapittāsṛakaṇḍūśvasatṛṣāpahā
Hṛllāsaviṣavastyāsyasirōrukvāmikāsanut" (Bhā.pṛa.)]

"भद्रैला कटुका पाके रसे पित्ताग्निकृत् लघुः ।
रूक्षोष्णा रोचनी कासकफवातास्रश्वासहा ॥
हान्ति हृल्लासतृट्कण्डूशिरोवस्त्यास्यरुग्वमीः । " (कै.नि.)
["Bhadrailā kaṭukā pākē rasē pittāgnikṛt laghuḥ
Rukṣōṣṇā rōcanī kāsakaphavātāsṛaśvāsahā
Hanti hṛllāsatṛṭkaṇḍūśirōvastyāsyarugvamīḥ" (Kai.ni.)]

"एला तिक्ता च लघ्वी स्यात्कफवातविषव्रणान् ।
वस्तिकण्ठरुजो हन्ति मुखमस्तकशोधिनी ॥" (ध.नि.)
["Elā tiktā ca laghvī syātkaphavātaviṣavṛaṇān
Vastikaṇṭharujō hanti mukhamastakaśōdhinī" (Dha.ni.)]

"एलाद्वयं शीतळतिक्तमुक्तं
सुगन्धि पित्तार्त्तिकफापहारी ।
करोति हृद्रोगमलार्त्तिवस्ति-
शूलघ्नमत्र स्थविरा गुणाढ्या ॥" (रा.नि.)
["Elādvayaṃ śītaḷatiktamuktaṃ

sugandhi pittārttikaphāpahārī
Karōti hṛdrōgamalārttivasti-
śūlaghnamatṛa sthavirā guṇāḍhyā" (Rā.ni.)]

"स्थूलैला रेचनी तीक्ष्णा लघूष्णा कफपित्तजित् ।
हल्लासविषवस्त्यास्यशिरोरुग्वमिकासनुत् ॥" (म.वि.)
["Sthūlailā rēcanī tīkṣṇā laghūṣṇā kaphapittajit
Hṛllāsaviṣavastyāsyaśirōrugvamikāsanut" (Ma.vi.)]

Remarks: In Kerala, seeds of *Amomum microstephanum* Baker are also used as *pērēlaṃ* in the formulations.

Coll. No. AVS 2450

Amorphophallus paeoniifolius **(Dennst.) Nicolson var. companulatus (Decne.) Sivad.**

(A. campanulatus *Decne.*)

Araceae : (सूरण–कुलम्)

Eng	:	Elephant foot yam
Hin	:	Sūraṇ, Jamīkand (सूरण, जमीकन्द)
Kan	:	Suvarṇagaḍḍa (ಸುವರ್ಣಗಡ್ಡ)
Mal	:	Cēna (ചേന)
San	:	Sūraṇaḥ (सूरणः)
Tam	:	Karuṇaikkiḻanku (கருணைக் கிழங்கு)
Tel	:	Kandagaḍḍa (కందగడ్డ)

Distribution: Throughout India, cultivated

The plant: A stout herbaceous plant with underground hemispherical depressed dark brown corm; leaves compound, large, solitary, petiole stout, mottled, 60–90 cm long, leaflets 5–12.5 cm long of variable width, obovate or oblong, acute, strongly and many-nerved; male and female inflorescences contiguous, neuters absent, appendage of spadix subglobose or amorphous, equalling or longer than the fertile region, spathe campanulate, pointed, strongly, closely veined, greenish pink externally, base within purple, margins recurved, undulate and crisped, male inflorescence subturbinate, female 7.5cm or more long; fruits obovoid 2–3 seeded red berries.

Parts used: corms

Properties and uses: The corms are acrid, astringent, thermogenic, irritant, anodyne, anti-inflammatory, antihaemorrhoidal, haemostatic, expectorant, carminative, digestive, appetiser, stomachic, anthelmintic, liver tonic, aphrodisiac, emmenagogue, rejuvenating and tonic. They are useful in vitiated conditions of *vāta* and *kapha,* arthralgia, elephantiasis, tumours, inflammations, haemorrhoids, haemorrhages, vomiting, cough, bronchitis, asthma, anorexia, dyspepsia, flatulence, colic, constipation, helminthiasis hepatopathy, splenopathy, amenorrhoea, dysmenorrhoea, seminal weakness, fatigue, anaemia and general debility.

The roots are ophthalmic and emmenagogue, and are useful in ophthalmia, amenorrhoea and boils.

"सूरणः स्याच्छत्रकः स्यान्महानाळस्त्रिशीर्षपात् ।
त्र्यंकुरश्चंचुमारिश्च छत्रवृन्तस्सितात्मकः ॥" (अ.म.)

Amorphophallus paeoniifolius var. campanulatus

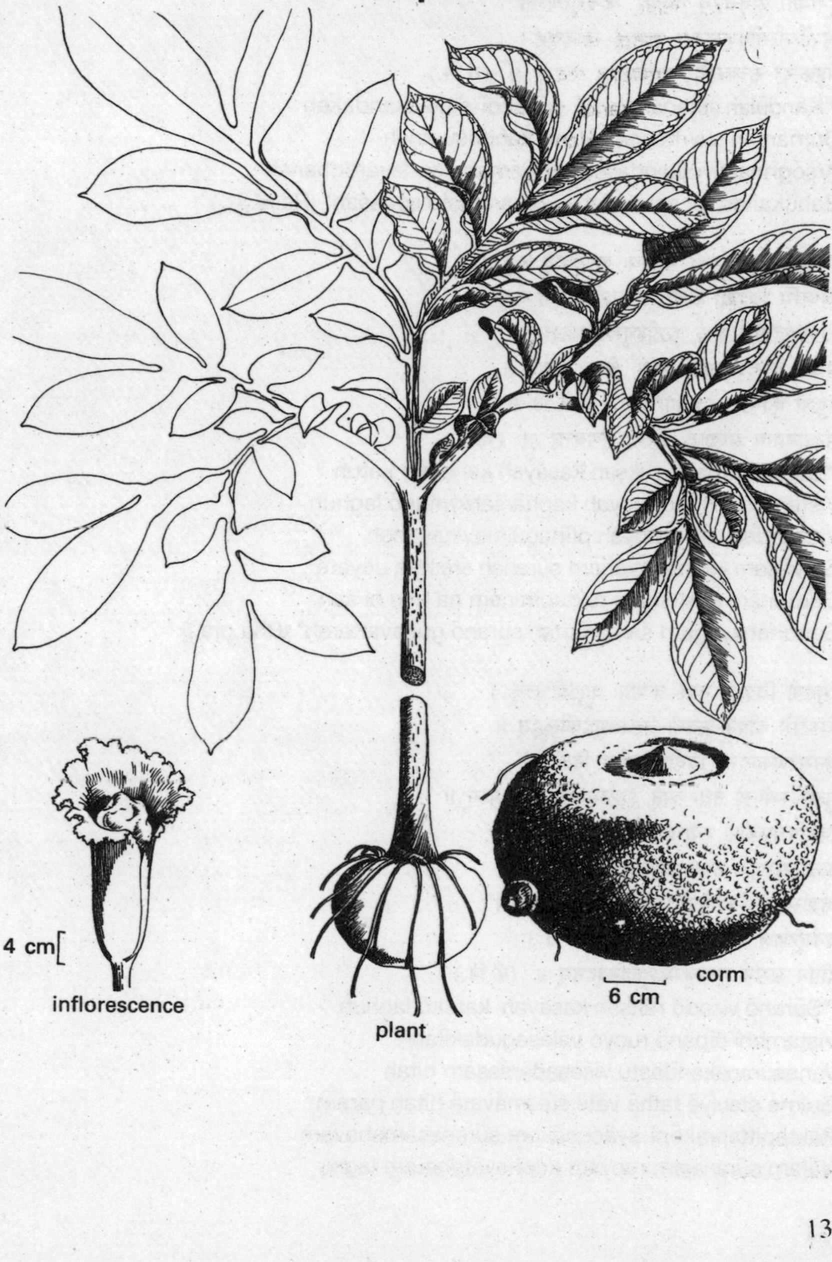

["Sūraṇaḥ syācchatṛakaḥ syātmahānāḷastṛiśīṛṣapāt
Tṛyaṁkuraścaṁcumāriśca chatṛavṛntassitātmakaḥ" (A.ma.)]

"सूरणः कन्द ओळश्च कन्दळो|र्शोघ्न इत्यपि ।" (भा.प्र.)
["Sūraṇaḥ kanda ōḷaśca kandaḷōḷṛśōghna ityapi" (Bhā.pṛa.)]

"कण्डूलः सूरणः कन्दी सुकन्दी स्थूलकन्दकः ।
दुर्नामारि सुवृत्तश्च वातारिः कन्दसूरणः ॥
अर्शोघ्नस्तीव्रकन्दश्च कन्दार्हः कन्दवर्द्धनः ।
बहुकन्दो रुच्यकन्दः सूरकन्दस्तु षोडशः ॥" (रा.नि.)
["Kaṇḍūlaḥ sūraṇaḥ kandī sukandī sthūlakandakaḥ
Duṛnāmāri suvṛttaśca vātāriḥ kandasūraṇaḥ
Aṛśōghnastīvṛakandaśca kandāṛhaḥ kandavaṛddhanaḥ
Bahukandō rucyakandaḥ sūrakandastu ṣōḍaśaḥ" (Rā.ni.)]

"सूरणो दीपनो रूक्षः कषायः कण्डुकृत् कटुः ।
विष्टंभि विशदो रुच्यः कफार्शःकृन्तनो लघुः ॥
विशेषादर्शसे पथ्यः प्ळीहगुल्मविनाशनः ।
सर्वेषां कन्दशाकानां सूरणः श्रेष्ठ उच्यते ॥
ददूणां कुष्ठिनां रक्तपित्तिनां न हितो हि सः ।
सन्धानयोगं सम्प्राप्तः सूरणो गुणवत्तरः ॥" (भा.प्र.)
["Sūraṇō dīpanō rūkṣaḥ kaṣāyaḥ kaṇḍukṛt kaṭuḥ
Viṣṭambhi viśadō rucyaḥ kaphāṛśaḥkṛntanō laghuḥ
Viśēṣādaṛśasē pathyaḥ plīhagulmavināśanaḥ
Saṛvēṣāṃ kandaśākānāṃ sūraṇaḥ śṛēṣṭha ucyatē
Dadrūṇāṃ kuṣṭhināṃ raktapittināṃ na hitō hi saḥ
Sandhānayōgaṃ sampṛāptaḥ sūraṇō guṇavattaraḥ" (Bhā.pṛa.)]

"सूरणो विशदो रूक्षः कषायः कटुको लघुः ।
विष्टंभि दीपनो रुच्यो वलासगुदकीलहृत् ॥
वनसूरणकन्दस्तु विशेषादर्शसां हितः ।
गुल्मे स्थौल्ये तथा वाते श्ळेष्मवाते हितः परम् ॥
रक्तपित्तप्रकोपी स्याच्छाकं सूरणसंभवम् ।
नाळं सूरणजं रुच्यं कफवातहरं लघु ॥
अर्शसां तु विशेषेण हितं कामाग्निदीपनम् ।
वनसूरणजं रूक्षं नाळं कटुविपाकि च ।
दीपनं स्रंसनं गुल्मकृमिशूलनिषूदनम् ॥" (कै.नि.)
["Sūraṇō viśadō rūkṣaḥ kaṣāyaḥ kaṭukō laghuḥ
Viṣṭambhi dīpanō rucyō valāsagudakīlahṛt
Vanasūraṇakandastu viśēṣādaṛśasāṃ hitaḥ
Gulmē staulyē tathā vātē śḷēṣmāvatē hitaḥ paraṃ
Raktapittapṛakōpī syācchākaṃ sūraṇasambhavaṃ
Nāḷaṃ sūraṇajaṃ rucyaṃ kaphavātaharaṃ laghu

Aṛśasāṃ tu viśēṣēṇa hitaṃ kāmāgnidīpanaṃ
Vanasūraṇajaṃ rūkṣaṃ nāḷaṃ kaṭuvipāki ca
Dīpanaṃ sṛamsanaṃ gulmakṛmi śūlaniṣūdanaṃ" (Kai.ni.)]

"दीपनः सूरणो रुच्यः कफघ्नो विशदो लघुः ।
विशेषादर्शसां पथ्यः..................॥" (अ.हृ.सू.)
["Dīpanaḥ sūraṇō rucyaḥ kaphaghnō viśadō laghuḥ
Viśēṣādaṛśasāṃ pathyaḥ .... " (A.hṛ.Sū.)]

"शूरणः कटुकरुच्यदीपनः
पाचनः कृमिकफानिलापहः ।
श्वासकासवमनार्शसां हरः
शूलगुल्मशमनोऽस्रदोषकृत् ॥" (रा.नि.)
["Śuraṇaḥ kaṭukarucyadīpanaḥ
pācanaḥ kṛmikaphānilāpahaḥ
Śvāsakāsavamanāṛśasāṃ haraḥ
śūlagulmaśamanōʃsṛadōṣakṛt" (Rā.ni.)]

"विशेषादर्शसां पथ्यः .... (सो..नि.)
["Viśēṣādaṛśasāṃ pathyaḥ ...." (Sō.ni.)]

"सूरणो दीपनो रूक्षः कफार्शःकृन्तनो लघुः ।
तद्वदन्यो वज्रकन्दः कफघ्नः पित्तरक्तकृत् ॥" (म.वि.)
["Sūraṇō dīpanō rūkṣaḥ kaphāṛśaḥkṛntanō laghuḥ
Tadvadanyō vajṛakandaḥ kaphaghnaḥ pittaraktakṛt" (Ma.vi.)]

"सूरणो दीपनो रूक्षः कषायः कटुकण्डुकृत् ।
विष्टंभि विशदो रुच्यः कफार्शःकृन्तनो लघुः ॥
नाळं सूरणकं रुच्यं कफवातहरं लघुः ।
अर्शसां तु विशेषेण हितं कामाग्निदीपनम् ॥" (म.पा.नि.)
["Sūraṇō dīpanō rūkṣaḥ kaṣāyaḥ kaṭukaṇḍukṛt
Viṣṭambhi viśadō rucyaḥ kaphāṛśaḥkṛntanō laghuḥ
Nāḷaṃ sūraṇakaṃ rucyaṃ kaphavātaharaṃ laghuḥ
Aṛśasāṃ tu viśēṣēṇa hitaṃ kāmāgnidīpanaṃ" (Ma.pā.ni.)]

"ईषत्कषायः कटुका रूक्षा विष्टंभिनो गुरवः कफवातळः पित्तहरश्च ।" (सु.सू.)
["Īṣatkaṣāyaḥ kaṭukā rūkṣā viṣṭambhinō guravaḥ kaphavātaḷaḥ pittaharaśca" (Su.Sū.)]

"ചേന നന്നു കഫത്തിന്നും രുചിക്കും ദഹനത്തിനും
ലഘുവായിട്ടിരിപ്പോന്നു വിശദം താനുമേറ്റവും.
കാട്ടുചേന വിശേഷിച്ചുമർശ്ശസ്സിനേറ്റവും ഗുണം
ഗുൽമം വാതകഫം മേദസ്സിത്യാദീനാഞ്ച നാശനം." (ഗു.പാ.)
["Cēna nannu kaphattinnuṃ rucikkuṃ dahanattinuṃ

Laghuvāyiṭṭirippōnnu viśadaṃ tānumēttavuṃ
Kāṭṭucēna viśēṣiccumaṛśśassinnēttavuṃ guṇaṃ
Gulmaṃ vātakaphaṃ medassityādīnañca nāśanaṃ." (Gu.pā.]

Remarks: The wild variety of this, *vanasūraṇa,* is said to be more effective in the treatment of haemorrhoids. But this has to be washed, boiled in butter milk and dried a few times and thus purified before use.

Coll. No. AVS 1478

Anacardium occidentale **Linn.**

Anacardiaceae : (आम्र–कुलम्)

Eng	:	Cashewnut tree
Hin	:	Dūk, Kājū (दूक्, काजू)
Kan	:	Gērumara, Turakagēru (ಗೇರುಮರ. ತುರಕಗೇರು)
Mal	:	Kaśumāvu̩, Pa̩rankimāvu̩ (കശുമാവ്, പറങ്കിമാവ്)
San	:	Vṛkkabījaḥ, Vṛkkaphalaḥ, Vēnāmraḥ (वृक्कबीजः, वृक्कफलः, वेनाम्रः)
Tam	:	Muntiri (முந்திரி)
Tel	:	Gīḍimāvriḍi (జీడిమామిడి)

Distribution: Cultivated and wild especially on the sea coast

The plant: A small tree with short, thick, crooked trunk; leaves large, obovate, rounded at the apex; inflorescence terminal, longer than the leaves; flowers yellow, streaked with pink; fruits greenish grey, nuts on yellow or scarlet flesh pedicel.

Parts used: roots, bark, leaves, fruits

Properties and uses: The roots are considered purgative. The bark has alterative properties and is used along with the inflorescence for the treatment of snakebite. The bark and leaves are useful in odontalgia and ulitis. The gum from the bark is recommended in leprosy, ringworm, corns and obstinate ulcers. Fruits are acrid, sweet, thermogenic, aphrodisiac, trichogenous and anthelmintic, and are useful in vitiated conditions of *vāta* and *kapha,* skin diseases, dysentery, haemorrhoids and anorexia. They are used for preventing hair loss and to increase the growth of hair. The kernels constitute a highly nutritious and concentrated food. A delicious drink is also derived from the spongy thalamus.

"गुच्छपुष्पो वृक्कबीजः पृथक्बीजो रुजाकरः ।
अग्न्याह्वोऽरुष्करः क्षुद्रः स्निग्धः पीतफलः स्मृतः ॥" (स्व.)
["Gucchapuṣpō vṛkkabījaḥ pṛthagibījō rujākaraḥ
Agnyāhvōʃruṣkaraḥ kṣudraḥ snigdhaḥ pītaphalaḥ smṛtaḥ" (Sva.)]

"वेनाम्रोऽथ बहिर्बीजो प्रोक्तः शोफहरश्च सः" (स्व.)
["Vēnāmrọʃtha bahiṛbījaḥ prōktaḥ śōphaharaśca saḥ" (Sva.)]

Anacardium occidentale

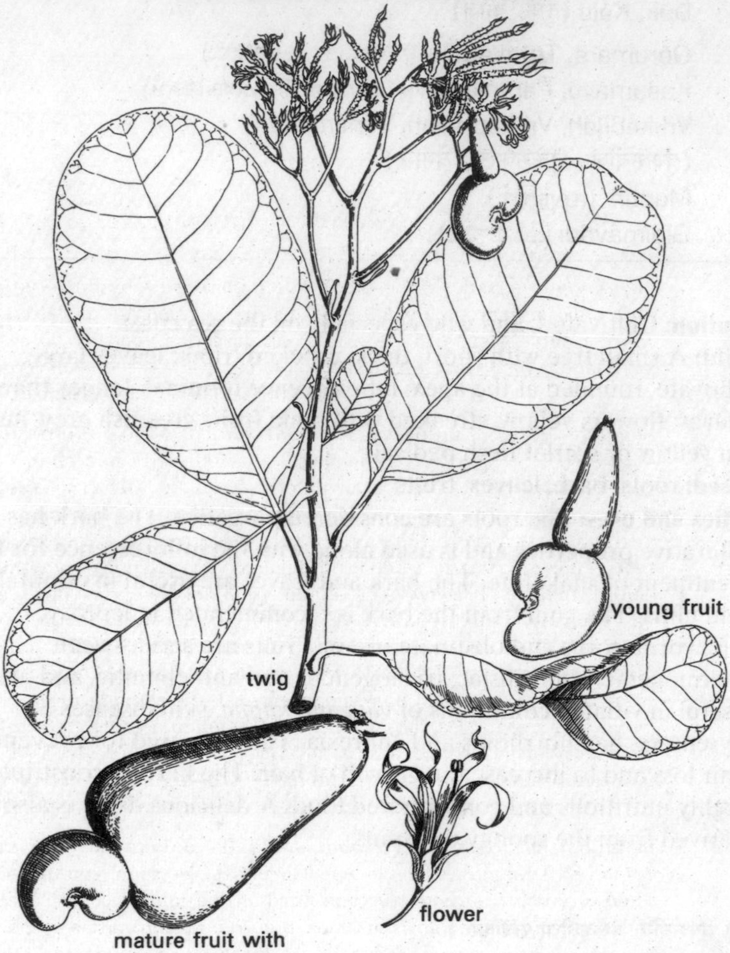

"काजूतको वृत्तपत्रो गुच्छपुष्पश्च पार्वती ।
स्निग्धपीतफलश्चैव पृथग्बीजो ह्यरुष्करः ॥" (शा.नि.)
["Kājūtakō vṛttapatrō gucchapuṣpaśca pārvatī
Snigdhapītaphalaścaiva pṛthagbījō hyaruṣkaraḥ" (Sā.ni.)]

"गुणैर्भल्लातवत् ज्ञेयं विशेषादस्य बीजकम् ।
सुभृष्टं मधुरं स्निग्धं हृद्यं वृष्यं रसायनम् ॥
कफवातहरं श्वासकासघ्नं बलपुष्टिकृत् ।
बीजास्थितैलमस्यैव तीक्ष्णं दाहकरं परम् ॥
अग्निवत् स्फोटजनकं व्रणक्लेदरुजादिकृत् ।
सुसंस्कृतं साधुसिद्धं युक्त्या चैतत् प्रयोजितम् ॥
श्वित्रकुष्टविसर्पादीन् नाशयेन्नात्र संशयः ।
ईषत् कषाय मधुरं फलमस्यरुचिप्रदम् ॥
कृमिघ्नं दीपनं पथ्यं वृष्यं वातकफापहम् ।
वेनाम्रस्त्वक् कषायः स्यात् त्वच्यो व्रण्यः कफापहः ॥
विषकण्डूकुष्ठशोफश्वित्रवीसर्पनाशनः ।" (स्व.)
["Guṇairbhallātavat jñēyaṃ viśēṣādasya bījakaṃ
Subhṛṣṭaṃ madhuraṃ shigdhaṃ hṛdyaṃ vṛṣyaṃ rasāyanaṃ
Kaphavātaharaṃ śvāsakāsaghhaṃ balapuṣṭikṛt
Bījāsthitailamasaiva tīkṣṇaṃ dāhakaraṃ paraṃ
Agnivat sphōṭajanakaṃ vraṇaklēdarujādikṛt
Susaṃskṛtaṃ sādhusiddhaṃ yuktyā caitat prayōjitaṃ
Śvitṛakuṣṭhavisaṛpādīn nāśayēnnātṛa saṃśayaḥ
Iṣat kaṣāyamadhuraṃ phalamasya rucipṛadaṃ
Kṛmighnaṃ dīpanaṃ pathyaṃ vṛṣyaṃ vātakaphāpahaṃ
Vēnāmṛastvak kaṣāyaḥ syāt tvacyō vṛaṇyaḥ kaphāpahaḥ
Viṣakaṇḍūkuṣṭhaśōphaśvitṛavīsarpanāśanaḥ" (Sva.)]

"काजूतकस्तु तुवरो मधुरोष्णो लघुः स्मृतः ।
धातुवृद्धिकरो वातकफगुल्मोदरज्वरान् ॥
कृमिव्रणाग्निमान्द्यानि कुष्ठा च श्वेतकुष्ठकम् ।
संग्रहण्यर्शानाहान्नाशयेदिति कीर्त्तितः ॥" (नि.र.)
["Kājūtakastu tuvarō madhurōṣṇō laghuḥ smṛtaḥ
Dhātuvṛddhikarō vātakaphagulmōdarajvarān
Kṛmivṛaṇāgnimāndyāni kuṣṭhā ca śvētakuṣṭhakaṃ
Saṃgrahaṇyaṛśānāhānnāśayēditi kīṛttitaḥ" (Ni.ra.)]

Coll. No. AVS 2410

Anacyclus pyrethrum **DC.**

Asteraceae : (भृङ्गराज–कुलम्)

Eng	:	Pellitory
Hin	:	Akarkarā (अकरकरा)
Kan	:	Akkalakara (ಅಕ್ಕಲಕರ)
Mal	:	Akkikkaṛuka, Akkṛāvu (അക്കിക്കറുക, അക്രാവ്)
San	:	Agragrāhī, Ākārakarabhaḥ (अग्रग्राही, आकारकरभः)
Tam	:	Akkirakkāram, Akkalkārā (அக்கிரக்காரம், அக்கல்காரா)
Tel	:	Akarākaramu (అకరాకరము)

Distribution: Indigenous to north Africa, introduced into south Europe

The plant: A perennial, procumbent plant with numerous stems and somewhat downy branches; leaves radical, stalked, smooth, pinnatisect into linear, subulate segments, cauline leaves sessile; branches one-headed, involucral scales lanceolate, acuminate, brown at the edge, receptacle convex; ray flowers white, purplish beneath.

The fresh root is fusiform, fleshy and very pungent, producing a sensation of cold followed by heat. When dry it is brownish externally and whitish internally. It tastes hot, induces salivation and causes a burning sensation in the stomach when ingested.

Parts used: roots

Properties and uses: Roots are acrid, astringent and are a valuable sialogogue and regarded as a tonic to the nervous system. They are anti-inflammatory, depurative and powerful irritant. A decoction of the root is useful as a gargle in dental caries, odontalgia, pharyngitis and tonsilitis. It is used to treat paralysis, hemiplegia, cephalalgia, chronic ophthalmia, epilepsy, cholera, rheumatism and typhus fever. Powdered root is given with honey for epilepsy. It is recommended as a masticatory in vitiated *vāta* conditions of the face.

"अग्रग्राही परस्त्रैणः प्रतीकः प्रीतिकारकः ।
आकारकरभश्चैव फिरङ्गारी सुतेजनः ॥" (स्व.)
["Agragrāhī parastraiṇaḥ pratīkaḥ prītikārakaḥ
Akārakarabhaścaiva phirangārī sutējanaḥ" (Sva.)]

Anacyclus pyrethrum

(Courtesy: NBRI, Lucknow.)

"आकारकरभश्चैवाकल्लकोऽथ ह्यकल्लकः ।" (शा.नि.)

["Ākārakarbhaścaivākallakōʃtha hyakallakaḥ" (Śā.ni.)]

"कटुतिक्तोष्णवीर्योऽसौ मेहहा वस्तिशूलहृत् ।
शुक्ळमूत्रामयान् हन्याद्दन्तशूलविनाशनः ॥
वीर्यस्तंभकरोऽप्येषः शीलितः क्ळैब्यकृत् परम् ।
तन्त्रानाडीं ज्ञानशक्तिं क्रमात्तन्नाशयेत् ध्रुवम् ॥" (स्व.)
["Kaṭutiktōṣṇavīryōʃsau mēhahā vastiśūlahṛt
Śukḷamūtṛāmayān hanyāddantaśūlavināśanaḥ
Vīryastambhakarōʃpyēṣaḥ śīlitaḥ kḷaibyakṛtparaṃ
Tantṛanāḍīṃ jñānaśktiṃ kṛamāttannāśayēt dhṛuvaṃ" (Sva.)]

"अकल्लकोष्णो वीर्येण बलकृत् कटुको मतः ।
प्रतिश्यायं च शोफं च वातं चैव विनाशयेत् ॥ (नि.र.)
["Akallakōṣṇō vīryēṇa balakṛt kaṭukō mataḥ
Pṛatiśyāyaṃ ca śōphaṃ ca vātaṃ caiva vināśayēt (Ni.ra.)]

Coll. No. AVS 2451

***Anamirta cocculus* (Linn.) Wight & Arn.**

(A.paniculata *Colebr.*)

Menispermaceae (गुडूची–कुलम्)

Eng	:	Levant berries, Fish berries, Crow killer
Hin	:	Kākamārī (काकमारी)
Kan	:	Kākamāri, Kāyamari (ಕಾಕಮಾರಿ, ಕಾಯಮರಿ)
Mal	:	Poḷḷa, Kollakkāya, Pēṯṯumarunnụ (പൊള്ള, കൊല്ലക്കായ, പേറ്റുമരുന്ന)
San	:	Garaḷaphalā, Kākamārī (गरळफला, काकमारी)
Tam	:	Kākamāri (காகமாரி)
Tel	:	Garaḷaphala, Kākinicampaceṭṭu (గరళఫల, కాకినిచంపచెట్టు)

Distribution: Throughout India in forests

The plant: A large,woody,climbing shrub with vertically furrowed ash-coloured bark and glabrous young parts; leaves large, simple, alternate, long-petioled, petioles thickened at the base and apex, broadly ovate, subcoriaceous, cordate or truncate at the base, acute or acuminate, 5-nerved with tufts of hairs in the axils of the nerves except the basal ones; flowers greenish in long panicles, drooping from the nodes of the old wood; fruits drupes, kidney shaped, turning red on ripening.

Parts used: leaves, fruits

Properties and uses: The fruits are bitter, astringent, thermogenic, expectorant, antifungal, anthelmintic and depurative. They are useful in vitiated conditions of *kapha* and *vāta,* bronchitis, dermatophytosis, foul ulcers, inflammations, flatulence, chronic skin diseases and ringworm. The tender leaves are used by the tribals for the contraction of the uterus immediately after delivery.

"गरळा काकमारी च काकाह्वा काकनाशिका ।
काकनाशी विषफला मत्स्यघ्नी मत्स्यनाशिका ॥" (स्व.)
["Garaḷā kākamārī ca kākāhvā kākanāśikā
Kākanāśī viṣaphalā matsyaghnī matsyanāśikā" (Sva.)]

"काकमारीफलं तीक्ष्णं कषायोष्णं कटु स्मृतम् ।
रक्तशुद्धिकरं तिक्तं कृमिजन्तुविनाशकम् ॥
शोफव्रणश्वासकासकण्डूत्वग्दोषनाशनम् ।

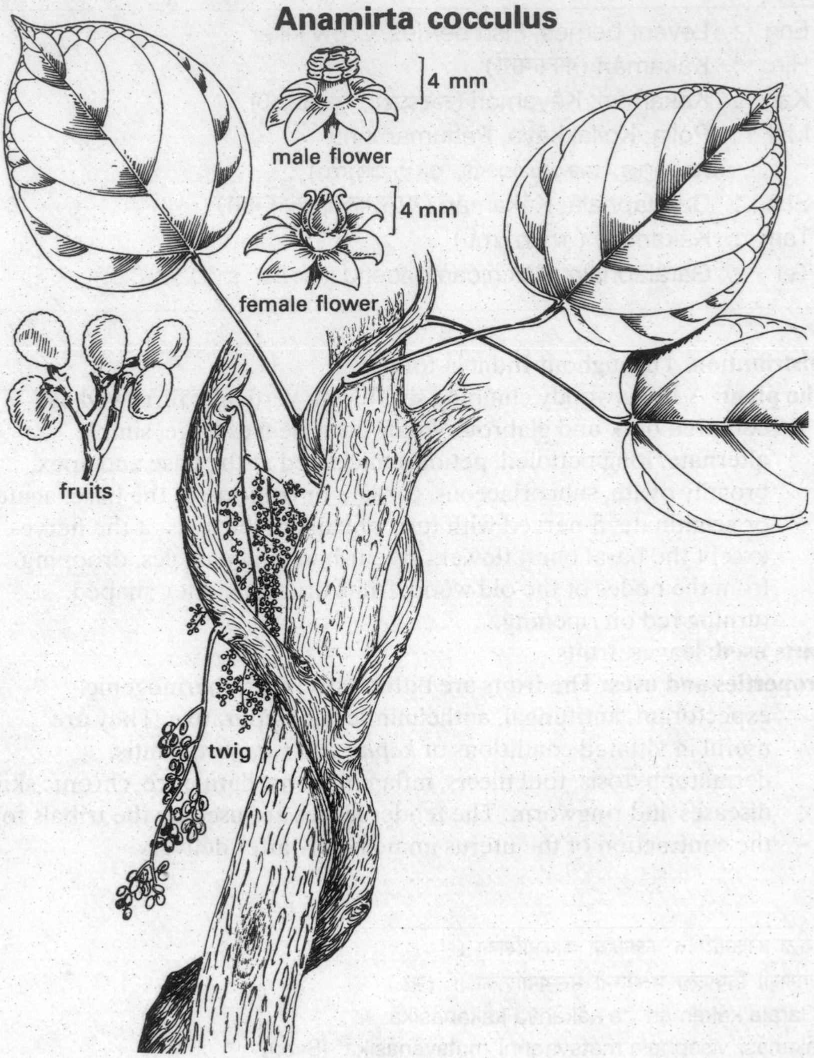
Anamirta cocculus
4 mm
male flower
4 mm
female flower
fruits
twig

कफवातहरं प्रोक्तं दुष्टव्रणहरं परम् ॥" (स्व.)
["Kākamārīphalaṃ tīkṣṇaṃ kaṣāyōṣṇaṃ kaṭu smṛtaṃ
Raktaśuddhikaraṃ tiktaṃ kṛmijantuvināśakaṃ
Śōphavraṇaśvāsakāsakaṇḍūtvagdōṣanāśanaṃ
Kaphavātaharaṃ prōktaṃ duṣṭavraṇaharaṃ paraṃ" (Sva.)]

Coll. No. AVS 2452

Ananas comosus **(Linn.) Merrill**

(A.sativus *Schultes f.*)

Bromeliaceae (अनंनास–कुलम्)

Eng	:	Pineapple
Hin	:	Anānās (अनानास)
Kan	:	Anasahannu (ಅನಸಹಣ್ಣು)
Mal	:	Kaitaccakka, Kappaccakka, Anānās (കൈതച്ചക്ക, കപ്പച്ചക്ക, അനനാസ്)
San	:	Anamnāsam̩, Bahunētraphalam̩ (अनंनासं, बहुनेत्रफलं)
Tam	:	Annāśippal̲am̩ (அன்னாசிப்பழம்)
Tel	:	Annasapan̩d̩u (అనాసపండు)

Distribution: Throughout India,cultivated

The plant: A herbaceous perennial with a short stout stem; leaves numerous, spirally and compactly arranged, linear-lanceolate, acuminate, margins spiny,toothed, shining on the upper surface, those subtending the inflorescence small, much reduced, reddish; heads terminal, ovoid, bracteoles reddish, numerous, triangluar-ovate to oblong-ovate, imbricate ; fruits composite, succulent, bearing a crown of leaves.

Parts used: fruits, leaves

Properties and uses: The unripe fruits are sour, cooling, appetiser, digestive, anthelmintic, cathartic, cardiotonic, uterine tonic, emmenagogue and febrifuge. They are useful in vitiated conditions of *pitta,* anorexia, dyspepsia, helminthiasis, constipation, cardiac debility, haematemesis, sexually transmitted diseases, amenorrhoea, dysmenorrhoea and fever.

The ripe fruits are sweet, cooling emollient, diuretic, carminative, digestive, cardiotonic, sudorific, styptic, lithontriptic, antiscorbutic, febrifuge and tonic. They are useful in vitiated conditions of *pitta,* strangury, dyspepsia, flatulence, colic, hyperacidity, cardiac debility, haematemesis, haemoptysis, jaundice, renal and vesical calculi,scabies, pruritus, fever and general debility.

The leaves are anthelmintic, abortifacient and emmenagogue, and are useful in induction of abortion, helminthiasis, amenorrhoea, dysmenorrhoea and whooping cough.

Ananas comosus

"अनंनासं पारवती चामं कौतुकसंज्ञकम् ।" (नि.र.)
["Anamnāsaṃ pāravatī cāmaṃ kautukasamjñakaṃ" (Ni.ra.)]

"अनंनासमपक्वन्तु रुच्यं हृद्यं गुरुर्मतम् ।
कफपित्तकरं चैव प्रोक्तं चान्नमरोचकम् ।
श्रमं क्ळमं नाशयति तत्पक्वं स्वादु पित्तहृत् ।
रसातपविकारांश्च नाशयेदिति कीर्त्तितम् ॥" (नि.र.)
["Anamnāsamapakvantu rucyaṃ hṛdyaṃ gururmataṃ
Kaphapitttakaraṃ caiva prōktaṃ cānnamarōcakaṃ
Śramaṃ kḷamaṃ nāśayati tatpakvaṃ svādu pittahṛt
Rasātapavikārāmśca nāśayēditi kīrttītaṃ" (Ni.ra.)

"बहुनेत्रफलं चाम्ळं कृमिघ्नं मधुरं सरम् ।
बल्यं वातहरं रुच्यं श्ळेष्मळं तर्पणं गुरु ॥" (रा.व.)
["Bahunētraphalaṃ cāmḷaṃ kṛmighnaṃ madhuraṃ saraṃ
Balyaṃ vātaharaṃ rucyaṃ śḷēṣmaḷaṃ tarpaṇaṃ guru" (Rā.va.)]

"आमं त्वनानसफलं सरमम्ळं सुदीपनम् ।
रजःप्रवर्त्तकं स्निग्धं रक्तस्तंभनकृत् हिमम् ॥
परन्त्वत्युपयोगेन गर्भस्रावकरं च तत् ।
पक्वं फलं स्वादु शीतं मूत्रळं रक्तरोधनम् ॥
अग्निदीप्तिकरं हृद्यं स्वेदनं त्वग्विकारनुत् ।
अश्मरीगुल्मशूलघ्नं विषदोषहरं सरम् ॥
पत्रं तु शस्तं हिध्मायां रेचनं कृमिरोगजित् ।" (स्व.)
["Āmaṃ tvanānasaphalaṃ saramamḷaṃ sudīpanaṃ
Rajaḥpravarttakaṃ snigdhaṃ raktastambhanakṛt himaṃ
Parantvatyupayōgēna garbhasrāvakaraṃ ca tat
Pakvaṃ phalaṃ svādu śītaṃ mūtraḷaṃ raktarōdhanaṃ
Agnidīptikaraṃ hṛdyaṃ svēdanaṃ tvagvikāranut
Aśmarīgulmaśūlaghnaṃ viṣadōṣaharaṃ saraṃ
Patraṃ tu śastaṃ hidhmāyāṃ rēcanaṃ kṛmirōgajit" (Sva.)]

Coll.No. AVS 1059

Andrographis paniculata **(Burm.f.) Wall. ex Nees**

Acanthaceae (वाशा–कुलम्)

Eng	:	Green chiretta, Kalmegh, Creat
Hin	:	Kālamēgh, Kalpaāath (कालमेघ, कल्पनाथ)
Kan	:	Nelabēru (ನೆಲಬೇರು)
Mal	:	Nilavēppụ, Kiriyātta (നിലവേപ്പ്, കിരിയാത്ത)
San	:	Bhunimbaḥ, Kirātatiktaḥ (भूनिम्ब :, किराततिक्त :)
Tam	:	Nilavempu (நிலவேம்பு)
Tel	:	Nēlavēmu (నేలవేము)

Distribution: Throughout India,in the plains, also in forests as undergrowth

The plant: An erect, branched annual herb, 0.3 m to 0.9 m in height with quadrangular branches; leaves simple, lanceolate, acute at both ends, glabrous, main nerves 4–6 pairs; flowers small, pale but blotched and spotted with brown and purple distant in lax spreading axillary and terminal racemes or panicles, calyx-lobes glandular pubescent, anthers bearded at the base; fruits linear capsules, acute at both ends; seeds numerous, yellowish brown, subquadrate.

Parts used: whole plant

Properties and uses: The plant is bitter, acrid, cooling, laxative, vulnerary, antipyretic, antiperiodic, anti-inflammatory, expectorant, depurative, sudorific, anthelmintic, digestive and stomachic. It is useful in hyperdipsia, burning sensation, wounds, ulcers, chronic fever, malarial and intermittent fevers, inflammations, cough, bronchitis, skin diseases, leprosy, pruritus, intestinal worms, dyspepsia, flatulence, colic, diarrhoea, dysentery, haemorrhoids and vitiated conditions of *pitta.*

"किराततिक्तः कैरातः कटुतिक्तः किरातकः ।
काण्डतिक्तोऽनार्यतिक्तो भूनिम्बो रामसेनकः ॥" (भा.प्र.)
["Kirātatiktaḥ kairātaḥ kaṭutiktaḥ kirātakaḥ
Kāṇḍatiktōʃnāryatiktō bhūnimbō rāmasēnakaḥ " (Bhā.pṛa.)]

Andrographis paniculata

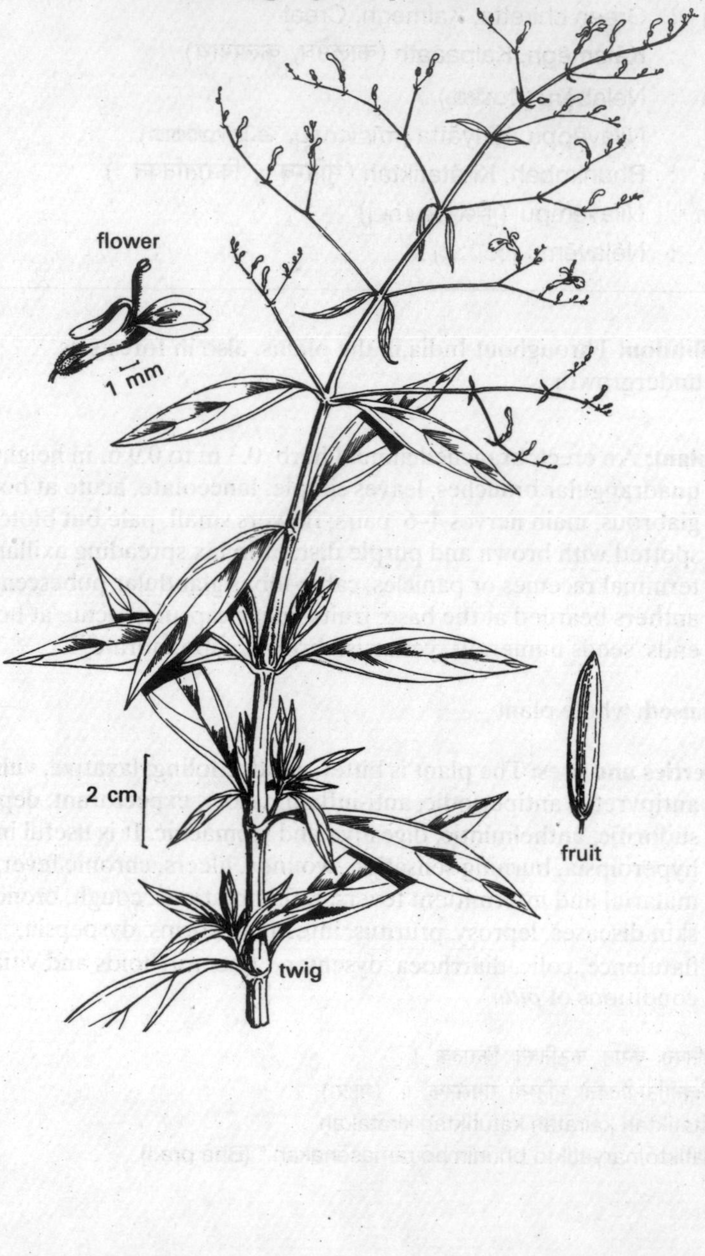

"उपनिम्ब : कुनिम्बश्च निस्सारो भूमिनिम्बकः ।
कथितो निम्बपर्यायैः भूमिपर्यायपूर्वकैः ॥" (अ.म.)
["Upanimbaḥ kunimbaśca nissārō bhūminimbakaḥ
Kathitō nimbaparyāyaiḥ bhūmiparyāyapūrvakaiḥ" (A.ma.)]

"किराततिक्तको हैमः काण्डतिक्तः किरातकः ।
भूनिम्बोऽनार्यतिक्तश्च किरातो रामसेनकः ॥" (ध.नि.)
["Kirātatiktakō haimaḥ kāṇḍatiktaḥ kirātakaḥ
Bhūnimbōऽnāryatiktaśca kirātō rāmasēnakaḥ" (Dha.ni.)]

"किरातः सारको रूक्षः शीतळस्तिक्तको लघुः ।
सन्निपातज्वरश्वासकफपित्तास्रदाहनुत् ॥
कासशोफतृषाकुष्ठज्वरव्रणकृमिप्रणुत् ।" (भा.प्र.)
["Kirātaḥ sārakō rūkṣaḥ śītaḷastiktakō laghuḥ
Sannipātajvaraśvāsakaphapittāsṛadāhanut
Kāsaśōphatṛṣākuṣṭhajvaravṛaṇakṛmipṛaṇut" (Bhā.pṛa.)]

"भूनिम्बो वातळस्तिक्तः कफपित्तज्वरापहः ।
व्रणसंरोपणः पथ्यः कुष्ठकण्डूतिशोफनुत् ॥" (रा.नि.)
["Bhūnimbō vātaḷastiktaḥ kaphapittajvarāpahaḥ
Vṛaṇasamrōpaṇaḥ pathyaḥ kuṣṭhakaṇḍūtiśōphanut" (Rā.ni.)]

"भूनिम्बो वातळस्तिक्तो व्रणरोपणकारकः ।
सरः शीतः पथ्यकरो लघु रूक्षस्तृषापहः ॥
कफं पित्तं ज्वरं कुष्ठं कण्डूं शोफं कृमींस्तथा ।
सन्निपातज्वरं दाहं शूलं मेहं व्रणं तथा ॥
श्वासं कासं च प्रदरं शोषं चार्शोऽरुचिं जयेत् ।" (नि.र.)
["Bhūnimbō vātaḷastiktō vṛaṇarōpaṇakārakaḥ
Saraḥ śītaḥ pathyakarō laghu rūkṣastṛṣāpahaḥ
Kaphaṃ pittaṃ jvaraṃ kuṣṭhaṃ kaṇḍūṃ śōphaṃ kṛmīmstathā
Sannipātajvaraṃ dāhaṃ śūlaṃ mēhaṃ vṛaṇaṃ tathā
Śvāsaṃ kāsaṃ ca pṛadaraṃ śōṣaṃ cārśōऽruciṃ jayēt" (Ni.ra.)]

"भूनिम्बः शीतळो रूक्षो रसे तिक्तो लघुः सरः ।
वातळः कफपित्तास्रकुष्ठमेहापहो हरेत् ॥
श्वासकासतृषादाहारुचिशोफज्वरकृमीन् ।" (कै.नि.)
["Bhūnimbaḥ śītaḷō rūkṣō rasē tiktō laghuḥ saraḥ
Vātaḷaḥ kaphapittāsṛakuṣṭhamēhāpahō harēt
Śvāsakāsatṛṣādāhāruciśōphajvarakṛmīn" (Kai.ni.)]

"भूनिम्बो वातळो रूक्षः कफपित्तज्वरापहा ।" (रा.व.)
["Bhūnimbō vātaḷō rūkṣaḥ kaphapittajvarāpahā" (Rā.va.)]

शूलापहो मलध्वंसी कृमिघ्नो बालकप्रिय ः ।" (सो.नि.)

["Śūlāpahō maladhvaṁsī kṛmighnō bālakapṛiyaḥ" (So.ni.)]

Remarks: Many Sanskrit treatises mention two kinds of '*kirātatikta*' viz. '*bhūniṁba*' and '*nēpāḷaniṁba*' and these have been translated into Malayalam as '*nilavēppu*' and '*kiriyātta*', respectively.

All the commentaries on 'Bhāvapṛakāśaṃ', `Kaiyadēvanighaṇṭu', etc., have identified *kiratatikta* as *Swertia chirayita.* None of these commentators have made any mention about *Andrographis paniculata.* But Acarya P.V. Sharma in his 'Dravyaguṇavijñān' identifies *bhūniṁba* as *A.paniculata* and assigns a Sanskrit name *kālamēghā* to it. *Bhūniṁba,* as we know it is one of the synonyms of *kirātatikta.* However, it is to be noted that the same author has given the Latin name *Swertia chirayita* to *kirātatikta.*

Anyhow, it is worth mentioning that *kirātatikta* or *bhūniṁba* has been correctly translated into Tamil as *nilavēṁpu.*

While in north India and some parts of Kerala *S. chirayita* is the drug used for *kirātatikta,* in certain other parts of Kerala *Andrographis paniculata (nilavēppu)* is in use. However, throughout Kerala *bhūniṁba,* one of the synonyms of *kirātatikta* has been for long wrongly translated into Malayalam as *puttiricuṇḍa (Solanum indicum)* and used in formulations wherever the word *bhūniṁba* occurs.

Nēpāḷaniṁba (Swertia chirayita) gets its name from the fact that it occurs abundantly in Nepal, while *kirātatikta (Andrographis paniculata)* is indigenous to India and grows plentifully throughout.

Coll. No. AVS 1391

Anethum graveolens **Linn.**

(Anethum sowa *Roxb. ex DC.*
Peucedanum graveolens *Linn.* (in part))
Apiaceae (शतपुष्पा–कुलम्)

Eng	:	Dill, Garden dill, Anet
Hin	:	Sōyā (सोया)
Kan	:	Sabbasige (ಸಬ್ಬಸಿಗೆ)
Mal	:	Śatakuppa (ശതകുപ്പ)
San	:	Śatapuspa (शतपुष्पा)
Tam	:	Śatakuppi (சதகுப்பி)
Tel	:	Śatakuppivittulu (శతకుప్పివిత్తులు)

Distribution: Throughout India, cultivated

The plant: A glabrous aromatic annual herb, 30–90 cm in height with hollow finely grooved stem, striped dark green and white with bluish spots; leaves compound, 2–3 pinnate, bluishgreen, segments filiform, leafsheath surrounds the stem; flowers yellow, in flat compound umbels; fruits narrowly winged, vittae large and conspicuous.

Parts used: fruits

Properties and uses: The fruits are acrid, bitter, thermogenic, deodorant, digestive, carminative, stomachic, anthelmintic, anodyne, anti-inflammatory, diuretic, emmenagogue, galactagogue, expectorant, cardiotonic, anaphrodisiac, febrifuge, sudorific, antispasmodic, antidysenteric, alexeteric and vulnerary. They are useful in halitosis, flatulence, colic, dyspepsia, intestinal worms, odontalgia, arthralgia, inflammation, strangury, amenorrhoea, dysmenorrhoea, agalactia, hiccough, cough, asthma, bronchitis, spermatorrhoea, fever, ulcers, skin diseases, splenopathy, hepatopathy, uropathy, gleet, syphilis, haemorrhoids and cardiac debility.

"मिसिरुद्दिष्टा घोषा शतपुष्पा सेतिका शष्पा चेति ।
कारव्युत्कटपुष्पी मगधी मधुपुष्पिकाप्यतिच्छत्रा ॥" (अ.म.)
["Misiruddiṣṭā ghōṣā śatapuṣpā sētikā śaṣpā cēti
Kāravyutkaṭapuṣpī magadhī madhupuṣpikāpyaticchatṛā" (A.ma.)]

"शतपुष्पा शताह्वा च मधुरा कारवी मिसिः ।

Anethum graveolens

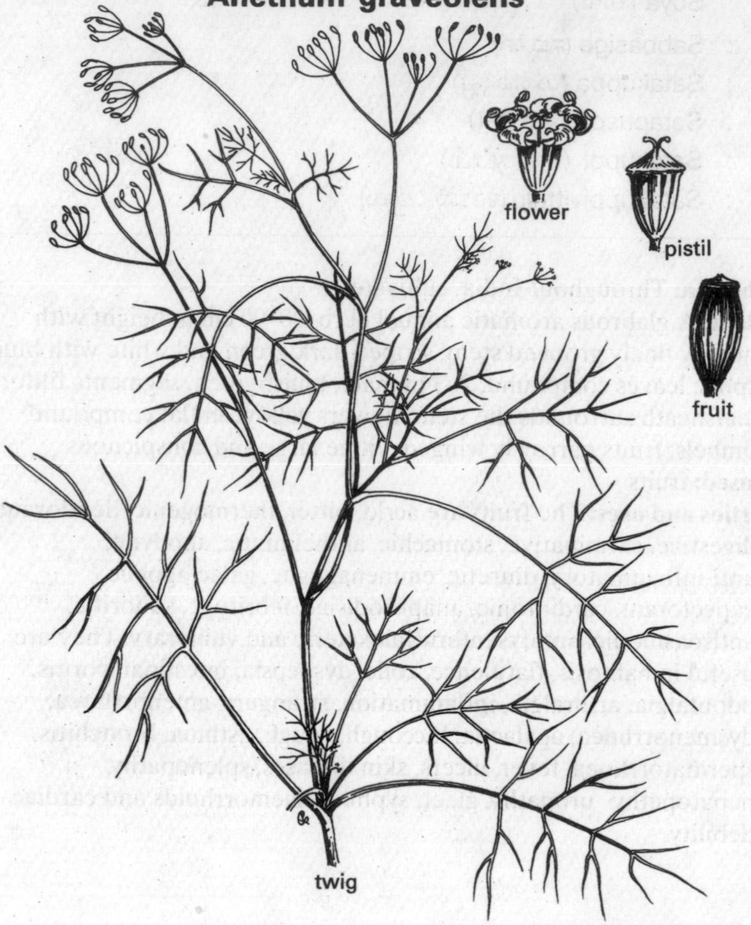

अतिलम्बी सितछत्रा संहिता छत्रिकापि च ॥" (भा.प्र.)
["Śatapuṣpā śatāhvā ca madhurā kāravīmisiḥ
Atilambī sitachatrā samhitā chatṛikāpi ca " (Bhā.pṛa.)]

"शताह्वा शतपुष्पा च मिसिर्घोषा च पोतिका ।
अहिछत्राऽप्यवाक्पुष्पी माधवी कारवी शिफा ॥
संघातपत्रिका छत्रा वज्रपुष्पा सुपुष्पिका ।
शतप्रसूना बहळा पुष्पाह्वा शतपत्रिका ॥
वनपुष्पा भूरिपुष्पा सुगन्धा सूक्ष्मपत्रिका ।
गन्धारिकाऽतिच्छत्रा च चतुर्विंशति नामका ॥" (रा.नि.)
["Śatāhvā śatapuṣpā ca misiṛghōṣā ca pōtikā
Ahicchatṛāʃpyavākpuṣpī mādhavī karavī śiphā
Ṣamghātapatṛikā chatṛā vajṛapuṣpā supuṣpikā
Satapṛasūnā bahaḷā puṣpāhvā śatapatṛikā
Vanapuṣpā bhūripuṣpā sugandhā sūkṣmapatṛikā
Gandhārikāʃticchatṛā ca caturvimśati nāmakā" (Rā.ni.)]

"शतपुष्पा सूक्ष्मपत्रा पीतपुष्पाऽतिछत्रका ।
प्रसिद्धा क्षेत्रविख्याता दीपनोक्ता महर्षिभिः ॥" (शा.नि.)
["Śatapuṣpā sūkṣmapatṛā pītapuṣpāʃtichatṛakā
Pṛasiddhā kṣētṛavikhyātā dīpanōktā mahaṛṣibhiḥ" (Śā.ni.)]

"लघूष्णा कटुका पाके कफवातनिबर्हणि ।
अन्नगन्धहरा रुच्या शाकसौगन्ध्यदा मिसिः ॥" (म.नि.)
["Laghūṣṇā kaṭukā pākē kaphavātanibaṛhaṇi
Annagandhaharā rucyā sākasaugandhyadā misiḥ " (Ma.ni.)]

"शतपुष्पा लघुस्तीक्ष्णा पित्तकृत् दीपनी कटुः
उष्णा ज्वरानिलश्ळेष्मव्रणशूलाक्षिरोगहृत् ॥" (भा.प्र.)
["Śatapuṣpā laghustīkṣnā pittakṛt dīpanī kaṭuḥ
Uṣṇā jvarānilaśḷēṣmavṛanaśūlākṣirōgahṛt" (Bhā.pṛa.)]

"शताह्वा कटुका तिक्ता स्निग्धोष्णा श्ळेष्मवातजित् ।
ज्वरनेत्रव्रणान् हन्ति वस्तिकर्मणि शस्यते ॥
शतपुष्पादळं चोक्तं वृष्यं रुधिरगुल्मजित् ।
वातघ्नं दीपनं स्तन्यं पित्तकृत् रुचिदायकम् ॥" (ध.नि.)
["Śatāhvā kaṭukā tiktā snigdhōṣṇā śḷēṣmavātajit
Jvaranētṛavṛaṇān hanti vastikaṛmaṇi śasyatē
Śatapuṣpādaḷaṃ cōktaṃ vṛṣyaṃ rudhiragulmajit
Vātaghnaṃ dīpanaṃ stanyaṃ pittakṛt rucidāyakaṃ" (Dha.ni.)]

"शतपुष्पा कटुस्तिक्ता तीक्ष्णोष्णा दीपनी लघुः ।

पित्तळा कफवातघ्नी मेध्या स्निग्धा ज्वरापहा ॥
निहन्ति शूलदाहाक्षिरोगतृष्णावमिव्रणान् ।" (कै.नि.)
[`Śatapuṣpā kaṭustiktā tīkṣṇōṣṇā dīpanī laghuḥ
Pittaḷā kaphavātaghnī mēdhyā snigdhā jvarāpahā
Nihanti śūladāhākṣirōgatṛṣṇāvamivraṇān'' (Kai.ni.)]

"शताह्वा पित्तळा लघ्वी तिक्ता कट्वग्निदीपनी ।
उष्णा मेध्या वस्तिकर्मप्रशस्ता कफनाशिनी ॥
वातं ज्वरं च शूलं च योनिशूलं च नाशयेत् ।
आध्मानं चक्षुरोगं च व्रणं चैव विनाशयेत् ॥" (नि.र.)
[`Śatāhvā pittaḷā laghvī tiktā kaṭvagnidīpanī
Uṣṇā mēdhyā vastikarmapraśastā kaphanāśinī
Vātaṃ jvaraṃ ca śūlaṃ ca yōniśūlaṃ ca nāśayēt
Ādhmānaṃ cakṣurōgaṃ ca vraṇaṃ caiva vināśayēt'' (Ni.ra.)]

"शताह्वा तु कटुस्तिक्ता स्निग्धा श्ळेष्मातिसारनुत् ।
ज्वरनेत्रव्रणघ्नी च वस्तिकर्मणि शस्यते ॥" (रा.नि.)
[`Śatāhvā tu kaṭustiktā snigdhā śḷēṣmātisāranut
Jvaranētravraṇaghnī ca vastikarmaṇi śasyatē'' (Rā.ni.)]

"शतपुष्पा लघुस्तीक्ष्णा पित्तकृद्दीपनी कटुः ।
उष्णा ज्वरानिलश्ळेष्मव्रणशूलाक्षिरोगजित् ॥" (म.पा.नि.)
[`Śatapuṣpā laghustīkṣṇā pittakṛddīpanī kaṭuḥ
Uṣṇā jvarānilaśḷēṣmavraṇaśūlakṣirōgajit'' (Ma.pā.ni.)]

"शताह्वा कफवातार्श आमातीसारशूलनुत् ।
तीक्ष्णोष्णा कटुका पाके रुच्या पित्ताग्निवर्द्धनी ॥" (सो.नि.)
[`Śatāhvā kaphavātārśa āmātīsāraśūlanut
Tīkṣṇōṣṇā kaṭukā pākē rucyā pittāgnivarddhanī'' (Sō.ni.)]

എരിച്ചുകച്ചിരിപ്പോന്നു ചതകുപ്പയുടെ രസം
സ്നിഗ്ദ്ധമായുഷ്ണമായുള്ളു കഫപിത്തവിനാശനം
തീപ്പുണ്ണിനേറ്റവും നന്നു വസ്തിഗുന്മത്തിനുത്തമം (ഗു.പാ.)
[`Ericcukaccirippōnnu catakuppayuṭe rasaṃ
Snigddhamāyuṣṇamāyuḷḷu kaphapittavināśanaṃ
Tīppuṇṇinēṟṟavuṃ nannu vastigulmattinuttamaṃ'' (Gu.pā.)]

Coll. No. AVS 1481

Anisomeles malabarica **(Linn.) R.Br.**

Lamiaceae (तुळसी–कुलम्)

Eng	:	Malabar catmint
Hin	:	Cōdhārā (चोधारा)
Kan	:	Karitumbi (ಕರಿತುಂಬಿ)
Mal	:	Karintumpa (കരിന്തുമ്പ)
San	:	Vaikuṇṭhaḥ, Mahādrōṇaḥ (वैकुण्ठः, महाद्रोणः)
Tam	:	Pēyimaruṭṭi, Pēyāmeraṭṭi (பேய்மருட்டி, பேயாமெரட்டி)
Tel	:	Mogabīrāku (మొగబీరాకు)

Distribution : Throughout south India (Deccan plateau)

The plant : An erect shrub about 1.8 m in height with obtusely tetragonous and softly white-tomentose stems and branches; leaves simple, opposite, very thick, aromatic, oblong-lanceolate, acute, pale above, white below, crenate-serrate, softly woolly; flowers purple, in dense whorls of more or less interrupted spikes; fruits nutlets, ellipsoid, compressed, the inner face slightly angular, the dorsal rounded, smooth, brown.

Parts used : whole plant

Properties and uses : The plant is acrid, bitter, aromatic, intellect promoting, stomachic, anthelmintic, febrifuge and sudorific. It is useful in halitosis, epilepsy, hysteria, amentia, anorexia, dyspepsia, colic, flatulence, intestinal worms, fever arising from teething in children, intermittent fevers, vitiated conditions of *vāta* and *kapha,* gout, swellings and diarrhoea.

"तृतीयस्तु महाद्रोणः स्तम्भो देवकृतस्तथा ।
वैकुण्ठो वनजन्मा च व्रणकीटरिपुः स्मृतः ॥" (अ.म.)
[`Tṛtīyastu mahādrōṇaḥ stambho devakṛtastathā
Vaikuṇṭhō vanajanma cā vṛaṇakīṭaripuḥ smṛtaḥ" (A.ma.)]

"अन्या चैव महाद्रोणा कुरुम्बा देवपूर्वका ।
दिव्यपुष्पी महाद्रोणी देवीकाण्डा षडाह्वया ॥" (रा.नि.)
[`Anyā caiva mahādrōṇā kurumbā dēvapūrvakā

Anisomeles malabarica

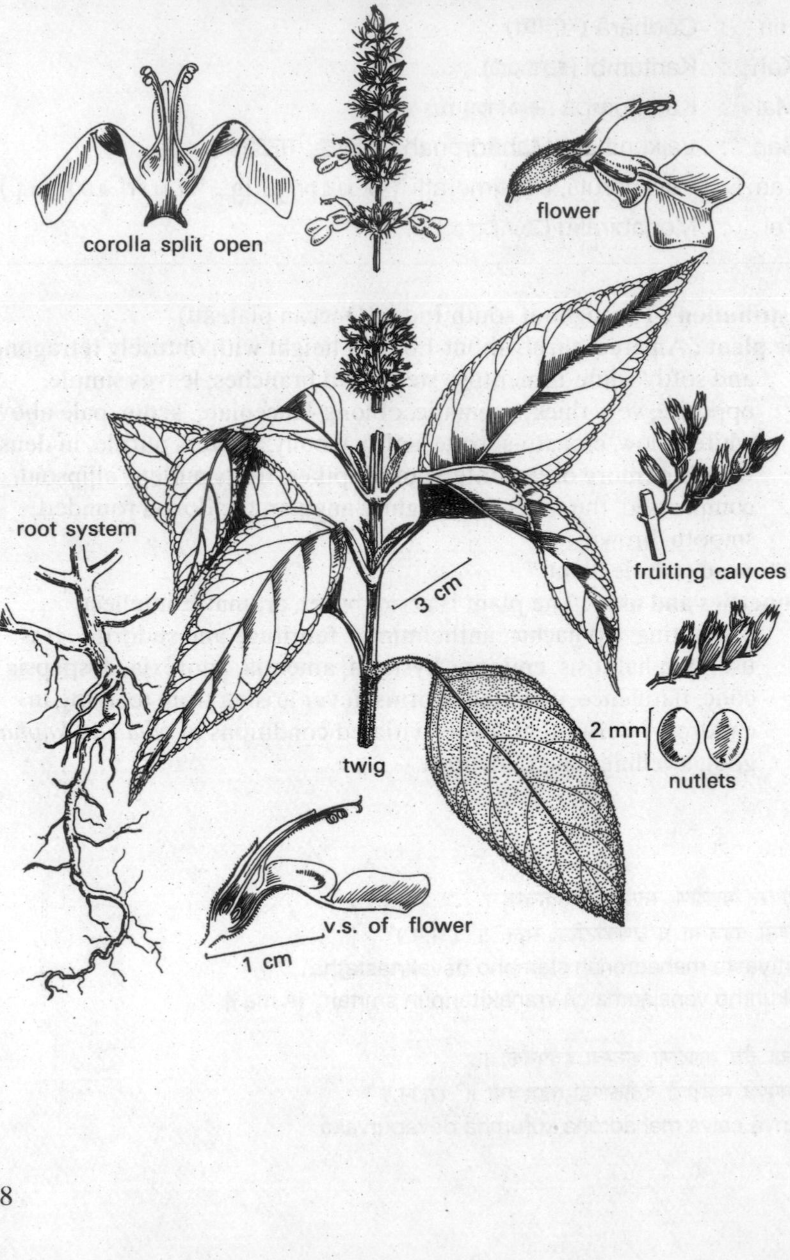

Divyapuṣpī mahādrōṇī dēvīkāṇḍā ṣaḍāhvayā'' (Rā.ni.)]

"देवद्रोणी कटुस्तिक्ता मेध्या वातार्त्तिभूतनुत् ।
कफमान्द्यापहा चैव युक्त्या पारदशोधने ॥" (रा.नि.)
[`Dēvadrōṇī kaṭustiktā mēdhyā vātārttibhūtanut
Kaphamāndyāpahā caiva yuktyā pāradaśōdhanē'' (Rā.ni.)]

"कुतुम्बरं तत्सदृशं सूतिकाशूलजित्परम् ।" (हृ.प्रि.)
[`Kutumbaraṃ tatsadṛśaṃ sūtikāśūlajitparaṃ'' (Hṛ.pri.)]

"കരിന്തുമ്പയുമീവണ്ണം വിശേഷാത് രുചികൃത്പരം." (ഗു.പാ.)
[`Karintumpayumīvaṇṇaṃ viśēṣāt rucikṛtparaṃ'' (Gu.pā.)]

Coll. No. AVS 1687

Annona squamosa **Linn.**

Annonaceae (काष्ठदारु–कुलम्)

Eng	:	Custard apple, Sugar apple
Hin	:	Sītāphal (सीताफल)
Kan	:	Sītāphala (ಸಿತಾಫಲ)
Mal	:	Sītappaḷaṃ, Attaccakka (സീതാപ്പഴം, ആത്തച്ചക്ക)
San	:	Sītāphalaṃ (सीताफलं)
Tam	:	Sītāppaḻaṃ (சீத்தாப்பழம்)
Tel	:	Sītāapanḍu (సీతాపండు)

Distribution : Throughout India, cultivated

The plant : A small tree about 6.0 m in height; leaves simple, alternate, bifarious, oblong-lanceolate or elliptic obtuse, glabrous above, lateral nerves 8–11 pairs ascending; flowers yellowish green, solitary, leaf-opposed or 2–4 on short extra axillary branchlets, sepals and petals three each; fruits yellowish green, globose with well marked areoles easily breaking into large pieces; seeds hard, brownish black, smooth.

Parts used : roots, leaves, fruits, seeds

Properties and uses : The roots are powerful purgative, and are useful in mental depression and spinal disorders. The leaves are suppurative and insecticidal, and are useful in destroying lice, proctoptosis in children and as a poultice to produce suppuration. The fruits are sweet, haematinic, cooling, sedative, stimulant, expectorant, maturant and tonic. They are useful in anaemia, burning sensation, vitiated conditions of *pitta,* vomiting, cough, malignant tumours, and for strengthening muscles. The seeds are abortifacient and insecticidal and are useful in destroying lice in the hair.

"सीताफलं गण्डगात्रं वैदेहीवल्लभं तथा ।
कृष्णबीजं चाग्रिमाख्यमातृप्यं बहुबीजकम् ॥" (शा.नि.)
[`Sītāphalaṃ gaṇḍagātraṃ vaidēhīvallabhaṃ tathā
Kṛṣṇabījaṃ cāgrimākhyamātṛpyaṃ bahubījakaṃ'' (Śā.ni.)]

Annona squamosa

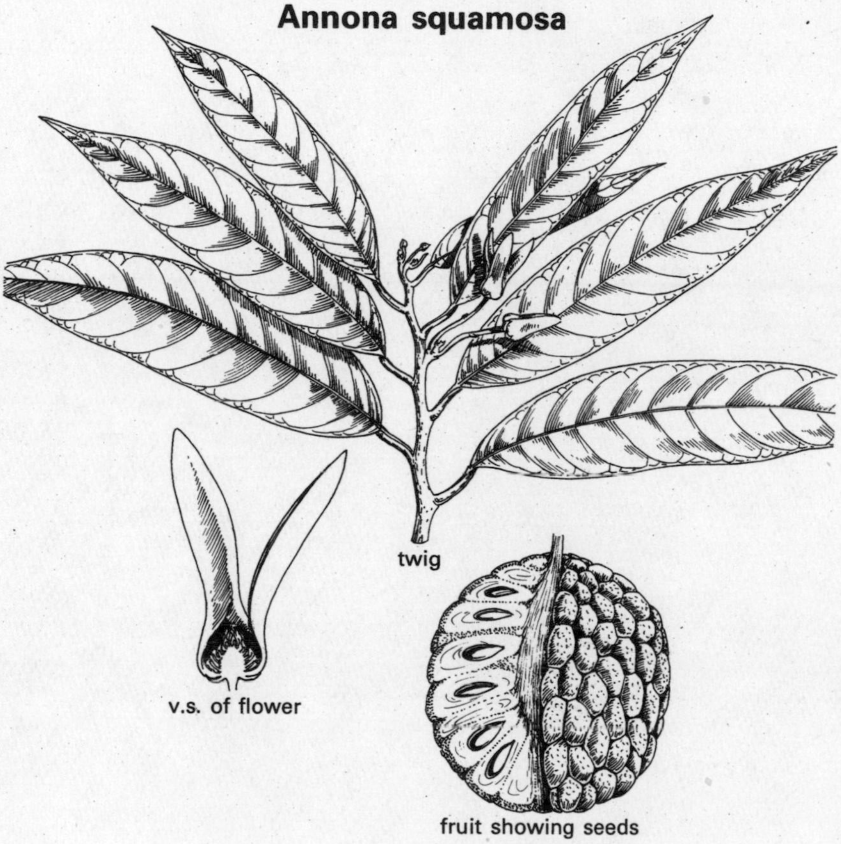

"तर्पणं रक्तकृत् स्वादु शीतळं हृद्यमेव च ।
बलदं मांसकृत् दाहरक्तपित्तमरुत्प्रणुत् ॥" (शा.नि.)
[Taṛpaṇaṃ raktakṛt svādu śītaḷaṃ hṛdyamēva ca
Baladaṃ māṃsakṛt dāharaktapittamarutpṛaṇut'' (Śā.ni.)]

"सीताफलं तु मधुरं शीतं हृद्यं बलप्रदम् ।
वातळं कफकृत् स्वादु पुष्टिकृत् पित्तनाशनम् ॥" (नि.र.)
[`Sītāphalaṃ tu madhuraṃ śītaṃ hṛdyaṃ balapṛadaṃ
Vātaḷaṃ kaphakṛt svādu puṣṭikṛt pittanāśanaṃ'' (Ni.ra.)]

Coll. No. B.S.I. (S.V.) 10886

Anogeissus latifolia (Roxb. ex DC.) Wall. ex Guill & Perr.

Combretaceae (हरीतकी–कुलम्)

Eng	:	Axle wood
Hin	:	Dhavā, Dhaurā, Bākalī (धवा, धौरा, बाकली)
Kan	:	Dinduge (ದಿಂದುಗೆ)
Mal	:	Veḷḷanava, Maḻukkāññiraṃ (വെള്ളനവ, മഴുക്കാഞ്ഞിരം)
San	:	Dhavaḥ (धवः)
Tam	:	Veḷḷanagai, Veḷḷanamai (வெள்ளநகை, வெள்ளநமை)
Tel	:	Cerimānu, Sirikarra (చెరిమాను, సిరికఱ్ఱ)

Distribution : Throughout India,in deciduous forests

The plant : A large deciduous tree upto 30 m in height with a clear bole of 15 m and with greenish or greyish white smooth bark exfoliating in irregular thin scales; leaves elliptic or suborbicular, obtuse at the apex, rounded or sometimes cordate at base, glabrous when fully grown, midrib prominent, pink, main nerves 6–10 pairs arching, prominent on the lower side, leaves turning red before falling; flowers sessile in small dense heads; fruits small, many in a globular head, yellowishbrown, winged, beaked with the persistent calyx enclosing a single seed.

Parts used : roots, bark, leaves, fruits

Properties and uses : The roots are astringent, acrid, thermogenic and stomachic. They are useful in vitiated conditions of *kapha* and *vāta,* and abdominal disorders. The bark is astringent, acrid, cooling, vulnerary, anti-inflammatory, urinary astringent, haemostatic, constipating, depurative and rejuvenating. It is useful in vitiated conditions of *kapha* and *vāta,* wounds and ulcers, inflammations, diabetes, haemorrhages, haemoptysis, diarrhoea, dysentery, haemorrhoids, skin diseases, leprosy, hepatopathy, erysipelas, ophthalmia and general debility. The leaf juice is good for otopyorrhea. The fruits are acrid, astringent, sweet, cooling and constipating. They are useful in vitiated conditions of *kapha* and *pitta,* diarrhoea and dysentery.

"धव इति शकटाक्षः स्यात् कषायमधुरच्छदो गौरः ।

Anogeissus latifolia

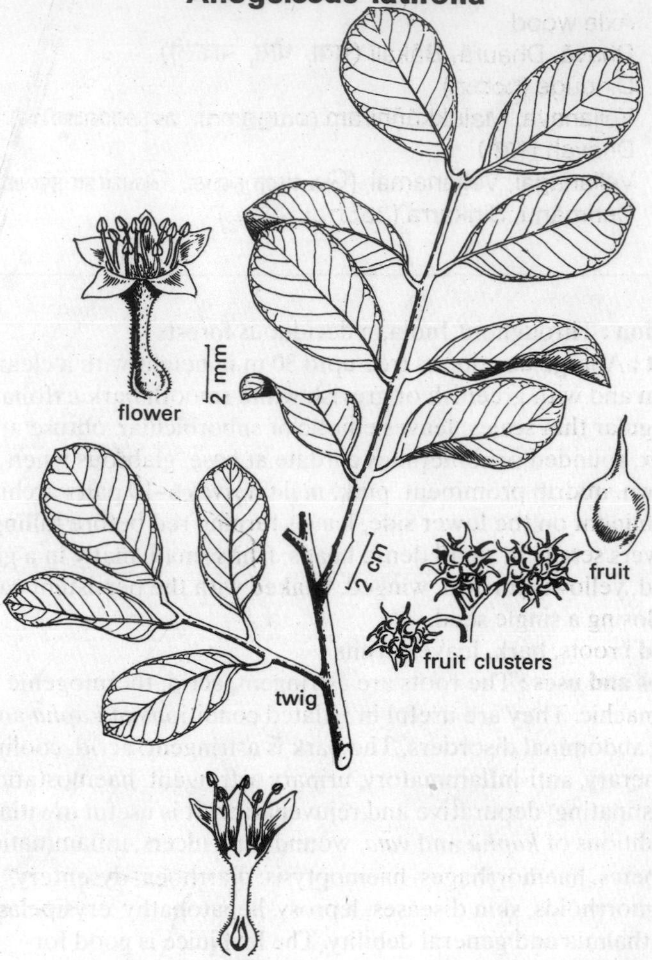

श्वेतफलः सितवृक्षः पर्यायैः पाण्डुरश्चेति ॥" (अ.म.)
["Dhava iti śakaṭākṣaḥ syāt kaṣāyamadhuracchadō gauraḥ
Śvētaphalaḥ sitavṛkṣaḥ paryāyaiḥ pāṇḍuraścēti" (A.ma.)]

"धवो धटो नन्दतरुः स्थिरो गौरो धुरन्धर : ।" (भा.प्र.)
["Dhavō dhaṭō nandataruḥ sthirō gaurō dhurandharaḥ" (Bhā.pṛa.)]

"धवो दृढतरुर्गौरः कषायो मधुरत्वचः ।
शुक्ळवृक्षः पाण्डुतरुर्धवळः पाण्डुरो नव ।" (रा.नि.)
["Dhavō dṛḍhatarurgauraḥ kaṣāyō madhuratvacaḥ
Śukḷavṛkṣaḥ pāṇḍutarurdhavaḷaḥ pāṇḍurō nava" (Rā.ni.)]

"धवः शीतः प्रमेहार्शःपाण्डुपित्तकफापहः ।
मधुरस्तुवरस्तस्य फलं च मधुरं मनाक् ॥" (भा.प्र.)
["Dhavaḥ śītaḥ pṛamēhāṛśaḥpāṇḍupittakaphāpahaḥ
Madhurastuvarastasya phalaṃ ca madhuraṃ manāk" (Bhā.pṛa.)]

"धवस्तु तुवरः शीतो मधुरः कटुको मतः ।
दीपनो रुचिकृत् चैव पाण्डुरोगप्रमेहजित् ॥
कफपित्तर्शवातानां नाशकः परिकीर्त्तितः ॥
फलं चास्य हिमं स्वादु रूक्षं च तुवरं मतम् ॥
मलस्तम्भकरं चैव वातळं कफपित्तजित् ।
मूलं कटुकषायं च पित्तकृद्दीपनं परम् ॥" (नि.र.)
["Dhavastu tuvaraḥ śītō madhuraḥ kaṭukō mataḥ
Dīpanō rucikṛt caiva pāṇḍurōgapṛamēhajit
Kaphapittāṛśavātānāṃ nāśakaḥ parikīṛttitaḥ
Phalaṃ cāsya himaṃ svādu rūkṣaṃ ca tuvaraṃ mataṃ
Malastambhakaraṃ caiva vātaḷaṃ kaphapittajit
Mūlaṃ kaṭukaṣāyaṃ ca pittakṛddīpanaṃ paraṃ" (Ni.ra.)]

"सुरासवोपयोगी च कषायमधुरो हिमः ।
पाण्डुमेहप्रशमनः कफपित्तहरो धवः ॥" (म.नि.)
["Surāsavōpayōgī ca kaṣāyamadhurō himaḥ
Pāṇḍumēhapṛaśamanaḥ kaphapittaharō dhavaḥ" (Ma.ni.)]

"धवः कषायः कटुकः कफघ्नोऽनिलनाशनः ।
पित्तप्रकोपणो रुच्यो विज्ञेयो दीपनः परः ॥" (रा.नि.)
["Dhavaḥ kaṣāyaḥ kaṭukaḥ kaphaghnōऽnilanāśanaḥ
Pittapṛakōpaṇō rucyō vijñēyō dīpanaḥ paraḥ" (Rā.ni.)]

"धवस्तु तुवरः शीतो मधुरो मेहपाण्डुहा ।
कफपित्तहरं, तस्य फलं स्वादु कषायकम् ॥
हिमं रूक्षं गुरु स्तम्भी वातळं कफपित्तजित् " (कै. नि.)
["Ḍhavastu tuvaraḥ śītō madhurō mēhapāṇḍuhā
Kaphapittaharaṃ, tasya phalaṃ svādu kaṣāyakaṃ
Himaṃ rūkṣaṃ guru stambhī vātaḷaṃ kaphapittajit" (Kai.ni.)]

Aphanamixis polystachya (Wall.) Parker

(Amoora rohituka *(Roxb.) Wight & Arn.*)

Meliaceae (निम्ब–कुलम्)

Eng	:	Rohituka tree
Hin	:	Harin-hārā हरिन–हारा
Kan	:	Mullumuntala (ಮುಲ್ಲುಮುಂತಲ)
Mal	:	Cemmaraṃ (ചെമ്മരം)
San	:	Rōhītakaḥ (रोहीतकः)
Tam	:	Malampuḷuvan, Semmaraṃ (மலம் புழுவன், செம்மரம்)
Tel	:	Sēvamānu (సేవమాను)

Distribution : Throughout India,in evergreen forests

The plant : A medium to large sized tree, 18–25 m in height with a cylindrical bole and a heavy crown, bark greyish brown to dark brown, rough, exfoliating in circular flakes, wood reddish brown, leaves large, imparipinnate, leaflets opposite, 9–17 in number, elliptic-oblong or oblong-lanceolate, acuminate, glabrous on both surfaces; male flowers numerous in axillary panicles, female or bisexual flowers larger than male in axillary or supra-axillary solitary spikes; fruits globular, smooth, yellow when ripe, opening by 3-valved; seeds with scarlet aril.

Parts used : bark, seeds

Properties and uses: The bark is acrid, astringent, bitter, vulnerary, digestive, anthelmintic, depurative, urinary astringent, ophthalmic and refrigerant. It is useful in splenomegaly, liver disorders, tumour, ulcer, dyspepsia, intestinal worms, skin diseases, leprosy, diabetes, ophthalmopathy, jaundice, haemorrhoids, burning sensation, rheumatoid arthritis and leucorrhoea. The seeds are acrid, refrigerant, laxative, anodyne and anthelmintic. They are useful in ulcers, ophthalmopathy, otopathy, myalgia, skin diseases, intestinal worms, burning sensation and vitiated conditions of *vāta.*

"रोहीतको रोहितको रोही दाडिमपुष्पकः"
["Rōhītakō rōhitakō rōhī dāḍimapuṣpakaḥ" (Bhā.pra.)]

"रोहीतको रोहितकश्चय रोहितः
कुशाल्मलिर्दाडिमपुष्पसंज्ञकः

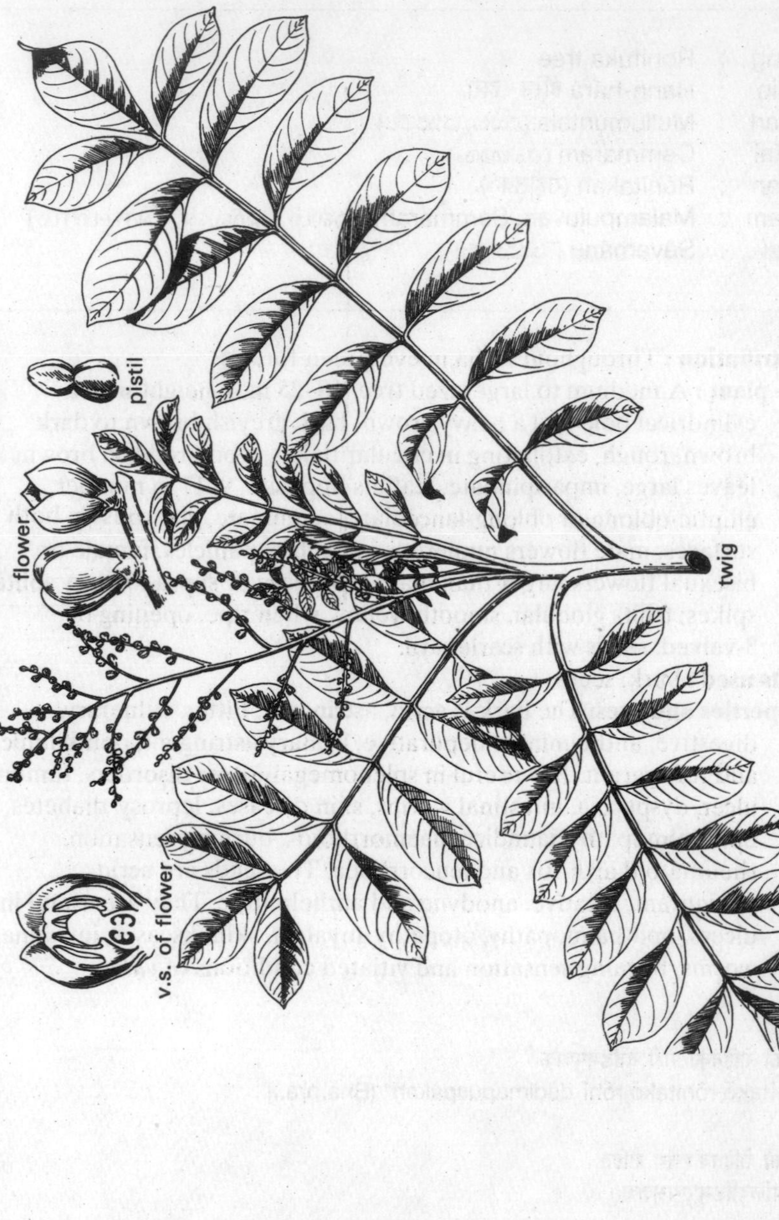

Aphanamixis Polystachya

सदाप्रसूनः स च कूटशाल्मलि-
र्विरोचनः शाल्मलिको नवाह्वयः ॥
सप्ताह्वः श्वेतरोहितः सितपुष्पः सिताह्वयः
शिताङ्गः शुक्ळरोहितो लक्ष्मीवान् जनवल्लभः ॥" (रा.नि.)
["Rōhītakō rōhitakaśca rōhitaḥ
kuśālmaliṛdāḍimapuṣpasaṃjñakaḥ
Sadāpṛasūnaḥ sa ca kūṭaśālmaliṛ-
virōcanaḥ śālmalikō navāhvayaḥ
Saptāhvaḥ śvētarōhitaḥ sitapuṣpaḥ sitāhvayaḥ
Sitāngaḥ śukḷarōhitō lakṣmīvān janavallabhaḥ" (Rā.ni.)]

"रोहीतके रोहितको रोही दाडिमपुष्पकः ।
कुशाल्मलिः शाल्मलिको रोचनः कूटशाल्मलिः ॥
रक्तपुष्पः सदापुष्पो रक्तघ्नः प्ळीहनाशनः ।
द्वितीयः श्वेतपुष्पश्च रोही रोहितकस्तथा ॥
क्षारयोग्यो युगो योज्यो लक्ष्मी सर्वजनप्रियः ।" (सो.नि.)
["Rōhītakē rōhitakō rōhī dāḍimapuṣpakaḥ
Kuśālmaliḥ śālmalikō rōcanaḥ kūṭaśālmaliḥ
Raktapuṣpaḥ sadāpuṣpō raktaghnaḥ pḷīhanāśanaḥ
Dvitīyaḥ śvētapuṣpaśca rōhī rōhītakastathā
Kṣārayōgyō yugō yōjyō lakṣmī saṛvajanapṛiyaḥ" (Sō.ni.)]

"रोहीतकः प्ळीहघाती रुच्यो रक्तप्रसादनः । (भा.प्र.)
["Rōhītakaḥ pḷīhaghāti rucyō raktapṛasādanaḥ" (Bhā.pṛa.)]

"रोहीतको यकृत्प्ळीहगुल्मोदरहरः सरः ॥
श्वेतो रोहीतकश्चान्यः कटूष्णमुभयं स्मृतम् ॥
कर्णरोगहरं चैव विषवेगविनाशनम् ।" (ध.नि.)
["Rōhītakō yakṛtpḷīhagulmōdaraharaḥ saraḥ
Śvētō rōhītakaścanyaḥ kaṭūṣṇamubhayaṃ smṛtaṃ
Kaṛṇarōgaharaṃ caiva viṣavēgavināśanaṃ" (Dha.ni.)]

रोहीतकः कटुस्तिक्तः सरोष्णः कफवातनुत् ।
प्ळीहोदरयकृद्गुल्ममांसमेदोविषापहः ॥
भूतानाहविबन्धास्रकफशूलरुजापहः ॥
(प्ळीहानां नाशयेद्रोही स्तन्यो रक्तप्रसादनः ॥
कर्णकाख्यामयं हन्यात् सर्वव्रणनिषूदनः ।)" (कै.नि.)
["Rōhītakaḥ kaṭustiktaḥ sarōṣṇaḥ kaphavātanut
Pḷīhōdarayakṛdgulmamāmsamēdōviṣāpahaḥ
Bhūtānāhavibandhāsṛakaphaśūlarujāpahaḥ
(Pḷīhānāṃ nāśayēdrōhī stanyō raktapṛasādanaḥ
Kaṛṇakākhyāmayaṃ hanyāt saṛvavṛaṇaniṣūdanaḥ") (Kai.ni.)]

"रोहीतकद्वयं स्निग्धं तुवरं कटुकं मतम् ।
रक्तप्रसादनं तिक्तं शीतळं च सरं मतम् ॥
कृमिप्ळीहरक्तदोषव्रणकर्णरुजापहम् ।
विषं नेत्ररुजं गुल्मयकृत्कफविनाशनम् ॥
वातं विबन्धं मांसं च मेदं शूलं च नाशयेत् ।
आनाहं भूतबाधा च नाशयेदिति कीर्त्तितम् ॥" (नि.र.)
["Rōhītakadvayaṃ snigdhaṃ tuvaraṃ kaṭukaṃ mataṃ
Raktaprasādanaṃ tiktaṃ śītaḷaṃ ca saraṃ mataṃ
Kṛmipḷīharaktadōṣavraṇakarṇarujāpahaṃ
Viṣaṃ nētrarujaṃ gulmayakṛtkaphavināśanaṃ
Vātaṃ vibandhaṃ māṃsaṃ ca mēdaṃ śūlaṃ ca nāśayēt
Anāhaṃ bhūtabādhā ca nāśayēditi kīrttitaṃ" (Ni.ra.)]

"रोहीतकौ कटुस्निग्धौ कषायौ च सुशीतळौ ।
कृमिदोषव्रणप्ळीहरक्तनेत्रामयापहौ ॥ " (रा.नि.)
["Rōhītakau kaṭusnigdhau kaṣāyau ca suśītaḷau
Kṛmidōṣavraṇapḷīharaktanētrāmayāpahau" (Rā.ni.)]

"रोहीतकः सरो गुल्मयकृत्प्ळीहोदरापहः ।"(म.वि.)
["Rōhītakaḥ sarō gulmayakṛtpḷīhōdarāpahaḥ" (Ma.vi.)]

"रोहीतको यकृत्प्ळीहगुल्मोदरहरः परम् । " (सो.नि.)
["Rōhītakō yakṛtpḷīhagulmōdaraharaḥ paraṃ" (Sō.ni.)]

Remarks : In Kerala, *rōhītakaṃ* is identified as *Aphanamixis polystachya.* Dr. Koman (1919), however, is of the opinion that the bark of this plant does not have the effect on the spleen to the extent reported. Hence, further research is needed to confirm this identity.

In north India it is the bark of *Tecoma undulata* which is used for *rōhītaka.* 'The Ayurvedic Formulary of India' says that *Aphanamixis polystachya* can be used as a substitute for this.

`Rājanighaṇṭu', `Dhanvantarinighaṇṭu', and `Nighaṇṭuratnākaraṃ' describe two kinds of *rōhītakaṃ.* Some identify these two as two different drugs under the botanical names *Tecoma undulata* and *Aphanamixis polystachya (Amoora rohituka).*

Aquilaria agallocha Roxb.

Thymeleaceae (अगुरु–कुलम्)

Eng	:	Aloe wood, Eagle wood
Hin	:	Agar (अगर)
Kan	:	Kṛiṣṇāgāru (ಕೃಷ್ಣಾಗರು)
Mal	:	Akil, Kārakil (അകിൽ, കാരകിൽ)
San	:	Aguruḥ, Kṛṣṇāguruḥ (अगुरुः कृष्ण?गुरुः)
Tam	:	Agaṛ, Agalicandanām, Krsnaguru (அகர், அகலிசந்தனம், கிருஷ்ணாகுரு)
Tel	:	Kṛṣṇāgaru (కృష్ణాగరు)

Distribution : In the forests of Bhutan, Bengal, Assam and Myanmar

The Plant : A large evergreen tree about 21 m in height and 1.5–2.4 m in girth with somewhat straight and fluted stem; leaves linear-lanceolate to ovate-oblong, 5–9 cm long, silky glossy and faintly parallel nerved; flowers small, greenish on very slender pilose petioles in shortly peduncled umbels, on younger branchlets, perianth about 5 mm long, slightly hairy outside, stamens alternate the perianth, filaments red at the apex, ovary tawny-tomentose; fruits slightly compressed, yellowish tomentose capsules.

Commercially used fragrant-resinous agar wood is formed in the interior of the old tree. The tree contains plenty of oleoresin and has irregular dark patches. The wood burns with a bright flame giving off a pleasnt smell.

Parts used : Fragrant resinous wood and oil

Properties and uses : The wood is acrid, bitter, thermogenic, digestive, carminative, deodorant, sudorific, anodyne, anti-inflammatory, anti-leprotic, depurative, cardiotonic, rejuvenating and tonic. It is useful in vitiated conditions of *vāta* and *kapha,* halitosis, dyspepsia, anorexia, caridac debility, skin disease, leprosy, foul ulcers, hypothermia, inflmmations, rheumatoid arthritis, cough, asthma, hiccough, albuminuria and general debility. An external application of *agaru* is very useful in vomiting in children, pectoralgia due to pneumonia and cephalalgia.

The oil is astringent, acrid, bitter, thermogenic, depurative, alexeteric and antileprotic. It is useful in vitiated conditions of *vāta* and *kapha,* rheumatoid arthritis, cough, asthma, bronchitis, leprosy, skin diseases and foul ulcers.

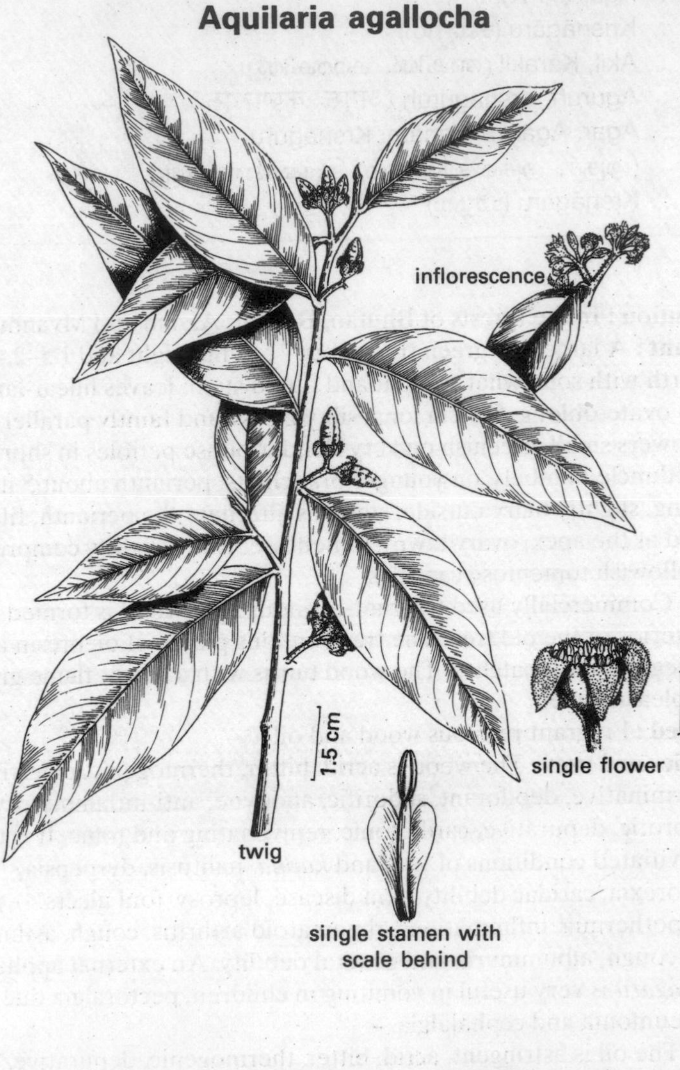
Aquilaria agallocha
inflorescence
single flower
3 mm
1.5 cm
twig
single stamen with
scale behind

"जोङ्गकमगुरु वराङ्गं चानार्यं शीतशिवकं भवति ।
कृष्णागुरु लोहं स्यात् कृमिजग्धं चागुरु प्रवरम् ॥"(अ.म.)
["Jōngakamaguru varāngaṃ cānāryaṃ śītaśivakaṃ bhavati
Kṛṣṇāguru lōhaṃ syāt kṛmijagdhaṃ cāguru pṛavaraṃ" (A.ma.)]

"अगुरु प्रवरं लोहं राजार्हं योगजं तथा ।
वांशिकं कृमिजं चापि कृमिजग्धमनार्यकम् ॥" (भा.प्र)
["Aguru pṛavaraṃ lōhaṃ rājāṛhaṃ yōgajaṃ tathā
Vāṁśikaṃ kṛmijaṃ cāpi kṛmijagdhamanāryakaṃ" (Bhā.pṛa.)]

"कृष्णागुरु स्यादगुरु शृङ्गारं विश्वरूपकम् ।
शीर्षं कालागुरु केश्यं वसुकं कृष्णकाष्ठकम् ॥
धूपार्हं वल्लरं गन्धराजकं द्वादशाह्वयम् ।" (रा.नि.)
["Kṛṣṇāguru syādaguru śṛngāraṃ viśvarūpakaṃ
Śīṛṣaṃ kālāguru kēśyaṃ vasukaṃ kṛṣṇakāṣṭhakaṃ
Dhūpāṛhaṃ vallaraṃ gandharājakaṃ dvādaśāhvayaṃ" (Rā.ni.)]

"कृष्णागुरुः श्रेष्ठवृक्षो जोङ्गकं विश्वरूपकम् ।
अगरु प्रवरं लौहं कृमिजग्धमनार्यकम् ॥
राजार्हं तच्च मलिनं कालेयं शीर्षकं लघु ।" (कै.नि.)
["Kṛṣṇāguruḥ śṛēṣṭhavṛkṣō jōngakaṃ viśvarūpakaṃ
Aguru pṛavaraṃ lauhaṃ kṛmijagdhamanāryakaṃ
Rājāṛhaṃ tacca malinaṃ kālēyaṃ śīṛṣakaṃ laghu" (Kai.ni.)]

"उष्णवीर्योऽनिलहरः सुगन्धो धूपयोगिकः ।
लेपनोद्वर्तने युक्तो धूमपाने तथाऽगुरुः ॥" (म. नि.)
["Uṣṇāvīryō'nilaharaḥ sugandhō dhūpayōgikaḥ
Lēpanōdvartanē yuktō dhūmapānē tathā'guruḥ" (Ma.ni.)]

"अगुरूष्णं कटु त्वच्यं तिक्तं तीक्ष्णं च पित्तळम् ।
लघु कर्णाक्षिरोगघ्नं शीतवातकफप्रणुत् ॥
कृष्णं गुणाधिकं तत्तु लोहवद्वारि मज्जति ।
अगुरूप्रभवः स्नेहः कृष्णागुरुसमः स्मृतः ॥ " (भा.प्र.)
["Agurūṣṇaṃ kaṭu tvacyaṃ tiktaṃ tīkṣṇaṃ ca pittaḷaṃ
Laghu kaṛṇākṣirōgaghnaṃ śītavātakaphapraṇut
Kṛṣṇaṃ guṇādhikaṃ tattu lōhavadvāri majjati
Agurūpṛabhavaḥ snēhaḥ kṛṣṇāgurusamaḥ smṛtaḥ" (Bhā.pra.)]

"कटुतिक्तोष्णमगुरु स्निग्धं वातकफापहम् ।
श्रुतिनेत्ररुजं हन्ति माङ्गल्यं कुष्ठनुत् परम् ॥"(ध.नि.)
["Kaṭutiktōṣṇamaguru snigdhaṃ vātakaphāpahaṃ
Śrutinētrarujaṃ hanti māngalyaṃ kuṣṭhanut paraṃ" (Dha.ni.)]

"कृष्णागुरु कटूष्णञ्च तिक्तं लेपे च शीतळम् ।
पाने पित्तहरं किञ्चित् त्रिदोषघ्नमुदाहृतम् ॥ " (रा.नि.)
["Kṛṣṇāguru kaṭūṣṇañca tiktaṃ lēpē ca śītaḷaṃ
Pānē pittaharaṃ kiñcit tridōṣaghnamudāhṛtaṃ" (Rā.ni)]

"कृष्णागुरुः कटुस्तिक्तस्तीक्ष्णोष्णः पित्तळो लघुः ।
कर्णाक्षिरोगत्वग्दोषशीतवातकफप्रणुत् ॥
कृष्णः प्रधानमगुरुः लोहवन्मज्जते जले ।
अगुरु प्रभवः स्नेहः कृष्णागुरुसमः स्मृतः ॥ (कै.नि.)
["Kṛṣṇāguruḥ kaṭustiktastīkṣṇōṣṇaḥ pittaḷō laghuḥ
Karṇākṣirōgatvagdōṣaśītavātakaphapraṇut
Kṛṣṇaḥ pradhānamaguruḥ lōhavanmajjatē jalē
Aguruprabhavaḥ snēhaḥ kṛṣṇāgurusamaḥ smṛtaḥ" (Kai.ni.)]

"अगुरुस्तु सुगन्धिः स्यादुष्णस्तिक्तः कटुः स्मृतः ।
स्निग्धो मङ्गळदो रुच्यो धूपयोग्यश्च पित्तळः ॥
तीक्ष्णो वातकफौ हन्ति कर्णनेत्ररुजापहः ।
कुष्ठनाशकरः प्रोक्तो लेपे चोद्वर्तने शुभः ॥" (नि.र.)
["Agurustu sugandhiḥ syāduṣṇastiktaḥ kaṭuḥ smṛtaḥ
Snigdhō maṅgaḷadō rucyō dhūpayōgyaśca pittaḷaḥ
Tīkṣṇō vātakaphau hanti karṇanētrarujāpahaḥ
Kuṣṭhanāśakaraḥ prōktō lēpē cōdvartanē śubhaḥ" (Ni.ra.)]

"अगुरुसारस्नेहस्तिक्तकटुकषायाः दुष्टव्रणशोधनाः कृमि–
कफकुष्ठानिलहराश्च। " (सु.सू.)
["Agurusārasnēhastiktakaṭukaṣāyāḥ duṣṭavraṇaśōdhanāḥ
kṛmikaphakuṣṭhānilaharāśca" (Su.Sū.)]

"അകിലുഷ്ണമെരിച്ചിട്ടും കച്ചിട്ടും രസമായ് വരും
സ്നിഗ്ദ്ധമായിട്ടിരിപ്പോന്നു കഫവാതവിനാശകൃത്.
പ്രധാനം കാരകിലതു മംഗല്യം കുഷ്ഠനാശനം
വാതപിത്തകഫശ്വാസകാസകർണ്ണാക്ഷിരോഗജിത്
ശ്രമക്ലമങ്ങളെന്നോരോന്നുണ്ടായാലാശു നാശയേത്." (ഗു.പാ.)
["Akiluṣṇamericciṭṭuṃ kacciṭṭuṃ rasamāyvaruṃ
Snigddhamāyiṭṭirippōnnu kaphavātavināśakṛt
Pradhānaṃ kārakilatu maṅgalyaṃ kuṣṭhanāśanaṃ
Vātapittakaphaśvāsakāsakarṇākṣirōgajit
Śramaklamaṅṅaḷennōrōnnuṇṭāyālāśu nāśayēt." (Gu.pā.)]

Remarks: 'Ayurvedic Materia Medicas' mention two kinds of *aguru* viz. *kṛṣṇāguru* and *svētāguru* (the black and white varieties, respectively). In several parts of south India the white variety (*Dysoxylum malabaricum* Bedd. ex Hiern) is in use. But it is the black variety, i.e. *Aquilaria agallocha* Roxb., that has to be used as *aguru,* as it possesses all the properties mentioned in the text.

Coll. No. AVS 2453

***Arachis hypogaea* Linn**

Fabaceae : (अपराजिता–कुलम्)

Eng	:	Groundnut, Peanut, Monkeynut
Hin	:	Mūṅg-phalī (मूँग–फली)
Kan	:	Nīlakaḍali (ನೀಲಕಡಲಿ)
Mal	:	Nilakkaṭala (നിലക്കടല)
San	:	Bhūcaṇakaḥ, Maṇḍapī (भूचणकः, मण्डपी)
Tam	:	Vēṛkkaṭalai (வேர்க்கடலை)
Tel	:	Vēruśenagalu (వేరుశనగలు)

Distribution : Throughout India, cultivated

The Plant : A branched hairy annual herb with erect branches trailing on the ground; leaves compound, pulvinate, 8–12 cm long, leaflets oblong to obovate, entire; flowers yellow, axillary, fascicled; fruits pods, ripening underground, leathery, containing 1–3 seeds; each seed with a thin brown seed-coat and two fleshy white cotyledons rich in oil and proteins.

Parts used : seeds, oil

Properties and uses : The seeds are sweet, oleagenous, aphrodisiac, galactagogue, constipating and tonic and are useful in agalactia, diarrhoea and general debility. The oil is sweet, purgative and emollient, and is used in nephropathy and dislocated joints.

"द्वित्रिबीजो भूचणकः स्नेहाढ्यो रक्तबीजकः ।
भूवाचि शब्दपूर्वोऽयं चणकः सितसूपकः ॥ (स्व.)
["Dvitṛibījō bhūcaṇakaḥ snēnāḍhayō raktabījakaḥ
Bhūvāci śabdapūrvōऽyaṃ caṇakaḥ sitasūpakaḥ]" (Sva.)]

"भूशिम्बिका रक्तबीजा त्रिबीजा स्नेहबीजका ।
मण्डपी भूमिजा भूस्था तथा भूचणका स्मृता ॥" (शा.नि.)
["Bhūśimikā raktabījā tṛibījā snēhabījakā
Maṇḍapī bhūmijā bhūsthā tathā bhūcaṇakā smṛtā" (Śā.ni.)]

"बलपुष्टिकरो ह्येष मधुरः परमं गुरुः ।
विष्टंभि दुर्ज्जरोऽत्यर्थं श्ळेष्मपित्तकरः परम् ॥

Plate 8

Arachis hypogaea

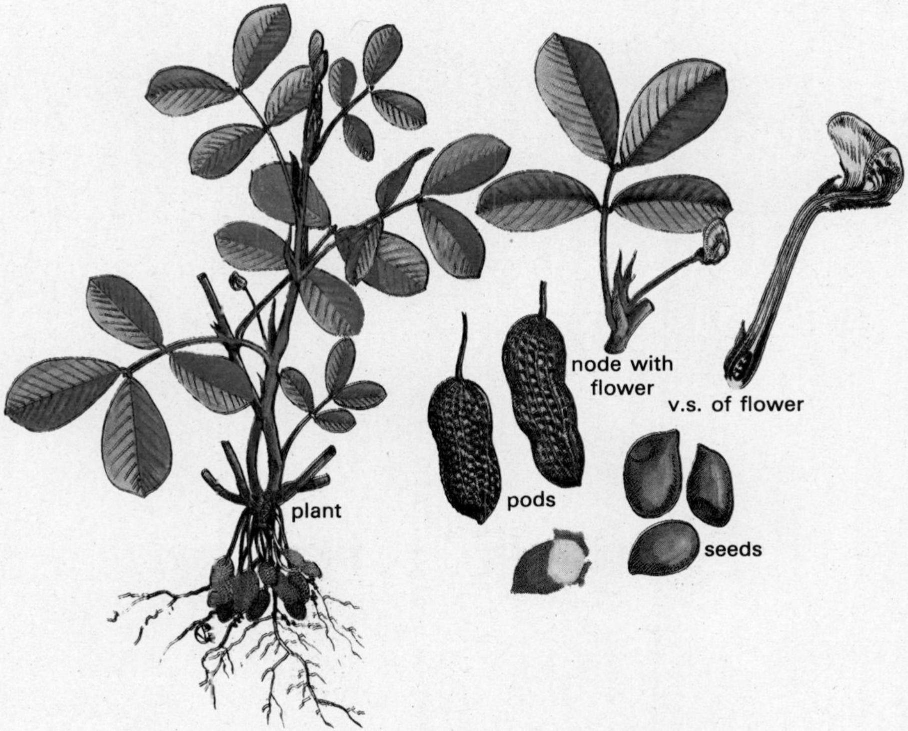

तत्तैलं मधुरं रुच्यं स्निग्धं रेचनकं स्मृतम् ।
दोषदूष्यादि संचिन्त्य यथार्हं तच्च योजयेत् ॥ (स्व.)
["Balapuṣṭikarō hyēṣa madhuraḥ paramaṃ guruḥ
Viṣṭambhi durjjarōꞋtyarthaṃ ślēṣmapittakaraḥ paraṃ
Tattailaṃ madhuraṃ rucyaṃ snigdhaṃ rēcanakaṃ smṛtaṃ
Dōṣadūṣyādi samcintya yathārhaṃ tacca yōjayēt" (Sva.)]

"मण्डपी मधुरा स्निग्धा वातळा कफकारिका ।
ग्राहिका बद्धवर्च्चश्च तत्तैलं तद्गुणं स्मृतम् ॥ " (शा.नि.)
["Maṇḍapī madhurā snigdhā vataḷā kaphakārikā
Grāhikā baddhavarccāśca tattailam tadguṇam smṛtaṃ" (Sā.ni.)]

Coll. No. AVS 2454

***Areca catechu* Linn.**

Arecaceae : (पूग–कुलम्)

Eng	:	Arecanut tree, Betelnut tree
Hin	:	Supārī (सुपारी)
Kan	:	Adike (ಅಡಿಕೆ)
Mal	:	Kavunnụ, Kamunnū, Kamukụ, Aṭaykkāmaraṃ (കവുങ്ങ്, കമുങ്ങ്, കമുക്, അടയ്ക്കാമരം)
San	:	Pūgaḥ (पूगः)
Tam	:	Pākkumaraṃ (பாக்குமரம்)
Tel	:	Vakka, Pōka (వక్క, పోక)

Distribution : Cultivated throughout India

The plant : A tall slender unbranched palm with a crown of leaves, stem annulate; leaves pinnate with a conspicuous sheath; flowers in spadix, male many at the upper portion, female much larger and few at the base; fruits 3.8 – 5 cm long, smooth, orange or scarlet when ripe.

Parts used: roots, leaves, fruits

Properties and uses : A decoction of the root is a reputed cure for sore lips. The juice of tender leaves is mixed with oil and is used as an embrocation in cases of lumbago. The nuts are used either raw or cured. They are cooling, astringent, diuretic, digestive, anthelmintic, aphrodisiac, nervine tonic and emmenagogue. They are useful in urinary disorders, anorexia and general debility. In veterinary medicine, they are employed as a vermifuge especially for tape worm. Chewing of nuts facilitates salivation and prevents decay of teeth; but its continued use blackens and loosens them. The constant use of this nut might result in oral carcinoma. The juice of tender nuts in small doses is a good laxative. The burnt nut is often used as dentifrice.

"पूगः स्रंसी चिक्को घोण्टाफलश्च गोपफलः ।
गोपः कैडर्यफलः कालत्वग्गुवाकफल उद्वेगी ॥
पूगी पूगफलाह्वः ताम्बूलफलश्च पट्टिकः प्रोक्तः ।" (अ.म.)
["Pūgaḥ sraṃsī cikkō ghōṇṭāphalaśca gōpaphalaḥ
Gōpaḥ kaiḍaryaphalaḥ kālatvagguvākaphala udvēgī
Pūgī pūgaphalāhvaḥ tāmbūlaphalaśca paṭṭikaḥ prōktaḥ" (A.ma.)]

Areca catechu

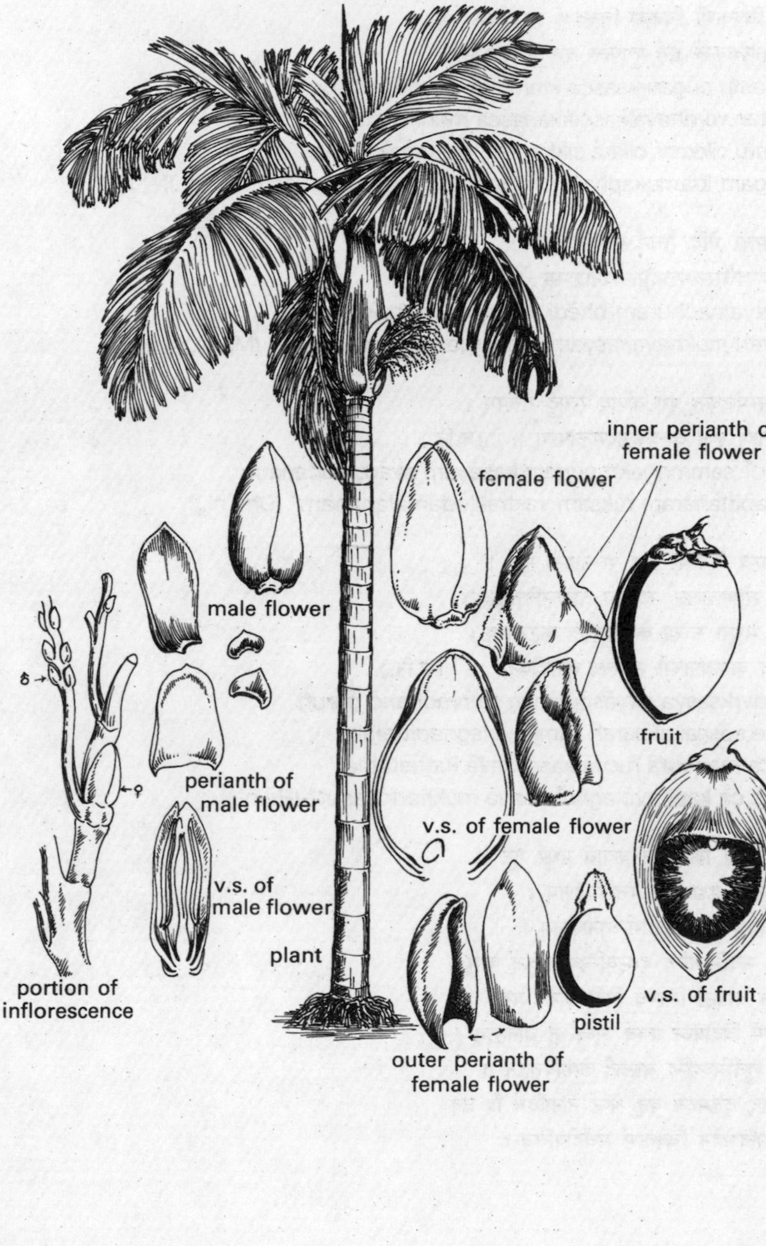
inner perianth of
female flower
female flower
male flower
perianth of
male flower
v.s. of
male flower
plant
portion of
inflorescence
fruit
v.s. of female flower
pistil
v.s. of fruit
outer perianth of
female flower

"घोण्टा पूगी च पूगश्च गुवाकः क्रमुकस्य च ।
फलं पूगीफलं प्रोक्तमुद्वेगं च तदीरितम् ॥ "(भा.प्र.)
["Ghōṇṭā pūgī ca pūgaśca guvākaḥ kṛamukasya ca
Phalaṃ pūgīphalaṃ prōktamudvēgaṃ ca tadīritaṃ" (Bhā.pṛa.)]

"पूगस्तु पूगवृक्षश्च क्रमुको दीर्घपादपः ।
वल्कतरुर्दृढवल्कश्चिक्कणश्च मुनिर्मतः ॥
पूगस्तु चिक्कणी चिक्का चिक्कणं श्ळक्ष्णकं तथा ।
उद्वेगं क्रमुकफलं ज्ञेयं पूगफलं वसु ॥" (रा.नि.)
["Pūgastu pūgavṛkṣaśca kṛamukō dīrghapādapaḥ
Valkataruṛdṛḍhavalkaścikkaṇaśca muniṛmataḥ
Pūgastu cikkaṇī cikkā cikkaṇaṃ śḷakṣṇakaṃ tathā
Udvēgaṃ kṛamukaphalaṃ jñēyaṃ pūgaphalaṃ vasu" (Rā.ni.)]

"कषायमधुरं भेदि रोचनं मोहकृद् गुरुः ।
पूगन्तु मुखवैरस्यमलदौर्गन्ध्यनाशनम् "(म.नि.)
["Kaṣāyamadhuraṃ bhēdi rōcanaṃ mōhakṛd guruḥ
Pūgantu mukhavairasyamaladauṛgandhyanāśanaṃ" (Ma.ni.)]

"भेदी सम्मोहकृत् पूगं कषायं स्वादु रोचनम् ।
कफपित्तहरं रूक्षं वक्त्रक्ळेदमलापहम् ॥ " (ध.नि.)
["Bhēdī sammōhakṛt pūgaṃ kaṣāyaṃ svādu rōcanaṃ
Kaphapittaharaṃ rūkṣaṃ vaktṛakḷēdamalāpahaṃ" (Dha.ni.)]

"पूगवृक्षस्य निर्यासो हिमः सम्मोहनो गुरुः ।
विपाके सोष्णकक्षारः साम्ळो वातघ्नपित्तळः ॥
सेरी च मधुरा रुच्या कषायाम्ळा कटुस्तथा ।
पथ्या च कफवातघ्नी सारिका मुखदोषनुत् ॥ " (रा.नि.)
["Pūgavṛkṣasya niryāsō himaḥ saṁmōhanō guruḥ
Vipākē sōṣṇakakṣāraḥ sāmḷō vātagnapittaḷaḥ
Sērī ca madhurā rucyā kaṣāyāmḷā kaṭustathā
Pathyā ca kaphavātaghnī sārikā mukhadōṣanut" (Rā.ni.)]

पूगं रूक्षं सरं किञ्चित् कषायं मधुरं गुरु ॥
रोचनं मोहनं हृद्यं कफपित्तनिबर्हणम् ।
दीपनं वक्त्रवैरस्यमलदौर्गन्ध्यनाशनम् ॥
आर्द्रं तु गर्वभिष्यन्दि दृष्ट्यग्निमान्द्यकृत् परम् ।
शुष्कं तु वातळं स्निग्धं त्रिदोषशमंन परम् ॥
स्विन्नपूगं त्रिदोषघ्नं पक्वं शुष्कं तु वातळम् ।
पक्वार्द्रं गुर्वभिष्यन्दि बालार्द्रं कफपित्तहृत् ॥
पूंग स्याद् दृढमध्यं यत् श्रेष्टं नानाविघं हि तत्
पाकदेशादिभेदेन चिक्कणं सर्वदोषजित् ॥

(कृमिहृत् पूगपुष्पं तु कषायं मधुरं गुरु) (कै.नि.)
["Pūgaṃ rūkṣaṃ saraṃ kiñcit kaṣāyaṃ madhuraṃ guru
Rōcanaṃ mōhanaṃ hṛdyaṃ kaphapittanibarhaṇaṃ
Dīpanaṃ vaktravairasyamaladaurgandhyanāśanaṃ
Ārdraṃ tu gurvabhiṣyandi dṛṣṭyagnimāndyakṛt paraṃ
Śuṣkaṃ tu vātaḷaṃ snigdhaṃ tridōṣaśamanaṃ paraṃ
Svinnapūgaṃ tridōṣaghnaṃ pakvaṃ śuṣkaṃ tu vātaḷaṃ
Pakvārdraṃ gurvabhiṣyandi bālārdraṃ kaphapittahṛt
Pūgaṃ syāt dṛḍhamadhyaṃ yat śrēṣṭhaṃ nānāvidhaṃ hi tat
Pākadēśādibhēdēna cikkaṇaṃ sarvadōṣajit
(Kṛmihṛt pūgapuṣpaṃ tu kaṣāyaṃ madhuraṃ guru) " (Kai.ni.)]

पक्वं तु वातळं रूक्षं भेदनं कफनाशनम् ।
शुष्कमग्निकरं पूगं कषायं मधुरं परम् ॥
गुर्वभिष्यन्दि मधुरं तोयधृग्वह्निनाशनम् ॥
पूगमादौ विषं घोरं द्वितीये भेदि दुर्जरम् ।
तृतीयादिषु पातव्यं सुधातुल्यं रसायनम् ॥
पुगीफलं मोहकरं स्वादु रुच्यं कषायकम् ।
रूक्षं सरं च मधुरं गुरु पथ्यं च दीपनम् ॥
किञ्चित्कटु च संप्रोक्तं मुखवैरस्य नाशकम् ।
वमिं क्लेदं त्रिदोषघ्नं मलं वातं कफं तथा ॥
पित्तं दुर्गन्धतां चैव नाशयेदिति कीर्त्तितम् ।
आर्द्रं पूगीफलं प्रोक्तं तुवरं कण्ठशुद्धिकृत् ॥
अभिष्यन्दि सरं चैव गुरु दृष्ट्यग्निमान्द्यकृत् ।
रक्तदोषं मुखमलं पित्तं चामं कफं तथा ॥
आध्मानमुदरं चैव नाशयेदिति कीर्त्तितम् ।
शुष्कं पूगीफलं रुच्यं पाचकं रेचकं तथा ॥
स्निग्धं च वातळं चैव कण्ठरुग्घृत्रिदोषनुत् ।
पर्णं विना केवलं तु भक्षितं शोफपाण्डुकृत् ॥
पक्वं चार्द्रं पूगफलं छेदकं च त्रिदोषहृत् ।
शुष्कं पक्वीकृतं तत्तु स्निग्धं वातकरं मतम् ॥
त्रिदोषनाशकं चैवं तद्बालं सर्वदोषहृत् ।
पूगवृक्षस्य निर्यासो मोहनः शीतळो गुरुः ॥
पाके चोष्णः पित्तळं च पटुश्चाम्ळः प्रकीर्त्तितः ।
वातनाशकरश्चैव मुनिभिः परिकीर्त्तितः ॥" (नि.र.)
["Pakvaṃ tu vātaḷaṃ rūkṣaṃ bhēdanaṃ kaphanāśanaṃ
Suṣkamagnikaraṃ pūgaṃ kaṣāyaṃ madhuraṃ paraṃ
Gurvabhiṣyandi madhuraṃ tōyadhṛgvahnināśanaṃ
Pūgamādau viṣaṃ ghōraṃ dvitīyē bhēdi durjjaraṃ
Tṛtīyādiṣu pātavyaṃ sudhātulayaṃ rasāyanaṃ
Pūgīphalaṃ mōhakaraṃ svādu rucyaṃ kaṣāyakaṃ
Rūkṣaṃ saraṃ ca madhuraṃ guru pathyaṃ ca dīpanaṃ
Kiñcitkaṭu ca samprōktaṃ mukhavairasya nāśakaṃ

Vamīṃ kḷēdaṃ tṛidōṣaghnaṃ malaṃ vātaṃ kaphaṃ tathā
Pittaṃ durgandhatāṃ caiva nāśayēditi kīrttitaṃ
Ārdraṃ pūgīphalaṃ prōktaṃ tuvaraṃ kaṇṭhaśuddhikṛt
Abhiṣyandi saraṃ caiva guru dṛṣṭyagnimāndyakṛt
Raktadōṣaṃ mukhamalaṃ pittaṃ cāmaṃ kaphaṃ tathā
Ādhmānamudaraṃ caiva nāśayēditi kīrttitaṃ
Śuṣkaṃ pūgīphalaṃ rucyaṃ pācakaṃ rēcakaṃ tathā
Snigdhaṃ ca vātaḷaṃ caiva kaṇṭharugghṛtṛidōṣanut
Parṇaṃ vinā kēvalaṃ tu bhakṣitaṃ śōphapāṇḍukṛt
Pakvaṃ cārdraṃ pūgaphalaṃ chēdakaṃ ca tṛidōṣahṛt
Śuṣkaṃ pakvīkṛtaṃ tattu snigdhaṃ vātakaraṃ mataṃ
Tṛidōṣanāśakaṃ caiva tadbālaṃ sarvadōṣahṛt
Pūgavṛkṣasya niryāsō mōhanaḥ śītaḷō guruḥ
Pākē cōṣṇaḥ pittaḷaṃ ca paṭuścāmḷaḥ prakīrttitaḥ
Vātanāśakaraścaiva munibhiḥ parikīrttitaḥ" (Ni.ra)]

"ചവർത്തു മധുരിച്ചുള്ളോന്നടയ്ക്കാ തു പ്രമേഹകൃത്
പാരം രുചിയെയുണ്ടാക്കും വിരേചനകരം പരം" (ഗു.പാ.)
["Cavarttu madhuriccuḷḷōnnaṭaykkā tu pramēhakṛt
Pāraṃ ruciyeyuṇṭākkuṃ virēcanakaraṃ paraṃ". (Gu.pā.)]

Remarks: There is a variety of this plant growing in the north Canara district of Karnataka State known under the Malayalam names, *kānakavuṅṅu* and *cūṇḍapākku*. Its botanical name is *Areca dicksonii* Roxb. or *Pinanga dicksonii* Blume. The fruit of this plant is so small that it is just enough for chewing once only.

Argemone mexicana

Plate 9

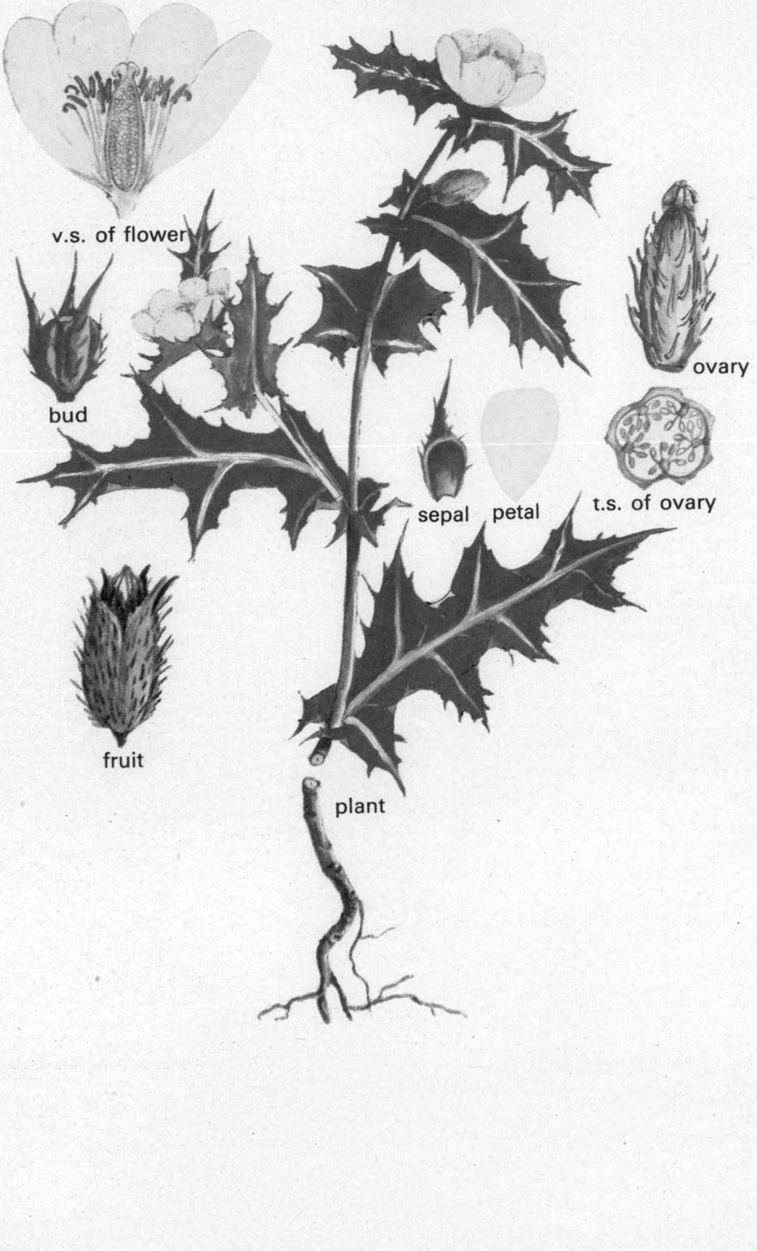

Coll. No. AVS 2167

Argemone mexicana **Linn.**

Papaveraceae : (अहिफेन–कुलम्)

Eng	:	Mexican poppy, Yellow Mexican poppy, Prickly poppy
Hin	:	Bhaṭbhāṃṭ, Phāraṃgī dhattūrā (भटभांट, फारंगी धत्तूरा)
Kan	:	Araśina, Ummatta, Dattūrigida (ಅರಶಿನ, ಉಮ್ಮತ್ತ, ದತ್ತೂರಿಗಿಡ)
Mal	:	Ponnummattu̥, Kanṭankattiri (പൊന്നുമ്മത്ത്, കണ്ടൻകത്തിരി)
Sam	:	Svarṇakṣīrī, Brahmadantī (स्वर्णक्षीरी, ब्रह्मदन्ती)
Tam	:	Kuṭiyōṭṭi, Ponnummattai (குடியோட்டி, பொன்னும்மத்தை)
Tel	:	Brahmadanḍicettu (బ్రహ్మదండిచెట్టు)

Distribution : Throughout the hotter parts of India,in areas upto 1,500 m elevation on road sides and waste places

The plant : A strong,branched,prickly annual, 60 – 90 cm in height with yellow latex; leaves simple, sessile, spiny, semi-amplexicaul, sinuate-pinnatifid, variegated with white, spinous, veins white; flowers large, bright yellow, terminal on short leafy branches; fruits prickly capsules, oblong-ovoid, opening by 4 – 6 valves; seeds numerous.

Parts used : whole plant

Properties and uses : The plant is bitter, acrid, cooling, vulnerary, diuretic, purgative, anti-inflammatory, expectorant, aphrodisiac, emetic, depurative, anodyne, anthelmintic, antipyretic, ophthalmic, stomachic and sedative.

The roots are useful in guinea-worm infestation, skin diseases, leprosy, pruritus, blennorrhagia, inflammations, all types of poisoning, constipation, flatulence, colic, malarial fever and vesicular calculus. The leaves are useful in cough, wounds, ulcers and skin diseases. The seeds are useful in vitiated conditions of *kapha,* cough, asthma, pertussis, skin diseases, leprosy, ulcers, wounds, odontalgia, dental caries, constipation, rheumatalgia, colic and flatulence. The latex is useful in dropsy, jaundice, skin diseases, leprosy, blisters, indolent ulcers, conjunctivitis, inflammations, burning sensation and malarial fever. The oil is useful in indolent ulcers, wounds, leprosy, skin diseases, constipation, flatulence, colic and rheumatalgia.

"कण्टकी कण्टपत्रा च पीतपुष्पा क्षुपा भवेत् ।
स्वर्णक्षीरी कण्टफला कृष्णबीजा च सुस्थिरा ॥" (शि.नि.)

["Kaṇṭakī kaṇṭapatṛā ca pītapuṣpā kṣupā bhavėt
Svaṛṇakṣīrī kaṇṭaphalā kṛṣṇabījā ca susthirā" (Śi.ni.)]

"गदितेह हेमदुग्धा काञ्चनदुग्धा च काञ्चनक्षीरी ।
कनकाभिधानसहितो ब्रूते तां दुग्धपर्यायः ॥" (अ.म.)
["Gaditēha hēmadugdhā kāñcanadugdhā ca kañcanakṣīrī
Kanakābhidhānasahitō brūtē tāṃ dugdhaparyāyaḥ" (A.ma.)]

"क्षीरिणी काञ्चनक्षीरी कटुपर्णी च कर्षणी ।
तिक्तदुग्धा हैमवती हेमदुग्धा हिमावती ॥
स्वर्णक्षीरी स्वर्णदुग्धा सुवर्णक्षीरिकाऽपि च ।
हेमाह्वा कनकक्षीरी हेमक्षीरी च काञ्चनी ॥" (ध.नि.)
["Kṣīriṇī kāñcanakṣīrī kaṭuparṇī ca karṣaṇī
Tiktadugdhā haimavatī hēmadugdhā himāvatī
Svaṛṇakṣīrī svaṛṇadugdhā suvaṛṇakṣīrikāʃpi ca
Hēmāhvā kanakakṣīrī hēmakṣīrī ca kāñcanī" (Dha.ni.)]

"क्षीरिणी काञ्चनक्षीरी कर्षणी कटुपर्णिका ।
तिक्तदुग्धा हैमवती हिमदुग्धा हिमावती ॥
हिमाद्रिजा पीतदुग्धा यवचिञ्चा हिमोद्भवा ।
हैमी च हिमजा चेति चतुरेकगुणाह्वया ॥
स्वर्णक्षीरी स्वर्णदुग्धा स्वर्णाह्वा रुग्मिणी तथा ।
सुवर्णा हेमदुग्धी च हेमक्षीरी च काञ्चनी ॥" (रा.नि.)
["Kṣīriṇī kāñcanakṣīrī karṣaṇī kaṭuparṇikā
Tiktadugdhā haimavatī himadugdhā himāvatī
Himādrijā pītadugdhā yavaciñcā himōdbhavā
Haimī ca himajā cēti caturēkaguṇāhvayā
Svaṛṇakṣīrī svaṛṇadugdhā svaṛṇāhvā rugmiṇī tathā
Suvaṛṇā hēmadugdhī ca hemakṣīrī ca kāñcanī" (Rā.ni.)]

"हेमाह्वा रेचनी तिक्ता भेदिन्युत्क्ळेशकारिणी ।
कृमिकण्डूविषानाहकफपित्ताम्रकुष्ठनुत् ॥" (भा.प्र.)
["Hēmāhvā recanī tiktā bhēdinyuklēśakāriṇī
Kṛmikaṇḍūviṣānāhakaphapittāsṛakuṣṭhanut" (Bhā.pra.)]

"तिक्ता तु काञ्चनक्षीरी पित्तकृमिविषापहा ।
शोधनी दोषसङ्घातशमनी रक्तपित्तजित् ॥
क्षीरिणीयुगळं तिक्तं कृमिपित्तकफापहम् ।" (ध.नि.)
["Tiktā tu kāñcanakṣīrī pittakṛmiviṣāpahā
Sōdhanī dōṣasanghātaśamanī raktapittajit
Kṣīriṇīyugaḷaṃ tiktaṃ kṛmipittakaphāpahaṃ" (Dha.ni.)]

"क्षीरिणी कटुतिक्ता च रेचनी शोफतापनुत् ।
कृमिदोषकफघ्नी च पित्तज्वरहरा च सा ॥

स्वर्णक्षीरी हिमा तिक्ता कृमिपित्तकफापहा ।
मूत्रकृच्छ्राश्मरीशोफदाहज्वरहरा परा ॥" (रा.नि.)
["Kṣīriṇī kaṭutiktā ca rēcanī śōphatāpanut
Kṛmidōṣakaphaghnī ca pittajvarahara ca sā
Svaṛṇakṣīrī himā tiktā kṛmipittakaphāpahā
Mūtṛakṛcchṛāśmarīśōphadāhajvaraharā parā" (Rā.ni.)]

"स्वर्णक्षीरी हिमा तिक्ता सा कण्डूविनाशिका ।
वातरक्तं कृमीं पित्तं कफं कृच्छ्रं च नाशयेत् ॥
जूर्त्यश्मरीशोफदाहज्वरकुष्ठविनाशिनी ।
मूलं चास्य चोक इति गुणाः पूर्वोक्तवत्स्मृताः ॥" (नि.र.)
["Svaṛṇakṣīrī himā tiktā sā kaṇḍūvināśikā
Vātaraktaṃ kṛmīṃ pittaṃ kaphaṃ kṛcchṛaṃ ca nāśayēt
Jūṛtyaśmarīśōphadāhajvarakuṣṭhavināśinī
Mūlaṃ cāsya cōka iti guṇāḥ pūṛvōktavatsmṛtāḥ" (Ni.ra.)]

"तस्याः क्षीरं बिन्दुमात्रं नेत्रे क्षिप्तं घृताप्लुतम्
शुक्ळं च ह्यधिमांसं च नेत्रान्ध्यं चैव नाशयेत् ॥" (ग.नि.)
["Tasyāḥ kṣīraṃ bindumātṛaṃ nētṛē kṣiptaṃ ghṛtāpḷutaṃ
Śukḷaṃ ca hyadhimāṃsaṃ ca nētṛāndhyaṃ caiva nāśayēt" (Ga.ni.)]

"उत्क्ळेशिनी प्रमदिनी भेदिनी हेमदुग्धिका ।
कफपित्तहरा ऽऽनाहकामलापाण्डुनाशनी ॥" (म.नि)
["Utkḷēśinī pṛamadinī bhēdinī hēmadugdhikā
Kaphapittaharā ʃʃnāhakāmalāpāṇḍunāśanī" (Ma.ni.)]

"स्वर्णक्षीरी सरा तिक्ता मादन्युत्क्ळेदनी जयेत् ।
कण्डूकृमिविषानाहकफपित्तास्रकामलाः ॥" (कै.नि.)
["Svaṛṇakṣīrī sarā tiktā mādanyutkḷēdanī jayēt
Kaṇḍūkṛmiviṣānāhakaphapittāsṛakāmalāḥ]" (Kai.ni.)]

"हेमाह्वा रेचनी तिक्ता मन्दाग्न्युत्क्ळेदकारिणी ।
कृमिकण्डूकफानाहविषकुष्ठविनाशिनी ।" (म.पा.नि.)
["Hēmāhvā rēcanī tiktā mandāgnyutkḷēdakāriṇī
Kṛmikaṇḍūkaphānāhaviṣakuṣṭhavināśinī" (Ma.pā.ni.)]

"हेमदुग्धा हिमा तिक्ता श्ळेष्मपित्तापहृत्सरः ।" (सो.नि.)
["Hēmadugdhā himā tiktā śḷēṣmapittāpahṛtsaraḥ" (Sō.ni.)]

Remarks : Acharya P.V. Sharma in his `Dravyaguṇavijñān' refers to this plant and argues very correctly that the plant mentioned as *kāñcanakṣīrī* in `Suśṛutasaṃhitā' (Bhagandarapṛakaraṇaṃ)' is not *Argemone mexicana* but *Euphorbia thomsoniana* Boiss. which grows in Kashmir. For, *Argemone mexicana* is a plant indigenous to Mexico. The synonyms *haimavatī* and *himāvatī* given by the authors of different `Materia Medica' make it clear that this is a plant growing in the Himalayas and therefore it is only proper that this has to be identified as *Euphorbia thomsoniana* Boiss. referred to by Dr Sharma.

Synonyms given by Abhidhānamañjarī (गतितेह हेमदुग्धा .... दुग्धपर्यायः),
Dhanvantarinighaṇṭu (स्वर्णक्षीरी .... च काञ्चनी)
and by Rājanighaṇṭu (स्वर्णक्षीरी स्वर्णदुग्धा .... च काञ्चनी)
seem very appropriate to *Argemone mexicana.*

Perhaps the scarcity of *Euphorbia thomsoniana* Boiss., which grows in Kashmir at an altitude of 2,100 m, induced the practitioners of Ayurvedic medicines to use *Argemone mexicana* Linn. as a substitute and hence its current popularity.

Coll. No.AVS 2216

Argyreia nervosa (Burm.f.) Boj.

(A. speciosa *Sweet*)

Convolvulaceae : (त्रिवृत्–कुलम्)

Eng	:	Elephant creeper
Hin	:	Samandār-kā-pat, Samudraśōṣ (समन्दार–का–पत, समुद्रशोष)
Kan	:	Candrapāda (ಚಂದ್ರಪಾದ)
Mal	:	Maṛikkunni, Maṛutuṭari, Samudrappacca (മറിക്കുന്നി, മറുതുടരി, സമുദ്രപ്പച്ച)
San	:	Vṛddhadārukaḥ, Bastāntṛī (वृद्धदारुकः, बस्तान्त्री)
Tam	:	Samuttirappaccai, Samuttirappālai (சமுத்திரப்பச்சை, சமுத்திரப்பாலை)
Tel	:	Candrapāda (చంద్రపాద)

Distribution : Throughout India,in areas upto 900 m elevation

The plant: A very large climbing shrub with woody, white, tomentose stems; leaves simple, large, ovate, acute, base cordate, glabrous above, white tomentose beneath; flowers large, purple, silky-pubescent without in long-peduncled cymes, corolla tubular-infundibuliform; fruits dry, globose, apiculate.

Parts used : roots

Properties and uses : The roots are acrid, bitter, astringent, sweet, emollient, thermogenic, roborant, appetiser, digestive, carminative, aperient, cardiotonic, anti-inflammatory, expectorant, diuretic, aphrodisiac, rejuvenating, intellect promoting, brain tonic, nervine tonic and tonic.They are useful in vitiated conditions of *kapha* and *vāta,* emaciation, wounds, ulcers, anorexia, dyspepsia, flatulence, colic, constipation, cardiac debility, inflammations, cough, bronchitis, strangury, seminal weakness, nervous weakness, cerebral disorders, synovitis, haemorrhoids, obesity, hoarseness, syphilis, anaemia, diabetes, tuberculosis, arthritis, ascites, leucorrhoea and general debility.

"बस्तान्त्री विषगन्धा वयोजरदारिका छगळान्त्री ।
विषपत्रिकान्त्रवस्ता पर्यायैर्वृद्धदारुकं भवति ॥" (अ.म.)
[Bastāntṛī viṣagandhā vayōjaradārikā chagaḷāntṛī
Viṣapatṛikāntṛavastā paryāyaiṛvṛddhadārukaṃ bhavati" (A.ma.)]

"वृद्धदारुक आवेगी जुङ्गको दीर्घवालुकः ।
वृद्धः कोटरपुष्पी स्यादजान्त्री छगळान्त्र्यपि ॥" (ध.नि.)

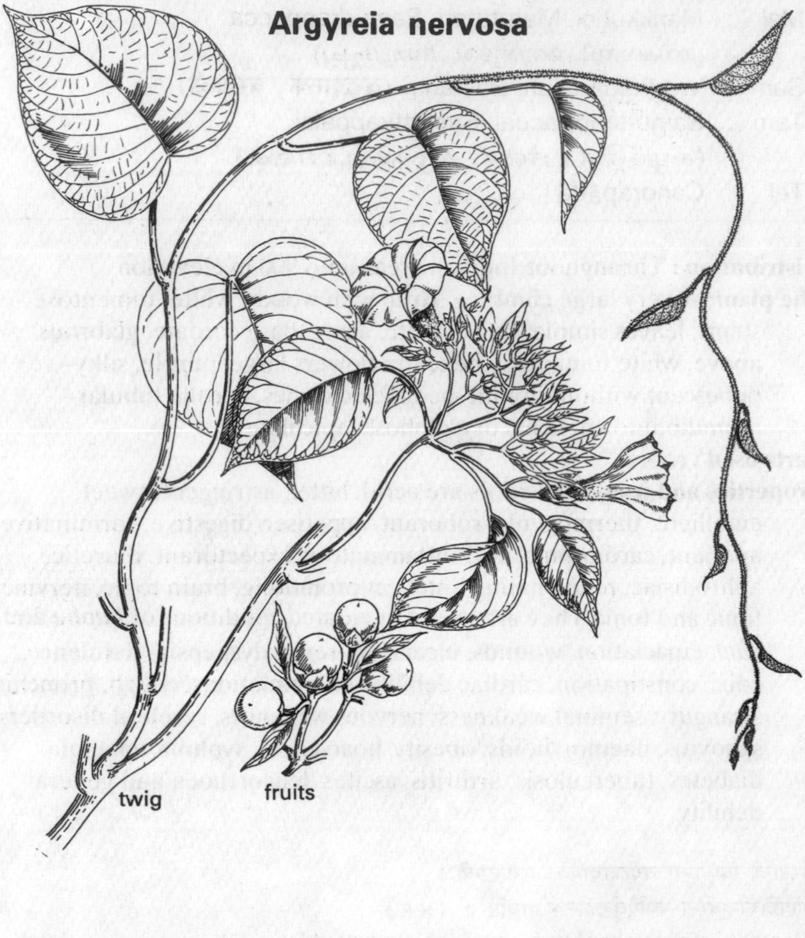
Argyreia nervosa
twig
fruits

["Vṛddhadāruka āvēgī juṅgakō dīrghavālukaḥ
Vṛddhaḥ kōṭarapuṣpī syādajāntṛī chagaḷāntryapi"(Dha.ni.)]

"वृद्धदारुक आवेगी जोङ्गको जीर्णबालकः ।
अन्तः कोटरपुष्पी स्यात् श्यामा महिषवल्लरी ॥
अजान्त्री तु महाश्यामा वल्लरी दीर्घबालकः ।" (कै.नि.)
["Vṛddhadāruka āvēgī jōṅgakō jīṇabālakaḥ
Antaḥ kōṭarapuṣpī syāt śyāmā mahiṣavallarī
Ajāntrī tu mahāśyāmā vallarī dīrghabālakaḥ " (Kai.ni.)]

"वृद्धदारुः कषायोष्णः कटुस्तिक्तो रसायनः ।
वृष्यो वातामवातार्शःशोफमेहकफप्रणुत् ॥
शुक्ळायुर्बलमेधाग्निस्वरकान्तिकरः सरः ।" (भा.प्र.)
["Vṛddhadāruḥ kaṣāyōṣṇaḥ kaṭustiktō rasāyanaḥ
Vṛṣyō vātāmavātārśaḥśōphamēhakaphapraṇut
Śukḷāyuṛbalamēdhāgnisvarakāntikaraḥ saraḥ" (Bhā.pra.)]

"वृद्धदारुः कटुस्तिक्तस्तथोष्णः कफवाताजित् ।
श्वयथुकृमिमेहास्रवातोदरहरः परः ॥" (ध.नि.)
["Vṛddhadāruḥ kaṭustiktastathōṣṇaḥ kaphavātajit
Śvayathukṛmimēhāsṛavātōdaraharaḥ paraḥ" (Dha.ni.)]

"वृद्धदारुः कटुस्तिक्तः कषायोष्णो रसायनः ।
शुक्ळायुर्बलमेध्याग्निस्वरकान्तिकरः सरः ॥
शोफामवातवातास्रवातमेहकफापहः ।" (कै.नि.)
["Vṛddhadāruḥ kaṭustiktaḥ kaṣāyōṣṇō rasāyanaḥ
Śukḷāyuṛbalamēdhyāgnisvarakāntikaraḥ saraḥ
Śōphāmavātavātāsṛavātamēhakaphāpahaḥ" (Kai.ni.)]

"साधारणो वृद्धदारुः कटुस्तिक्तः कषायकः ।
रसायनोष्णो मधुरो मेध्यः स्वर्यः सरोऽग्निदः ॥
कान्तिधातुकरो बल्यो रुच्यः पुष्टिकरो लघुः ।
उपदंशं पाण्डुरोगं क्षयं कासं प्रमेहकम् ॥
वातरक्तं चामवातं वातं शोफं कफं जयेत् ।" (नि.र.)
["Sādhāraṇō vṛddhadāruḥ kaṭustiktaḥ kaṣāyakaḥ
Rasāyanōṣṇō madhurō mēdhyaḥ svaryaḥ sarōʃgnidaḥ
Kāntidhātukarō balyō rucyaḥ puṣṭikarō laghuḥ
Upadaṁśaṃ pāṇḍurōgaṃ kṣayaṃ kāsaṃ pramēhakaṃ
Vātaraktaṃ cāmavātaṃ vātaṃ śōphaṃ kaphaṃ jayēt" (Ni.ra.)]

वृद्धदारो ग्रहोन्मादपापालक्ष्मीविनाशनः ।
अपस्मारामवातघ्नः शोफशूलापहोऽग्निकृत् ॥
बल्यः कण्ठ्योऽस्थिसंधानकारी वातरुजापहः ।

विषूचीप्रतितून्यादिव्याधिघाती रसायनम् ॥" (सो.नि.)
["Vṛddhadārō grahōnmādapāpālakṣmī vināśanaḥ
Apasmārāmavātaghnaḥ śōphaśūlāpahōʃgnikṛt
Balyaḥ kaṇṭhyōʃsthisaṁdhānakārī vātarujāpahaḥ
Viṣucīpratitūnyādivyādhighātī rasāyanaṃ" (So.ni.)]

"स्रंसिनी गुल्महृद्रोगविषारोचकनाशिनी ।
बस्तान्त्री कफरोगघ्नी मूत्रकृच्छ्रविनाशिनी ॥" (म.नि.)
["Sraṁsinī gulmahṛdrōgaviṣārōcakanāśinī
Bastāntrī kapharōgaghnī mūtrakṛcchravināśinī" (Ma.ni.)]

"वृद्धदारुः कषायोष्णः सरस्तिक्तो रसायनम् ।
वृष्यो वातामवातास्राशोफमेहकफान् जयेत् ॥" (म.वि.)
["Vṛddhadāruḥ kaṣāyōṣṇaḥ sarastiktō rasāyanaṃ
Vṛṣyō vātāmavātāsraśōphamēhakaphān jayēt" (Ma.vi.)]

Remarks: `*Bastāntṛī*' of *Śyāmādigaṇa* (Aṣṭāṅgahṛdayaṃ) and *vṛddhadāru* of `*Mahārāsnādikaṣāyaṃ*' (*Sahasrayōgaṃ*) are interpreted as *maṛikkunni* in Malayalam by most of the commentators.

In the '*Aruṇōdaya*' commentary on Aṣṭāṅgahṛdayaṃ the Malayalam name *maṛutuṭari* is given for *bastāntṛī*. In the 'Oṣadhinighaṇṭu' of Kumaran Krishnan, the Sanskrit-Malayalam dictionary of Kanippayoor and 'Ayurvēdaviśvakōśaṃ' of Pandit K.K. Panickar, *chagaḷāntṛī*, *vṛddhadāruka*, and *vṛddadāru* are translated into Malayalam as *maṛikkunni. Bastāntṛi* is *maṛutuṭari* or *maṛukuṭari* according to 'Ayurvēdaviśvakōśaṃ'. But there is no mention of this word *bastāntṛī* in 'Oṣadhinighaṇṭu' or Sanskrit-Malayalam dictionary. *Maṛikkunni* and *maṛutuṭari* are treated as two distinct raw drugs in 'Oṣadhinighāṇṭu' and 'Ayurvēdaviśvakōśaṃ'. In the 'Ayurvedic Formulary of India' also *bastāntṛī* and *vṛddhadāru* are treated as two distinct ones, giving the Latin name as *Argyreia speciosa* and *Ipomoea petaloidea*, respectively. In the 'Glossary of Vegetable Drugs in Bṛhattrayī, *Ipomoea pes-caprae* is the Latin name given for *chagaḷāntṛī* and *bastāntṛī* is treated as a synonym of *chagaḷāntṛī*. But in the `Pharmacognosy of Ayurvedic Drugs' both *Argyreia speciosa* and *Ipomoea pes-caprae* are regarded as *vṛddhadāruka*, giving the Malayalam names *samudrapacca* for *Argyreia speciosa* and *aḍampu* or *cuvanna aḍampu* for *Ipomoea pes-caprae.* Dr S.N. Nesamani considers *Argyreia speciosa* as *samudrapacca* in his book 'Auṣadhasasyaṅṅaḷ.' The commentators of 'Bhāvapṛakāśaṃ', 'Kaiyadēvanighaṇṭu' etc., are of the opinion that the Latin name of *vṛddhadāru* is *Argyreia speciosa.*

As *chagaḷāntrī* is a synonym of *bastāntṛī* and as *maṛikkunni* is the Malayalam name given for *chagaḷāntrī* it amounts to regard *bastāntṛī* as *maṛikkunni* itself. Hence, the Malayalam name *maṛikkunni* is applicable to *bastāntṛī* as well as *vṛddhadāru.*

It is strange to note that all the Sanskrit synonyms of *vṛddhadāru* are given to *Rourea santaloides* W. & A. also, in `Indian Medicinal Plants'. Being highly poisonous it is not advisable to use as *vṛddhadāru.*

Thus, it is clear that in Kerala *Argyreia nervosa (A.speciosa)* is being used for *maṛutuṭari, maṛikkunni* and *samudrapacca.*

Coll. No. AVS 1691

Aristolochia bracteolata **Lam.**

Aristolochiaceae : (ईश्वरी–कुलम्)

Eng	:	Worm killer, Bracteated birthwort
Hin	:	Kīramār, Kīṭamār (कीरमार, कीटमार)
Kan	:	S̱anajalihallu (ಸನಜಲಿಹಲ್ಲು)
Mal	:	Aṭṭukoṭṭappāla, Aṭutinnāppāla (ആട്ടുകൊട്ടപ്പാല, ആടുതിന്നാപ്പാല)
San	:	Ḵīṭamārī (कीटमारी)
Tam	:	Aṭutinnāppālai (ஆடுதின்னாப்பாலை)
Tel	:	Gāḍidagaḍapāku (గాడిదగడపాకు)

Distribution: Bengal, Western Peninsula, Gujarat, Deccan, Kerala and Karnataka

The plant: A perennial prostrate herb with weak, glabrous stems; leaves simple, alternate, reniform or broadly ovate, cordate at the base with a wide sinus upto 7.5 cm in diameter, finely reticulately veined; flowers solitary with a large sessile orbicular bract at the base, perianth tube cylindric with dark purple lip having revolute margins; fruits oblong-ellipsoid 12-ribbed glabrous capsules; seeds deltoid with slightly cordate base.

Parts used: roots, leaves

Properties and uses: The roots and leaves are bitter, acrid, thermogenic, anthelmintic, cathartic, anti-inflammatory, emmenagogue, vulnerary, appetiser, sudorific and antiperiodic, and are useful in vitiated conditions of *kapha* and *vāta,* intestinal worms (especially round worms), constipation, inflammations, amenorrhoea, dysmenorrhoea, foul ulcers, boils, syphilis, gonorrhoea, dyspepsia, colic, skin diseases, eczema, arthralgia and intermittent fevers.

"कीटमारी धूम्रपत्रा गृद्ध्रपत्रा च कीटहा ।
कीटारिः कत्रपुङ्खा च भृङ्गी गृद्ध्राणिरष्टधा ॥" (स्व.)
["Kīṭamārī dhūmṛapatṛā gṛddhṛapatṛā ca kīṭahā
Kīṭāriḥ katṛapuṅkhā ca bhṛṅgī gṛddhṛāṇiraṣṭadhā " (Sva.)]

"कीटारिः कीटमारी च भृङ्गी कीटकहा तथा ।" (शा.नि.)
["Kīṭāriḥ kīṭamārī ca bhṛṅgī kīṭakahā tathā (Śā.ni.)]

Aristolochia bracteolata

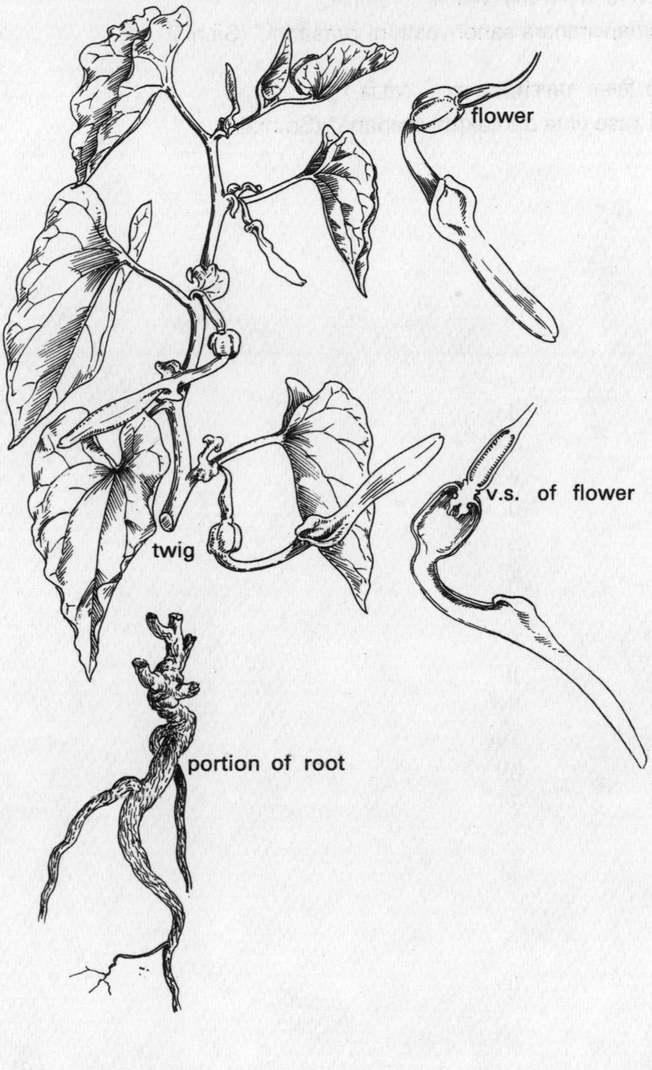

कटूष्णा कीटमारी स्यात् तिक्ता दीपनरेचनी ।
कासगुल्मरजोदोषविषवीसर्पनाशिनी ॥
विषमज्वरजिद्व्रण्या जन्तुघ्नी शोफशूलनुत् ।" (स्व.)
["Kaṭūṣṇā kīṭamārī syāt tiktā dīpanarēcanī
Kāsagulmarajōdōṣavisavīsarpanāśinī
Viṣamajvarajidvraṇyā jantughnī śōphasūlanut" (Sva.)]

"वातश्ळेष्मज्वरहरा सन्ध्यस्थीनि प्रसारिणी ॥" (शा.नि.)
["Vātaśḷēṣmajvaraharā sandhyasthīni prasāriṇī" (Śā.ni.)]

"कीटमारी रसे तिक्ता दन्तकृमिविषापहा ।" (सो.नि.)
["Kīṭamārī rasē tiktā dantakṛmiviṣāpahā" (Sō.ni.)]

Coll. No. AVS 1443

***Aristolochia indica* Linn.**

(A.lanceolata *Wt.*)

Aristolochiaceae : (ईश्वरी–कुलम्)

Eng	:	Indian birthwort
Hin	:	Iśvarmūl, Isarmūl (ईश्वरमूल, ईसरमूल)
Kan	:	Īsvaberusa (ಈಸ್ವಬೆರುಸ)
Mal	:	Karaḷayaṃ, Iśvaramulla, Karaḷakaṃ, Garuḍakkoṭi (കരളയം, ഈശ്വരമുല്ല, കരളകം, ഗരുഡക്കൊടി)
San	:	Garaḷikā, Iśvarī (गरळिका, ईश्वरी)
Tam	:	Karuṭakkoṭi, Iśvaramūlī (கருடக்கொடி, ஈசுவரமூலி)
Tel	:	Ēśvaraveru (ఈశ్వరవేరు)

Distribution : Throughout India,at low elevations, on hedges and bushes

The plant : A perennial shrubby glabrous twiner with a long woody root-stock; leaves simple, alternate, short-petioled, entire with somewhat undulate margins; flowers greenish white or light purplish in axillary cymes or fascicles with swollen or inflated basal part, contracted middle part and narrowly funnel-shaped distal part; fruits rounded or oblong or hexagonal, septicidal 6-valved capsules opening from below upwards; seeds flat, winged.

Parts used: roots, leaves, fruits

Properties and uses: The roots are bitter, acrid, astringent, thermogenic, purgative, anodyne, depurative, digestive, anthelmintic, stomachic, cardiotonic, anti-inflammatory, diuretic, sudorific, febrifuge, antiperiodic, emmenagogue and tonic. They are useful in ulcers, vitiated conditions of *kapha* and *vāta,* arthralgia, inflammations, leprosy, leucoderma, skin diseases, dyspepsia, intestinal worms, colic, flatulence, strangury, cardiac debility, fever, intermittent fever, cough, catarrh, amenorrhoea, dysmenorrhoea, dystocia, abdominal disorders in children and all types of poisonous bites and stings. Leaves are used to treat cholera, bowel complaints and intermittent fevers in children. A paste made out of the leaves is good for inflammations. The seeds are good for inflammation, biliousness, dry cough, arthralgia and dyspnoea in children.

"कीटमारिर्गरळिका सर्पिणी सर्पगन्धिला ।
ईश्वरी कृत्तिकावल्ली गारुडी नकुलप्रिया ॥
सुनन्देश्वरमूली च प्रोक्ता रुद्रजटाभिधा ।" (स्व.)

Aristolochia indica

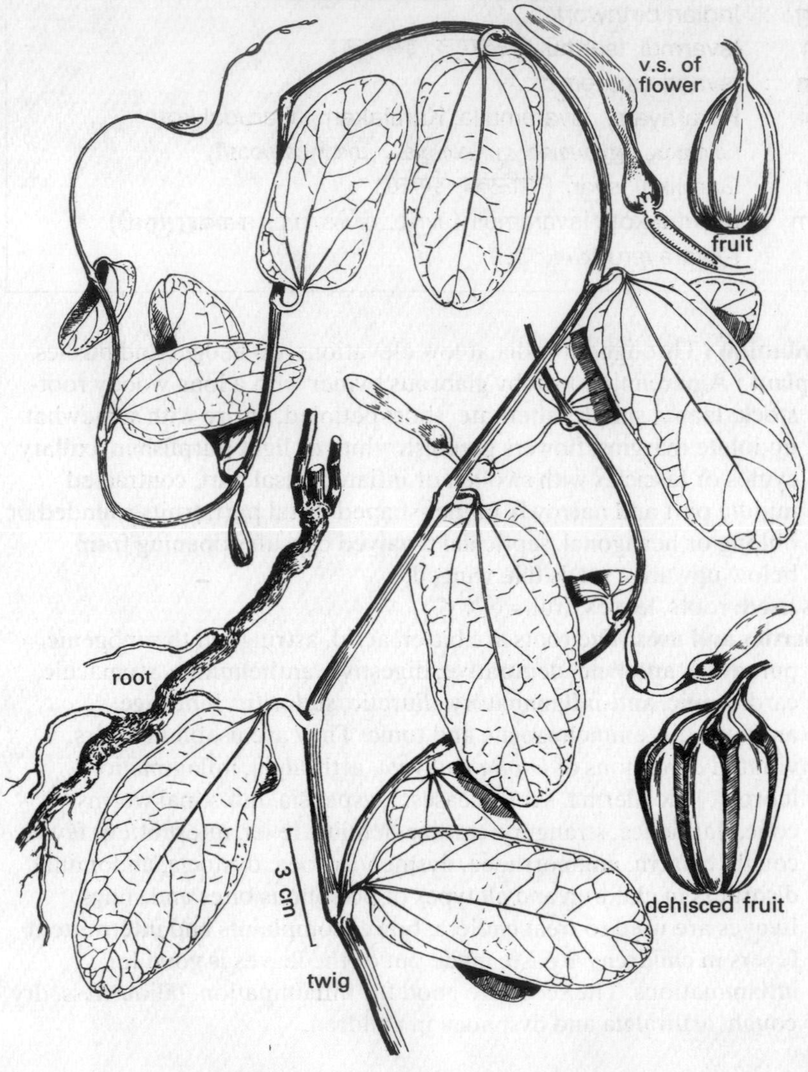

[`Kīṭamāriṛgaraḷikā sarpiṇī sarpagandhilā
Iśvarī kṛttikāvallī gāruḍī nakulapriyā
Sunandēśvaramūlī ca prōktā rudrajaṭābhidhā'' (Sva.)]

"क्ष्वेळवेगा करळका विषवेगा" (ज्योत्स्निका)
[`Kṣvēḷavēgā karaḷakā viṣavēgā'' (Jyōtsnikā)]

"गारुडी सर्वविषजित् कुष्ठघ्नी कफवातहा ।" (हृदयप्रिया)
[`Gāruḍī sarvaviṣajit kuṣṭhaghnī kaphavātahā'' (Hṛdayapriyā)]

"मूलं तिक्तमतीवास्य सुगन्धं च कषायकम् ।
विषहारि त्रिदोषघ्नं दीपनं पाचनं स्मृतम् ॥
कृमिघ्नमगदं प्रोक्तं ज्वरघ्नं कोष्ठशूलजित् ।
श्वासकासाङ्गमर्दादीन् सन्धिशोफं च नाशयेत् ॥" (स्व.)
[`Mūlaṃ tiktamatīvāsya sugandhaṃ ca kaṣāyakaṃ
Viṣahāri tridōṣaghnaṃ dīpanaṃ pācanaṃ smṛtaṃ
Kṛmighnamagadaṃ prōktaṃ jvaraghnaṃ kōṣṭhaśūlajit
Śvāsakāsāṅgamardādīn sandhiśōphaṃ ca nāśayēt'' (Sva.)]

Coll. No. AVS 2411

Artemisia nilagirica (Clarke) Pamp.

(=A.vulgaris *auct. non Linn.*)

Asteraceae : (भृङ्गराज–कुलम्)

Eng	:	Indian wormwood, Fleabane
Hin	:	Nāgdōnā, Davanā, Daunā (नागदोना, दवना, दौना)
Kan	:	Urigaṭṭige, Urruvalu (ಉರಿಗಟ್ಟಿಗೆ, ಉರುವಲು)
Mal	:	Makkippūvu̥, Māśipatṛi (മക്കിപ്പൂവ്, മാശിപത്രി)
San	:	Damanakaḥ, Damanaḥ (दमनकः, दमनः)
Tam	:	Māṣipattiri, Makkippū (மாசிபத்திரி, மக்கிப்பூ)
Tel	:	Māsipatri (మాసిపత్రి)

Distribution : Throughout India,in hilly districts, in areas upto 2,400 m elevation

The plant : A tall aromatic perennial shrub, often gregarious, pubescent or villous throughout; lower leaves ovate in outline deeply pinnatisect with small stipule-like lobes at the base, pubescent above, white - tomentose beneath, uppermost smaller, 3-fid or entire, lanceolate; flowers in subglobose heads, in spicate or suberect or horizontal panicled racemes, outer flowers female, very slender, inner disk flowers fertile, bisexual, bracts ovate or oblong, margins scarious, fruits oblong-ellipsoid minute achenes.

Parts used : leaves, flowering tops

Properties and uses : Leaves and flowering tops are bitter, astringent, acrid, thermogenic, aromatic, anodyne, anti-inflammatory, depurative, diuretic, emmenagogue, aphrodisiac, appetiser, digestive, stomachic, anthelmintic, febrifuge, deobstruent, alexeteric and haematinic. They are useful in vitiated conditions of *vāta* and *kapha,* cough, asthma, bronchitis, cephalalgia, nervous and spasmodic affections, inflammations, leprosy, skin diseases, pruritus, strangury, amenorrhoea, dysmenorrhoea, anorexia, dyspepsia, flatulence, colic, intestinal worms, fever, hysteria, measles and anaemia.

"ऋषिक्षमः सत्यपरः साधकः साधुगन्धिकः
साधुर्मुनिर्दमनकः दमनः कथ्यते बुधैः ॥ "(अ.म.)

[`Ṛṣikṣamaḥ satyaparaḥ sādhakaḥ sādhugandhikaḥ
Sādhurmunirdamanakaḥ damanaḥ kathyatē budhaiḥ'' (A.ma.)]

Artemisia nilagirica

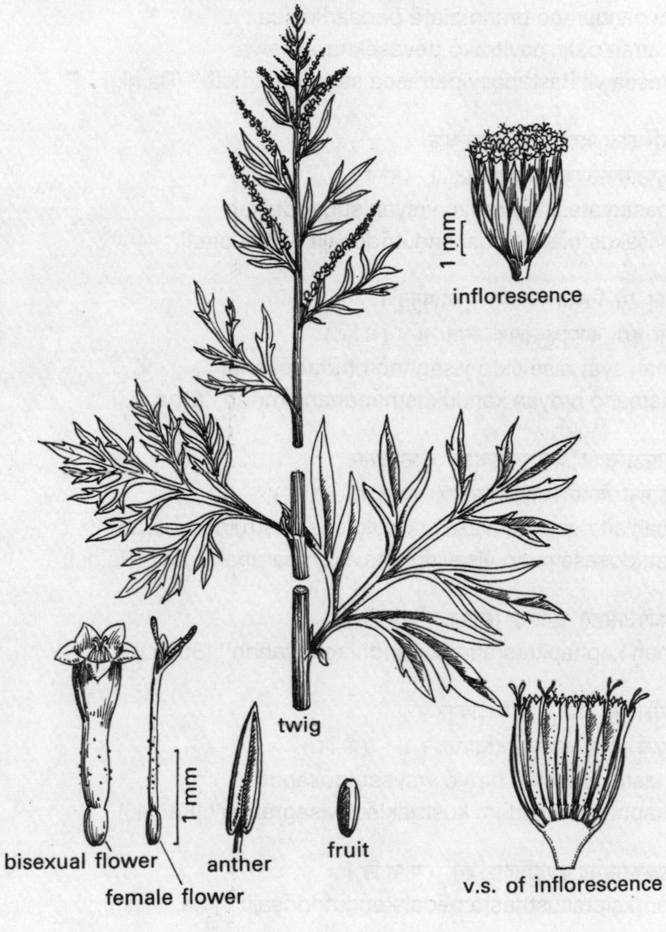

"उक्तो दमनको दान्तो मुनिपुत्रस्तपोधनः ।
गन्धोत्कटो ब्रह्मजटो विनीतः कलपत्रकः ॥ (भा.प्र)
[`Uktō damanakō dāntō muniputṛastapōdhanaḥ
Gandhōtkaṭō brahmajaṭō vinītaḥ kalapatṛakaḥ'' (Bha.pṛa.)]

"अथ दमनकस्तु दमनो दान्तो गन्धोत्कटो मुनिर्जटिलः ।
दण्डी च पाण्डुरागो ब्रह्मजटा पुण्डरीकश्च ॥
तापसपत्रः पत्री पवित्रको देवशेखरश्चैव ।
कुलपत्रश्च विनीतस्तपस्विपत्रश्च सप्तधात्रीकः ॥" (रा.नि.)
[`Atha damanakastu damanō dāntō gandhōlkaṭō munirjaṭilaḥ
Daṇḍī ca pāṇḍurāgō brahmajaṭā puṇḍarīkaśca
Tāpasapatṛaḥ patṛī pavitṛakō dēvaśēkharaścaiva
Kulapatṛaśca vinītastapasvipatṛaśca saptadhātṛīkaḥ'' (Rā.ni.)]

"दमनस्तुवरस्तिक्तो हृद्यो वृष्यः सुगन्धिकः ।
ग्रहणीविषकुष्ठास्रक्लेदकण्डूत्रिदोषजित् ॥" (भा.प्र.)
[`Damanastuvarastiktō hṛdyō vṛṣyaḥ sugandhikaḥ
Grahaṇīviṣakuṣṭhāsṛaklēdakaṇḍūtṛīdōṣajit'' (Bhā.pṛa.)]

"दमनः स्यात् रसे तिक्तो विषघ्नो भूतदोषनुत् ।
त्रिदोषशमनो हृद्यः कण्डूकुष्ठापहः स्मृतः ॥" (ध.नि.)
[`Damanaḥ syāt rasē tiktō viṣaghnō bhūtadōṣanut
Tṛidōṣaśamanō hṛdyaḥ kaṇḍūkuṣṭhāpahaḥ smṛtaḥ'' (Dha.ni.)]

"दमनः शीतळस्तिक्तः कषायकटुकश्च कुष्ठदोषहरः ।
द्वन्द्वत्रिदोषशमनो विषविस्फोटविकारहरणः स्यात् ॥" (रा.नि.)
[`Damanaḥ śītaḷastiktaḥ kaṣāyakaṭukaśca kuṣṭhadōṣaharaḥ
Dvandvatṛidōṣaśamanō viṣavisphōṭavikāraharaṇaḥ syāt'' (Rā.ni.))

"दमनः कफपित्तास्रहृत् सुगन्धि रसायनः ।" (सो.नि)
[`Damanaḥ kaphapittāsṛahṛt sugandhi rasāyanaḥ'' (Sō.ni.)]

"दमनस्तुवरस्तिक्तो हृद्यो वृष्यस्त्रिदोषनुत् ।
निहन्ति कफजं कण्डूं कुष्ठक्लेदविषग्रहान् ॥ " (कै.नि.)
[`Damanastuvarastiktō hṛdyō vṛsyastṛidōṣanut
Nihanti kaphajaṃ kaṇḍūṃ kuṣṭhaklēdaviṣagrahān'' [Kai.ni.)]

"दमनोऽक्षिप्रकुष्ठास्रमेदःकण्डूत्रिदोषजित्" (म.पा.नि.)
[`Damanōऽkṣipṛakuṣṭhāsṛamēdaḥkaṇḍūtṛidōṣajit'' [Ma.pā.ni.)]

Artocarpus communis

Plate 10

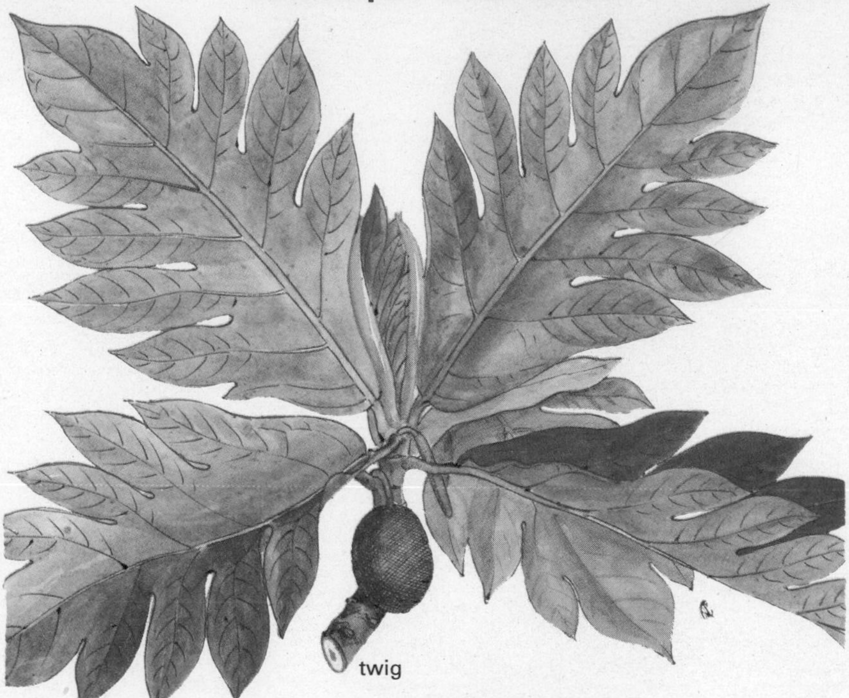

twig

fruit - part exposed

Coll. No. AVS 2455

Artocarpus communis **Forst.**

(=A.incisus *(Thunb.) Linn. f.*)

Moraceae : (वट–कुलम्)

Eng	:	Bread fruit
Hin	:	Bilātti kaṭhal (बिलात्ति कटहल)
Mal	:	Kaṭappilāvu̥, Śīmapḷāvu̥, Kaṭaccakka (കടപ്പിലാവ്, ശീമപ്ലാവ്, കടച്ചക്ക)
San	:	Kṣudrapanasaḥ (क्षुद्रपनसः)
Tam	:	Śīmaippalā (சீமைப்பலா)
Tel	:	Sīmapavara (సీమపవర)

Distribution : Cultivated throughout India

The plant : A tall, fast growing evergreen tree, 12–18 m in height with thick yellowish grey bark; leaves large, simple, incised, dark green; flowers in catkins; fruits prickly, globose, brownish or yellowish, composite, usually seedless.

Parts used : fruits, latex

Properties and uses : The fruits are bitter, sweet, acrid, cooling, diuretic, stomachic, cardiotonic, appetiser and galactagogue. They are useful in vitiated conditions of *pitta,* anorexia, flatulence, colic, cardiac debility and agalactia. The fruit is a tasty and nutritious vegetable. The latex is useful in external application for hyperadenosis and abscesses.

"पनसस्य तु पर्यायैः क्षुद्राल्पपदपूर्वकैः ।
प्रोच्यते क्षुद्रपनसः सोऽतिविस्तारपर्णकः ॥
निर्बीजफलपूर्णः स्यात् सदाफल इति स्मृतः ।" (स्व.)
[`Panasasya tu paryāyaiḥ kṣudrālpapadapūrvakaiḥ
Prōcyatē kṣudrapanasaḥ sōltivistārapaṛṇakaḥ
Niṛbījapḥalapūṛṇaḥ syāt sadāphala iti smṛtaḥ'' (Sva.)]

मधुरं कटुकं क्षुद्रपनसस्य फलं स्मृतम् ॥
मूत्रळं स्तन्यजननं पित्तास्रज्वरदाहनुत् ।
गुल्मशुलहरं रुच्यं हृद्रोगे च प्रशस्यते ॥ (स्व.)
[`Madhuraṃ kaṭukaṃ kṣudrapanasasya phalaṃ smṛtaṃ
Mūtraḷaṃ stanyajananaṃ pittāsṛajvaradāhanut
Gulmaśūlaharaṃ rucyaṃ hṛdrōgē ca praśasyatē'' (Sva.)]

Coll. No. AVS 2190

Artocarpus heterophyllus **Lam.**

(A. integrifolia *auct. non Linn.*)

Moraceae (वट–कुलम्)

Eng	:	Jackfruit tree
Hin	:	Kaṭhal, Cakki (कटहल, चक्की)
Kan	:	Halasu (ಹಲಸು)
Mal	:	Pḷāvụ, Pilāvụ (പ്ലാവ്, പിലാവ്)
San	:	Panasaḥ (पनसः)
Tam	:	Palāmaram (பலாமரம்)
Tel	:	Panasa (పనస)

Distribution : Throughout India

The plant : A large monoecious evergreen tree with very dense rounded crown, 18–25 m in height, bark black mottled with green, rough with warty excrescences, heartwood bright yellow, sapwood pale; leaves simple, alternate, coriaceous, entire, dark, shiny, green above, penninerved, lateral nerves 7–8 pairs, stipules sheathing, leaving a scar on falling; male flowers crowded on cylindrical receptacles; female flowers crowded on globose receptacles–both cauliflorous; fruits multiple, large, fleshy, globose or oblong, covered with tubercles; seeds oval, with a membranous testa, cotyledons unequal.

Parts used : roots, leaves, fruits, seeds, wood, latex

Properties and uses : The roots are credited with antidiarrhoeal property. The leaves are useful in fever, boils, wounds, skin diseases and vitiated conditions of *pitta* and *vāta.* The unripe fruits are acrid, astringent, carminative and tonic. They are useful in vitiated conditions of *kapha,* dyspepsia and debility. The ripe fruits are sweet, cooling, oleagenous, laxative, aphrodisiac and tonic, and are useful in vitiated conditions of *vāta* and *pitta,* and ulcers. The seeds are sweet, diuretic, aphrodisiac and constipating. The wood is a nervine sedative, and is useful in convulsions. The latex is useful in dysopia, ophthalmitis and pharyngitis.

"पनसः स्वर्णसारश्च मोरटो्ग्रज आहळः ।
महाफलो हविर्गन्धी मधुरो मोच उच्यते ॥" (अ.म.)

[`Panasaḥ svarṇasāraśca mōraṭōʃgraja āhaḷaḥ
Mahāphalō havirgandhī madhurō mōca ucyatē'' (A.ma.)]

Plate 11

Artocarpus heterophyllus

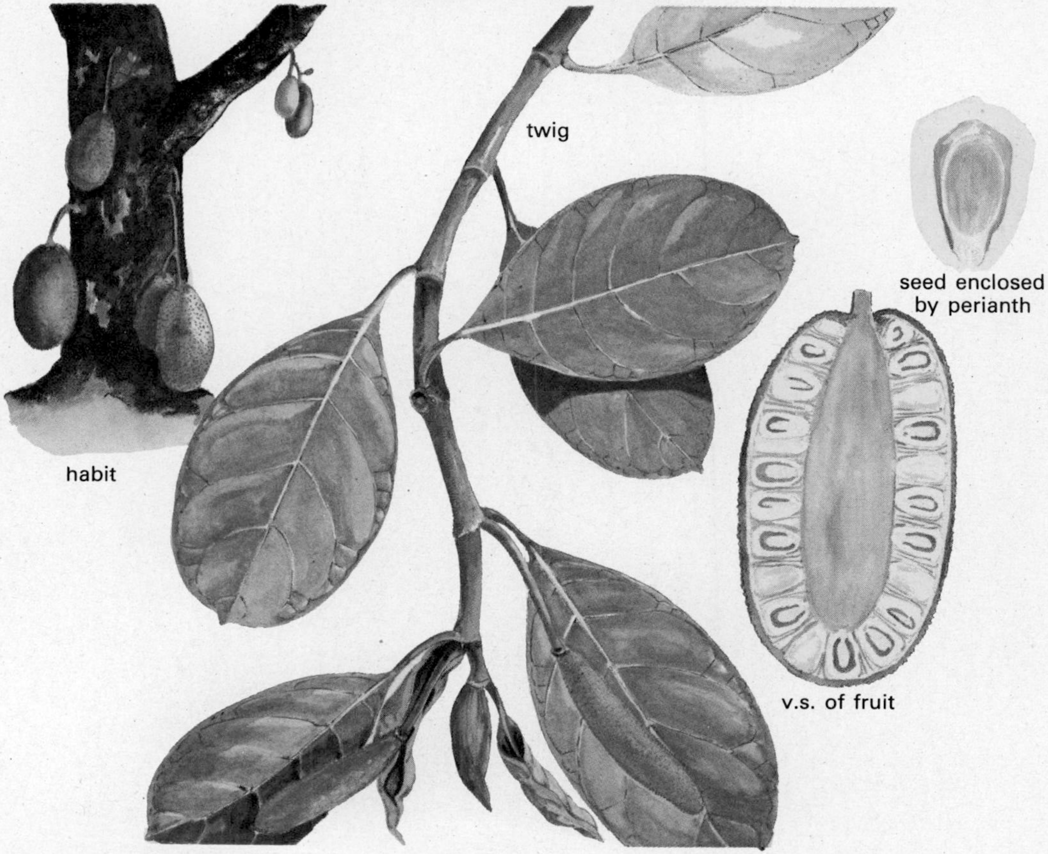

पनसस्तु महासर्जः फलिनः फलवृक्षकः ।
स्थूलकण्टफलश्चैव स्यान्मूलफलदः स्मृतः ॥
अपुष्पफलदः पूतफलो ह्यङ्गमितस्तथा । (रा.नि.)
[`Panasastu mahāsarjaḥ phalinaḥ phalavṛkṣakaḥ
Stūlakanṭaphalaścaiva syānmūlaphaladaḥ smṛtaḥ
Apuṣpaphaladaḥ pūtaphalō hyaṅgamitastathā'' (Rā.ni.)]

"श्ळेष्मातकसदृक्पत्रः स्यात् कण्टकिफलस्तथा ।
पनसस्त्वाशयफल आशयो गर्भकण्टकः ॥" (कै.नि.)
[`Sḷēṣmātakasadṛkpatraḥ syāt kanṭakiphalastathā
Panasastvāśayaphala āśayō garbhakanṭakaḥ'' (Kai.ni.)]

"पनशः कण्टकिफलः पनसोऽतिबृहत्फलः ।" (भा.प्र.)
[`Panaśaḥ kanṭakiphalaḥ panasō'tibṛhatphalaḥ'' (Bhā.pra.)]

"बृहत्स्थूलफलः प्रोक्तः पनसः कण्टकीफलः ।
मृदंगफलकश्चैव स्थूला काण्डफलस्तथा ॥
अपुष्पफलकश्चैव फलवार्षिक एव च ।" (स्व.)
[`Bṛhatsthūlaphalaḥ prōktaḥ panasaḥ kanṭakīphalaḥ
Mṛdaṃgaphalakaścaiva sthūlā kānḍaphalastathā
Apuṣpaphalakaścaiva phalavārṣika ēva ca'' (Sva.)]

"पनसं शीतळं पक्वं स्निग्धं पित्तानिलापहम् ।
तर्पणं बृंहणं स्वादु मांसळं श्ळेष्मळं भृशम् ॥
बल्यं शुक्ळप्रदं हन्ति रक्तपित्तक्षतव्रणान् ।
आमं तदेव विष्टंभि वातळं तुवरं गुरु ॥
दाहकृत् मधुरं बल्यं कफमेदोविवर्धनम् ।
पनसोद्भूतबीजानि वृष्याणि मधुराणि च ॥
गुरूणि बद्धविट्कानि सृष्टमूत्राणि संवदेत् ।
मज्जा पनसजो वृष्यो वातपित्तकफापहः ॥
विशेषात् पनसो वर्ज्यः गुल्मिभिर्मन्दवाह्निभिः ।" (भा.प्र.)
[`Panasaṃ śītaḷaṃ pakvaṃ snigdhaṃ pittānilāpahaṃ
Tarpaṇaṃ bṛṃhaṇaṃ svādu māṃsaḷaṃ śḷēṣmaḷaṃ bṛśaṃ
Balyaṃ śukḷapradaṃ hanti raktapittakṣatavraṇān
Amaṃ tadēva viṣṭambhi vātaḷaṃ tuvaraṃ guru
Dāhakṛt madhuraṃ balyaṃ kaphamēdōvivardhanaṃ
Panasōdbhūtabījāni vṛṣyāṇi madhurāṇi ca
Gurūṇi baddhaviṭkāni sṛṣṭamūtrāṇi saṃvadēt
Majjā panasajō vṛṣyō vātapittakaphāpahaḥ
Viśēṣāt panasō varjyaḥ gulmibhirmandavahnibhiḥ'' (Bhā. pra.)]

"पनसं तुवरं स्वादु गुरु विष्टंभि वातळम् ।
तिक्तं पनसपुष्पन्तु गुरु वक्त्रविशोधनम् ॥
पनसस्यफलं बालं कफमेदोविवर्धनम् ।

वातापित्तहरं बल्यं दाहघ्नं मधुरं गुरु ॥
तद्विशेषाद्विवर्ज्यं स्याद् गुल्मिभिर्दुर्बलाग्निभिः ।
रक्तपित्तहरं पक्वं विपाके स्वादु शीतळम् ॥
तर्पणं बृंहणं वृष्यं मांसळं श्ळेष्मळं भृशम् ।
बल्यं स्निग्धं जयेद्वातं क्षतरक्तक्षयानपि ॥
पनसोद्भूतबीजानि वृष्याणि मधुराणि च ।
गुरुणि बद्धवर्चांसि सृष्टमूत्राणि तानि च ॥
मज्जा तस्यापि पित्तघ्नो वृष्यः श्ळेष्मानिलापहः । " (कै.नि.)
[`Panasaṃ tuvaraṃ svādu guru viṣṭambhi vātaḷaṃ
Tiktaṃ panasapuṣpantu guru vaktṛaviśōdhanaṃ
Panasasyaphalaṃ bālaṃ kaphamēdōvivaṛdhanaṃ
Vātapittaharaṃ balyaṃ dāhaghnaṃ madhuraṃ guru
Tadviśēṣādvivaṛjyaṃ syād gulmibhiṛduṛbalāgnibhiḥ
Raktapittaharaṃ pakvaṃ vipākē svādu śītaḷaṃ
Taṛpaṇaṃ bṛṃhaṇaṃ vṛṣyaṃ māṃsaḷaṃ śḷēṣmaḷaṃ bṛśaṃ
Balyaṃ snigdhaṃ jayēdvātaṃ kṣataraktakṣayānapi
Panasōdbhūtabījāni vṛṣyāṇi madhurāṇi ca
Gurūṇi baddhavaṛcāṃsi sṛṣṭamūtṛāṇi tāni ca
Majjā tasyāpi pittaghnō vṛṣyaḥ śḷēṣmānilāpahaḥ'' (Kai.ni.)]

"रुच्यं पनसबीजं तु स्वादु वृष्यं बलप्रदम् ।
हृद्यं च, अस्यातियोगस्तु शुलाध्मानादिकृत् परम् ॥
वृन्तं पनसपत्रस्य किञ्चित्तिक्तं ज्वरापहम्
प्रोक्तं वातहरं चैव पत्रं चापि तथा स्मृतम् ॥
मूलक्वाथस्त्वतीसारवातशूलाग्निमान्द्यहृत् ।" (स्व.)
[`Rucyaṃ panasabījaṃ tu svādu vṛṣyaṃ balapṛadaṃ
Hṛdyaṃ ca, asyātiyōgastu śūlādhmānādikṛt paraṃ
Vṛntaṃ panasapatṛasya kiñcittiktaṃ jvarāpahaṃ
Pṛōktaṃ vātaharaṃ caiva patṛaṃ cāpi tathā smṛtaṃ
Mūlakvāthastvatīsāravātaśūlāgnimāndyahṛt'' (Sva.)]

पनसं मधुरं सुपिच्छिलं
गुरु हृद्यं बलवीर्यवृद्धिदम् ।
श्रमदाहविशोषनाशनं
रुचिकृद्ग्राहि च दुर्जरं परम् ॥
ईषत्कषायं मधुरं तद्बीजं वातळं गुरु ।
तत्फलस्य विकारघ्नं रुच्यं त्वग्दोषनाशनम् ॥
बालं तु नीरसं हृद्यं मध्यपक्वं तु दीपनम् ।
रुचिदं लवणाद्युक्तं पनसस्य फलं स्मृतम् ॥" (रा.नि.)
[`Panasaṃ madhuraṃ supicchilaṃ
guru hṛdyaṃ balavīryavṛddhidaṃ
Sṛamadāhaviśōṣanāśanaṃ
rucikṛdgrāhi ca duṛjaraṃ paraṃ

Īṣatkaṣāyaṃ madhuraṃ tadbījaṃ vātaḷaṃ guru
Tatphalasya vikāraghnaṃ rucyaṃ tvagdōṣanāśanaṃ
Bālaṃ tu nīrasaṃ hṛdyaṃ madhyapakvaṃ tu dīpanaṃ
Rucidaṃ lavaṇādyuktaṃ panasasya phalaṃ smṛtaṃ'' (Rā.ni.)]

पनसस्य फलं चामं मलावष्टंभकृन्मतम् ।
मधुरं दोषळं बल्यं तुवरं गुरु वातळम् ॥
कोमळं तच्च मधुरं गुरु बल्यं कफप्रदम् ।
मेदोवृद्धिकरं चैव दाहवातप्रपित्तनुत् ॥
तत्पक्वं शीतळं दाहि स्निग्धं वै तृप्तिकारकम् ।
धातुवृद्धिकरं स्वादु मांसळं च कफप्रदम् ॥
बल्यं पुष्टिकरं जन्तुकारकं दुर्जरं वृषम् ।
वातं क्षतक्षयं रक्तपित्तं चाशु व्यपोहति ॥
तस्य बीजन्तु मधुरं वृष्यं विष्टंभकं गुरु ।
तस्य पुष्पं गुरुस्तिक्तं मुखशुद्धिकरं मतम् ॥" (नि.र.)
[`Panasasya phalaṃ cāmaṃ malāvaṣṭambhakṛnmataṃ
Madhuraṃ dōṣaḷaṃ balyaṃ tuvaraṃ guru vātaḷaṃ
Kōmaḷaṃ tacca madhuraṃ guru balyaṃ kaphapradaṃ
Mēdōvṛddhikaraṃ caiva dāhavātaprapittanut
Tatpakvaṃ śītaḷaṃ dāhi snigdhaṃ vai tṛptikārakaṃ
Dhātuvṛddhikaraṃ svādu māṃsaḷaṃ ca kaphapradaṃ
Balyaṃ puṣṭikaraṃ jantukārakaṃ durjaraṃ vṛṣaṃ
Vātaṃ kṣatakṣayaṃ raktapittaṃ cāśu vyapōhati
Tasya bījantu madhuraṃ vṛṣyaṃ viṣṭambhakaṃ guru
Tasya puṣpaṃ gurustiktaṃ mukhaśuddhikaraṃ mataṃ'' (Ni.ra.)]

"ഇടിച്ചക്ക മതൃത്തുള്ളു കഫമേദോബലപ്രദം
വാതവും പിത്തവും ദാഹം ശമിപ്പാനും ഗുണം ഗുരു.
കൃമിക്കും ജഠരാഗ്നിക്കും ബലമില്ലാത്ത മർത്ത്യനും
ഗുന്മിക്കും ജഠരാഗ്നിക്കും നോവുള്ളൊരു ജനത്തിനും
ചക്കപ്പഴം ഭുജിക്കൊല്ലാ തിന്നാൽ സങ്കടമായ് വരും.
ചക്കക്കുരുക്കൾ വൃഷ്യങ്ങൾ മധുരങ്ങളതേറ്റവും
മലം തടുത്തു മൂത്രത്തെ ഒഴിപ്പിക്കുന്നതായ് വരും
മുളച്ച ചക്കക്കുരുവുകൾ മധുരം രസപാകയോഃ
വൃഷ്യം ത്രിദോഷശമനമേറ്റവും ബൃംഹണം ലഘു." (ഗു.പാ.)
[`Iṭiccakka matṛttuḷḷu kaphamēdōbalapradaṃ
Vātavuṃ pittavuṃ dāhaṃ śamippānuṃ guṇaṃ guru
Kṛmikkuṃ jaṭharāgnikkuṃ balamillātta marttyanuṃ
Gulmikkuṃ jaṭharāgnikkuṃ nōvuḷḷoru janattinuṃ
Cakkappaḻaṃ bhujikkollā tinnāl saṅkaṭamāyvaruṃ

Cakkakkurukkaḷ vṛṣyannaḷ madhurannaḷatĕṫṫavuṃ
Malaṃ taṭuttu mūṭratte oḷippikkunnatāyvaruṃ
Muḷacca cakkakkuruvukaḷ madhuraṃ rasapākayōḥ
Vṛṣyaṃ tṛidōṣaśamanamĕṫṫavuṃ bṛmhaṇaṃ laghu" (Gu.pā.)]

Coll. No. AVS 2456

Artocarpus hirsutus **Lam.**

Moraceae : (वट–कुलम्)

Eng	:	Wild jack
Kan	:	Hebbalasu (ಹೆಬ್ಬಲಸು)
Mal	:	Ayani, Ayaniplāvu, Āññali, Āññili (അയനി, അയനിപ്ലാവ്, ആഞ്ഞലി, ആഞ്ഞിലി)
San	:	Lakucaḥ (लकुचः)
Tam	:	Kāṭṭuppalā (காட்டுப்பலா)
Tel	:	Pejuta (పెజుట)

Distribution : Evergreen forests of the West Coast

The plant : A tall, evergreen tree with a straight bole and dense foliage; bark grey, smooth, sapwood white, heartwood yellowish brown; leaves ovate, stipules yellow, hairy; fruits spinous, oblong or cylindrical, 5–7.5 cm long, yellow when ripe.

Parts used : bark, leaves, fruits

Properties and uses : Unripe fruits are sour, astringent, sweet, thermogenic, indigestible, anaphrodisiac and constipating, and cause flatulence, colic, *tridōṣa* and *rakta* vitiations. The ripe fruits are sweet, sour, appetiser, cooling, aphrodisiac and indigestible. They are useful in vitiated conditions of *vāta* and *pitta* and anorexia. An infusion of the bark is applied to cure small pimples and cracks on the skin, and the powdered bark is used to heal sores. Dry leaves are useful in treating bubose and hydrocele.

"लकुचो लिकुचश्शालः कषायी दृढवल्कलः ।
डहुः कार्श्यश्च शूरश्च स्थूलस्कन्धो नवाह्वयः ॥ (रा.नि.)
[`Lakucō likucaśśālaḥ kaṣāyī dṛḍhavalkalaḥ
Ḍahuḥ kārśyaśca śūraśca sthūlaskandhō navāhvayaḥ'' (Rā.ni.)]

"लकुचः स्वरसे तिक्तः कषायोष्णो लघुस्तथा ।
कफदोषहरो दाही मलसंग्रहदायकः ॥" (रा.नि.)
[`Lakucaḥ svarasē tiktaḥ kaṣāyōṣṇō laghustathā
Kaphadōṣaharō dāhī malasaṃgrahadāyakaḥ'' (Rā.ni.)]

Artocarpus hirsutus

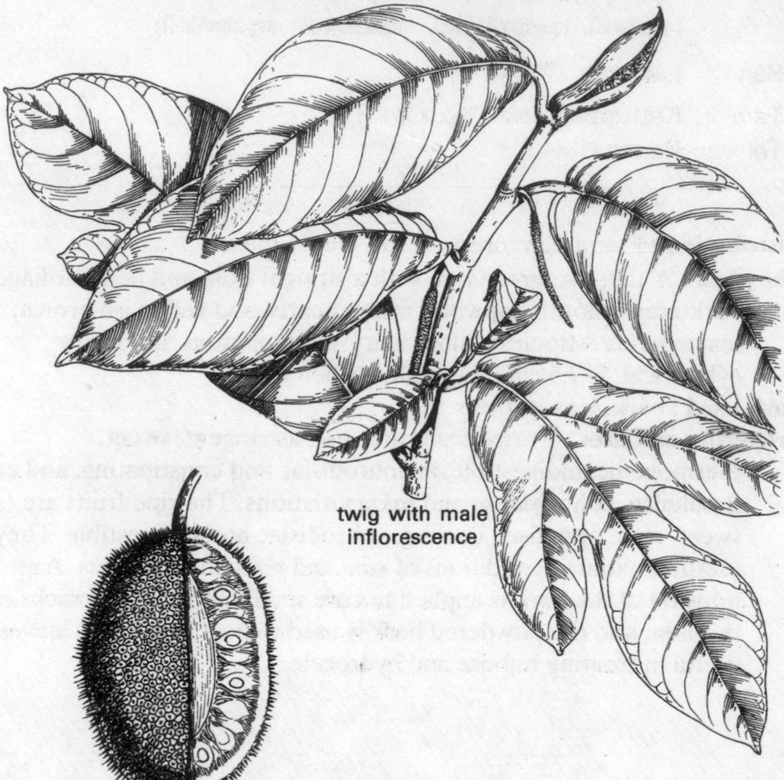

"आमं लकुचमुष्णं च गुरु विष्टंभकृत्तथा ।
मधुरं च तथाम्ळं च दोषत्रितयरक्तकृत् ॥
शुक्ळाग्निनाशनं वापि नेत्रयोरहितं स्मृतम् ।
सुपक्वं तत्तु मधुरमम्ळं चानिलपित्तहृत् ॥
कफवह्निकरं रुच्यं वृष्यं विष्टंभकं च तत् ।" (भा.प्र.)

[`Āmaṃ lakucamuṣṇaṃ ca guru viṣṭambhakṛttathā
Madhuraṃ ca tathāmḷaṃ ca dōṣatritayaraktakṛt
Śukḷāgninaśanaṃ vāpi nētrayōrahitaṃ smṛtaṃ
Supakvaṃ tattu madhuramamḷaṃ cānilapittahṛt
Kaphavahnikaraṃ rucyaṃ vṛṣyaṃ viṣṭambhakaṃ ca tat'' (Bhā.pra.)]

"लकुचं तुवरं चोष्णं फलेष्वप्यवरं गुरु ।
रक्तपित्तं वलासं च कुरुते हरतेऽनिलम् ॥
पक्वं तु स्वादु विष्टंभि वृष्यं दोषाग्निवर्द्धनम् ।" (कै.नि.)

[`Lakucaṃ tuvaraṃ cōṣṇaṃ phalēṣvapyavaraṃ guru
Raktapittaṃ valāsaṃ ca kurutēʃharatēʃnilaṃ
Pakvaṃ tu svādu viṣṭambhi vṛṣyaṃ dōṣāgnivarddhanaṃ'' (Kai.ni.)]

"लकुचं गुरु विष्टंभि स्वाद्वम्ळं रक्तपित्तजित् ।
श्ळेष्मकारी समीरघ्नमुष्णं शुक्ळाग्निनाशनम् ॥" (म.वि.)

[`Lakucaṃ guru viṣṭambhi svādvamḷaṃ raktapittajit
Śḷēṣmakārī samīraghnamuṣṇaṃ śukḷāgninaśanaṃ'' (Ma.vi.)]

"लकुचं गुरु विष्टंभि दोषकृत् शुक्ळशोषणम् ।" (सो.नि.)

[`Lakucaṃ guru viṣṭambhi dōṣakṛt śukḷaśōṣaṇaṃ'' (Sō.ni.)]

Coll. No. AVS 2148

Asparagus racemosus **Willd.**

Liliaceae : (रसोन–कुलम्)

Eng	:	Wild asparagus
Hin	:	Satāvar, Śatamūli (सतावर, शतमूलि)
Kan	:	Callagaḍḍa (ಚಲ್ಲಗಡ್ಡ)
Mal	:	Śatāvari, Śatāvali (ശതാവരി, ശതാവലി)
San	:	Śatāvarī, Ābhīru (शतावरी, आभीरु)
Tam	:	Kilāvari, Śatāvali (கிலாவரி, சதாவலி)
Tel	:	Satāvari, Callagadda (శతావరి, పల్లగడ్డ)

Distribution : Throughout India,in areas upto 1,400 m elevation, also cultivated

The plant : An armed, climbing undershrub with woody terete stems and recurved or rarely straight spines, young stems very delicate, brittle and smooth; leaves reduced to minute chaffy scales and spines; cladodes triquetrous, curved in tufts or 2–6; flowers white, fragrant, in simple or branched racemes on the naked nodes of the main shoots or in the axils of the thorns; fruits globular or obscurely 3-lobed, pulpy berries, purplish black when ripe, seeds with hard and brittle testa.The tuberous succulent roots are 30 cm to a metre or more in length, fascicled at the stem base, smooth, tapering at both ends.

Parts used : tuberous roots

Properties and uses : The roots are bitter, sweet, emollient, cooling, nervine tonic, constipating, galactagogue, ophthalmic, anodyne, aphrodisiac, diuretic, rejuvenating, carminative, appetiser, stomachic, antispasmodic and tonic. They are useful in nervous disorders, dyspepsia, diarrhoea, dysentery, tumours, inflammations, vitiated conditions of *vāta* and *pitta,* burning sensation, hyperdipsia, ophthalmopathy, nephropathy, hepatopathy, strangury, scalding of urine, throat infections, tuberculosis, cough, bronchitis, gleet, gonorrhoea, leucorrhoea, leprosy, epilepsy, fatigue, hyperacidity, colic, haemorrhoids, cardiac debility, hypertension, abortion, agalactia and general debility.

"बहुपुत्रा शतपदी शतमूली शतावरी ।

Asparagus racemosus

Plate 12

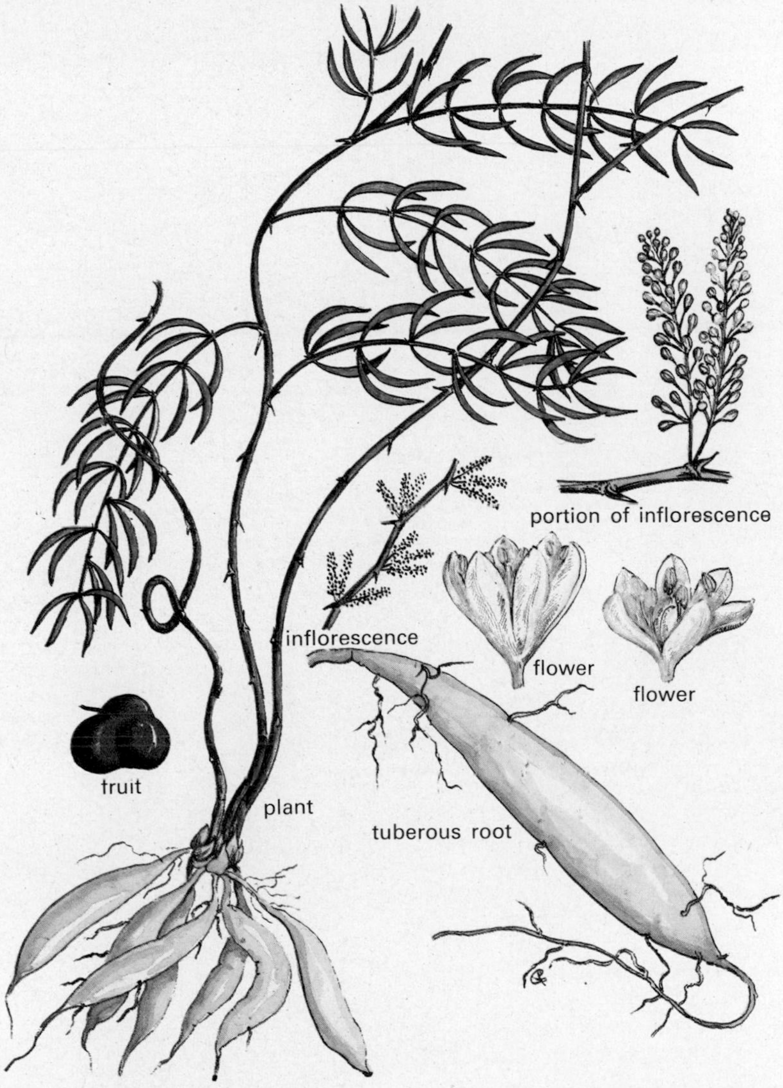

नारायणी द्वीपिशत्रुर्द्वीपिका धरकण्टका ॥
अभीरुस्तुंगिनी केशी पीवरी द्वीपपीवरी ।
सहस्रवीर्या मधुरा फणिजिह्वोर्ध्वकण्टका ॥
ऋष्यप्रोक्ता सूक्ष्मपत्रा महापुरुषदन्तिका ।" (कै.नि.)
[`Bahuputṛā śatapadī śatamūlī śatāvarī
Nārāyaṇī dvīpiśatṛuṛdvīpikā dharakaṇṭakā
Abhīrustuṁginī kēśī pīvarī dvīpapīvarī
Sahasṛavīryā madhurā phaṇijihvōṛdhvakaṇṭakā
Ṛṣyapṛōktā sūkṣmapatṛā mahāpuruṣadantikā'' (Kai.ni.)]

शतावरी शतपदी पीवरीन्दीवरी वरी ।
भीरुर्दीप्या द्वीपिशत्रुर्दीपिका/मरकण्टिका ॥
सूक्ष्मपत्रा सुपत्रा च बहुमूला शताह्वया ।
नारायणी स्वादुरसा शताह्वा लघुपर्णिका ॥
आत्मशल्या जटामूला शतवीर्या महौदनी ।
मधुरा शतमूला च केशिका शतनेत्रिका ॥
विश्वाख्या वैष्णवी कार्ष्णी वासुदेवी वरीयसी ।
दुर्मरा तेजवल्ली च स्यात्रयस्त्रिंशदाह्वया ॥
महाशतावरी वीरा तुङ्गिनी बहुपत्रिका ।
सहस्रवीर्या सुरसा महापुरुषदन्तिका ॥
ऊर्ध्वकण्टा महावीर्या फणिजिह्वा महाशता ।
शतवीर्या सुवीर्या च नामान्यस्यास्त्रयोदश ॥ (रा.नि.)
[`Śatāvarī śatapadī pīvarīndīvarī varī
Bhīruṛdīpyā dvīpiśatṛuṛdvīpikā/marakaṇṭikā
Sūkṣmapatṛā supatṛā ca bahumūlā śatāhvayā
Nārāyaṇī svādurasā śatāhvā laghuparṇikā
Atmaśalyā jaṭāmūlā śatavīryā mahaudanī
Madhurā śatamūlā ca kēśikā śatanētṛikā
Viśvākhyā vaiṣṇavī kāṛṣṇī vāsudēvī varīyasī
Duṛmarā tējavallī ca syāttṛayastṛiṁśadāhvayā
Mahāśatāvarī vīrā tunginī bahupatṛikā
Sahasṛavīryā surasā mahāpuruṣadantikā
Urdhvakaṇṭā mahāvīryā phaṇijihvā mahāśatā
Śatavīryā suvīryā ca nāmānyasyāstṛayōdaśa'' (Rā.ni.)]

"शतावरी गुरुः शीता तिक्ता स्वाद्वी रसायनी ।
मेधाग्निपुष्टिदा स्निग्धा नेत्र्या गुल्मातिसारजित् ॥
शुक्लस्तन्यकरी बल्या वातपित्तास्रशोफजित् ।
महाशतावरी मेध्या हृद्या वृष्या रसायनी ॥
शीतवीर्या निहन्त्यर्शोग्रहणीनयनामयान् ।" (भा.प्र.)
[`Śatāvarī guruḥ śītā tiktā svādvī rasāyanī
Mēdhāgnipuṣṭidā snigdhā nētṛyā gulmātisārajit
Śukḷastanyakarī balyā vātapittāsṛaśōphajit

Mahāśatāvarī mēdhyā hṛdyā vṛṣyā rasāyanī
Sītavīryā nihantyarśōgrahaṇīnayanāmayān'' (Bhā.pra.)]

"वातपित्तहरी वृष्या स्वादुतिक्ता शतावरी ।
महती चैव हृद्या च मेधाग्निबलवर्द्धिनी ॥
ग्रहण्यर्शोविकारघ्नी वृष्या शीता रसायनी ।
कफपित्तहरास्तिक्तास्तस्या एवाङ्कुरा स्मृताः ॥" (सु.सू.४६)
[`Vātapittaharī vṛṣyā svādutiktā śatāvarī
Mahatī caiva hṛdyā ca mēdhāgnibalavarddhinī
Grahaṇyarvśōvikāraghnī vṛṣyā śītā rasāyanī
Kaphapittaharastiktāstasyā ēvānkurā smṛtāḥ'' (Su.Sū.46.)]

"वातपित्तहरा वृष्या बल्या शीता रसायनी ।
स्वादुः शतावरी तैलघृतयोगेषु पूजिता ॥ " (म.नि.)
[`Vātapittaharā vṛṣyā balyā śītā rasāyanī
Svāduḥ śatāvarī tailaghṛtayōgēṣu pūjitā'' (Ma.ni.)]

"शतावरी हिमा तिक्ता रसे स्वादुः क्षयास्रजित् ।
वातपित्तहरा वृष्या रसायनवरा स्मृता ॥
सहस्रवीर्या मेध्या तु हृद्या वृष्या रसायनी ।
शीतवीर्या निहन्त्यर्शोग्रहणीनयनामयान् ॥
तदङ्कुरस्त्रिदोषघ्नो लघुरर्शःक्षयापहः ।" (ध.नि.)
[`Satāvarī himā tiktā rasē svāduḥ kṣayāsṛajit
Vātapittaharā vṛṣyā rasāyanavarā smṛtā
Sahasṛavīryā mēdhyā tu hṛdyā vṛṣyā rasāyanī
Sītavīryā nihantyarśōgrahaṇīnayanāmayān
Tadankurastṛidōṣaghnō laghurarśaḥkṣayāpahaḥ'' (Dha.ni.)]

"शतावर्यौ हिमे वृष्ये मधुरे पित्तजित्परे ।
कफवातहरे तिक्ते महाश्रेष्ठे रसायने ॥
शतावरीद्वयं वृष्यं मधुरं पित्तजिद्धिमम् ।
महती कफवातघ्नी तिक्ता श्रेष्ठा रसायने ॥
कफपित्तहरास्तिक्तास्तस्या एवाङ्कुरा स्मृता ।" (रा.नि.)
[`Satāvaryau himē vṛṣyē madhurē pittajitparē
Kaphavātaharē tiktē mahāśṛēṣṭhē rasāyanē
Satāvarīdvayaṃ vṛṣyaṃ madhuraṃ pittajiddhimaṃ
Mahatī kaphavātaghnī tiktā śṛēṣṭhā rasāyanē
Kaphapittaharāstiktāstasyā ēvānkurā smṛtā'' (Rā.ni.)]

"शतावरी हिमा तिक्ता स्वाद्वी गुर्वी रसायनी ।
सुस्निग्धा शुक्ळळा बल्या स्तन्यमेधाग्निपुष्टिदा ॥
चक्षुष्या वातपित्तास्रगुल्मातीसारशोफजित्
महाशतावरी हृद्या मेधग्निबलशुक्ळदा ॥
ग्रहण्यर्शोक्षिरोगघ्नी शीतवीर्या रसायनी ।

तदङ्कुरो लघुस्तिक्तो वृष्यो हृद्यस्त्रिदोषनुत् ॥
निहन्ति वातपित्तास्रग्रहणीगुदजक्षयान् ।" (कै.नि.)
[`Satavarī himā tiktā svādvī guṛvī rasāyanī
Susnigdhā śukḷaḷā balyā stanyamēdhāgnipuṣṭidā
Cakṣuṣyā vātapittāsṛagulmātīsāraśōphajit
Mahāśatāvarī hṛdyā mēdhāgnibalaśukḷadā
Grahaṇyaṛśōḷkṣirōgaghnī śītavīryā rasāyanī
Tadankurō laghustiktō vṛṣyō hṛdyastṛidōṣanut
Nihanti vātapittāsṛagrahaṇīgudajakṣayān'' (Kai.ni.)]

"शतावरी तु मधुरा शीता वृष्या च तिक्तका ।
रसायनी गुरुः स्वादुः स्निग्धा दुग्धप्रदा मता ॥
अग्निदीप्तिकरी बल्या मेध्या शुक्ळकरी मता ।
चक्षुष्या पुष्टिकृत्पित्तकफवातक्षयापहा ॥
रक्तदोषगुल्महन्त्री शोफातीसारनाशिनी ।
तैले घृते प्रयोगार्थ प्रशस्ता मुनिभिर्मता ॥
महाशतावरी हृद्या मेध्या चाग्निप्रदीपनी ।
शुक्ळळा शीतवीर्या च बल्या वृष्या रसायनी ॥
अर्शसंग्रहणीरोगनेत्ररोगविनाशिनी ।
गुणाह्यस्यास्तु विज्ञेयाः पूर्वायाः सदृशा गुणैः ॥ " (नि.र.)
[`Satāvarī tu madhurā śītā vṛṣyā ca tiktakā
Rasāyanī guruḥ svāduḥ snigdhā dugdhapṛadā matā
Agnidīptikarī balyā mēdhyā śukḷakarī matā
Cakṣuṣyā puṣṭikṛtpittakaphavātakṣayāpahā
Raktadōṣagulmahantṛī śōphātīsāranāśinī
Tailē ghṛtē pṛayōgāṛtha pṛaśastā munibhiṛmatā
Mahāśatāvarī hṛdyā mēdhyā cāgnipṛadīpanī
Sukḷaḷā śītavīryā ca balyā vṛṣyā rasāyanī
Aṛśaḥsaṃgrahaṇīrōganētṛarōgavināśinī
Guṇāhyasyāstu vijñēyāḥ pūṛvāyāḥ sadṛśā guṇaiḥ'' (Ni.ra.)]

"ശതാവരിക്കിഴങ്ങിൻെറ രസം കച്ചുമതൃത്തത്
ഗുണന്തു ബൃംഹണം മൂത്രദോഷഘ്നം വാതപിത്തജിത്
ഇന്ദ്രിയത്തെപ്പെരുപ്പിക്കും മേദോഗ്നിബലവർദ്ധനം." (ഗു.പാ.)
["Satāvarikkiḻanniṟe rasaṃ kaccumatṛttatụ
Guṇantu bṛmhaṇaṃ mūtṛadōṣaghnaṃ vātapittajit
Indriyattepperuppikkuṃ mēdōgnibalavaṛddhanaṃ" (Gu.pā.)]

Remarks: Most of the herbal dictionaries in Sanskrit describe two kinds of Asparagus viz. *śatāvarī* and *Mahāśatāvarī*. Of these, *Mahāśatāvarī* and its synonyms have been identified as *Asparagus sarmentosus* Linn.

In Kerala, however, all the different species of Asparagus are regarded as *śatāvarī*.

Coll. No. AVS 2194

Averrhoa carambola **Linn.**

Oxalidaceae : (चाङ्ेरी–कुलम्)

Eng	:	Carambola apple, Coromandel gooseberry
Hin	:	Kamarakh, Kamaraṁgā (कमरख, कमरंगा)
Kan	:	Dērehuḷi (ದೇರೆಹುಳಿ)
Mal	:	Caturappuḷi, Iruṁpanpuḷi (ചതുരപ്പുളി, ഇരുമ്പൻപുളി)
San	:	Kaṛmaraṅgaḥ, Kārukaḥ (कर्मरङ्गः, कारुकः)
Tam	:	Tāmarattai (தாமரத்தை)
Tel	:	Karamonga, Tāmaratama (కరమొంగ, తామరతమ)

Distribution: Throughout India, cultivated

The plant: A small,handsome evergreen tree about 9.0 m in height with close drooping branches; leaves compound, alternate, leaflets 5–11, glabrous, glaucous beneath, base oblique, acute; flowers variegated with white and purple in short racemes, chiefly axillary or sometimes springing from the stem; fruits ovoid, 5-angled, indehiscent, yellowish berry, seeds arillate.

Parts used: leaves, fruits

Properties and uses: The leaves are antipruritic, antipyretic and anthelmintic. They are useful in scabies, various types of poisoning, pruritus, intermittent fevers and intestinal worms.

The fruits are sweet, sour, thermogenic, constipating, febrifuge, antipyretic, antiscorbutic and tonic. They are useful in diarrhoea, vomiting, hyperdipsia, haemorrhoids, intermittent fever, hepatodynia, scabies, various kinds of poisoning and general debility.

"कर्मारः कर्मरकः पीतफलः कर्मरश्च मुद्गरकः ।
मुद्गरफलश्च धाराफलकस्तु कर्मारकश्चैव ॥" (रा.नि.)
[" Kaṛmāraḥ kaṛmarakaḥ pītaphalaḥ kaṛmaraśca mudgarakaḥ
Mudgaraphalaśca dhārāphalakastu kaṛmārakaścaiva" (Rā.ni.)]

"कर्मरङ्गं हिमं ग्राहि स्वाद्वम्ळं कफवातहृत् ।" (भा.प्र.)
["Kaṛmaraṅgaṃ himaṃ grāhi svādvamḷaṃ kaphavātahṛt" (Bhā.pra.)]

"कर्मारकोऽम्ळ उष्णश्च वातहृत् पित्तकारकः ।

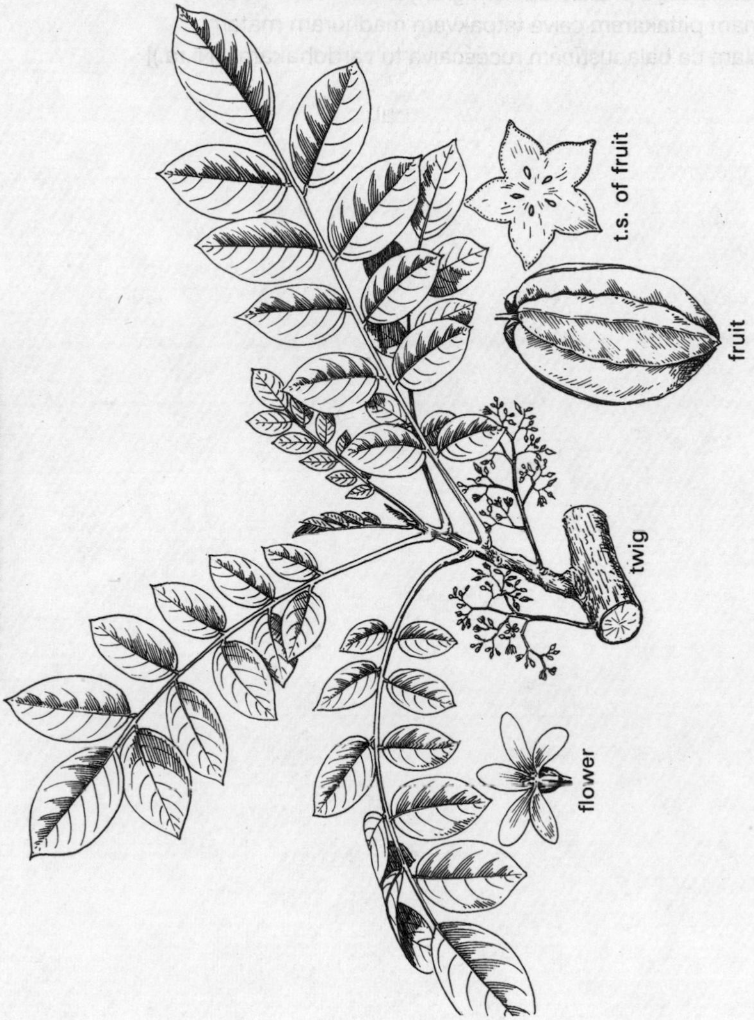

Averrhoa carambola

पक्वस्तु मधुराम्ळः स्याद् बलपुष्टिरुचिप्रदः ॥ (रा.नि.)
["Kaṛmārakōʃṁḷa uṣṇaśca vātahṛt pittakārakaḥ
Pakvastu madhurāmḷaḥ syād balapuṣṭirucipṛadaḥ" (Rā.ni.)]

"कर्मारस्य फलं चामं ग्राह्याम्ळं वातनाशकम् ।
उष्णं पित्तकरं चैव तत्पक्वं मधुरं मतम् ॥
अम्ळं च बलपुष्टीनां रुचेश्चैव तु वर्द्धकम् ॥" (नि.र.)
["Kaṛmārasya phalaṃ cāmaṃ grāhyāmḷaṃ vātanāśakaṃ
Uṣṇaṃ pittakaraṃ caiva tatpakvaṃ madhuraṃ mataṃ
Aṁḷaṃ ca balapuṣṭīnāṃ rucēścaiva tu vaṛddhakaṃ" (Ni.ra.)]

Coll. No. AVS 1971

Azadirachta indica **A. Juss.**

(Melia azadirachta *Linn.*)

Meliaceae : (निम्ब–कुलम्)

Eng	:	Neem tree, Margosa tree, Indian lilac
Hin	:	Nīṃ, Niṁb (नीम, निम्ब)
Kan	:	Turakabēvu, Huccabēvu, Cikkabēvu (ತುರಕಬೇವು. ಹುಚ್ಚಬೇವು. ಚಿಕ್ಕಬೇವು)
Mal	:	Vēppu, Āryavēppu, Āruvēppu, Kaippanvēppu (വേപ്പ്, ആര്യവേപ്പ്, ആരുവേപ്പ, കൈപ്പൻ വേപ്പ്)
San	:	Niṁbaḥ, Pṛabhadraḥ (निम्बः, प्रभद्रः)
Tam	:	Vēmpu, Vēppu (வேம்பு, வேப்பு)
Tel	:	Koṇḍavepa, Turakavepa (కొండవేప, తురకవేప)

Distribution: Throughout India,in deciduous forests, also widely cultivated

The plant: A medium to large sized tree, 15–20 m in height with a clear bole of 7.0 m having greyish to dark grey tubercled bark; leaves compound, imparipinnate, leaflets, subopposite, serrate, very oblique at base; flowers cream or yellowish white in axillary panicles, staminal tubes conspicuous, cylindric, widening above, 9–10 lobed at the apex; fruits one-seeded drupes with woody endocarp greenish yellow when ripe, seeds ellipsoid, cotyledons thick, fleshy and oily.

Parts used: bark, leaves, flowers, seeds, oil

Properties and uses: The bark is bitter, astringent, acrid, refrigerant, depurative, antiperiodic, vulnerary, demulcent, insecticidal, liver tonic, expectorant, urinary astringent, anthelmintic, pectoral and tonic. It is useful in vitiated conditions of *pitta,* hyperdipsia, leprosy, skin diseases, eczema, leucoderma, pruritus, intermittent and malarial fevers, wounds, ulcers, burning sensation, tumour, tubercular glands, anorexia, vomiting, dyspepsia, intestinal worms, hepatopathy, cough, bronchitis, urorrhea, diabetes, inflammation, amenorrhoea, lumbago, haemorrhoids, otalgia, syphilis and fatigue.

The leaves are bitter, astringent, acrid, depurative, antiseptic, ophthalmic, anthelmintic, alexeteric, appetiser, insecticidal, demulcent and refrigerant. They are useful in vitiated conditions of *pitta,* burning sensation, leprosy, skin diseases, leucoderma, pruritus, ophthalmopathy, intestinal worms, dyspepsia, ulcers, tuberculosis, boils, eczema and malarial and intermittent fevers.

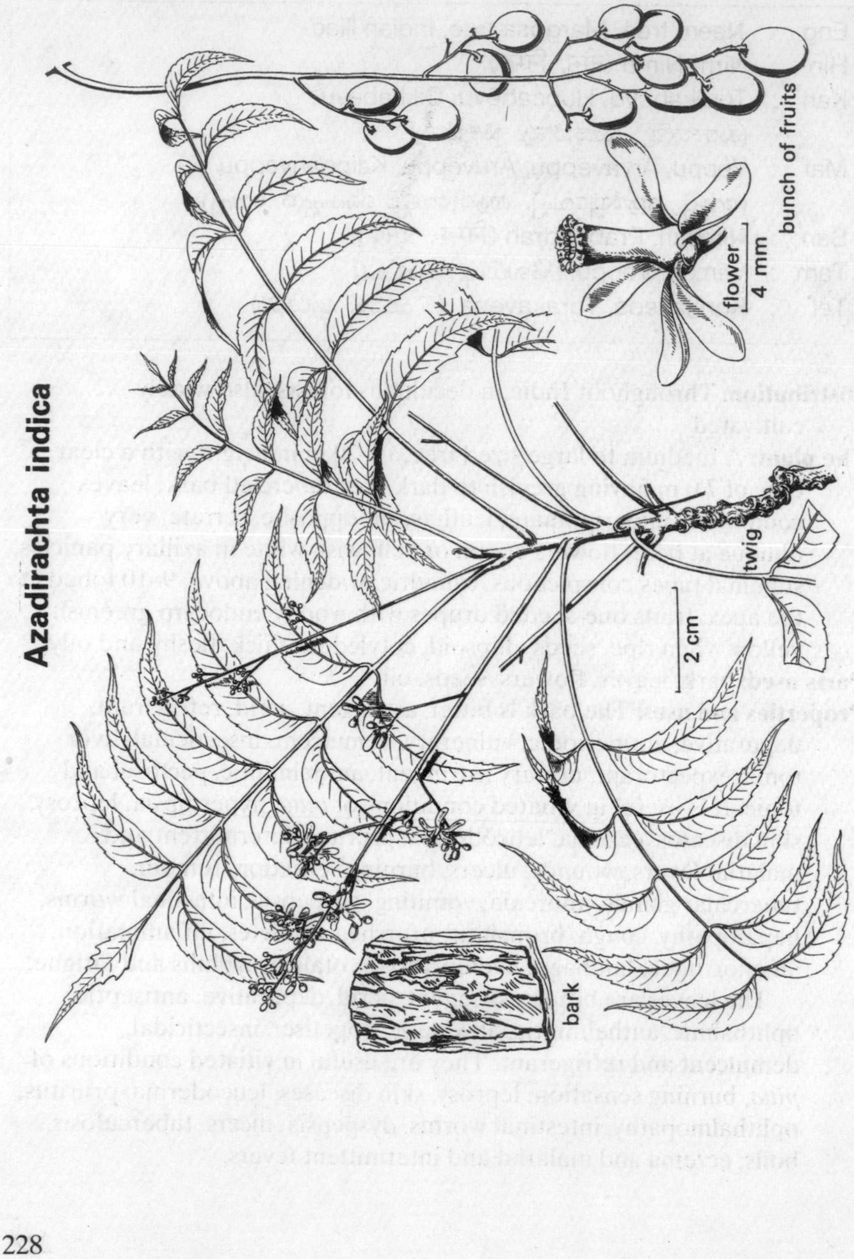
Azadirachta indica
bunch of fruits
flower
4 mm
twig
2 cm
bark

The flowers are bitter, refrigerant, ophthalmic, stomachic, anthelmintic and tonic. They are useful in vitiated conditions of *pitta* and *kapha,* burning sensation, ophthalmopathy, colic, dyspepsia, intestinal worms and general debility.

The seeds are bitter, acrid, thermogenic, purgative, emollient, anodyne, anthelmintic, depurative, vulnerary, uterine stimulant and urinary astringent. They are useful in tumours, leprosy, skin diseases, odontalgia, intestinal worms, haemorrhoids, pulmonary tuberculosis, ophthalmopathy, wounds, ulcers, constipation, dystocia, antenatal diseases, urorrhea and diabetes.

The oil is bitter, anthelmintic, anodyne and depurative. It is useful in vitiated conditions of *vāta,* chronic skin diseases, syphilitic sores, indolent ulcers, ringworm, scabies, intestinal worms, chronic malarial fever and leprosy.

"अथ निगदितः प्रभद्रः पिचुमन्दः पारिभद्रको निम्बः ।
काकफलः कीरेष्टो नेतारिष्टश्च सर्वतोभद्रः ॥
धमनो विशीर्णपर्णो पवनेष्टः पीतसारकः शीतः ।
वरतिक्तोऽरिष्टफलो ज्येष्ठामलकश्च हिंगुनिर्यासः ॥
छर्दनश्चाग्निधमनो ज्ञेया नाम्ना तु विंशतिः । " (रा.नि.)

["Atha nigaditaḥ prabhadraḥ picumandaḥ pāribhadrakō nimbaḥ
Kākaphalaḥ kīrēṣṭō nētāriṣṭaśca sarvatōbhadraḥ
Dhamanō viśīrṇaparṇō pavanēṣṭaḥ pītasārakaḥ śītaḥ
Varatiktō'riṣṭaphalō jyēṣṭhāmalakaśca himguniryāsaḥ
Chardanaścāgnidhamanō jñēyā nāmnā tu vimśatiḥ" (Rā.ni.)]

"निम्बः स्यात् पिचुमर्दश्च पिचुमन्दश्च तिक्तकः ।
अरिष्टः पारिभद्रश्च हिंगुनिर्यास इत्यपि ॥" (भा.प्र.)

["Nimbaḥ syāt picumardaśca picumandasca tiktakaḥ
Ariṣṭaḥ pāribhadraśca himguniryāsa ityapi" (Bhā.pra.)]

"निम्बो नियामनो नेता पिचुमन्दः सुतिक्तकः ।
अरिष्टः सर्वतोभद्रः सुभद्रः पारिभद्रकः ॥
शुकप्रियश्चीर्णपर्णो यवनेष्टो वरत्वचः ।
छर्दनो हिंगुनिर्यास पीतसारो रविप्रियः ॥" (सो.नि.)

["Nimbō niyāmanō nētā picumandaḥ sutiktakaḥ
Ariṣṭaḥ sarvatōbhadraḥ subhadraḥ pāribhadrakaḥ
Sukapriyaścīrṇaparṇō yavanēṣṭō varatvacaḥ
Chardanō himguniryāsaḥ pītasārō ravipriaḥ" (Sō.ni.)]

"निम्बस्तिक्तः कटुः पाके लघुः शीतोऽग्निवातकृत् ।
ग्राह्यहृद्यो जयेत् पित्तकफमेहज्वरकृमीन् ॥
कुष्ठकासारुचिश्वासहृल्लासश्वयथुव्रणान् ।
ग्राहि प्रवाळं निम्बस्य रक्तपित्तकफकृमीन् ॥
कुष्ठघ्नं वातजननं नेत्ररोगान् विनाशयेत् ।

तद्वत् पत्रणि निम्बस्य व्रणघ्नानि विशेषतः ॥
शलाका निम्बपत्रस्य कासश्वासविनाशिनी ।
कृमिघ्ना तु वरिष्ठा स्यात् कुष्ठज्वरविनाशिनी ॥
चक्षुष्यं निम्बपुष्पं च कृमिपित्तविषप्रणुत् ।
वातळं कटुपाकं स्यात् सर्वारोचकनाशनम् ॥
फलं तिक्तं रसे पाके कटुकं भेदनं लघु ।
अरूक्षमुष्णं कुष्ठघ्नं गुल्मार्शःकृमिमेहनुत् ॥
निम्बस्य पक्वं मधुरं सतिक्तं
स्निग्धं फलं शोणितपित्तरोगे ।
कफे प्रशस्तं नयनामयघ्नं
क्षतक्षयघ्नं गुरु पिच्छिलं च ॥
निम्बबीजस्य मज्जा च कृमिकुष्ठविशोधनः ।
नात्युष्णं निम्बजं तिक्तं कृमिकुष्ठकफप्रणुत् ॥
अभ्यङ्गान्नावनात् क्षीरभोजिनः पलितापहम् ।" (कै.नि.)

["Nimbastiktaḥ kaṭuḥ pākē laghuḥ śītō|gnivātakṛt
Grāhyahṛdyō jayēt pittakaphamēhajvarakṛmīn
Kuṣṭhakāsāruciśvāsahṛllāsaśvayathuvṛaṇān
Grāhi pṛavāḷaṃ nimbasya raktapittakaphakṛmīn
Kuṣṭhaghnaṃ vātajanaṃ nētrarōgān vināśayēt
Tadvat patṛāṇi nimbasya vṛaṇaghnāni viśēṣataḥ
Śalākā nimbapatṛasya kāsaśvāṣavināśinī
Kṛmighnā tu variṣṭhā syāt kuṣṭhajvaravināśinī
Cakṣuṣyaṃ nimbapuṣpaṃ ca kṛmipittaviṣapṛaṇut
Vātaḷaṃ kaṭupākaṃ syāt saṛvārōcakanāśanaṃ
Phalaṃ tiktaṃ rasē pākē kaṭukaṃ bhēdanaṃ laghu
Arūkṣamuṣṇaṃ kuṣṭhaghnaṃ gulmāṛśaḥkṛmimēhanut
Nimbasya pakvaṃ madhuraṃ satiktaṃ
snigdhaṃ phalaṃ śōṇitapittarōgē
Kaphē pṛaśastaṃ nayanāmayaghnaṃ
kṣatakṣayaghnaṃ guru picchilaṃ ca
Nimbabījasya majjā ca kṛmikuṣṭhaviśōdhanaḥ
Nātyuṣṇaṃ nimbajaṃ tiktaṃ kṛmikuṣṭhakaphapṛaṇut
Abhyaṅgānnāvanāt kṣīrabhōjinaḥ palitāpahaṃ" (Kai.ni.)]

"निम्बः शीतो लघुर्गाही कटुपाको|ग्निवातनुत् ।
अहृद्यः श्रमतृट्कासज्वरारुचिकृमिप्रणुत् ॥
व्रणपित्तकफच्छर्दिकुष्ठहल्लासमेहनुत् ।
निम्बपत्रं स्मृतं नेत्र्यं कृमिपित्तविषप्रणुत् ॥
वातळं कटुपाकं च सर्वारोचककुष्ठनुत् ।
नैम्बं फलं रसे तिक्तं पाके तु कटु भेदनम् ॥
स्निग्धं लघूष्णं कुष्ठघ्नं गुल्मार्शः कृमिमेहनुत् ॥ (भा.प्र.)
[Nimbaḥ śītō laghuṛgrāhī kaṭupākō|gnivātanut
Ahṛdyaḥ śramatṛṭkāsajvarāṛucikṛmipṛaṇut

Vṛaṇapittakaphacchardikuṣṭhahṛllāsamēhanut
Nimbapatṛaṃ smṛtaṃ nētṛyaṃ kṛmipittaviṣapṛaṇut
Vātaḷaṃ kaṭupākaṃ ca saṛvārōcakakuṣṭhanut
Naimbaṃ phalaṃ rasē tiktaṃ pākē tu kaṭu bhēdanaṃ
Snigdhaṃ laghūṣṇaṃ kuṣṭhaghnaṃ gulmāṛśaḥkṛmimēhanut"(Bhā.pṛa.)]

"निम्बस्तिक्तरसः शीतो लघुः श्लेष्मास्रपित्तनुत् ।
कुष्ठकण्डूव्रणान् हन्ति लेपहारादिशीलितः ॥
अपक्वं पाययेच्छोफं व्रणं पक्वं विशोधयेत् ।
नात्युष्णं निम्बजं तैलं कृमिकुष्ठकफापहम् ॥
वातरक्तप्रशमनं मदालक्ष्मीज्वरापहम् । " (ध.नि.)
["Nimbastiktarasaḥ śītō laghuḥ śḷēṣmāsṛapittanut
Kuṣṭhakaṇḍūvṛaṇān hanti lēpahārādiśīlitaḥ
Apakaṃ pāyayēcchōphaṃ vṛaṇaṃ pakvaṃ viśōdhayēt
Nātyuṣṇaṃ nimbajaṃ tailaṃ kṛmikuṣṭhakaphāpahaṃ
Vātaraktapṛaśamanaṃ madālakṣhmījvarāpahaṃ"(Dha.ni.)]

"प्रभद्रकः प्रभवति शीततिक्तकः
कफव्रणकृमिवमिशोफशान्तये ।
वलासभिद् बहुविषपित्तदोषजिद्
विशेषतो हृदयविदाहशान्तिकृत् ॥
निम्बतैलं तु नात्युष्णं कृमिकुष्ठकफापहम् । " (रा.नि.)
["Pṛabhadrakaḥ pṛabhavati śītatiktakaḥ
kaphavṛaṇakṛmivamiśōphaśāntayē
Valāsabhid bahuviṣapittadōṣajit
Viśēṣatō hṛdayavidāhaśāntikṛt
Nimbatailaṃ tu nātyuṣṇaṃ kṛmikuṣṭhakaphāpahaṃ" (Rā.ni.)]

निम्बवृक्षो लघुः शीतस्तिक्तो ग्राही कटुः स्मृतः ।
अग्निमान्द्यकरश्चैव व्रणशोधनकारकः ॥
शोफपाककरो बाले हितो रुद्यो मतो बुधैः ।
कृमिवान्तिव्रणकफशोफपित्तविषापहः ॥
वातं कुष्ठं च हृद्दाहं श्रमं कासं ज्वरं तृषां ।
अरुचिं रक्तदोषं च मेहं चैव विनाशयेत् ॥
कोमलः पल्लवश्चास्य ग्राहको वातकारकः ।
रक्तपित्तं नेत्ररोगं कुष्ठं चैव विनाशयेत् ॥
जीर्णपर्णं विशेषेण व्रणनाशकरं मतम् ।" (नि.र.)
["Nimbavṛkṣō laghuḥ śītastiktō grāhī kaṭuḥ smṛtaḥ
Agnimāndyakaraścaiva vṛaṇaśōdhanakārakaḥ
Sōphapākakarō bālē hitō rudyō matō budhaiḥ
Kṛmivāntivṛaṇakaphaśōphapittaviṣāpahaḥ
Vātaṃ kuṣṭhaṃ ca hṛddāhaṃ śṛamaṃ kāsaṃ jvaraṃ tṛṣāṃ
Arucim raktadōṣaṃ ca mēhaṃ caiva vināśayēt

Kōmaḷaḥ pallavaścāsya grāhakō vātakārakaḥ
Raktapittaṃ nētṛarōgaṃ kuṣṭhaṃ caiva vināśayēt
Jīṛṇapaṛṇaṃ viśēṣēṇa vṛaṇanāśakaraṃ mataṃ " (Ni.ra.)]

"निम्बवृक्षस्य पुष्पाणि पित्तघ्नानि विशेषतः ।
तिक्तानि च कृमिघ्नानि तथा कफहराणि च ॥
निम्बस्य सूक्ष्मशाखा तु कासश्वासार्शःगुल्महा ।
कृमिमेहहरा प्रोक्ता फलं चामं लघु स्मृतम् ॥
स्निग्धं च भेदकं चोष्णं मेहकुष्ठविनाशकम् ।
आमं फलं रसे तिक्तं पाके तु कटुकं मतम् ॥
स्निग्धं लघूष्णं कुष्ठघ्नं गुल्मार्शःकृमिमेहनुत् ।
निम्बबीजस्य मज्जा तु कुष्ठघ्नी कृमिनाशिनी ॥
निम्बतैलन्तु कुष्ठघ्नं तिक्तं कृमिहरं परम् ।
निम्बवृक्षस्य पञ्चाङ्गं रक्तदोषहरं मतम् ॥
पित्तं कण्डूं व्रणं दाहं कुष्ठं चैव विनाशयेत् । (शा. नि.)
["Nimbavṛkṣasya puṣpāṇi pittaghnāni viśēṣataḥ
Tiktāni ca kṛmighnāni tathā kaphaharāṇi ca
Nimbasya sūkṣmaśākhā tu kāsaśvāsāṛśaḥgulmahā
Kṛmimēhaharā prōktā phalaṃ cāmaṃ laghu smṛtaṃ
Ṣnigdhaṃ ca bhēdakaṃ cōṣṇaṃ mēhakuṣṭhavināśakaṃ
Amaṃ phalaṃ rasē tiktaṃ pākē tu kaṭukaṃ mataṃ
Snigdhaṃ laghūṣṇaṃ kuṣṭhaghnaṃ gulmāṛśaḥkṛmimēhanut
Nimbabījasya majjā tu kuṣṭhaghnī kṛmināśinī
Nimbatailantu kuṣṭhaghnaṃ tiktaṃ kṛmiharaṃ paraṃ
Nimbavṛkṣasya pañcāṅgaṃ raktadōṣaharaṃ mataṃ
Pittaṃ kaṇḍūṃ vṛaṇaṃ dāhaṃ kuṣṭhaṃ caiva vināśayēt " (Śā.ni.)]

വേപ്പിൻെറ തൊലി കച്ചുള്ളു ശീതമാകയുമുണ്ടത്
ക്രിമികുഷ്ഠവിഷം പിത്തം നാശയേദ് ദീപനം ഹിതം
അത്യുഷ്ണമല്ല വേപ്പെണ്ണ കച്ചിട്ടുള്ള രസം പരം
ധാതുക്കളെ കെടുപ്പിക്കും സന്നിപാതത്തിനും ഗുണം
വാതം കുഷ്ഠം ക്രിമികഫം വ്രണങ്ങൾക്കും ഗുണം തുലോം" (ഗു. പാ.)
["Vēppinṫe toli kaccuḷḷu śītamākayumuṇṭatụ
Kṛmikuṣṭhaviṣaṃ pittaṃ nāśayēd dīpanaṃ hitaṃ
Atyuṣṇamalla vēppeṇṇa kacciṭṭuḷḷa rasaṃ paraṃ
Dhātukkaḷe keṭuppikkuṃ sannipātattinuṃ guṇaṃ
Vātam kuṣṭhaṃ kṛmikaphaṃ vṛaṇaṅṅaḷkkuṃ guṇaṃ tulōṃ" (Gu.pā.)]

Bacopa monnieri

Plate 13

Coll. No. AVS 1426

Bacopa monnieri **(Linn.) Pennell**

(Monniera cuneifolia *Michx.*)
(Herpestis monniera *(Linn.) H.B. and K.*)
Scrophulariaceae : (कटुका–कुलम्)

Eng	:	Thyme leaved gratiola
Hin	:	Baramī, Jalnīṃ (बरमी, जलनीं)
Kan	:	Nīrbrahmi (ನೀರ್ಬ್ರಹ್ಮಿ)
Mal	:	Brāhmī, Nīṛbrahmi (ബ്രഹ്മി, നീർബ്രഹ്മി)
San	:	Brāhmī, Sarasvatī (ब्राह्मी, सरस्वती)
Tam	:	Nīṛpirami, Piramiyapūṇḍu (நீர்பிரமி, பிரமியபூண்டு)
Tel	:	Sambrāṇicettu (సాంబ్రాణిచెట్టు)

Distribution: Throughout India,in wet places upto 1,200 m elevation

The plant: A prostrate or creeping, juicy, succulent, glabrous annual herb rooting at the nodes with numerous ascending branches; leaves simple, opposite, decussate, sessile, obovate-oblong or spatulate, entire, fleshy, obscurely veined, punctate; flowers pale blue or whitish, axillary, solitary, on long slender pedicles; fruits ovoid, acute, 2-celled, 2-valved capsules, tipped with style base; seeds minute, numerous.

Parts used: whole plant

Properties and uses: The plant is astringent, bitter, sweet, cooling, laxative, intellect promoting, anodyne, carminative, digestive, anti-inflammatory, anticonvulsant, depurative, cardiotonic, bronchodilator, diuretic, emmenagogue, sudorific, febrifuge and tonic. It is useful in vitiated conditions of *kapha* and *vāta,* biliousness, neuralgia, inflammations, epilepsy, insanity, amentia, tumours, ulcers, splenomegaly, ascites, dyspepsia, flatulence, constipation, asthma, bronchitis, skin diseases, leprosy, leucoderma, erysipelas, syphilis, hoarseness, strangury, elephantiasis, dysmenorrhoea, sterility, fever and general debility.

"ब्राह्मी मेधाजननी रसाधिका सप्तला च यवतिक्ता ।
फेनवती च जलूका शब्दैः पर्यायवाचकैः कथिता ॥ " (अ.म.)
["Brāhmī mēdhājananī rasādhikā saptalā ca yavatikatā
Phēnavatī ca jalūkā śabdaiḥ paryāyavācakaiḥ kathitā" (A.ma.)]

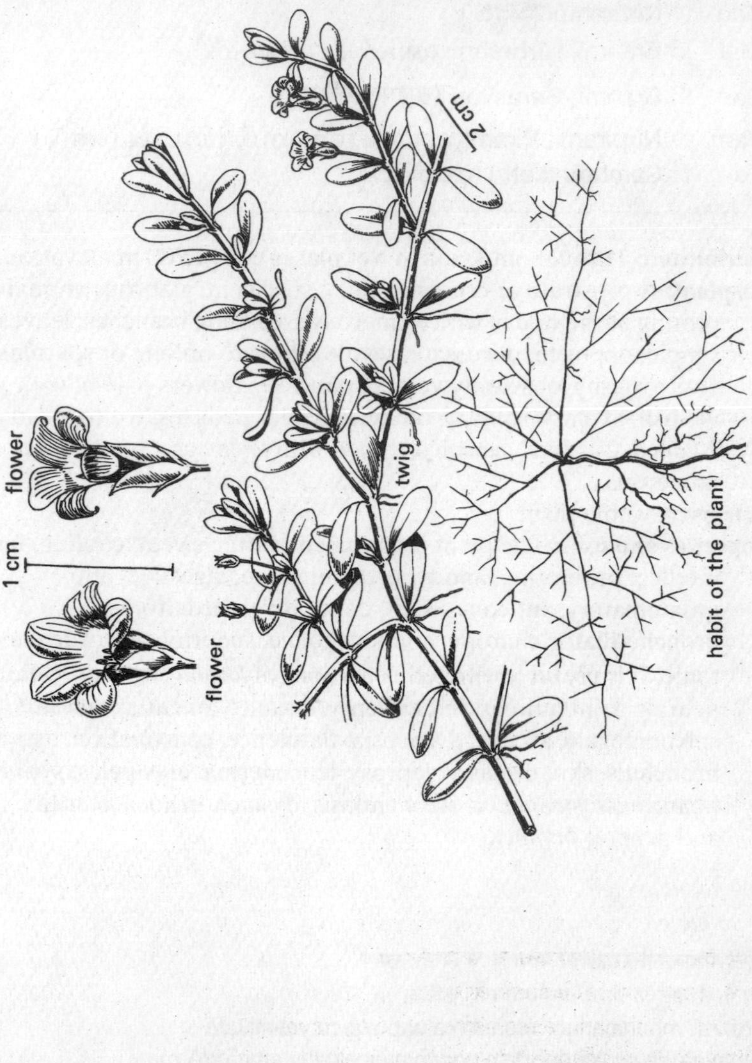

Bacopa monnieri

"ब्राह्मी सरस्वती सोमा सत्याह्वा ब्रह्मचारिणी ।" (म.पा.नि.)
["Brāhmī sarasvatī sōmā satyāhvā brahmacāriṇī" (Ma.pā.ni.)]

"ब्राह्मी कपोतवङ्गा च सोमवल्ली सरस्वती ।" (भा.प्र.)
["Brāhmī kapōtavaṅgā ca sōmavallī sarasvatī" (Bhā.pṛa.)]

"ब्राह्मी सौम्या विनिर्दिष्टा दिव्यतेजा महौषधी ।
कपोतवेगा त्वष्टा च सैव ब्रह्मसुवर्चला ॥" (ध.नि.)
["Brāhmī saumyā vinirdiṣṭā divyatējā mahauṣadhī
Kapōtavēgā tvaṣṭā ca saiva brahmasuvaṛcalā" (Dha.ni.)]

"ब्राह्मी हिमा सरा तिक्ता लघुर्मेध्या च शीतळा ।
कषाया मधुरा स्वादुपाकायुष्या रसायनी ॥
स्वर्या स्मृतिप्रदा कुष्ठपाण्डुमेहास्रकासजित् ।
विषशोफज्वरहरी ---------------------" (भा.प्र.)
["Brāhmī himā sarā tiktā laghuṛmēdhyā ca śītaḷā
Kaṣāyā madhurā svādupākāyuṣyā rasāyanī
Svaryā smṛtipṛadā kuṣṭhapāṇḍumēhāsṛakāsajit
Viṣaśōphajvaraharī ...."(Bhā.pṛa.)]

"ब्राह्मी शीता कषाया च तिक्ता बुद्धिप्रदा मता ।
मेधायुरग्निजननी सारका स्वादुळा लघुः ॥
कण्ठशुद्धिकरी हृद्या स्मृतिदा च रसायना ।
हृद्या मेहं विषं कुष्ठं पाण्डुं कासं ज्वरं जयेत् ॥
शोफकण्डूप्ळीहवातरक्तपित्तारुचिर्जयेत् ।
श्वासं शोषं सर्वदोषं कफवातामयान् जयेत् ॥" (नि.र.)
["Brāhmī śītā kaṣāyā ca tiktā buddhipṛadā matā
Mēdhāyuragnijananī sārakā svāduḷā laghuḥ
Kaṇṭhaśuddhikarī hṛdryā smṛtidā ca rasāyanā
Hṛdyā mēhaṃ viṣaṃ kuṣṭhaṃ pāṇḍuṃ kāsaṃ jvaraṃ jayēt
Śōphakaṇḍūpḷīhavātaraktapittārucirjayēt
Śvāsaṃ śōṣaṃ saṛvadōṣaṃ kaphavātāmayān jayēt" (Ni.ra.)]

"ब्राह्मी तु पिच्छिलायुष्या सरोन्मादविमर्दिनी ।
वयसःस्थापनी मेध्या वाक्स्वरस्मृतिदा परा ॥
तिक्ता हृद्या कटुः पाके श्वासश्ळेष्मनिकृन्तनी ।" (ग.नि.)
["Brāhmī tu picchilāyuṣyā sarōnmadavimaṛdinī
Vayasaḥsthāpanī mēdhyā vāksvarasmṛtidā parā
Tiktā hṛdyā kaṭuḥ pākē śvāsaśḷēṣmanikṛntanī " (Ga.ni.)]

"ब्राह्मी तु भेदिनी गुर्वी मेध्या तिक्ता कफापहा ।" (रा.व.)
["Brāhmī tu bhēdinī guṛvī mēdhyā tiktā kaphāpahā " (Rā.va.)]

"ब्राह्मी हिमा सरा स्वादुर्लघुर्मेध्या रसायनी ।

स्वर्या स्मृतिप्रदा कुष्ठपाण्डुमेहास्रकासजित् ॥
विषशोफज्वरहरा ------------" (म.पा.नि.,म.वि.)
["Brāhmī himā sarā svādurlaghurmēdhyā rasāyanī
Svaryā smṛtipradā kuṣṭhapāṇḍumēhāsṛakāsajit
Viṣaśōphajvaraharā ...." (Ma.pā.ni.,Ma.vi.)]

"ब्राह्मी सौम्या रसे तिक्ता शोफपाण्डुज्वरापहा ।
दीपनी कुष्ठकण्डूघ्नी प्लीहवातवलासजित् ॥ " (ध.नि.)
["Brāhmī saumyā rasē tiktā śōphāpāṇḍujvarāpahā
Dīpanī kuṣṭhakaṇḍūghnī plīhavātavalāsajit" (Dha.ni.)]

"ब्राह्मी च पिच्छिलायुष्या सरोन्मादविनाशिनी ।
वयसःस्थापनी मेधावाक्स्वरपित्तदा परम् ॥
तिक्ता हृद्या कटुः पाके श्वासश्ळेष्मनिकृन्तनी । " (सो. नि.)
["Brāhmī ca picchilāyuṣyā sarōnmādavināśinī
Vayasaḥsthāpanī mēdhāvāksvarapittadā paraṃ
Tiktā hṛdyā kaṭuḥ pākē śvāsaśḷēṣmanikṛntanī" (So.ni.)]

"ब्राह्मी तिक्ता सरा मेध्या कषाया स्वादुपाकतः ।
स्वर्या स्मृतिप्रदाऽऽयुष्या प्रोक्ता सा च रसायनी ॥
उन्मादापस्मृतिं हन्यात् विषशोफज्वरापहा ।
कफवातापहा सैव पाण्डुमेहास्रकासजित् ॥ " (स्व.)
["Brāhmī tiktā sarā mēdhyā kaṣayā svādupākataḥ
Svaryā smṛtipṛadāʃʃyuṣyā pṛōktā sā ca rasāyanī
Unmādāpasmṛtiṃ hanyāt viṣaśōphajvarāpahā
Kaphavātāpahā saiva pāṇḍumēhāsṛakāsajit" (Sva.)]
ബ്രഹ്മിക്കുള്ള രസം കൈയ്പു ഗുണം ശീതോഷ്ണമായ് വരും
കഫവാതങ്ങളർശസ്സും വ്രണഗുൽമോദരങ്ങളും
ഉണ്ടായ് വന്നാല് ശമിപ്പിക്കും വിരേചനകരം പരം (ഗു. പാ.)
["Brahmikkuḷḷa rasaṃ kayppu guṇaṃ śītōṣṇamāyvaruṃ
Kaphavātannaḷaṛśassuṃ vṛaṇagulmōdarannaḷuṃ
Unṭāyvannāl śamippikkuṃ virēcanakaraṃ paraṃ" (Gu.pā.)]

Remarks: In Kerala, *brāhmī* is identified as *Bacopa monnieri* and is sometimes called *nīṛbrahmi* also.

In north India, however, *brāhmī* is commonly identified as *Centella asiatica* (Linn.) Urban, which in Malayalam is known as *muttil* . It seems that this identification of *brāhmī* as *C. asiatica* has been in use for long in north India, as Hēmādri's 'Commentary on Aṣṭāṅgahṛdayaṃ' (Āyuṛvēdarasāyanaṃ) treats *maṇḍūkapaṛṇī (C.asiatica)* as a synonym of *brāhmī*.

Materia medicas like 'Rājanighaṇṭu' and 'Kaiyadēvanighaṇṭu' follow Hēmādrī in treating *maṇḍūkapaṛṇī* as a synonym of *brāhmī* leading to

confusion in the identity of *brāhmī*. The author of 'Dhanvantarinighaṇṭu', however, treats *maṇḍūkaparṇī* and *maṇḍūkī* as synonyms of *ādityabhaktā (Helianthus annuus* Linn.). P.V. Sharma in 'Dravyaguṇavijñān' follows Hēmādri and identifies *maṇḍūkaparṇī* as *brāhmī* and gives a description of *Centella asiatica.* Besides, he uses a Sanskrit name *aindrī* for *Bacopa monnieri* and adds a few properties to it, apart from those that are given for *laghu brāhmī* by 'Rājanighaṇṭu'. But it must be noted that nowhere has *aindrī* been identified as *brāhmī*. In Kerala, *aindrī* is identified under the Malayalam name *kāṭṭuveḷḷari (Citrullus colocynthis* (L.) Schrader).
It has to be pointed out that *brāhmī* and *maṇḍūkaparṇī (maṇḍūkī)* are entirely different plants, as Suśrutasaṁhitā in 'Rasāyanavidhi' describes *Maṇḍūkaparṇīsvarasarasāyana* and *Brāhmīsvarasarasāyana* separately. Again *brāhmī* and *maṇḍūkī* have been regarded as two drugs in the formulation of Aṣṭāṅagaghṛtaṃ in 'Aṣṭāṅgahṛdayaṃ' (Uttaraṃ- Chap.I).

"वचेन्दुलेखा मण्डूकी शङ्खपुष्पी शतावरी ।
ब्रह्मसोमामृता ब्राह्मी ------------॥"
["Vacēndulēkhā maṇḍūkī śaṅkhapuṣpī śatāvarī
Brahmasōmāmṛtā brāhmī........................")

Besides, the famous Commentary on 'Aṣṭāṅgahṛdayaṃ' by Aruṇadatta (Saṛvāṅgasudarī) treats *maṇḍūkaparṇī* as *maṇḍūkī* only. Further 'Bhāvapṛakāśaṃ', 'Madanapālanighaṇṭu' and 'Madanavinōdaṃ' after describing the properties of *brāhmī* state that *maṇḍūkaparṇī* possesses also the same properties (तद्वत् मण्डूकपर्णिनी). Hence, these two are entirely different drugs.

The `Glossary of vegetable drugs in Bṛahattṛayī' and the `Ayurvedic Formulary of India' identify *brāhmī* as *Bacopa monnieri* and *maṇḍūkaparṇī* and *maṇḍūkī* as *Centella asiatica.*

Thus, we have to conclude that the *brāhmī (nīṛbrahmi)* has to be identified as *Bacopa monnieri* and *maṇḍūkaparṇī (muttil)* as *Centella asiatica.*

Coll. No. AVS 1435

Baliospermum montanum **(Willd.) Muell-Arg.**

(B.axillare *Bl.*)

Euphorbiaceae : (एरण्ड–कुलम्)

Hin	:	Dantī (दन्ती)
Kan	:	Kāḍuharalu (ಕಾಡುಹರಲು)
Mal	:	Nāgandanti, Danti (നാഗദന്തി, ദന്തി)
San	:	Dantī (दन्ती)
Tam	:	Nākatanti (நாகதந்தி)
Tel	:	Adaviāmudamu, Kondaāmudamu (అడవిఆముదము, కొండఆముదము)

Distribution: Throughout India

The plant: A stout undershrub 0.9 – 1.8 m in height with herbaceous branches from the roots; leaves simple, sinuate-toothed, upper ones small, lower ones large, sometimes palmately 3–5 lobed; flowers numerous, in axillary racemes with male flowers above and a few females below; fruits capsules, 8–13 mm long, obovoid, seeds ellipsoid, smooth, mottled.

Parts used: roots, leaves, seeds

Properties and uses: The roots are acrid, thermogenic, purgative, anti-inflammatory, anodyne, digestive, anthelmintic, diuretic, diaphoretic, rubefacient, febrifuge and tonic. They are useful in anasarca, dropsy, flatulence, constipation, jaundice, haemorrhoids, leprosy, skin diseases, strangury, vesical calculi, wounds, splenomegaly, anaemia, leucoderma, fever and vitiated conditions of *vāta.* The leaves are good for asthma and bronchitis. The seeds are drastic purgative, rubefacient, hydragogue and stimulant, and are useful in vitiated conditions of *vāta,* inflammations and flatulence.

"निर्दिश्यते निकुम्भो दन्ती चित्रा मुकुळका शीघ्रा ।
उपचित्रा च विशल्या घुणप्रिया तीक्ष्णरेचनी चेति ॥
सैवेरण्डफला प्रोक्ता काकोदुम्बरपत्रिका ।
स्रंसनी च मुकुन्देति शब्दैः पर्यायवाचकैः ॥ " (अ.म.)

["Nirddiśyatē nikumbhō dantī citrā mukuḷakā śīghrā
Upacitra ca viśalyā ghuṇapriyā tīkṣṇarēcanī cēti
Saivēraṇḍaphalā prōktā kākōdumbarapatrikā

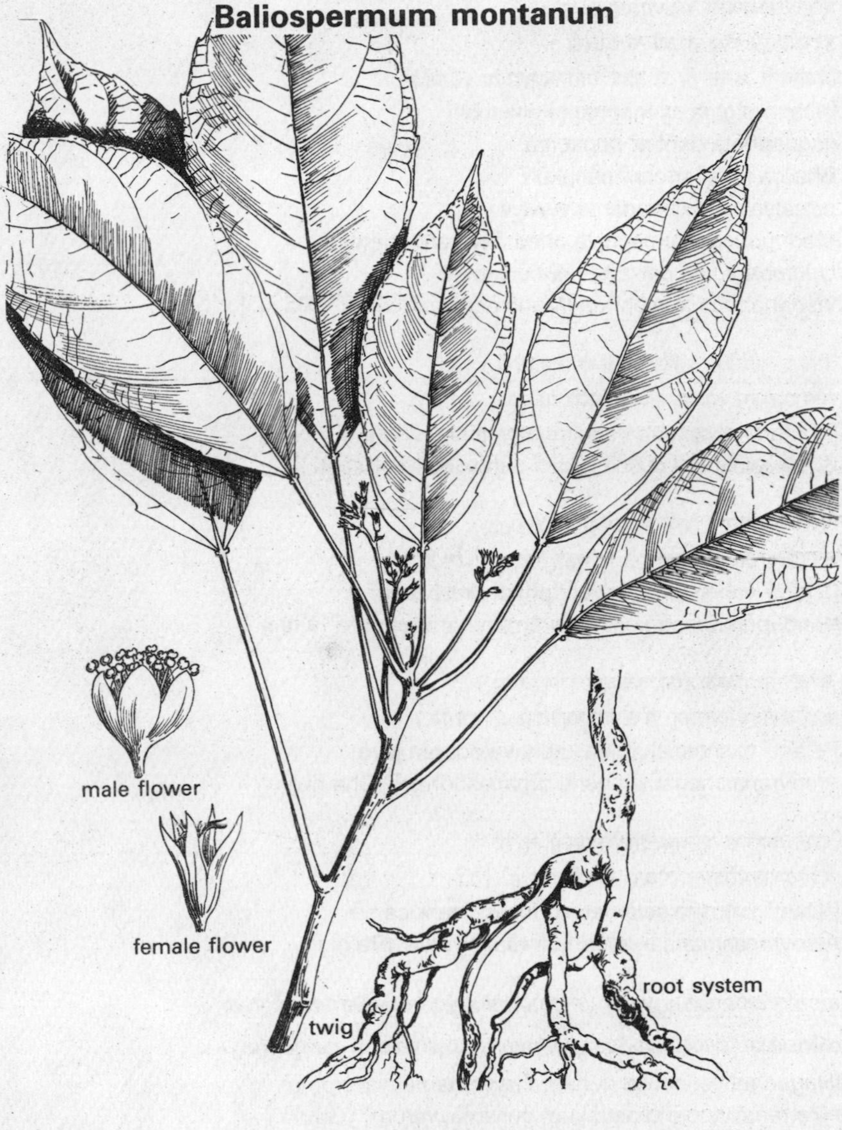
Baliospermum montanum
male flower
female flower
twig
root system

Sṛamsanī ca mukundēti śabdaiḥ paryāyāvacakaiḥ" (A.ma.)]

"दन्ती शीघ्रा श्येनघण्टा निकुम्भी
नागस्फोता दन्तिनी चोपचित्रा ।
भद्रा रूक्षा रोचनी चानुकूला
निःशल्या स्याद्वक्रदन्ता विशल्या ॥
मधुपुष्पैरण्डफला भद्राण्येरण्डपत्रिका ।
उदुंबरदळा चैव तरुणी चाणुरेवती ॥
विशोधनी च कुम्भी च ज्ञेया चाग्निकराह्वया । "(रा.नि.)
["Dantī śīghṛā śyēnaghaṇṭā nikuṁbhī
nāgasphōtā dantinī cōpacitṛā
Bhadrā rūkṣā rōcanī cānukūlā
niḥśalyā syādvakṛadantā viśalyā
Madhupuṣpairaṇḍaphalā bhadrāṇyēraṇḍapatṛikā
Uduṁbaradaḷā caiva taruṇī cāṇurēvatī
Viśōdhanī ca kuṁbhī ca jñēyā cāgnikarāhvayā " (Rā.ni.)]

"तिक्ता कृमिविषच्छर्दिर्कफास्रघ्नी विशोधनी ।
कोष्ठशूलहरा चोष्णा नागिनी सर्वदोषजित् ॥" (म.नि.)
["Tiktā kṛmiviṣacchaṛdiṛkaphāsṛaghnī viśōdhanī
Kōṣṭhaśūlaharā cōṣṇā nāginī saṛvadōṣajit" (Ma.ni.)]

"दन्ती वह्निसमा पाके शोफदद्रुविनाशिनी ।
कण्डूपामापहा कुष्ठध्वंसिनी कृमिहृत् परा ॥ " (ग.नि.)
["Dantī vahnisamā pākē śōphadadruvināśinī
Kaṇḍūpāmāpahā kuṣṭhadhvaṁsinī kṛmihṛt parā" (Ga.ni.)]

"दन्ती तीक्ष्णोष्णकटुका कफवातोदरान् जयेत् ।
अर्शोव्रणाश्मरीशूलान् हन्ति दीपनशोधनी ॥" (ध.नि.)
["Dantī tīkṣṇōṣṇakaṭukā kaphavātōdarān jayēt
Aṛśōvṛaṇāśmarīśūlān hanti dīpanaśōdhanī"(Dha.ni.)]

"दन्ती कटूष्णा शूलामत्वग्दोषशमनी च सा ।
अर्शोव्रणाश्मरीशल्यशोधनी दीपनी परा ॥" (रा.नि.)
["Dantī kaṭūṣṇā śūlāmatvagdōṣaśamanī ca sā
Aṛśōvṛaṇāśmarīśalyaśōdhanī dīpanī parā"(Rā.ni.)]

നാഗദന്തിയെരിച്ചുള്ളു ഗുണം തീക്ഷ്ണോഷ്ണമായ് വരും
നിറത്തെ തെളിയിപ്പാനുമെത്രയും ഗുണമായ് വരും (ഗു.പാ.)
[Nāgadantiyericcuḷḷu gunaṃ tīkṣṇōṣṇamāyvaruṃ
Niṛatte teḷiyippānumetṛayuṃ guṇamāyvaruṃ" (Gu.pā.)]

Remarks: 'Abhidhānamañjari' describes two more varieties of this plant viz. *veḷutta nāgadanti* and *ceṛunāgadanti.*

"दन्तीद्वयं सरं पाके रसे च कटुदीपनम् ।
गुदाङ्कुराश्मशूलार्शःकण्डूकुष्ठविदाहनुत् ॥
तीक्ष्णोष्णं हन्ति पित्तास्रकफशोफोदरकृमीन् ।" (भा.प्र)
["Dantīdvayaṃ saraṃ pākē rasē ca kaṭudīpanaṃ
Gudāṅgurāśmaśūlārśaḥkaṇḍūkuṣṭavidāhanut
Tīkṣṇōṣṇaṃ hanti pittāsṛakaphaśōphōdarakṛmīn "(Bhā.pṛa.)]

'Bhāvapṛakāśaṃ' describes two varieties *bṛhaddantī* and *laghudantī* (big and small) and gives the same properties for both and its commentator identifies *bṛhaddantī* as *Jatropha glandulifera* Roxb.
However, the synonyms given for *dantī*, *viśalayā* is considered to be *mēntōnni (Gloriosa superba* Linn.) and *nikuṁbha* as *nālkōlppakonna* (white variety of *Operculina turpethum* (Linn.) Silva Manso) by Ayurvedic practitioners.

'The Indian Medicinal Plants, gives the Malayalam names *dantika, nīṛvāḷaṃ kaṭālāvaṇakku, nāgadanti* and *nīraṭimuttu* for *Baliospermum montanum* and says that the seeds are some times used as a substitute for *Croton tiglium.* (Again, the author adds that the root is considered cathartic, and is useful in anasarca, dropsy and jaundice.) From these quotations it is clear that the Malayalam name *nīṛvāḷaṃ (Croton tiglium)* given for this is a misnomer.

However, in all Ayurvedic preparations wherever the names *dantī* and *nāgadantī* are mentioned, the root of *B. montanum* is being used.

Coll. No. AVS 2286

***Bambusa arundinacea* (Retz.) Willd.**

Bambusaceae : (वंश–कुलम्)

Eng	:	Thorny bamboo
Hin	:	Bāṁs, Kaṇṭabāṁs (बाँस, कण्टबाँस)
Kan	:	Bedru (ಬೆದ್ರು)
Mal	:	Muḷa, Illi (മുള, ഇല്ലി)
San	:	Vaṁśaḥ, Vēṇuḥ (वंशः, वेणुः)
Tam	:	Muḷmūṅkil (முள்மூங்கில்)
Tel	:	Vedurubiyyam, Veduruppu (వెదురుబియ్యం, వెదురుప్పు)

Distribution: Throughout India,in areas upto 2,100 m elevation

The plant: A tall thorny bamboo upto 30 m in height with many stems, tufted on stout root stock, nodes prominent, the lowest rooting, internodes upto 45 cm long, stem sheath coriaceous, orange-yellow, streaked, glabrous or puberulous beneath, base rounded, ciliate, tip stiff, midrib narrow, leaf sheaths with a short bristly auricle, ligule short; spikelets glabrous, yellow or yellowish green, in very long panicles, often occupying the whole stem, floral glumes, 3–7 in number, the uppermost 1–3 male or neuter, lodicules 3, hyaline, 1–3 nerved, ciliate; fruits oblong grains, beaked by the style base, grooved on one side.

Parts used: roots, leaves, sprouts, grains and bamboo manna

Properties and uses: The roots are sweet, astringent, cooling, laxative, depurative, diuretic and tonic. They are useful in vitiated conditions of *kapha* and *pitta,* leprosy, skin diseases, burning sensation, discolourations, strangury, ringworm, ulorrhea, arthralgia and general debility. The leaves are sweet, astringent, cooling, emmenagogue, ophthalmic, vulnerary, constipating and febrifuge. They are useful in vitiated conditions of *pitta,* ophthalmopathy, lumbago, haemorrhoids, diarrhoea, gonorrhoea, amenorrhoea, dysmenorrhoea, wounds, skin diseases and fever. The sprouts are acrid, bitter, laxative, thermogenic, anti-inflammatory, digestive, carminative, anthelmintic and diuretic. They are useful in inflammations, ulcers and wounds, dyspepsia, nausea, intestinal worms, flatulence and strangury. The grains are acrid, sweet, thermogenic, anthelmintic, aphrodisiac, alexeteric and tonic. They are useful in vitiated conditions of *kapha,* urorrhea, intestinal worms

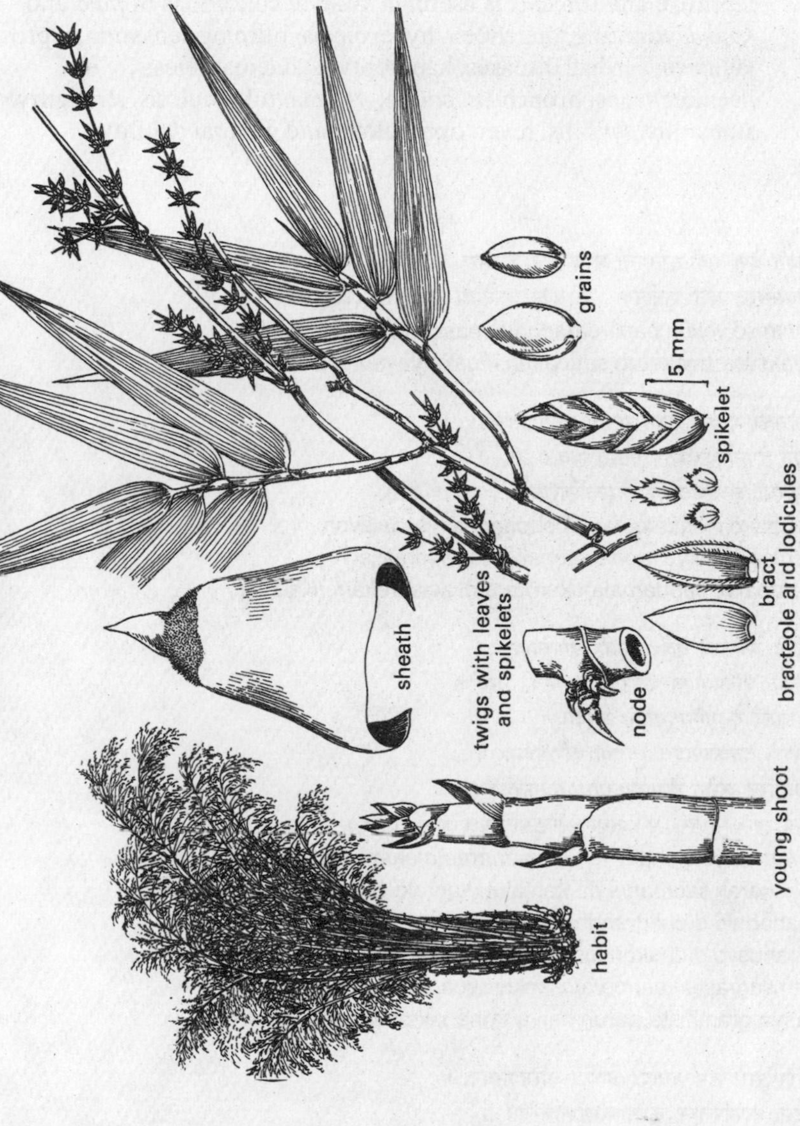

Bambusa arundinacea

and general debility.

The 'bamboo manna' is the siliceous secretion found in the internodes of the stems of various species of bamboo. It occurs in fragments or masses, and is translucent or transparent and of bluish white colour. It is astringent, acrid, sweet, cooling, expectorant, constipating, cardiotonic, haemostatic, aphrodisiac, diuretic, febrifuge and tonic. It is useful in vitiated conditions of *pitta* and *kapha,* vomiting, diarrhoea, hyperdipsia, burning sensation, leprosy, jaundice, cardiac diseases, haemoptysis, haematemesis, haemorrhages, bronchitis, cough, asthma, tuberculosis, strangury, stomatitis, syphilis, fever, ophthalmia and general debility.

"वंशो वेणुः पर्वी शतपर्वा मस्करश्च कल्माषः ।
त्वक्सारस्तृणकेतुः सुतीनकः कीचका यवफला स्यात् ॥" (अ.म.)
["Vaṁśō vēṇuḥ paṛvī śatapaṛvā maskaraśca kalmāṣaḥ
Tvaksārastṛṇakētuḥ sutīnakaḥ kīcakā yavaphalā syāt" (A.ma.)]

"कीचको मस्करो वंशी सुपर्वा षट्पदालयः ।
वंशो वेणुर्यवफलस्तृणकेतुस्तृणध्वजः ॥
शतपर्वा शब्दमालः कर्मारस्त्वाचिसारकः । " (कै.नि.)
["Kīcakō maskarō vaṁśī supaṛvā ṣaṭpadālayaḥ
Vaṁśō vēṇuṛyavaphalastṛṇakētustṛṇadhvajaḥ
Satapaṛvā śabdamālaḥ kaṛmārastvacisārakaḥ" (Kai.ni.)]

"वंशो यवफलो वेणुः कर्मारस्तृणकेतुकः ।
मस्करः शतपर्वा च कण्टालुः कण्टकी तथा ॥
महाबलो दृढग्रन्थिर्दृढपत्रो धनुर्द्रुमः ।
धनुष्यो दृढकाण्डश्च विज्ञेयो बाणभूमितः ॥
वंशाग्रस्तु करीरो वंशाङ्कुरश्च यवफलाङ्कुरः ।
तस्य ग्रन्थिस्तु परुः पर्व तथा काण्डसन्धिश्च ॥ " (रा.नि.)
["Vaṁśō yavaphalō vēṇuḥ kaṛmārastṛṇakētukaḥ
Maskaraḥ śatapaṛvā ca kaṇṭāluḥ kaṇṭakī tathā
Mahābalō dṛḍhagrandhiṛdṛḍhapatṛō dhanuṛdrumaḥ
Dhanuṣyō dṛḍhakāṇḍaśca vijñēyō bāṇabhūmitaḥ
Vaṁśāgrastu kanīrō vaṁśāṅkuraśca yavaphalāṅkuraḥ
Tasya granthistu paruḥ paṛva tathā kāṇḍasandhiśca " (Rā.ni.)]

"वंशः सरो हिमः स्वादुः कषायो वस्तिशोधनः ।
छेदनः कफपित्तघ्नः कुष्ठास्रव्रणशोफजित् ॥
तत्करीरः कटुः पाके रसे रूक्षो गुरुः सरः ।
कषायः कफकृत् स्वादुर्विदाही वातपित्तळः ॥" (भा.प्र.)
["Vaṁśaḥ sarō himaḥ svāduḥ kaṣāyō vastiśōdhanaḥ

Chēdanaḥ kaphapittaghnaḥ kuṣṭhāsṛavṛaṇaśōphajit
Tatkarīraḥ kaṭuḥ pākē rasē rūkṣō guruḥ saraḥ
Kaṣāyaḥ kaphakṛt svāduṛvidāhī vātapittaḷaḥ" (Bhā.pṛa.)]

"वंशस्त्वम्ळः कषायश्च कटुतिक्तश्च शीतळः ।
मूत्रकृच्छ्रप्रमेहार्शःपित्तदाहास्रनाशनः ॥
पित्तास्रदाहकृच्छ्रघ्नो रुचिकृत्पर्वनिर्गुणम् ।" (ध.नि.)
["Vaṁśastvamḷaḥ kaṣāyaśca kaṭutiktaśca śītaḷaḥ
Mūṭrakṛcchṛapṛamēhāṛśaḥpittadāhāsṛanāśanaḥ
Pittāsṛadāhakṛcchṛaghnō rucikṛtpaṛvaniṛguṇaṃ" (Dha.ni.)]

"वंशौ त्वम्ळौ कषायौ च किञ्चित्तिक्तौ च शीतळौ ।
मूत्रकृच्छ्रप्रमेहार्शःपित्तदाहास्रनाशनौ ॥
करीरं कटुतिक्ताम्ळं कषायं लघु शीतळम् ।
पित्तास्रदाहकृच्छ्रघ्नं रुचिकृत् पर्व निर्गुणम् ॥" (रा.नि.)
["Vaṁśau tvamḷau kaṣāyau ca kiñcittiktau ca śītaḷau
Mūṭrakṛcchṛapṛamēhāṛśaḥpittadāhāsṛanāśanau
Karīraṃ kaṭutiktāmḷaṃ kaṣāyaṃ laghu śītaḷam
Pittāsṛadāhakṛcchṛaghnaṃ rucikṛt paṛva niṛguṇaṃ" (Rā.ni.)]

"वंशस्तु शीतळः स्वादुः कषायो वस्तिशोधनः ।
छेदनः कफपित्तास्रकुष्ठशोफव्रणापहः ॥
तत्करीरः कटुः पाके रसे रूक्षो गुरुः सरः ।
कषायः श्लेष्मळः स्वादुर्विदाही वातपित्तळः ॥" (कै.नि.)
["Vaṁśastu śītaḷaḥ svāduḥ kaṣāyō vastiśōdhanaḥ
Chēdanaḥ kaphapittāsṛakuṣṭhaśōphavṛaṇāpahaḥ
Tatkarīraḥ kaṭuḥ pākē rasē rūkṣō guruḥ saraḥ
Kaṣāyaḥ śḷēṣmaḷaḥ svāduṛvidāhī vātapittaḷaḥ" (Kai.ni.)]

"वंशो व्रणास्रसंभारभेदनः शोफनाशनः ।
वेणोः करीराः गुरवः कफमारुतकोपनाः ॥" (सो.नि.)
["Vaṁśō vṛaṇāsṛasambhārabhēdanaḥ śōphanāśanaḥ
Vēṇōḥ karīraḥ guravaḥ kaphamārutakōpanāḥ" (Sō.ni.)]

"वंशोऽम्ळस्तुवरस्तिक्तः शीतळः सारको मतः ।
वस्तिशुद्धिकरः स्वादुच्छेदनो भेदको मतः ॥
कफं रक्तरुजं पित्तं कुष्ठं शोफं व्रणं तथा ।
मूत्रकृच्छ्रप्रमेहार्शान् दाहञ्चैव विनाशयेत् ॥ " (नि.र.)
["Vaṁśōʼmḷastuvarastiktaḥ śītaḷaḥ sārakō mataḥ
Vastiśuddhikaraḥ svāducchēdanō bhēdakō mataḥ
Kaphaṃ raktarujaṃ pittaṃ kuṣṭhaṃ śōphaṃ vṛaṇaṃ tathā
Mūṭrakṛcchṛapṛamēhāṛśān dāhañcaiva vināśayet" (Ni.ra.)]

Eng	:	Bamboo grains
Hin	:	Bāms kā cāval (बाँस का चावल)
Kan	:	Biḍrakki (ಬಿದಿರುಅಕ್ಕಿ)
Mal	:	Muḷayari (മുളയരി)
San	:	Vaṁ śayavaṃ (वंशयवं)
Tam	:	Mūṅkil ariśi (மூங்கில் அரிசி)
Tel	:	Vedūrubēaṃ (వెదురుబియ్యం)

"वेणुजो वेणुबीजश्च वंशजो वंशतण्डुलः ।
वंशधान्यं च वंशाह्वो वेणुवंशद्विधा यवं॥" (रा.नि.)
["Vēṇujō vēṇubījaśca vaṁśajō vaṁśataṇḍulaḥ
Vaṁśadhānyaṃ ca vaṁśāhvō vēṇuvaṁśadvidhā yavaṃ" (Rā.ni.)]

"शीतः कषायो मधुरस्तु रूक्षो
मेहकृमिश्ळेष्मविषापहश्च ।
पुष्टिं च वीर्यं च बलं च दत्ते
पित्तापहो वेणुयवः प्रशस्तः ॥" (रा.नि.)
["Sītaḥ kaṣāyō madhurastu rūkṣō
mēhakṛmiśḷēṣmaviṣāpahaśca
Puṣṭiṃ ca vīryaṃ ca balaṃ ca dattē
pittāpahō vēṇuyavaḥ praśastaḥ" (Rā.ni.)]

Eng	:	Bamboo manna
Hin	:	Vaṁ śalōc (वंशलोच)
Kan	:	Biḍru (ಬಿದಿರು)
Mal	:	Muḷaṅkarppūraṃ, Muḷaṅkallū (മുളങ്കർപ്പൂരം, മുളങ്കല്ല്)
San	:	Vaṁ śarōcanā (वंशरोचना)
Tam	:	Muḷaṅkarpūraṃ (மூளங்கற்பூரம்)
Tel	:	Vedūruppu (వెదురుప్పు)

"वंशजा तु भवेद्वांशी वंशक्षीरी च वांशिका ।
वंशोद्भवा वेणुभवा वैणवी तृणकेतकी ॥
वंशरोचनिका चेति पर्यायैर्वंशरोचना ।" (अ.म.)
["Vaṁśajā tu bhavēdvāṁśī vaṁśakṣīrī ca vāṁśikā
Vaṁśōdbhavā vēṇubhavā vaiṇavī tṛṇakētakī
Vaṁśarōcanikā cēti paryāyairvaṁśarōcanā" (A.ma.)]

"स्याद्वंशरोचना वांशी तुगाक्षीरी तुगा शुभा ।
त्वक्क्षीरी वंशजा शुभ्रा वंशक्षीरी च वैणवी ॥" (भा.प्र.)
["Syādvaṁśarōcanā vāṁśī tugākṣīrī tugā śubhā
Tvakkṣīrī vaṁśajā śubhrā vaṁśakṣīrī ca vaiṇavī" (Bhā.pra.)]

"वंशजा बृंहणी वृष्या बल्या स्वाद्वी च शीतळा ।
तृष्णाकासज्वरश्वासक्षयपित्तास्रकामलाः ॥
हरेत् कुष्ठं व्रणं पाण्डुं कषाया वातकृच्छ्रजित् ।" (भा.प्र.)
["Vaṁśajā bṛmhaṇī vṛṣyā balyā svādvī ca śītaḷā
Tṛṣṇākāsajvaraśvāsakṣayapittāsṛakāmalāḥ
Harēt kuṣṭhaṃ vṛaṇaṃ pāṇḍuṃ kaṣāyā vātakṛcchṛajit" (Bhā.pṛa.)]

"तुगा रूक्षा तु तुवरा मधुरा रक्तशुद्धिकृत् ।
शीता शुभावहा ग्राही वृष्या धातुविवर्धनी ॥
बल्या क्षयश्वासकासरक्तदोषारुचिप्रणुत् ।
रक्तपित्तं ज्वरं कुष्ठं कामलां पाण्डुरोगकम् ॥
दाहं तृषां व्रणं मूत्रकृच्छ्रं दाहं च नाशयेत् ।
वातघ्नी चैव विज्ञेया वैद्यशास्त्रविशारदैः ॥" (नि.र.)
["Tugā rūkṣā tu tuvarā madhurā raktaśuddhikṛt
Sītā śubhāvahā grāhī vṛṣyā dhātuvivaṛdhanī
Balyā kṣayaśvāsakāsaraktadōṣārucipṛaṇut
Raktapittaṃ jvaraṃ kuṣṭhaṃ kāmalāṃ pāṇḍurōgakaṃ
Dāhaṃ tṛṣāṃ vṛaṇaṃ mūtṛakṛcchṛaṃ dāhaṃ ca nāśayēt
Vātaghnī caiva vijñēyā vaidyaśāstṛaviśāradaiḥ" (Ni.ra.)]

Coll. No. AVS 1638

Barringtonia acutangula **(Linn.) Gaertn.**

Barringtoniaceae : (समुद्रफल–कुलम्)

Eng	:	Indian oak, Small Indian oak
Hin	:	Samudraphal (समुद्रफल)
Kan	:	Hōlekavau (ಹೊಲೆಕವು)
Mal	:	Nīṛpēḷu, Aṫṫupēḷu, Samudraphalam (നീർപേഴ്, ആറ്റുപേഴ്, സമുദ്രഫലം)
San	:	Samudraphalaḥ (समुद्रफलः)
Tam	:	Samuttirappaḻam (சமுத்திரப் பழம்)
Tel	:	Kanapa, Kanigi (కనప, కనిగి)

Distribution: Throughout India,in deciduous and evergreen forests, mostly along the banks of rivers, streams and tanks

The plant: A medium sized glabrous tree 10–15 m in height with pale grey slender young branches and rough dark brown bark; leaves simple, alternate, obovate-oblong or elliptic-cuneate, the margins minutely denticulate or crenulate, main nerves 10–13 pairs; flowers fragrant, dark scarlet, in pendulous many flowered racemes; fruits bluntly quadrangular, narrowed towards the ends, crowned by a small persistent calyx.

Parts used: roots, leaves, fruits

Properties and uses: The roots are bitter, cooling, aperient, antipyretic, stimulant and emetic. They are useful in catarrh, intermittent fevers, splenomegaly and constipation. It is similar to `cinchona' in action when administered in malarial fever. The leaves are bitter, constipating and tonic, and are useful in diarrhoea and dysentry. The fruits are acrid, bitter, cooling, anthelmintic, galactagogue, alexeteric, vulnerary, depurative, emetic, purgative, expectorant, diuretic, emmenagogue and antipyretic. They are useful in vitiated conditions of *pitta,* colic, intestinal worms, agalactia, wounds, ulcers, skin diseases, leprosy, splenomegaly, cough, bronchitis, strangury, dysmenorrhoea, intermittent fevers, ophthalmitis, cephalalgia, lumbago, syphilis, nasal catarrh and hallucinations.

"समुद्रनाम प्रथमं पश्चात् फलमुदाहरेत् ।
समुद्रफलमित्यादि नाम वाच्यं भिषग्वरैः ॥" (रा.नि.)

Barringtonia acutangula

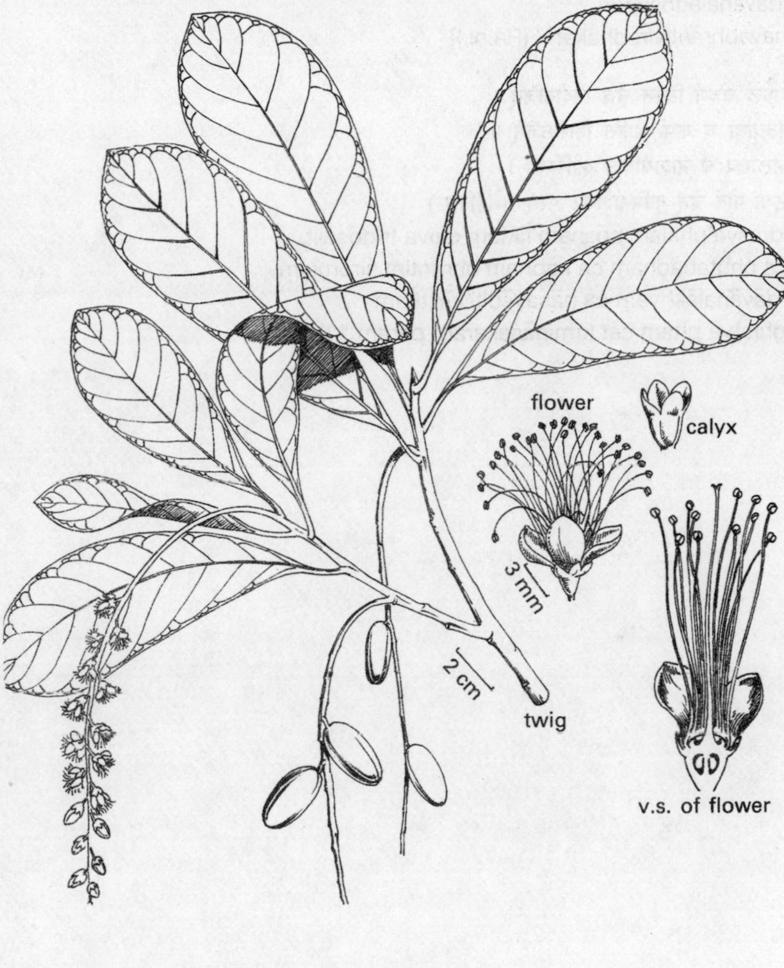

["Samudranāma prathamaṃ paścāt phalamudāharēt
Samudraphalmityādi nāma vācyaṃ bhiṣagvaraiḥ" (Rā.ni.)]

"फलं समुद्रस्य कटूष्णकारी
वातापहं भूतनिरोधकारी ।
त्रिदोषदावानलदोषहारी
कफामयभ्रान्तिविरोधकारी ॥" (रा.नि.)
["Phalaṃ samudrasya kaṭūṣṇakārī
vātāpahaṃ bhūtanirōdhakarī
Tṛidōṣadāvānaladōṣahārī
kaphāmayabhṛāntivirōdhakārī " (Rā.ni.)]

"समुद्रस्य फलं चोष्णं तिक्तं चैव त्रिदोषजित् ।
वातं च भूतबाधां च कफं भ्रान्तिं शिरोरुजम् ॥
दोषं दावानलाख्यं च नाशयेदिति कीर्त्तितम् ।
जलेन घृष्ट्वा पीतं चेत् कृमिनाशकरं परम् ॥" (नि.र.)
["Samudrasya phalaṃ cōṣṇaṃ tiktaṃ caiva tṛidōṣajit
Vātaṃ ca bhūtabādhāṃ ca kaphaṃ bhṛāntiṃ śirōrujaṃ
Dōṣaṃ dāvānalākhyaṃ ca nāśayēditi kīṛttitaṃ
Jalēna ghṛṣṭvā pītaṃ cēt kṛmināśakaraṃ paraṃ " (Ni.ra.)]

Coll. No. AVS 1498

Basella alba var. *rubra* (Linn.) Stewart

(=B.rubra *Linn.*)

Basellaceae (उपोदिका–कुलम्)

Eng	:	Indian spinach
Hin	:	Pōi, Lālbāclu (पोय, लालबाचलु)
Kan	:	Bansalī (ಬಸ್ಸಲಿ)
Mal	:	Vaśaḷaccīra, Baśaḷaccīra (വശളച്ചീര, ബശളച്ചീര)
San	:	Upōdikā (उपोदिका)
Tam	:	Vaśaḷakkīrai, Śivappu vaśaḷakkīrai (வசளக்கீரை, சிவப்பு வசளக்கீரை)
Tel	:	Baccali (బచ్చలి)

Distribution: Throughout India, cultivated

The plant: A perennial succulent glabrous twining herb with white or red branches; leaves simple, alternate, broadly ovate, acute or acuminate, cordate at base, thick, lamina narrowed into petiole; flowers white or red in spikes, bracteoles longer than perianth; fruits red, white or black, globose, utricle enclosed in the perianth.

Parts used: stems, leaves

Properties and uses: The stems and leaves are sweet, cooling, emollient, aphrodisiac, laxative, haemostatic, appetiser, sedative, diuretic, demulcent, maturate and tonic. They are useful in vitiated conditions of *pitta,* burning sensation, constipation, flatulence, anorexia, haemorrhages, haemoptysis, sleeplessness, pruritus, leprosy, urticaria, ulcers, dysentery, gonorrhoea, balanitis, strangury, fatigue and general debility. They are especially useful as a laxative in children and pregnant women.

"उपोदक्यूर्ध्वगा वल्ली पिच्छिलच्छदना स्थिरा ।
वृत्तपत्रा रक्तदण्डा रक्तबीजा च सा स्मृता ।।" (शि.नि.)
["Upōdakyūrdhvagā vallī picchilacchadanā sthirā
Vṛttapatrā raktadaṇḍā raktabījā ca sā smṛtā " (Śi.ni.)]

"पोतक्युपोदिका सा तु माळवी मृतवल्लरी ।" (भा.प्र.)
["Pōtakyupōdikā sā tu māḷavī mṛtavallarī" (Bhā.pṛa.)]

"पोतक्युपोदका मत्स्यकाळी सुतुङ्गी सङ्कटी ।

Basella alba var. rubra

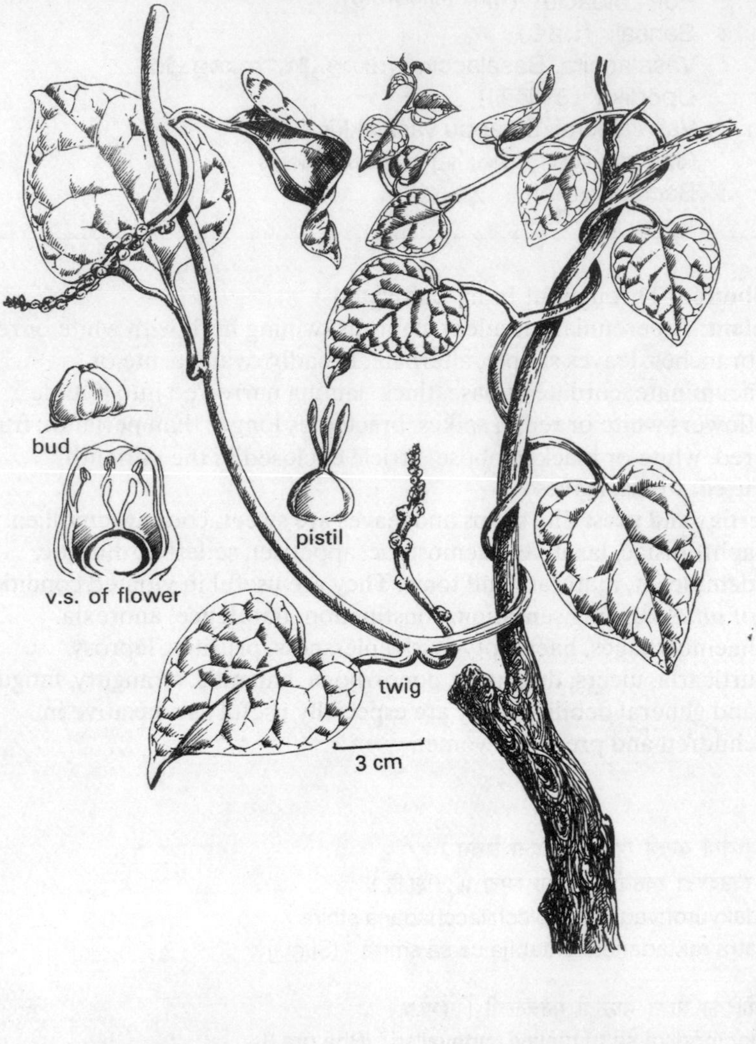

कळम्बिका वृकान्त्री च तुरङ्गी कण्टकी तथा ॥
मदघ्नी पिच्छिला ज्ञेया वृत्ता मदळिका मता ।" (कै.नि.)
["Pōtakyupōdakā matsyakāḷī sutungī sankaṭī
Kaḷambikā vṛkāntrī ca turangī kaṇṭakī tathā
Madaghnī picchilā jñēyā vṛttā madaḷikā matā" (Kai.ni.)]

"पोतकी शीतळा स्निग्धा श्ळेष्मळा वातपित्तनुत् ।
अकण्ठ्या पिच्छिला निद्राशुक्ळदा रक्तपित्तजित् ॥
बलदा रुचिकृत् पथ्या बृंहणी तृप्तिकारिणी ।" (भा.प्र.)
["Pōtakī śītaḷā snigdhā śḷēṣmaḷā vātapittanut
Akaṇṭhyā picchilā nidrāśukḷadā raktapittajit
Baladā rucikṛt pathyā bṛṁhaṇī tṛptikāriṇī" (Bhā.pra.)]

उपोदका हिमा स्निग्धा स्वादुपाकरसा सरा ।
सक्षारा श्ळेष्मळा बल्या निद्राशुक्ळातिपुष्टिदा ॥
अकण्ठ्या पिच्छिला हन्ति रक्तपित्तमदानिलान् । (कै.नि.)
["Upōdakā himā snigdhā svādupākarasā sarā
Sakṣārā śḷēṣmaḷā balyā nidrāśukḷātipuṣṭidā
Akaṇṭhyā picchilā hanti raktapittamadānilān" (Kai.ni.)]

"उपोदकी कषायोष्णा कटुका मधुरा च सा ।
निद्राʃʃलस्यकरी रुच्या विष्टंभश्ळेष्मकारिणी ॥" (रा.नि.)
["Upōdakī kaṣāyōṣṇā kaṭukā madhurā ca sā
Nidrāʃʃlasyakarī rucyā viṣṭambhaśḷēṣmakāriṇī" (Rā.ni.)]

"उपोदका सरा स्निग्धा बल्या श्ळेष्मकरी हिमा ।
स्वादुपाकरसा वृष्या वातापित्तमदापहा ॥" (सो.नि.)
["Upōdakā sarā snigdhā balyā śḷēṣmakarī himā
Svādupākarasā vṛṣyā vātapittamadāpahā" (Sō.ni.)]

"ഏറ്റം തണുപ്പു വശളയ്ക്കതിനും മധുരം രസം
ഗുന്മപ്രമേഹവും പിത്തം തീപ്പുണ്ണും വിഷമെന്നോരോ
ദണ്ഡങ്ങളെ ശമിപ്പിപ്പാൻ ശക്തിയുണ്ടതിനേറ്റവും." (ഗു.പാ.)
["Ēṟṟaṃ taṇuppu vaśaḷaykkatinuṃ madhuraṃ rasaṃ
Gulmapramēhavuṃ pittaṃ tīppuṇṇuṃ viṣamennōrō
Daṇḍaṅṅaḷe śamippippān śaktiyuṇṭatinēṟṟavuṃ" (Gu.pā.)]

Coll. No. AVS 1161

Bauhinia variegata **Linn.**

Caesalpiniaceae : (कण्टकीकरञ्ज-कुलम्)

Hin	:	Kancanar (काञ्चनार)
Kan	:	Kempumandāra (ಕೆಂಪುಮಂದಾರ)
Mal	:	Mandāraṃ, Cuvannamandāraṃ, Malayakatti, Koṅṅu, Koṅṅumandāraṃ (മന്ദാരം, ചുവന്നമന്ദാരം, മലയകത്തി, കൊങ്ങ്, കൊങ്ങുമന്ദാരം)
San	:	Kāñcanāraḥ, Kōvidāraḥ (काञ्चनारः, कोविदारः)
Tam	:	Śigappu mandāraii (சிகப்பு மந்தாரை)
Tel	:	Devakāncanamu (దేవకాంచనము)

Distribution: Throughout India,in areas upto 1,800m elevation

The plant: A moderate sized deciduous tree with vertically cracked grey bark, wood moderately hard, greyish brown with irregular darker patches; leaves of 2 leaflets, connate for about two-thirds up, leaflets ovate, rounded at apex, 10–15cm long, pubescent beneath when young, coriaceous; flowers white or pink, the uppermost petal darker and variegated, usually appearing before the leaves in short axillary or terminal racemes, stamens 5, staminodes absent, fruits flat dehiscent pods, seeds 10–15.

Parts used: roots, bark

Properties and uses: The roots and bark are astringent, acrid, cooling, constipating, depurative, anthelmintic, vulnerary, anti-inflammatory and styptic. They are useful in vitiated conditions of *pitta* and *kapha*, diarrhoea, dysentery, skin diseases, leprosy, intestinal worms, tumours, wounds, ulcers, inflammations, scrofula, proctoptosis, haemorrhoids, haemoptysis, cough, menorrhagia and diabetes.

"काञ्चनारः काञ्चनको गण्डारिः शोणपुष्पकः ।
कोविदारश्चमरिकः कुद्दाळो युग्मपत्रकः ॥
कुण्डली ताम्रपुष्पश्चाश्मन्तकः स्वल्पकेसरी ।" (भा.प्र.)
["Kāñcanāraḥ kāñcanakō gaṇḍāriḥ śōṇapuṣpakaḥ
Kōvidāraścamarikaḥ kuddāḷō yugmapatṛakaḥ
Kuṇḍalī tāmṛapuśpaścāśmantakaḥ svalpakēsarī" (Bhā.pṛa.)]

"आस्फोतकः कोविदारः कुण्डलः कुण्डली कुली ।

Bauhinia variegata

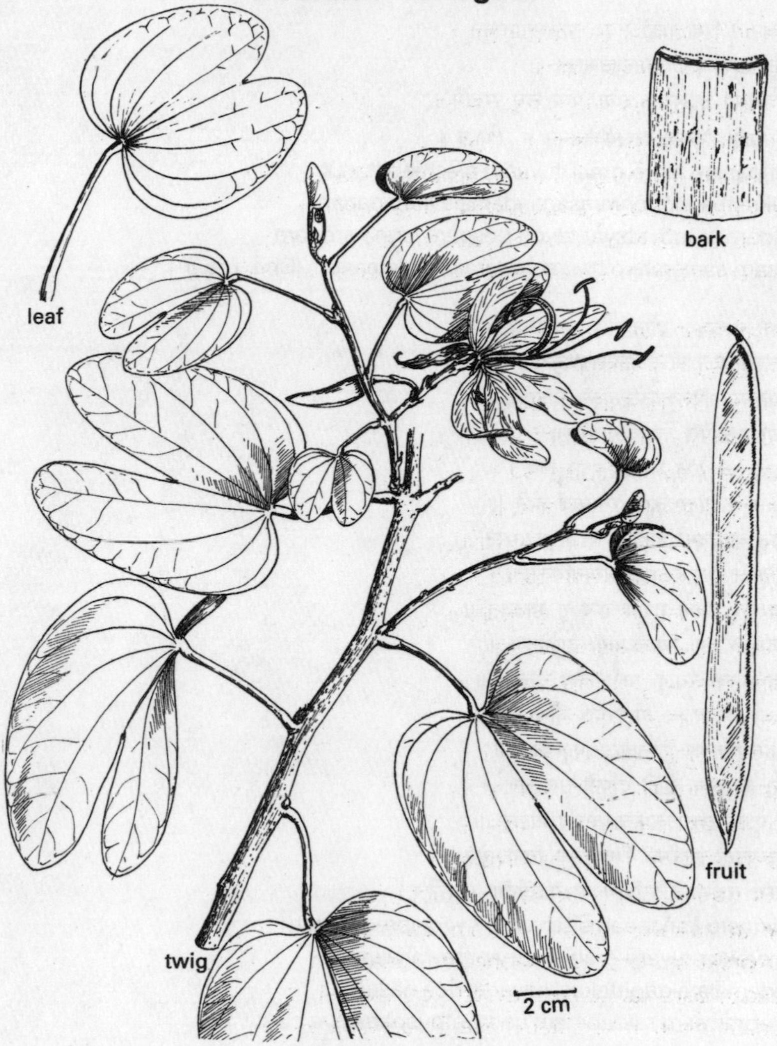

उद्दाळकश्चमरिकः कुद्दाळः स्वल्पकेसरः ॥
कोलीयाशाः काञ्चनको भ्रमरेष्टो मनोहरः ।
रक्तपुष्पोऽपरः श्वेतः पाकारिः काञ्चनारकः ॥" (कै.नि.)
["Asphōtakaḥ kōvidāraḥ kuṇḍalaḥ kuṇḍalī kulī
Uddāḷakaścamarikaḥ kuddāḷaḥ svalpakēsaraḥ
Kōlīyāśāḥ kāñcanakō bhṛamarēṣṭō manōharaḥ
Raktapuṣpōʃparaḥ śvētaḥ pākāriḥ kāñcanārakaḥ" (Kai.ni.)]

"काञ्चनारो हिमो ग्राही तुवरः श्ळेष्मपित्तनुत् ।
कृमिकुष्ठगुदभ्रंशगण्डमालाव्रणापहः ॥
कोविदारोऽपि तद्वत्स्यात् तयोः पुष्पं लघु स्मृतम् ।
रूक्षं संग्राहि पित्तास्रप्रदरक्षयकासनुत् ॥" (भा.प्र.)
["Kāñcanārō himō grāhī tuvaraḥ śḷēṣmapittanut
Kṛmikuṣṭhagudabhṛaṁśagaṇḍamālāvṛaṇāpahaḥ
Kōvidārōʃpi tadvatsyāt tayōḥ puṣpaṃ laghu smṛtaṃ
Rūkṣaṃ saṁgrāhi pittāsṛapṛadarakṣayakāsanut" (Bhā. pṛa.)]

"रक्तस्तु काञ्चनः शीतः सरो ह्यग्निप्रदीपनः।
संप्रोक्तस्तुवरो ग्राही कफपित्तव्रणकृमीन् ॥
गण्डमालारक्तपित्तकुष्ठवातांश्च नाशयेत् ।
गुदभ्रंशं रक्तपित्तं नाशयेत्पुष्पमस्य च ॥
शीतळं तुवरं रूक्षं संग्राहि मधुरं लघु ।
पित्तं क्षयं च प्रदरं कासं रक्तरुजं हरेत् ॥
श्वेतस्तु काञ्चनो ग्राही तुवरो मधुरः स्मृतः ।
रुच्यो रूक्षः श्वासकासपित्तरक्तविकारहा ।
क्षतप्रदरनुत् प्रोक्तो गुणाश्चान्ये तु रक्तवत् ॥
कोविदारो दीपनः स्यात्कषायो व्रणरोपणः ।
संग्राहि सारकः स्वादुः पर्णशाकेषु चोत्तमः ॥
मूत्रकृच्छ्रं त्रिदोषञ्च शोषं दाहं कफं तथा ।
वातं हरेत्पुष्पगुणाः रक्तकाञ्चनपुष्पवत् ॥
पीतस्तु काञ्चनो ग्राही दीपनो व्रणरोपणः ।
तुवरो मूत्रकृच्छ्रस्य कफवाय्वोश्च नाशनः ॥
काञ्चन्युक्ता शीर्षरुजं त्रिदोषञ्च विनाशयेत् ।
स्तन्यस्य वर्धनकरी ऋषिभिः सूक्ष्मदर्शिभिः ॥ (नि.र.)
["Raktastu kāñcanaḥ śītaḥ sarō hyagnipṛadīpanaḥ
Saṁpṛōktastuvarō grāhī kaphapittavṛaṇakṛmīn
Gaṇḍamālāraktapittakuṣṭ havātāṁśca nāśayēt
Gudabṛaṁśaṃ raktapittaṃ nāśayētpuṣpamasya ca
Śītaḷaṃ tuvaraṃ rūkṣaṃ saṁgrāhi madhuraṃ laghu
Pittaṃ kṣayaṃ ca pṛadaraṃ kāsaṃ raktarujaṃ harēt
Śvētastu kāñcanō grāhī tuvarō madhuraḥ smṛtaḥ
Rucyō rūkṣaḥ śvāsakāsapittaraktavikārahā
Kṣatapṛadaranut pṛōktō guṇāścānyē tu raktavat

Kōvidārō dīpanaḥ syātkaṣāyō vraṇarōpaṇaḥ
Saṁgrāhī sārakaḥ svāduḥ parṇaśākēṣu cōttamaḥ
Mūtrakṛcchraṃ tridōṣaṃ ca śōṣaṃ dāhaṃ kaphaṃ tathā
Vātaṃ harēt puṣpaguṇāḥ raktakāñcanapuṣpavat
Pītastu kāñcanō grāhī dīpanō vraṇarōpaṇaḥ
Tuvarō mūtrakṛcchrasya kaphavāyvōśca nāśanaḥ
Kāñcanyuktā śīrṣarujaṃ tridōṣaṃ ca vināśayēt
Stanyasya vardhanakarī ṛṣibhiḥ sūkṣmadarśibhiḥ" (Ni.ra.)]

"कोविदारः कषायः स्यात् संग्राही व्रणरोपणः ।
दीपनः कफवातघ्नो मूत्रकृच्छ्रनिबर्हणः ॥" (रा.नि.)
["Kōvidāraḥ kaṣāyaḥ syāt saṁgrāhī vraṇarōpaṇaḥ
Dīpanaḥ kaphavātaghnō mūtrakṛcchranibarhaṇaḥ" (Rā.ni.)]

"कोविदारः कषायस्तु संग्राही व्रणरोपणः ।
गण्डमालागुदभ्रंशशमनः कुष्ठकेशहा ॥" (ध.नि.)
["Kōvidāraḥ kaṣāyastu saṁgrāhī vraṇarōpaṇaḥ
Gaṇḍamālāgudabhraṁśaśamanaḥ kuṣṭhakēśahā " (Dha.ni.)]

"कोविदारो हिमो ग्राही कषायः कफपित्तजित् ।
गण्डमालागुदभ्रंशव्रणकुष्ठकृमीन् जयेत् ॥
तद्वच्च काञ्चनो ज्ञेयः तयोः पुष्पं हिमं गुरु ।
कषायं मधुरं पाके रसे संग्राहि रोचनम् ॥
रूक्षं कासक्षयश्वासपित्तास्रप्रदरापहम् ॥" (कै.नि.)
["Kōvidārō himō grāhī kaṣāyaḥ kaphapittajit
Gaṇḍamālāgudabhraṁśavraṇakuṣṭhakṛmīn jayēt
Tadvacca kāñcanō jñēyaḥ tayōḥ puṣpaṃ himaṃ guru
Kaṣāyaṃ madhuraṃ pākē rasē saṁgrāhi rōcanaṃ
Rūkṣaṃ kāsakṣayaśvāsapittāsrapradarāpahaṃ" (Kai.ni.)]

"कोविदारः कटुः पाके कषायो मधुरः परम् ।
कफपित्तहरो ग्राही किञ्चिन्मारुतकोपनम् ॥" (सो.नि.)
["Kōvidāraḥ kaṭuḥ pākē kaṣāyō madhuraḥ paraṃ
Kaphapittaharō grāhī kiñcinmārutakōpanaṃ" (Sō.ni.)]

"काञ्चनारो हिमो ग्राही तुवरः श्लेष्मपित्तनुत् ।
कृमिकुष्ठगुदभ्रंशगण्डमालाव्रणापहः ॥
कोविदारोऽपि तद्वत्स्यात्पुष्पं शीतं तयोर्लघू ।
रूक्षं संग्राहि पित्तास्रप्रदरक्षतकासनुत् ॥" (म.पा.नि.)
["Kāñcanārō himō grāhī tuvaraḥ śḷēṣmapittanut
Kṛmikuṣṭhagudabhraṁśagaṇḍamālāvraṇāpahaḥ
Kōvidārōʃpi tadvatsyātpuṣpaṃ śītaṃ tayōrlaghū
Rūkṣaṃ saṁgrāhi pittāsrapradarakṣatakāsanut" (Ma.pā.ni.)]

"മന്താരപ്പൂ തണുത്തുള്ളു ഗുരുവാകയുമുണ്ടത്
പിത്തശ്ലേഷ്മങ്ങളെത്തീർപ്പാൻ ശക്തിയുണ്ടതിനേറ്റവും." (ഗു.പാ)
["Mantārappū taṇuttuḷḷu guruvākayumuṇṭatụ
Pittaśḷēṣmannaḷettīṛppān saktiyuṇṭatinēṯṯavauṃ" (Gu.pā.)]

Remarks: In `Śāligrāmanighaṇṭubhūṣaṇaṃ', *kōvidāra* is identified as *Bauhinia variegata* and *B. purpurea.* But in `Kaiyadēvanighaṇṭu' *B.variegata* is the Latin name given for *kāñcanāra* and *B.purpurea* for *kōvidāra.* In 'Nighaṇṭuratnākaraṃ' five types viz. *raktakāñcanāraṃ, svētakāñcanāraṃ, kōvidāraṃ, pītakāñcanāraṃ* and *kāñcanī* are mentioned.

"कोविदारः श्वेतपुष्पो सुशिम्बो युग्मपत्रकः ।
दृढकाष्ठो रक्तसारः पादपः पर्वतो भवेत् ॥
काञ्चनारो महान् किञ्चित् युग्मपत्रोऽथ शिम्बकः ।
कषायो रक्तपुष्पश्च काननादौ प्रजायते ॥
कोविदारः पीतपुष्पः युग्मपत्रोऽल्पवृक्षकः।"
["Kōvidāraḥ śvētapuṣpō suśimbō yugmapatṛakaḥ
Dṛḍhakāṣṭhō raktasāraḥ pādapaḥ paṛvatō bhavēt
Kāñcanārō mahān kiñcit yugmapatṛōʃtha śimbakaḥ
Kaṣāyō raktapuṣpaśca kānanādau pṛajāyatē
Kōvidāraḥ pītpuṣpaḥ yugmapatṛōʃlpavṛkṣakaḥ"]

'Śivadattanighaṇṭu' refers to three kinds of *kāñcanāra* viz. white, red and yellow, based on the colour of the flowers. The Latin names for *kāñcanāra* as given in the commentary of `Dhanvantarinighaṇṭu', commentary of `Rājanighaṇṭu' and `Bhāvapṛakāśaṃ' are *B.purpurea, B.acuminata* and *B. variegata,* respectively. In `Dravyaguṇavijñān' *kāñcanāra* is identified as *B. variegata* indicating *B.purpurea* as *raktakōvidāra,* and *B.tomentosa* as *pītakāñcanāra.* In 'Indian Medicinal Plants' the Sanskrit name given for *B. tomentosa* is *pītakāñcanāra* and for *B. racemosa śvētakāñcanāra.* There is also a mention that *raktapuṣpakōvidāra* is *B.purpurea,* and *kōvidāra* and *raktapuṣpā* is *B. variegata.*

In `The Ayurvedic Formulary of India' *kōvidāra* is identified as *B. variegata.*

For *kōvidāra* and *kāñcanāra,* in certain parts of Kerala *B. tomentosa (maññamandāraṃ)* is being used.

Coll. No. AVS 1985

Benincasa hispida (Thunb.) Cogn.

(B. cerifera *Savi*)

Cucurbitaceae : (कोशातकी–कुलम्)

Eng	:	Ash gourd, White gourd melon
Hin	:	Pēṭhā, Raksā (पेठा, रकसा)
Kan	:	Būḍikumbala (ಬೂದಿಕುಂಬಲ)
Mal	:	Kuṁ paḷaṃ (കുമ്പളം)
San	:	Kūśmāṇḍaḥ (कूश्माण्डः)
Tam	:	Pūśaṇikkāi (பூசணிக்காய்)
Tel	:	Būḍidagummadi (బూడిదగుమ్మడి)

Distribution: Cultivated throughout India in plains and hills

The plant: A large trailing gourd climbing by means of tendrils; leaves large, hispid beneath; flowers yellow, unisexual, male peduncle 7.5–10 cm long, female peduncle shorter; fruits broadly cylindric, 30–45 cm long, hairy throughout, ultimately covered with a waxy bloom.

Parts used: fruits, seeds

Properties and uses: The fruits are sweet, cooling, styptic, laxative, diuretic, tonic, aphrodisiac and antiperiodic. They are useful in asthma, cough, diabetes, haemoptysis, haemorrhages from internal organs, epilepsy, fever and vitiated conditions of *pitta.* The seeds are sweet, cooling and anthelmintic, and are useful in dry cough, fever, urethrorrhea, syphilis, hyperdipsia and vitiated conditions of *pitta.*

"कूश्माण्डः ककुभण्डं पुष्यफला कोहळी बृहत्फला च ।
फलराजो गुळयोगी महाफलः कथ्यते गुळफलाख्यः ॥
कूश्माण्डोऽन्यो लट्वा लट्वाकः कूहळश्च कूश्माण्डी ।
अंगुलको वृत्तफलः शूकफलः पीतपुष्पः स्यात् ॥" (अ.म.)
["Kūśmāṇḍaḥ kakubhaṇḍaṃ puṣyaphalā kōhaḷi bṛhatphalā ca
Phalarājō guḷayōgī mahāphalaḥ kathyatē guḷaphalākhyaḥ
Kūśmāṇḍō∫nyō laṭvā laṭvākaḥ kūhaḷaśca kūśmāṇḍī
Amgulakō vṛttaphalaḥ śūkaphalaḥ pītapuṣpaḥ syāt" (A.ma.)]

"कश्माण्डं स्यात्पुष्पफलं पीतपुष्पं बृहत्फलम् ।" (भा.प्र.)
["Kūśmāṇḍaṃ syātpuṣpaphalaṃ pītapuṣpaṃ bṛhatphalaṃ" (Bhā.pra.)]

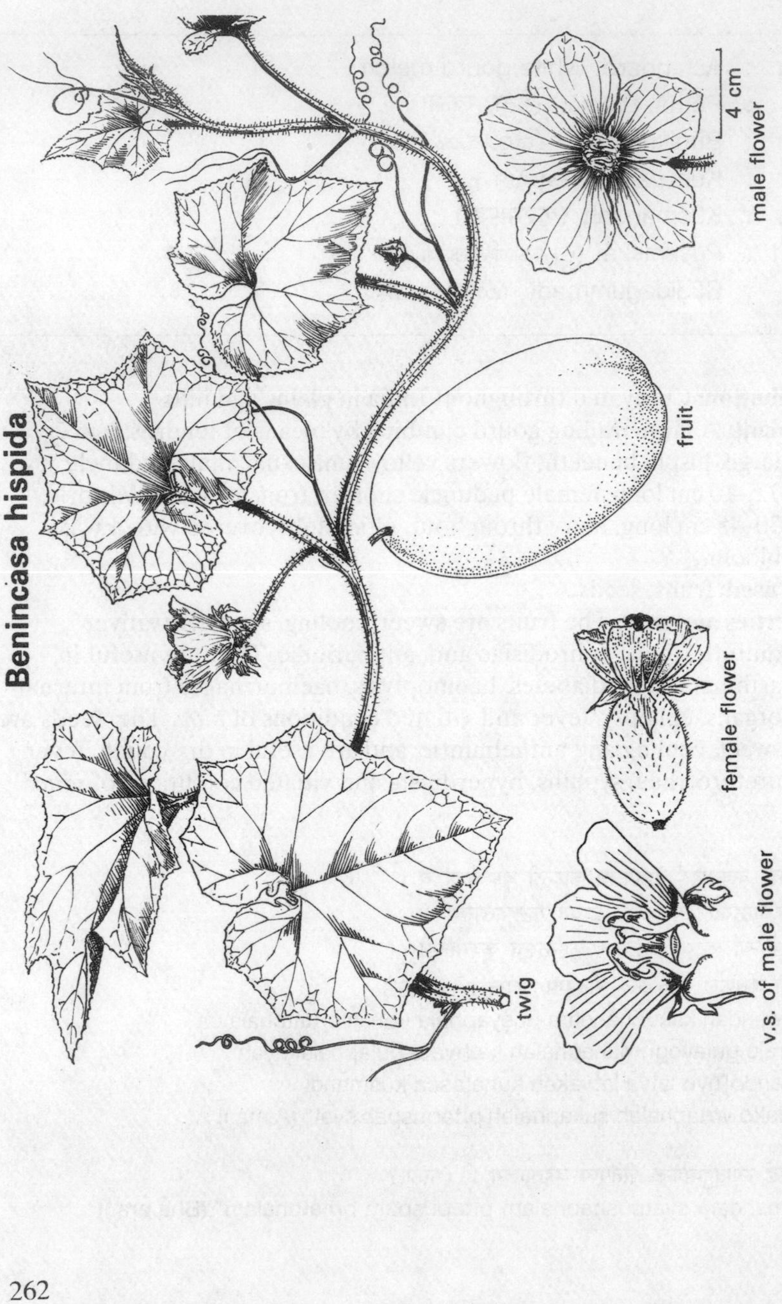
Benincasa hispida
4 cm
male flower
fruit
female flower
v.s. of male flower
twig

"कूश्माण्डं बृंहणं वृष्यं गुरु पित्तास्रवातनुत् ।
बालं पित्तापहं शीतं मध्यमं कफकारकम् ॥
वृद्धं नातिहिमं स्वादु सक्षारं दीपनं लघु ।
वस्तिशुद्धिकरं चेतोरोगहृत् सर्वदोषजित् ॥" (भा.प्र.)
["Kūśmāṇḍaṃ bṛṃhaṇaṃ vṛṣyaṃ guru pittāsravātanut
Bālaṃ pittāpahaṃ śītaṃ madhyamaṃ kaphakārakaṃ
Vṛddhaṃ nātihimaṃ svādu sakṣāraṃ dīpanaṃ laghu
Vastiśuddhikaraṃ cētōrōgahṛt sarvdōṣajit" (Bhā. pra.)]

"कूश्माण्डकफलं वृष्यं पुष्टिकृद्धातुवर्द्धकम् ।
वस्तिशुद्धिकरं बल्यमतिस्वादु च शीतळम् ॥
गुरु रूक्षं सारकं च हृद्यं कफकरं मतम् ।
मूत्राघातं प्रमेहं च मूत्रकृच्छ्राश्मरीं तृषां ॥
अरोचकं वातपित्तं पित्तं रक्तरुजं तथा ।
वातोरेतोविकारं च नाशयेदिति तन्मतम् ॥
तत्कोमळं चातिशीतं दोषकृत्पित्तहारकम् ।
तन्मध्यमं कफकरं पक्वं किञ्चिच्च शीतळम् ॥
दीपकं च लघु स्वादु क्षारं वस्तेश्च शुद्धिदम् ।
सर्वदोषहरं पथ्यं पक्वमज्जा च माधुरी ।
वस्तिशुद्धिकरी वृष्या पित्तनाशकरी मता ॥ " (नि.र.)
["Kuśmāṇḍakaphalaṃ vṛṣyaṃ puṣṭikṛddhātuvarddhakaṃ
Vastiśuddhikaraṃ balyamatisvādu ca śītaḷaṃ
Guru rūkṣaṃ sārakaṃ ca hṛdyaṃ kaphakaraṃ mataṃ
Mūtrāghātaṃ pramēhaṃ ca mutrakṛcchrāśmarīṃ tṛṣāṃ
Arōcakaṃ vātapittaṃ pittaṃ raktarujaṃ tathā
Vātōrētōvikāraṃ ca nāśayēditi tanmataṃ
Tatkōmaḷaṃ catiśītaṃ dōṣakṛtpittahārakaṃ
Tanmadhyamaṃ kaphakaraṃ pakvaṃ kiñcicca śītaḷaṃ
Dīpakaṃ ca laghu svādu kṣāraṃ vastēśca śuddhidaṃ
Sarvadōṣaharaṃ pathyaṃ pakvamajjā ca mādhurī
Vastiśuddhikarī vṛṣyā pittanāśakarī matā" (Ni.ra.)]

"पित्तघ्नं तेषु कूश्माण्डं बालं, मध्यं कफावहम् ।
शुक्ळं लघूष्णं सक्षारं दीपनं वस्तिशोधनम् ॥
सर्वदोषहरं हृद्यं पथ्यं चेतोविकारिणाम् । " (सु.सू.४६)
["Pittaghnaṃ tēṣu kuśmāṇḍaṃ bālaṃ, madhyaṃ kaphāvahaṃ
Śukḷaṃ laghūṣṇaṃ sakṣāraṃ dīpanaṃ vastiśōdhanaṃ
Sarvadōṣaharaṃ hṛdyaṃ pathyaṃ cētōvikāriṇāṃ" (Su.Sū.46)]

"वल्लीफलानां प्रवरं कूश्माण्डं वातपित्तजित् ।
वस्तिशुद्धिकरं वृष्यं हृद्यं चेतोविकारजित् ॥ " (ध.नि.)
["Vallīphalānāṃ pravaraṃ kuśmāṇḍaṃ vātapittajit
Vastiśuddhikaraṃ vṛṣyaṃ hṛdyaṃ cētōvikārajit" (Dha.ni.)]

"मूत्राघातहरं प्रमेहशमनं कृच्छ्राश्मरीच्छेदनं
विण्मूत्रग्ळपनं तृषार्तिशमनं जीर्णाङ्गपुष्टिप्रदम् ।
वृष्यं स्वादुतरं त्वरोचकहरं बल्यञ्च पित्तापहं
कूश्माण्डं प्रवरं वदन्ति भिषजो वल्लीफलानां पुनः ॥" (रा.नि.)
["Mūtrāghātaharaṃ pramēhaśamanaṃ kṛcchrāśmarīcchēdanaṃ
viṇmūtraglapanaṃ tṛṣārtiśamanaṃ jīrṇāṅgapuṣṭipradaṃ
Vṛṣyaṃ svādutaraṃ tvarōcakaharaṃ balyañca pittāpahaṃ
kūśmāṇḍaṃ pravaraṃ vadanti bhiṣajō vallīphalānāṃ punaḥ " (Rā.ni.)]

"कूश्माण्डं भेद्यभिष्यन्दि विष्टम्भि वातपित्तजित् ।
वस्तिशुद्धिकरं वृष्यं स्वादुपाकरसं गुरु ॥
विशेषात् पित्तनुत् बालं, मध्यं चैव कफापहम् ।
पक्वं लघूष्णं सक्षारं दीपनं पाचनं तथा ॥
सर्वदोषहरं हृद्यं पथ्यं चेतोविकारनुत् । " (सो.नि.)
["Kūśmāṇḍaṃ bhēdyabhiṣyandi viṣṭambhi vātapittjit
Vastiśuddhikaraṃ vṛṣyaṃ svādupākarasaṃ guru
Viśēṣāt pittanut bālaṃ, madhyaṃ caiva kaphāpahaṃ
Pakvaṃ laghūṣṇaṃ sakṣāraṃ dīpanaṃ pācanaṃ tathā
Sarvadōṣaharaṃ hṛdyaṃ pathyaṃ cētōvikāranut" (Sō.ni.)]

കുമ്പളത്തണ്ടു ദോഷഘ്നം സന്നിപാതജ്വരപാഹം
മൂത്രകൃച്ഛ്രാശ്മരീദാഹമിത്യാദിക്കും ഗുണം തുലോം

കുമ്പളത്തില തിക്തോഷ്ണം ശീതമാകയുമുണ്ടത്
കളഞ്ഞീടും ജ്വരാഷ്ഠീലാവാതാനാഹങ്ങളെ ദ്രുതം
ഹൃദ്യമാകയുമുണ്ടേറ്റം ലഘുവാകയുമുണ്ടത്.
വള്ളിമേൽ കാച്ചതിൽ ശ്രേഷ്ഠം കൂശ്മാണ്ഡം വാതപിത്തജിത്
പാകത്തിങ്കൽ മതൃത്തുള്ളു വസ്തിശുദ്ധികരം ഗുരു.
ഞെട്ടുകെട്ടതു സുക്ഷാരം നന്നു ബുദ്ധിഭ്രമത്തിനും
ദോഷങ്ങളെക്കളഞ്ഞീടും പുരാണമതിലും ഗുണം. (ഗു.പാ.)
["Kumpaḷattaṇṭu dōṣaghnaṃ sannipātajvarāpahaṃ
Mūtrakṛcchrāśmarīdāhamityādikkuṃ guṇaṃ tulōṃ
Kumpaḷattila tiktōṣṇaṃ śītamākayumuṇṭatu
Kaḷaññīṭuṃ jvarāṣṭhīlavatānāhannaḷe drutaṃ
Hṛdyamākayumaṇṭēṟṟaṃ laghuvākayumuṇṭatu.
Vaḷḷimēl kāccatil śreṣṭhaṃ kūśmāṇḍaṃ vātapittajit
Pākattiṅkal matṛttuḷḷu vastiśuddhikaraṃ guru
Ñeṭṭukeṭṭatu sukṣāraṃ nannu buddhibhramattinuṃ
Dōṣannaḷekkaḷaññīṭuṃ purāṇamatiluṃ guṇaṃ " (Gu.pā.)]

Remarks: The author of `Abhidhānamañjarī' describes *laṭvā,* a second variety of *kūśmāṇḍa (Benincasa hispida),* which in Kerala is called *narikumpaḷanna* or *ceṛukumpaḷanna.* Because of this description in `Abhidhanamañjarī', in Kerala some are of the opinion that the smaller one is better to be used as a drug.

Coll. No. AVS 2546

Beta vulgaris **Linn.**

Chenopodiaceae : (वास्तुक–कुलम्)

Eng	:	Beetroot, Garden beet
Hin	:	Cukkandār, Pālak (चुक्कनदार, पालक)
Kan	:	Bīṭurūtu (ಬೀಟುರೂಟು)
Mal	:	Bīṭṭrūṭṭū, ceñcīra, Neycīra (ബീറ്റ്റൂട്ട്, ചെഞ്ചീര, നെയ്ചീര)
San	:	Pālakyā (पालक्या)
Tam	:	Ceñcīrai (செஞ்சீரை)
Tel	:	Bīṭrūtu (బీట్రూటు)

Distribution: Cultivated in many parts of India

The plant: An annual or biennial tuberous herb with condensed stem; leaves simple in rosettes, ovate, cauline; flowers 2–3 in a cluster or sometimes solitary on a long slender spike, appearing usually in the second year.

The tuberous napiform tap root when fully grown is fleshy and purplish red in colour.

Parts used: taproot, leaves, seeds

Properties and uses: The swollen roots are sweet, expectorant and tonic, and are useful in psychopathy, cough, inflammations and general debility. The leaves are sweet, acrid, cooling, diuretic, anti-inflammatory, purgative, anodyne and tonic. They are useful in cuts and burns, strangury, inflammations, paralysis, otalgia, cephalalgia, liver and spleen disorders, constipation, vitiated conditions of *pitta* and general debility. The seeds are bitter, expectorant, diuretic, aphrodisiac, carminative and emmenagogue, and are useful in cough, asthma, strangury, inflammation, flatulence, anorexia, amenorrhoea and dysmenorrhoea.

"पालक्या वर्त्तुळवती वर्त्तुळा पिछिलावती ।
प्रोक्ता पालकिनी सद्भिस्तथा पिछिलपात्रिका ॥ " (अ.म.)
["Pālakyā vaṛttuḷavatī vaṛttuḷā pichilāvatī
Pṛōktā pālakinī sadbhistathā pichilapatṛikā" (A.ma.)]

Beta vulgaris

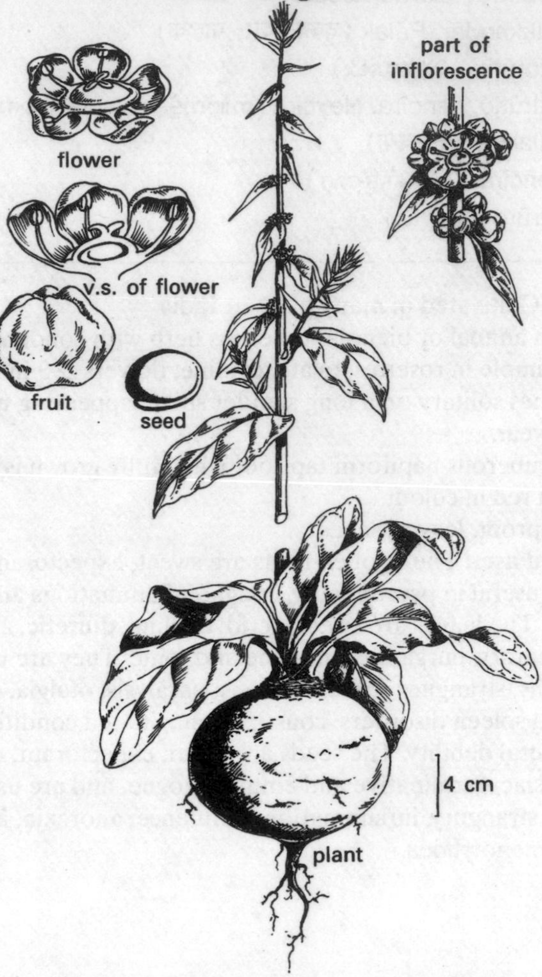

"पालिङ्क्या वास्तुकाकारा छर्दिका च्चिरितच्छदा । " (भ.प्र.)
["Pālinkyā vāstukākārā chardikā ciritacchadā" (Bhā.pra.)]

"पालिङ्क्या वातळा शीता श्ळेष्मळा भेदिनी गुरुः ।
विष्टम्भिनी मदश्वासपित्तरक्तविषापहा ॥ " (भा.प्र.)
["Pālinkyā vātaḷā śītā śḷeṣmaḷā bhēdinī guruḥ
Viṣṭambhinī madaśvāspittaraktaviṣāpahā" (Bhā.pra)]

"पालक्यमीषत् कटुकं मधुरं पथ्यशीतळम् ।
रक्तपित्तहरं ग्राहि ज्ञेयं सन्तर्पणं परम् ॥ " (रा.नि)
["Pālakyamīṣat kaṭukaṃ madhuraṃ pathyaśītaḷaṃ
Raktapittaharaṃ grāhi jñēyaṃ santarpaṇaṃ paraṃ" (Rā.ni.)]

"पालक्यामिति वर्णयन्ति सुधियो गुर्वी सरा पिच्छिला
शीता श्ळेष्मकरी च रक्तशमनी पित्तं विषं नाशयेत् । " (शा.नि.)
["Pālakyāmiti varṇayanti sudhiyō gurvī sarā picchilā
śītā śḷēṣmakarī ca raktaśamanī pittaṃ viṣaṃ nāśayēt" (Śā. ni.)]

"पालक्या पिच्छिला गुर्वी श्ळेष्मळा भेदिनी हिमा । " (अ.सं.)
["Pālakyā picchilā gurvī śḷēṣmaḷā bhēdinī himā" (A.saṁ.)]

Betula utilis D.Don

(B.bhojpathra *Wall.*)

Betulaceae : (भूर्ज–कुलम्)

Eng	:	Himalayan silver birch, Jacquemon tree
Hin	:	Bhōjpatra (भोजपत्र)
Kan	:	Būrjjamara (ಬೂರ್ಜ್ಜಮರ)
Mal	:	Bhūṛjamaraṃ, Bhujapatṛaṃ (ഭൂർജ്ജമരം, ഭൂജപത്രം)
San	:	Bhūṛjaḥ, Bahuḷavalkalaḥ (भूर्जः, बहुळवल्कलः)
Tam	:	Bhūṛjjamaraṃ (பூர்ச்சமரம்)
Tel	:	Būrjapatramu (బూర్జపత్రము)

Distribution: Himalayas, in areas upto 4,200 m elevation

The plant: A medium sized deciduous tree upto 20 m in height with white bark having horizontal lenticels and pink inner layers, peeling off in large papery layers; young shoots, petioles and leaves silky; leaves simple, ovate, acute, sharply irregularly serrate, base cuneate or rounded, sticky when young with yellow resinous scales; flowers in catkins, male catkins at the tip of the long shoots, female spikes solitary on the top of the dwarf shoots; fruits narrower than the bracts, the wings narrower than the nut.

Parts used: bark

Properties and uses: The bark is astringent, acrid, thermogenic, alexeteric, deodorant, antibacterial, anticonvulsant, constipating, haemostatic, expectorant, carminative and tonic. It is useful in vitiated conditions of *tṛidōṣā*, convulsions, hysteria, epilepsy, bacterial infections, wounds, diarrhoea, dysentery, haemorrhages, haemoptysis, haematemesis, cough, bronchitis, dyspepsia, otalgia, ottorrhoea, jaundice, bilious fever, leprosy, skin diseases and general debility.

"भूर्जः स्यात् भुजपत्रश्चर्म्याह्वश्छत्रपत्रश्च ।
तनुपत्रश्च मृदुत्वक् पर्यायैर्यन्त्रपत्र इति ॥ " (अ.म.)
["Bhūṛjaḥ syāt bhujapatṛaścaṛmyāhvaśchaṭrapatṛaśca I
Tanupatṛaśca mṛdutvak paṛyāyaiṛyantṛapatṛa iti " (A.ma.)]

"भूर्जो भुजो बहुपुटो बहुत्वक्को मृदुच्छदः ।
चित्रपत्रः छत्रपत्रो लेख्यपत्रोऽथ भूरुहः ॥ (म.नि.)
["Bhūṛjō bhujō bahupuṭō bahutvakkō mṛducchadaḥ
Citrapatṛaḥ chaṭrapatṛō lēkhyapatṛōʃtha bhūruhaḥ (Ma.ni.)]

Betula utilis

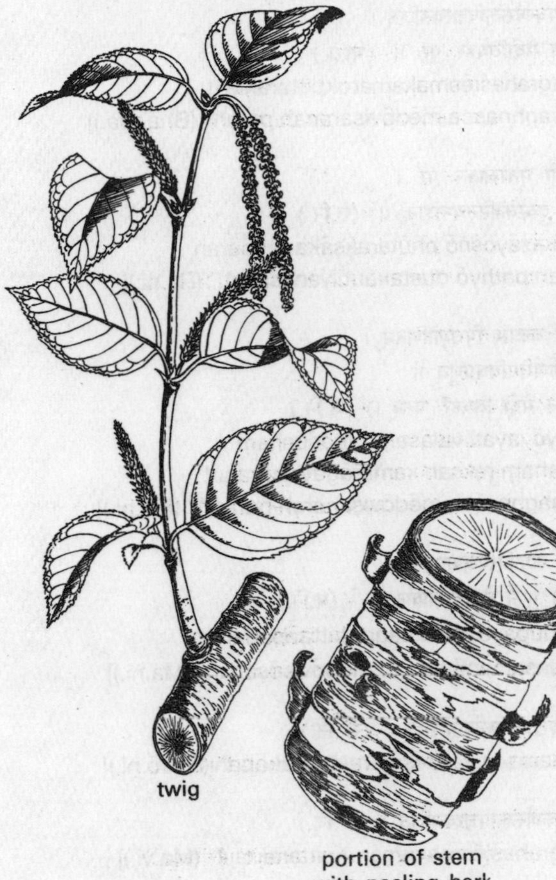

"भूर्जपत्रः स्मृतो भूर्जश्चर्मी बहुळवल्कलः । " (भा.प्र.)
["Bhūrjapatraḥ smṛtō bhūrjaścarmī bahuḷavalkalaḥ" (Bhā.pra.)]

"भूर्जो वल्कद्रुमो भूर्जः सुचर्मा भूर्जपत्रकः ।
चित्रत्वग्बिन्दुपत्रश्च रक्षापत्रो विचित्रकः ॥
भूतघ्नो मृदुपत्रश्च शैलेन्द्रस्थोऽद्रिभूमिजः ।" (रा.नि.)
["Bhūrjō valkadrumō bhūrjaḥ sucarmā bhūrjapatrakaḥ
Citratvagbindupatraśca rakṣāpatrō vicitrakaḥ
Bhūtaghnō mṛdupatraśca śailēndrasthō'dribhūmijaḥ" (Rā.ni.)]

"भूर्जो भूतग्रहश्ळेष्मकर्णरुक्पित्तरक्तजित् ।
कषायो राक्षसघ्नश्च मेदोविषहरः परः ॥" (भा.प्र.)
["Bhūrjō bhūtagrahaśḷēṣmakarṇarukpittaraktajit
Kaṣāyō rākṣasaghnaśca mēdōviṣaharaḥ paraḥ" (Bhā.pra.)]

"भूर्जः कटुकषायोष्णो भूतरक्षाकरः परः ।
त्रिदोषशमनः पथ्यो दुष्टकौटिल्यनाशनः ॥" (रा.नि.)
["Bhūrjaḥ kaṭukaṣāyōṣṇō bhūtarakṣākaraḥ paraḥ
Tridōṣaśamanaḥ pathyō duṣṭakauṭilyanāśanaḥ" (Rā.ni.)]

भूर्जः कषायो जयति वलासं पित्तशोणितम् ।
मेदो भूतग्रहं रक्षः कर्णरोगविषप्रणुत् ॥
(कषायो राक्षसघ्नश्च मेदो विषहरः परम् ।) (कै.नि.)
["Bhūrjaḥ kaṣāyō jayati valāsaṃ pittaśōṇitaṃ
Mēdō bhūtagrahaṃ rakṣaḥ karṇarōgaviṣapraṇut
(Kaṣāyō rākṣasaghnaśca mēdōviṣaharaḥ paraṃ)" (Kai.ni.)]

"ग्रहघ्नो धुपयोगे च कफपित्तविषापहः ।
मङ्गल्यः पापशमनो भूर्जो मेदोविशोषणः ॥ " (म.नि.)
["Grahaghnō dhūpayōgē ca kaphapittaviṣāpahaḥ
Maṅgalyaḥ pāpaśamanō bhūrjō mēdōviśōṣaṇaḥ" (Ma.ni.)]

"भूर्जो व्रणहरश्चैव श्ळेष्मरक्तप्रकोपहृत् ।" (सो.नि.)
["Bhūrjō vraṇaharaścaiva śḷēṣmaraktaprakōpahṛt" (Sō.ni.)]

"भूर्जो भूतग्रहश्ळेष्मकर्णरुक्पित्तरक्तजित् ।" (म.वि.)
["Bhūrjō bhūtagrahaśḷēṣmakarṇarukpittaraktajit" (Ma.vi.)]

Coll. No. AVS 1028

Biophytum sensitivum (Linn.) DC.

Oxalidaceae : (चाङ्गेरी–कुलम्)

Hin	:	Lajjālu, Lakṣmaṇā (लज्जालु, लक्ष्मणा)
Mal	:	Mukkutti (മുക്കുറ്റി)
San	:	Viparītalajjālu, Jhullapuṣpaḥ (विपरीतलज्जालु, झुल्लपुष्पः)
Tam	:	Tiṇṭāṉāḻi (தீண்டாநாழி)
Tel	:	Pulicenta (పులిచింత)

Distribution: Throughout the hotter parts of India as weeds in moist shady places

The plant: A slender erect annual with a rosette of leaves on top of the stem; leaves abruptly pinnate, sensitive, leaflets opposite, 6–12 pairs, the terminal pair being the largest, oblong, apiculate at the apex, glabrous, pale beneath; flowers yellow, dimorphic, peduncles many, slender upto 10 cm long, fruits ellipsoid capsules; seeds prominently ridged, transversely striate.

Parts used: whole plant

Properties and uses: The plant is bitter, thermogenic, diuretic, lithontriptic, suppurative, expectorant, stimulant and tonic. It is useful in strangury, urinary calculi, hyperdipsia in bilious fevers, wounds, abscesses, gonorrhoea, asthma, phthisis, stomachalgia and snake bite.

"लज्जालुर्वैपरीत्यान्या अल्पक्षुपबृहद्दळा ।
वैपरीत्या तु लज्जालुर्ह्यभिधाने प्रयोजयेत् ॥" (रा.नि.)
["Lajjāluṛvaiparītyānyā alpakṣupabṛhaddaḷā
Vaiparītyā tu lajjāluṛhyabhidhānē pṛayōjayēt" (Rā.ni.)]

"झुल्लपुष्पोज्वलत्पुष्पः कृछ्रहा लघुवृक्षकः ।
पीतपुष्पः पंक्तिपत्रस्तथा लज्जालुकः स्मृतः ।" (शा.नि)
["Jhullapuṣpōjvalatpuṣpaḥ kṛchṛahā laghuvṛkṣakaḥ
Pītapuṣpaḥ paṃktipatṛastathā lajjālukaḥ smṛtaḥ" (Sā.ni.)]

Biophytum sensitivum

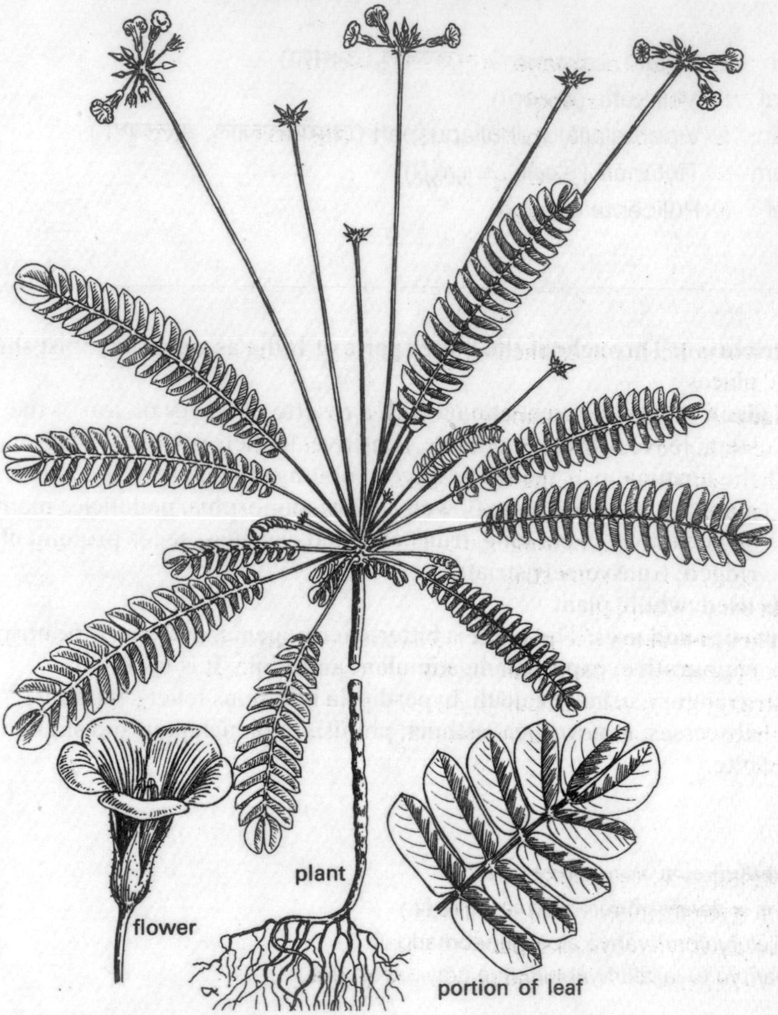

"निष्कण्टका क्षुद्रपादी निश्शाखा क्षुपवृक्षका ।
लज्जालुवत् प्रयोक्तव्यं हृद्यं शुलहरं च तत् ॥" (स्व.)
["Niṣkaṇṭakā kṣudrapādī niśśākhā kṣupavṛkṣakā
Lajjāluvat pṛayōktavyaṃ hṛdyaṃ śūlaharaṃ ca tat" (Sva.)]

"लज्जालुर्वैपरीत्याह्वा कटुरुष्णा कफामनुत् ।
रसे नियामकोऽत्यन्तनानाविज्ञानकारकः ॥ " (रा.नि.)
["Lajjāluṛvaiparītyāhvā kaṭuruṣṇā kaphāmanut
Rasē niyāmakōʃtyantanānāvijñānakārakaḥ" (Rā.ni.)]

"झुल्लपुष्पः सृष्टमूत्रो मूत्रकृच्छ्रहरः परः ।" (शा.नि)
["Jhullapuṣpaḥ sṛṣṭamūtṛō mūtṛakṛcchṛaharaḥ paraḥ" (Śā.ni.)]

Coll. No. AVS 1160

***Bixa orellana* Linn.**

Bixaceae : (सिन्दूरी–कुलम्)

Eng	:	Arnotta plant, Annatto plant
Hin	:	Sindūriyā, Lātkān (सिन्दूरिया, लातकान)
Kan	:	Kappumankala, Rangamali (ಕಪ್ಪುಮಂಕಲ,ರಂಗಮಲಿ)
Mal	:	Kuppamaññaḷ, Kuraṅṅumaññaḷ (കുപ്പമഞ്ഞൾ, കുരങ്ങുമഞ്ഞൾ)
San	:	Sindūrī (सिन्दूरी)
Tam	:	Śappira vīrai, Uragumañjaḷ (சப்பிரவீரை, உரகுமஞ்சள்)
Tel	:	Jaffraceṭṭu (జఫ్రచెట్టు)

Distribution: Widely cultivated throughout India

The plant: A small handsome evergreen tree; leaves large, cordate acuminate, glabrous on both surfaces; flowers white or pink in terminal panicles; fruits reddish brown or green capsules, clothed with soft bristles; seeds trigonous covered with a red pulp.

Parts used: roots, bark, seeds

Properties and uses: The roots, bark and seeds are antiperiodic, antipyretic and astringent. They are useful in intermittent fevers and gonorrhoea. The pulp surrounding the seed is a mosquito repellent, and is useful to treat dysentery. A non-toxic dye, `Annatto dye', obtained from the pulp is used for colouring edible materials.

"सिन्दूरी रक्तबीजा च रक्तपुष्पा सुकोमळा " (भा.प्र)
["Sindūrī raktabījā ca raktapuṣpā sukōmaḷā" (Bhā.pra.)]

"सिन्दूरी वीरपुष्पश्च तृणपुष्पी करच्छदः ।
सिन्दूरपुष्पी शोणादिपुष्पी षडाह्वयः स्मृतः ॥" (रा.नि.)
["Sindūrī vīrapuṣpāśca tṛṇapuṣpī karacchadaḥ
Sindūrapuṣpī śōṇādipuṣpī ṣaḍāhvayaḥ smṛtaḥ" (Rā.ni.)]

"सिन्दूरी विषपित्तास्रतृष्णावान्तिहरी हिमा ।"(भ.प्र.)
["Sindūrī viṣapittāsṛatṛṣṇāvāntiharī himā" (Bhā.pra.)]

"सिन्दूरी कटुका तिक्ता कषाया श्ळेष्मवातजित् ।
शिरोर्त्तिशमनी भूतनाशा चण्डीप्रिया भवेत् ॥" (रा.नि.)
["Sindūrī kaṭukā tiktā kaṣāyā śḷēṣmavātajit

Bixa orellana

Plate 14

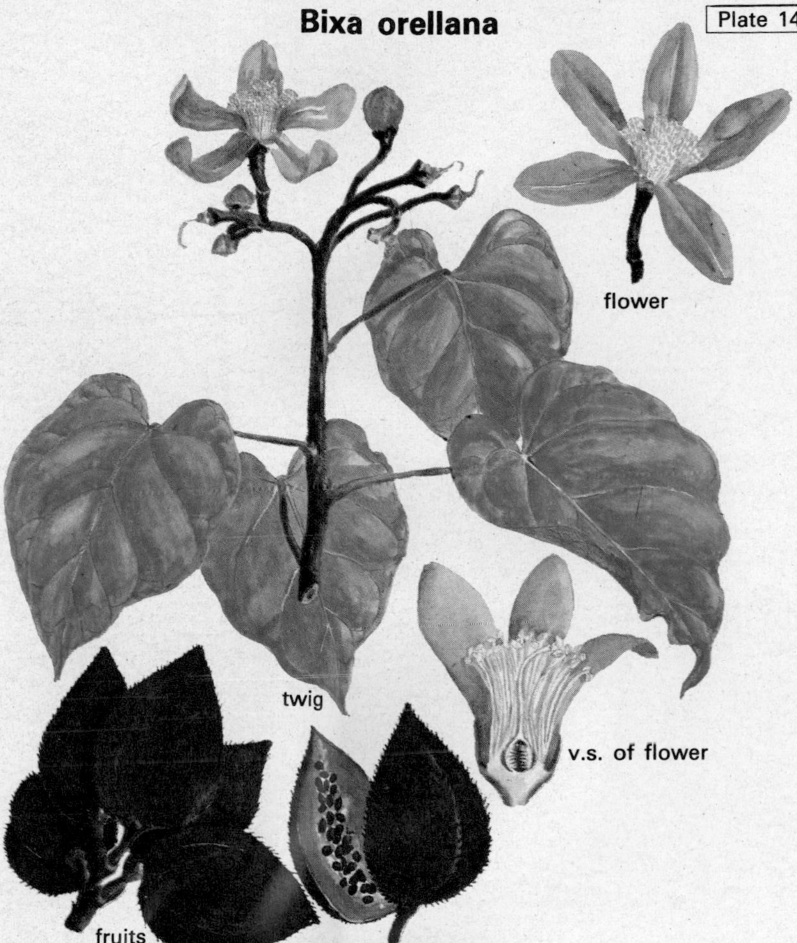

[Śīrōṛttiśamanī bhūtanāśā caṇḍīpriyā bhavēt " (Rā.ni.)]

കുപ്പമഞ്ഞൾ തുലോം തീക്ഷ്ണം പിത്തരക്തപ്രദൂഷണം
കാസശ്വാസങ്ങളാനാഹമർശസ്സും ഗുന്മമെന്നോരോ
ദണ്ഡങ്ങളെ ശമിപ്പിപ്പാനേറ്റവും നന്നിതുത്തമം. (ഗു.പാ.)

["Kuppamaññaḷ tulōṃ tīkṣṇaṃ pittaraktapradūṣaṇaṃ
Kāsaśvāsaṅṅaḷānāhamarśassuṃ gulmamennōrō
Daṇḍaṅṅaḷe śamippippānēṟṟavuṃ nannituttamaṃ" (Gu.pā.)]

Coll. No. AVS 1477

Blumea lacera **(Burm.f.) DC.**

Asteraceae : (भृङ्गराज–कुलम्)

Hin	:	Kukaraundhā (कुकरौन्धा)
Kan	:	Kukkaradru (ಕುಕ್ಕರದ್ರು)
Mal	:	Kukkuravṛkṣam, Ṛākkila (കുക്കുരവൃക്ഷം, റാക്കില)
San	:	Kukundaraḥ, Kukkuradry (कुकुन्दरः, कुक्कुरद्रु)
Tam	:	Kāṭṭumuḷḷaṅki (காட்டுமுள்ளங்கி)
Tel	:	Kukundaramu (కుకుందరము)

Distribution: Throughout India,in areas upto 600 m elevation

The plant: A herbaceous erect annual with a strong odour of turpentine upto 0.9 m in height, glandular, pubescent throughout; leaves simple, alternate, the lower petioled, often incised or lyrate, the upper sub-sessile, elliptic-oblong or obovate, 2.5 – 5 cm long; flowers yellow, numerous in heads, both terminal and axillary, corolla lobes glabrous; fruits subtetragonous achenes, not ribbed, crowned with white pappus hairs.

Parts used: whole plant

Properties and uses: The plant is bitter, astringent, acrid, thermogenic, errhine, anti-inflammatory, styptic, ophthalmic, digestive, anthelmintic, liver tonic, expectorant, febrifuge, antipyretic, diuretic, deobstruant and stimulant. It is useful in vitiated conditions of *pitta* and *kapha,* catarrh, cephalalgia, inflammation, ophthalmia, bruises, wounds, abdominal disorders, intestinal worms, liver disorders, haemorrhoids, haemorrhages, haematemesis, cough, bronchitis, leucorrhoea, fever, intermittent fevers, burning sensation, hyperdipsia, halitosis and cholera.

"कुकुन्दरस्ताम्रचूडः सूक्ष्मपत्रो मृदुच्छदः ।" (भा.प्र.)
["Kukundarastāmṛacūḍaḥ sūkṣmapatṛō mṛducchadaḥ" (Bhā.pṛa.)]

"कुक्कुरदुस्ताम्रचूडः सूक्ष्मपत्रो मृदुच्छदः ।" (म.वि)
["Kukkuradrustāmṛacūḍaḥ sūkṣmapatṛō mṛducchadaḥ" (Ma.vi.)]

"कुकुन्दरः कटुस्तिक्तो ज्वररक्तकफापहा ।

Blumea lacera

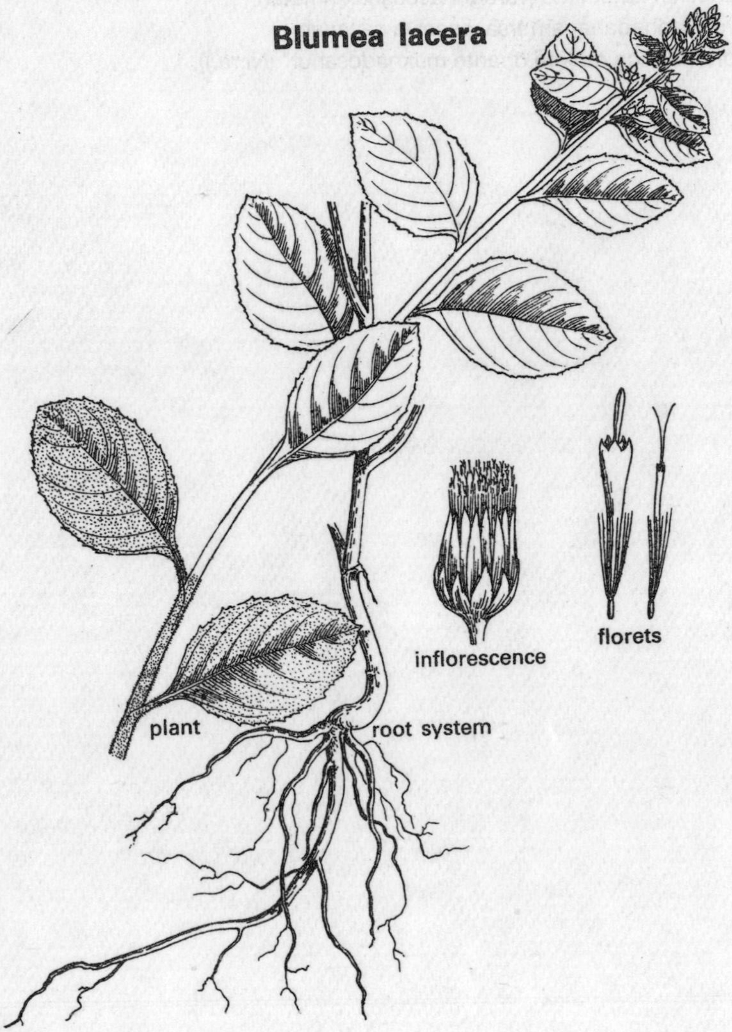

तन्मूलमार्द्रं निक्षिप्तं वदने मुखशोषहृत् ॥" (भा.प्र.)
["Kukundaraḥ kaṭustiktō jvararaktakaphāpahā
Tanmūlamārdraṃ nikṣiptaṃ vadanē mukhaśōṣahṛt" (Bhā.pṛa.)]

"कुकुन्दरः कटुस्तिक्तो ज्वरघ्नश्चोष्णकृन्मतः ।
रक्तरुक् कफदाहानां तृषायाश्चैव नाशनः ॥
अस्यार्द्रमूलञ्च मुखे धारिते मुखदोषनुत् ।" (नि.र.)
["Kukundaraḥ kaṭustiktō jvaraghnaścōṣṇakṛnmataḥ
Raktaruk kaphadāhānāṃ tṛṣayāścaiva nāśanaḥ
Asyārdramūlañca mukhē dhāritē mukhadōṣanut" (Ni.ra.)]

Coll. No. AVS 1112

Boerhaavia diffusa **Linn.**

Nyctaginaceae (पुनर्नवा–कुलम्)

Eng	:	Hogweed, Pigweed
Hin	:	Sānt, Gadahpurnā (सान्त, गदहपुरना)
Kan	:	Sanadika (ಸನದಿಕ)
Mal	:	Taviḻāma, Taḻutāma (തവിഴാമ, തഴുതാമ)
San	:	Punarṇavā, Śōphaghnī (पुनर्नवा, शोफघ्नी)
Tam	:	Mukkurattai, Mūkkarattai-kīrai (முக்குரத்தை, மூக்கரத்தைக்கீரை)
Tel	:	Attamamidi (అత్తమామిడి)

Distribution : Throughout India,as a weed in waste lands and road sides

The plant : A perennial diffuse herb with stout root stock and many procumbent branches; leaves simple, opposite, short-petioled in unequal pairs, ovate-oblong, acute or obtuse, rounded or subcordate at base, glabrous above, and whitish beneath; flowers pale rose coloured, small, short-stalked, in irregular clusters of terminal panicles at the ends of branches; fruits highly viscid, easily detachable, one-seeded, indehiscent with a thin pericarp.

Parts used : whole plant

Properties and uses : The plant is bitter, astringent, cooling, anthelmintic, diuretic, aphrodisiac, cardiac stimulant, diaphoretic, emetic, expectorant, anti-inflammatory, febrifuge, laxative and tonic. It is useful in all types of inflammations, strangury, leucorrhoea, ophthalmia, lumbago,myalgia, scabies, cardiac disorders, jaundice, anaemia, dyspepsia, constipation, cough, bronchitis and general debility.

"वृश्चीवो दीर्घदळः पुनर्नवो रक्तवृन्तश्च ।
जटिलः कठिल्लकः स्यात्सुनाशिका क्षुद्रवर्षाभूः ॥
वृश्चीवोऽन्यः श्वेतमूलः सद्योमण्डलपत्रकः ।
श्वेतपत्रश्चाम्ळशाको वैशाखश्च विरेचनी ॥
कठिल्लो महावर्षाभूर्वृषकेतुर्निगद्यते । " (अ.म.)

["Vṛścīvō dīrghadaḷaḥ punarṇavō raktavṛntaśca
Jaṭilaḥ kaṭhillakaḥ syātsunāśikā kṣudravarṣābhūḥ
Vṛścīvōऽnyaḥ śvētamūlaḥ sadyomaṇḍalapatṛakaḥ

Boerhaavia diffusa

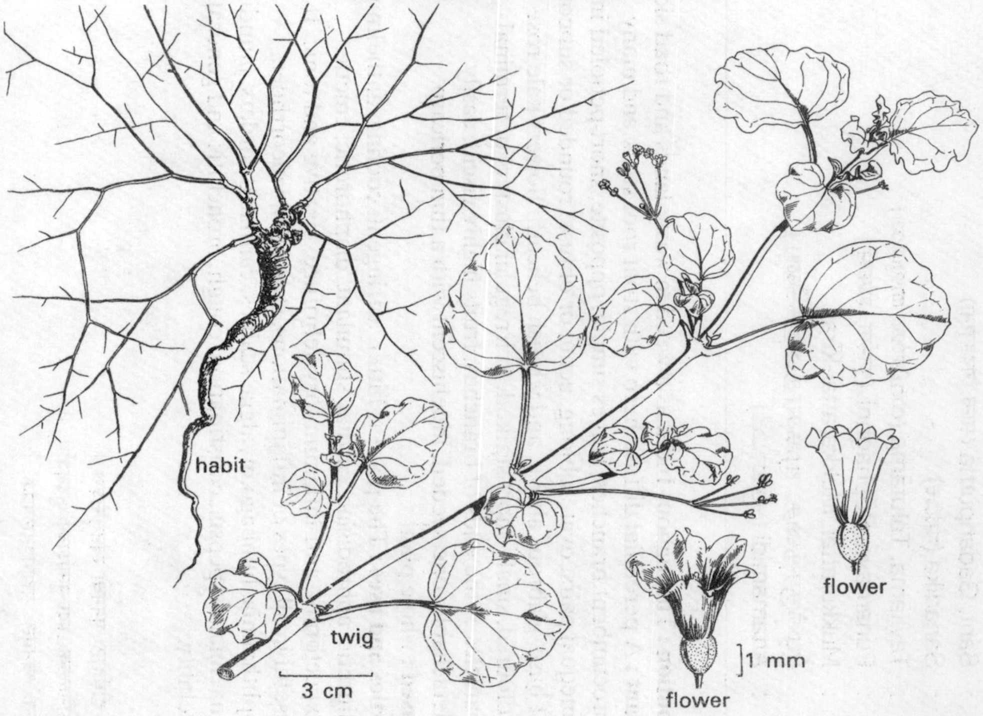

Śvētapatṛascām̱laśākō vaiśākhaśca virēcanī
Kaṭhillō mahāvarṣābhūṛvṛṣakētuṛnigadyatē" (A.ma.)]

"पुनर्नवा श्वेतमूला शोफघ्नी दीर्घपत्रिका ।
पुनर्नवाऽपरा रक्ता रक्तपुष्पा शिवाटिका ॥
शोफघ्नी क्षुद्रवर्षाभूर्वृषकेतुः कठिल्लका ।" (भा.प्र.)
["Punaṛnavā śvētamūlā śōphaghnī dīrghapatṛikā
Punaṛnavāʃparā raktā raktapuṣpā śivaṭikā
Śōphaghnī kṣudravaṛṣābhūṛvṛṣakētuḥ kaṭhillakā" (Bhā.pṛa.)]

"पुनर्नवो वृषकेतुः सदामण्डलपत्रकः ।
श्वेतमूलोऽथ वर्षाभूर्वृश्चीवः क्षुद्रपत्रकः
पुनर्नवोऽन्यो वैशाखोः रक्तवृन्तः कठिल्लकः ।
विकसा क्षुद्रवर्षाभू रक्तपुष्पा सिनाडिका ॥ "(म.नि.)
["Punaṛnavō vaṛṣakētuḥ sadāmaṇḍalapatṛakaḥ
Śvētamūlōʃtha vaṛṣābhūṛvṛścīvaḥ kṣudrapatṛakaḥ
Punaṛnavōʃnyō vaiśākhō raktavṛntaḥ kaṭhillakaḥ
Vikasā kṣudravaṛṣābhū raktapuṣpā sināḍikā" (Ma.ni.)]

"पुनर्नवा विशाखश्च कठिल्लः शशिवाटिका ।
पृथ्वी च सितवर्षाभूर्दीर्घपत्रः कठिल्लकः ॥
पुनर्नवाऽन्या रक्ताख्या क्रूरा मण्डलपत्रिका ।
रक्तकाण्डा वर्षकेतुर्लोहिता रक्तपत्रिका ॥
वैशाखी रक्तवर्षाभूः शोफघ्नी रक्तपुष्पिका ।
विकस्वरा विषघ्नी च प्रावृषेण्या च सारिणी ॥
वर्षाभवः शोणपत्रः शोणः सम्मिलितद्रुमः ।
पुनर्नवो नवो नव्यः स्याह्वाविंशतिसंज्ञया ॥
नीला पुनर्नवा नीला श्यामा नीलपुनर्नवा ।
कृष्णाख्या नीलवर्षाभूर्नीलिनी स्वाभिधान्विता ॥" (रा.नि.)
["Punaṛnavā viśākhaśca kaṭhillaḥ śaśivaṭikā
Pṛthvī ca sitavaṛṣābhūṛdīṛghapatṛaḥ kaṭhillakaḥ
Punaṛnavāʃnyā raktākhyā krūrā maṇḍalapatṛikā
Raktakāṇḍā vaṛṣakētuṛlōhitā raktapatṛikā
Vaiśākhī raktavaṛṣābhuḥ śōphaghnī raktapuṣpikā
Vikasvarā viṣaghnī ca pṛāvṛṣēṇya ca sariṇī
Vaṛṣābhavaḥ śōṇapatṛaḥ śōṇaḥ sammiḷitadrumaḥ
Punaṛnavō navō navyaḥ syāhvāvimśatisamjñayā
Nīlā punaṛnavā nīlā śyāmā nīlapunaṛnavā
Kṛṣṇākhyā nīlavaṛṣābhuṛnīlinī svābhidhānvitā" (Rā.ni.)]

"कटुः कषायानुरसा पाण्डुघ्नी दीपनी सरा ।
शोफानिलगरश्ळेष्महरी व्रण्योदरप्रणुत् ॥
पुनर्नवाऽरुणा तिक्ता कटुपाका हिमा लघुः ।
वातळा ग्राहिणी श्ळेष्मपित्तरक्तविनाशिनी ॥ " (भा.प्र.)
["Kaṭuḥ kaṣāyānurasā pāṇḍughnī dīpanī sarā
Sōphānilagaraśḷēṣmaharī vraṇyōdarapṛaṇut
Punaṛnavāʃruṇā tiktā kaṭupākā himā laghuḥ
Vātaḷā grāhiṇī śḷēṣmapittaraktavināśinī" (Bhā.pṛa.)]

"पुनर्नवा भवेदुष्णा तिक्ता रूक्षा कफापहा ।
सशोफपाण्डुहृद्रोगकासोरःक्षतशूलनुत् ॥
रक्ता पुनर्नवा तिक्ता सारिणी शोफनाशिनी ।
रक्तप्रदरदोषघ्नी पाण्डुपित्तप्रमर्दनी ॥ " (ध.नि.)
["Punaṛnavā bhavēduṣṇā tiktā rūkṣā kaphāpahā
Saśōphapāṇḍuhṛdrōgakāsōraḥkṣataśūlanut
Raktā punaṛnavā tiktā sāriṇī śōphanāśinī
Raktapṛadaradōṣaghnī pāṇḍupittapṛamardanī" (Dha.ni.)]

"उष्णानि स्वादुतिक्तानि वातप्रशमनानि च ।
तेषु पौनर्नवं शाकं विशेषात् शोफनाशनम् ॥ " (सु.सं.सू.४६)
["Uṣṇāni svādutiktāni vātapṛaśamanāni ca
Tēṣu paunaṛnavaṃ śākaṃ viśēṣāt śōphanāśanaṃ" (Su.sam.Sū.46.)]

"पुनर्नवस्यार्धपलं नवस्य
पिष्टं पिबेद्यः पयसाऽर्धमासम् ।
मासद्वयं तत्त्रिगुणं समं वा
जीर्णोऽपि भूयः स पुनर्नवः स्यात् ॥ " (अ.हृ.उ.)
["Punaṛnavasyārdhapalaṃ navasya
piṣṭaṃ pibēdyaḥ payasāʃṛdhamāsaṃ
Māsadvayaṃ tattṛiguṇaṃ samaṃ vā
jīṛṇōʃpi bhūyaḥ sa punaṛnavaḥ syāt" (A.hṛ.U.)]

"रसायनी शोफहरा सकषाया सतिक्तका ।
कफवातहरा ज्ञेया द्विविधा च पुनर्नवा ॥ " (म.नि.)
["Rasāyanī śōphaharā sakaṣāyā satiktakā
Kaphavātaharā jñēyā dvividhā ca punaṛnavā" (Ma.ni.)]

"श्वेता पुनर्नवा सोष्णा तिक्ता कफविषापहा ।
कासहृद्रोगशूलास्रपाण्डुशोफानिलार्तिनुत् ॥
रक्ता पुनर्नवा तिक्ता सारिणी शोफनाशिनि ।
रक्तप्रदरदोषघ्नी पाण्डुपित्तप्रमर्दिनी ॥
नीला पुनर्नवा तिक्ता कटूष्णा च रसायनी ।
हृद्रोगपाण्डुश्वयथुश्वासवातकफापहा ॥ " (रा.नि.)
["Śvētā punaṛnavā sōṣṇā tiktā kaphaviṣāpahā

Kāsahṛdrōgaśūlāsṛapāṇḍuśōphānilārtinut
Raktā punarṇavā tiktā sāriṇī śōphanāśinī
Raktapṛadaradōṣaghnī pāṇḍupittapṛamaṛdinī
Nīlā punarṇavā tiktā kaṭūṣṇā ca rasāyanī
Hṛdrōgapāṇḍuśvayathuśvāsavātakaphāpaha" (Rā.ni.)]

श्वेता पुनर्नवा तिक्ता चोष्णा कट्वी च तूवरा ।
रुच्याग्निदीपनी रूक्षा मधुरा पटु सारका ॥
हृद्या शोफं कफं वातं कासमर्शोव्रणं जयेत् ।
पाण्डून् विषोदरं शूलं हृद्रोगोरःक्षतापहा ॥
पौनर्नवी पर्णशाका चातिरूक्षा कफापहा ।
वाताग्निमान्द्यगुल्मघ्नी प्लीहशूलविनाशिका ॥ " (नि.र.)
["Śvētā punaṛnavā tiktā cōṣṇā kaṭvī ca tūvarā
Rucyāgnidīpanī rūkṣā madhurā paṭu sārakā
Hṛdyā śōphaṃ kaphaṃ vātaṃ kāsamaṛśōvṛaṇaṃ jayēṭ
Pāṇḍūn viṣōdaraṃ śūlaṃ hṛdrōgōraḥkṣatāpahā
Paunaṛnavī paṛṇaśākā cātirūkṣā kaphāpahā
Vātāgnimāndyagulmaghnī pḷīhaśūlavināśikā" (Ni.ra.)]

തവിഴാമയ്ക്കെരിച്ചിട്ടും കച്ചിട്ടും രസമായ്വരും
കഫവാതഹരം ഹൃദ്യം നന്നുശോഫോദരാർശസാം
ദീപനത്തെ വരുത്തീടും രുചിക്കും നന്നിതെത്രയും (ഗു. പാ.)
["Tavil̤āmaykkericciṭṭuṃ kacciṭṭuṃ rasamāy varuṃ
Kaphavātaharaṃ hṛdyaṃ nannu śōphōdarāṛśasāṃ
Dīpanatte varuttīṭuṃ rucikkuṃ nannitetṛayuṃ" (Gu.pā.)]

Remarks: In Ayurvedic dictionaries like 'Bhāvapṛakāśaṃ' two varieties of *punaṛnavā* are described, namely, the red and the white. But 'Rājanighaṇṭu' describes a third variety, the blue, besides the above two. The Commentators of all these dictionaries are agreed on the fact that the red variety is *Boerhaavia diffusa.* In 'Śāligrāmanighaṇṭubhūṣaṇaṃ' the white variety has been identified as *B. procumbense.* On the other hand, some Commentators identify this white variety as *Trianthema* species.

Trianthema and *Boerhaavia* species belong to different families. Besides, the *Trianthema* species neither contain the punarnavine alkaloid, nor does it possess white flowers. Therefore *śvētapunaṛnavā* cannot be *Trianthema* species.

`The Ayurvedic Formularly of India'identifies *śvētapunaṛnavā* as *Boerhaavia verticillata.*

The roots of the *Trianthema* species are often used to adulterate *punaṛnavā* roots. However, it is very easy to detect any adulteration of this root from the following two distinguishing characteristics of the *punaṛnavā* roots.

1. Plenty of starch grains can be seen in both the ground tissues and xylem

parenchyma of *punarnavā*, while in *Trianthema* species this cannot be seen.

2. The phloem around the xylem of *punarnavā* root has semicircular or crescentic patches, while that of *Trianthema* species is narrow strip only.

As *Boerhaavia verticillata* is not easily available in Kerala in sufficient quantities, double the quantities of *B. diffusa* are taken in instances where both these varieties are required as constituents of a formulation.

Bombax ceiba

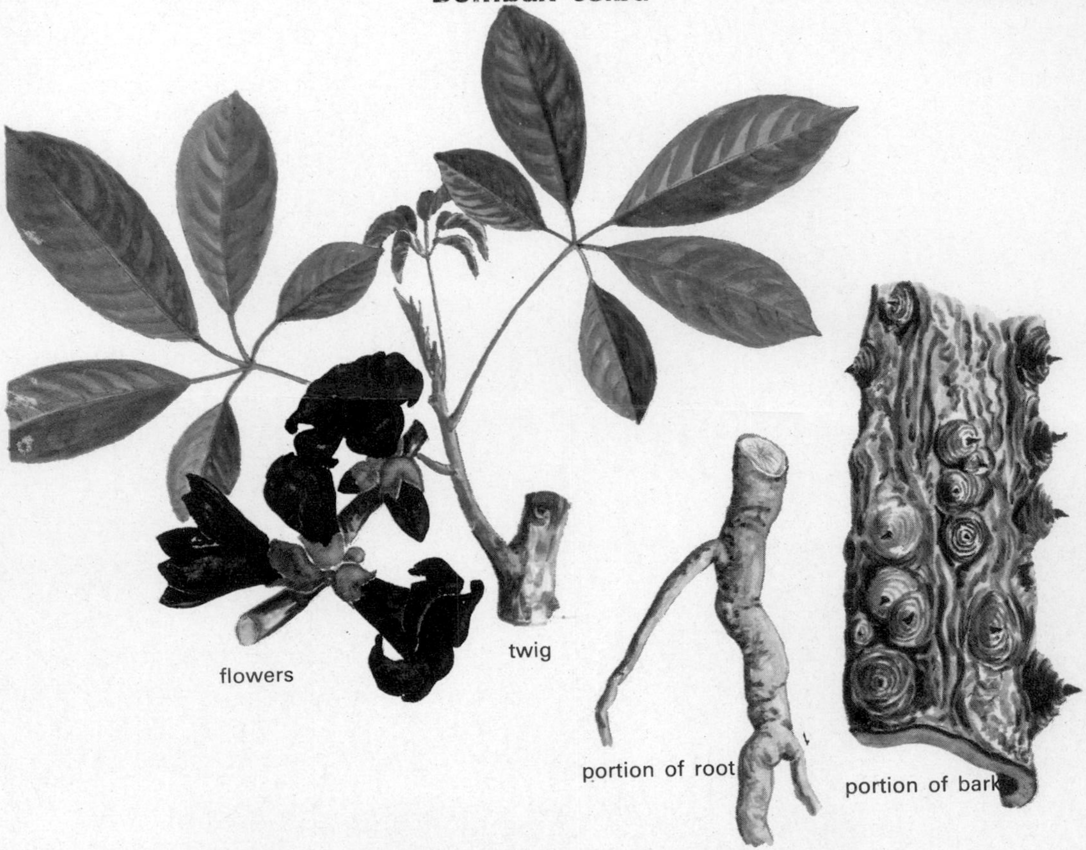

Bombax ceiba **Linn.**

(Salmalia malabarica *(DC.) Schott & Endlicher*)

Bombacaceae : (शाल्मली–कुलम्)

Eng	:	Red silk cotton tree
Hin	:	Śēmal, Sēmul (शेमल, सेमुल)
Kan	:	Būrugadamara (ಬೂರುಗದಮರ)
Mal	:	Ilavu̥, Elavu̥, Pūḷamaram, Muḷḷilavu̥ (ഇലവ്, എലവ്, പൂളമരം, മുള്ളിലവ്)
San	:	Sālmalī, Mōcā (शाल्मली, मोचा)
Tam	:	Ilavu, Muḷḷilavu (இலவு, முள்ளிலவு)
Tel	:	Muḷḷubūrugaceṭṭu, Koṇḍabūruga (ముళ్ళుబూరుగచెట్టు, కొండబూరుగ)

Distribution: Throughout India,in forests upto an elevation of about 1,500m, also raised in plantations.

The plant: A tall deciduous tree with a straight buttressed trunk having a clear bole of 24–30 m and spreading branches, bark grey or brown covered with hard, sharp, conical prickles; leaves large, spreading, glabrous, digitate, leaflets lanceolate, 3–7, entire; flowers red, numerous, appearing when the tree is bare of leaves, stamens many arranged in five bundles of 9–12 each and an inner bundle of 15; fruits capsules, dehiscing by 5 leathery or woody valves; seeds smooth, black or grey embedded in long white wool.

A gummy exudate obtained from the bark is dried and sold as `semul-gum' or `mocharas'. The dried gum is light brown in colour resembling the galls, and gradually becomes opaque and dark brown.

Parts used: roots, gum, bark, leaves, flowers, young fruits, seeds

Properties and uses: The roots are sweet, cooling, stimulant, tonic and demulcent, and are used in dysentery. The gum is astringent, cooling, stimulant, aphrodisiac, tonic, styptic and demulcent. It is useful in dysentery, haemoptysis of pulmonary tuberculosis, influenza, menorrhagia, burning sensation, strangury, haemorrhoids, blood impurities and vitiated conditions of *pitta*. The bark is mucilaginous, demulcent and emetic, and is used for fomenting and healing wounds. A paste of it is good for skin eruptions. Leaves are good for strangury and skin eruptions. Flowers are astringent and are good for skin troubles, splenomegaly and haemorrhoids. Young fruits are useful in calculus affections, chronic inflammations and ulceration of the bladder and kidney. Seeds are useful in treating gonorrhoea, chronic cystitis and vitiated conditions of *kapha*. A paste made out of the prickles is good for restoring skin colour especially on the face.

"शाल्मलिस्तु भवेन्मोचा पिच्छिला पूरणीति च ।
रक्तपुष्पा स्थिरायुश्च कण्टकाढ्या च तूलिनी ॥ " (भा.प्र.)
["Śālmalistu bhavēnmōcā picchilā pūraṇīti ca
Raktapuṣpā sthirāyuśca kaṇṭakāḍhyā ca tūlinī" (Bhā.pra.)]

"शाल्मलिश्चिरजीवी स्यात् पिच्छिलो रक्तपुष्पकः ।
कुक्कुटीः तूलवृक्षश्च मोचाख्यः कण्टकदुमः ॥
रक्तफलो रम्यपुष्पो बहुवीर्यो यमद्रुमः ।
दीर्घद्रुमः स्थूलफलो दीर्घायुस्तिथिभिर्मतः ॥" (रा.नि.)
["Śālmaliscirajīvī syāt picchilō raktapuṣpakaḥ
Kukkuṭīḥ tūlavṛkṣaśca mōcākhyaḥ kaṇṭakadrumaḥ
Raktaphalō ramyapuṣpō bahuvīryō yamadrumaḥ
Dīrghadrumaḥ sthūlaphalō dīrghāyustithibhirmataḥ"(Rā.ni.)]

"शाल्मलिः शीतळा स्वाद्वी रसे पाके रसायनी ।
श्ळेष्मळा पित्तवातास्रहारिणी रक्तपित्तजित् ॥
शाल्मलीपुष्पशाकं तु घृतसैन्धवसाधितम् ।
प्रदरं नाशयत्येव दुःसाध्यञ्च न संशयः ॥
रसे पाके च मधुरं कषायं शीतळं गुरु ।
कफापित्तास्रजिद् ग्राहि वातळं च प्रकीर्तितम् ॥" (भा.प्र.)
["Śālmaliḥ śītaḷā svādvī rasē pākē rasāyanī
Śḷēṣmaḷā pittavātāsrahāriṇī raktapittajit
Śālmalīpuṣpaśākaṃ tu ghṛtasaindhavasādhitaṃ
Pradaraṃ nāśayatyēva duḥsādhyañca na saṃśayaḥ
Rasē pākē ca madhuraṃ kaṣāyaṃ śītaḷaṃ guru
Kaphapittāsrajid grāhī vātaḷaṃ ca prakīrttitaṃ" (Bhā.pra.)]

"शाल्मली मधुरा वृष्या बल्या च तुवरा मता ।
शीतळा पिच्छिला लघ्वी स्निग्धा स्वाद्वी रसायना ॥
शुक्ळळा श्ळेष्मळा चैव धातुवृद्धिकरी मता ।
रक्तपित्तञ्च पित्तञ्च रक्तदोषञ्च नाशयेत् ॥
त्वग्रसो स्याद्ग्राहकः स्यात्तुवरः कफनाशनः ।
पुष्पं तु शीतळं तिक्तं गुरु स्वादु कषायकम् ॥
वातळं ग्राहकं रूक्षं कफपित्तविनाशकम् ॥
रक्तदोषहरं चैव गुणाह्येते फलस्य च ॥
कन्दो स्यान्मधुरः शीतो मलस्तम्भकरो मतः ।
शोफं दाहञ्च पित्तञ्च सन्तापञ्चैव नाशयेत् ॥ " (नि.र.)
["Śālmalī madhurā vṛṣyā balyā ca tuvarā matā

Śītaḷā picchilā laghvī snigdhā svādvī rasāyanā
Śukḷaḷa śḷēṣmaḷā caiva dhātuvṛddhikarī matā
Raktapittañaca pittañca raktadōṣañca nāśayēt
Tvagrasō syādgrāhakaḥ syāttuvaraḥ kaphanāśanaḥ
Puṣpaṃ tu śītaḷaṃ tiktaṃ guru svādu kaṣāyakaṃ
Vātaḷaṃ grāhakaṃ rūkṣaṃ kaphapittavināśakaṃ
Raktadōṣaharaṃ caiva guṇāhyētē phalasya ca
Kandō syānmadhuraḥ śītō malastambhakarō mataḥ
Śōphaṃ dāhañca pittaṇca santāpañcaiva nāśayēt" (Ni.ra.)]

"शाल्मली पिच्छिलो वृष्यो बल्यो मधुरशीतळः ।
कषायश्च लघुः स्निग्धः शुक्ळश्ळेष्मविवर्धनः ॥
तद्रसस्तद्गुणो ग्राही कषायः कफनाशकः ।
पुष्पं तद्वच्च निर्दिष्टं फलं तस्य तथाविधम् ॥" (रा.नि.)
["Śālmalī picchilō vṛṣyō balyō madhuraśītaḷaḥ
Kaṣāyaśca laghuḥ snighdhaḥ śukḷaśḷēṣmavivardhanaḥ
Tadrasastadguṇō grāhī kaṣāyaḥ kaphanāśakaḥ
Puṣpaṃ tadvacca nirdiṣṭaṃ phalaṃ tasya tathāvidhaṃ" (Rā.ni.)]

"वृष्या रसायनी शीता मधुरा रसपाकतः ।
रक्तपित्तहरा चैव शाल्मली धातुबृंहणी ॥" (म.नि.)
["Vṛṣyā rasāyanī śītā madhurā rasapākataḥ
Raktapittaharā caiva śālmalī dhātubṛmhaṇī" (Ma.ni.)]

"शाल्मली शीतळा स्निग्धा शुक्ळश्ळेष्मविवर्धिनी ।
कषायस्तद्रसो ग्राही पुष्पं तद्वत्तथा फलम् ॥" (ध.नि.)
["Śālmalī śītaḷā snigdhā śukḷaśḷēṣmavivardhinī
Kaṣāyastadrasō grāhī puṣpaṃ tadvattathā phalaṃ"(Dha.ni.)]

"शाल्मलिः शीतळा स्वाद्वी रसे पाके रसायनी ।
श्ळेष्मळा बृंहणी वृष्या स्निग्धा पित्तास्रनाशनी ॥
पुष्पं स्वादु रसे पाके रूक्षं तिक्तं हिमं गुरु ।
कषायं वातळं ग्राही कफपित्तास्रजित्परम् ॥ " (कै.नि.)
["Śālmaliḥ śītaḷā svādvī rasē pākē rasāyanī
Sḷēṣmaḷā bṛmhaṇī vṛṣyā snigdhā pittāsṛanāśanī
Puṣpaṃ svādu rasē pākē rūkṣaṃ tiktaṃ himaṃ guru
Kaṣāyaṃ vātaḷaṃ grāhī kaphapittāsṛajitparaṃ" (Kai.ni.)]

Eng	:	Semul-gum, Mocharas
Hin	:	Sēmur ka gōnd, Mōcras (सेमुर का गोन्द, मोचरस)
Mal	:	Ilavinpaśa (ഇലവിൻ പശ)
San	:	Mōcarasaḥ (मोचरसः)
Tam	:	Ilavupaśai (இலவுபசை)
Tel	:	Mōcasara (మోచసార)

"निर्यासः शाल्मलेः पिच्छा शाल्मलिर्वेष्टिकापि च ।
मोचस्रावो मोचरसो मोचनिर्यास इत्यपि ॥" (भा.प्र.)
["Niryāsaḥ śālmalēḥ picchā śālmalīrvēṣṭikāpi ca
Mōcasṛāvō mōcarasō mōcaniryāsa ityapi" (Bhā.pṛa.)]

"वयसःस्थापनो वृष्यो गुरु स्वादु रसायनः ।
स्निग्धः कफकरो गर्भस्थापको वातनाशनः ॥
अतिसारप्रवाहघ्नो रक्तरुक्पित्तदाहहा ।
आमातिसारशमनो रक्तातीसारनाशनः ॥" (नि.र.)
["Vayasaḥsthāpanō vṛṣyō guru svādu rasāyanaḥ
Snigdhaḥ kaphakarō gaṛbhasthāpakō vātanaśanaḥ
Ạtisārapṛavāhaghnō raktarukpittadāhahā
Amātisāraśamanō raktātīsāranāśanaḥ" (Ni.ra.)]

पक्वातिसारशमनो हन्ति घोरप्रवाहिकाम् ।
पिच्छिलः शुक्ळळः शीतः सन्धानः शाल्मलीरसः ॥" (म.नि.)
["Pakvātisāraśamanō hanti ghōrapṛavāhikāṃ
Picchilaḥ śukḷaḷaḥ śītaḥ sandhānaḥ śālmalīrasaḥ" (Ma.ni.)]

"मोचरसस्तु कषायः कफवातहरो रसायनो योगात् ।
बलपुष्टिं वर्णवीर्यप्रज्ञायुर्देहसिद्धिदो ग्राही ॥" (रा.नि.)
["Mōcarasastu kaṣāyaḥ kaphavātaharō rasāyanō yōgāt
Balapuṣṭiṃ vaṛṇavīryapṛajñāyuṛdēhasiddhidō grāhī "(Rā.ni.)]

"निर्यासः शीतळः स्निग्धो ग्राही वृष्यः कषायकः ।
प्रवाहिकाऽतिसारामकफपित्तास्रदाहनुत् ॥" (कै.नि.)
[Niryāsaḥ śītaḷaḥ snigdhō grāhī vṛsyaḥ kaṣāyakaḥ
Pṛavāhikāʃtisārāmakaphapittāsṛadāhanut" (Kai.ni.)]

Remarks: The bark and gum of this tree are more commonly used in Ayurvedic formulations. This resinous gum is different from other exudations in that it will not dissolve in water, but only gets bloated (swollen) on soaking.

Coll. No. AVS 2540

Borassus flabellifer **Linn.**

(B. flabelliformis *Roxb.*)

Arecaceae : (पूग–कुलम्)

Eng	:	Palmyra palm
Hin	:	Ṭār, Tāl (टार, ताल)
Kan	:	Tāḷimara (ತಾಳಿಮರ)
Mal	:	Karimpana (കരിമ്പന)
San	:	Tālaḥ, Tāladrumaḥ (तालः, तालद्रुमः)
Tam	:	Karumpanai, Nonkuppanai (கரும்பனை, நுங்குப்பனை)
Tel	:	Tāḍiceṭṭu (తాడిచెట్టు)

Distribution: Hotter parts of India, wild as well as cultivated

The plant: A tall palm attaining a height of about 30 m, with a black stem with a crown of leaves at the top; leaves 0.9 – 1.5 m in diameter, palmately fan shaped, rigidly coriaceous, cleft into many lobes, petiole edges with hard horny spinescent serratures; flowers unisexual, male spadix branched, female spadix simple; fruits large, subglobose drupes, on the greatly enlarged perianth.

Parts used: roots, leaves, inflorescences, fruits

Properties and uses: The roots are cooling, restorative, diuretic, stimulant and antiphlogistic. They are useful in hyperdipsia, burning sensation, strangury and inflammation. The juice of the leaf stalks and young roots is good for gastric catarrh and hiccough. The ash obtained by burning the infloresceneis a good antacid and antiperiodic, and is useful in hyperacidity, heart burn, bilious fever, splenomegaly, haepatomegaly and skin diseases. The fruits are sweet, cooling, laxative, sedative, anthelmintic, depurative, styptic, stomachic, aphrodisiac and tonic. They are useful in hyperdipsia, burning sensation, dyspepsia, flatulence, colic, constipation, intestinal worms, leprosy, skin diseases, haemorrhages, haemoptysis, vitiated conditions of *pitta* and *vatā* and general debility.

"उक्तस्तालस्तु तालो महातृणः सल्लकी शमोव्यासः ।
दीर्घतरुस्तृणराजो द्रुमेश्वरो लेख्यपत्रश्च ॥
ध्वजवृक्षोऽसितकायो दुरारुहो दीर्घवर्यश्च ।
चिरपाक्यः पितृबीजो दीर्घस्कन्धश्च पर्यायैः ॥ " (अ.म.)

Borassus flabellifer

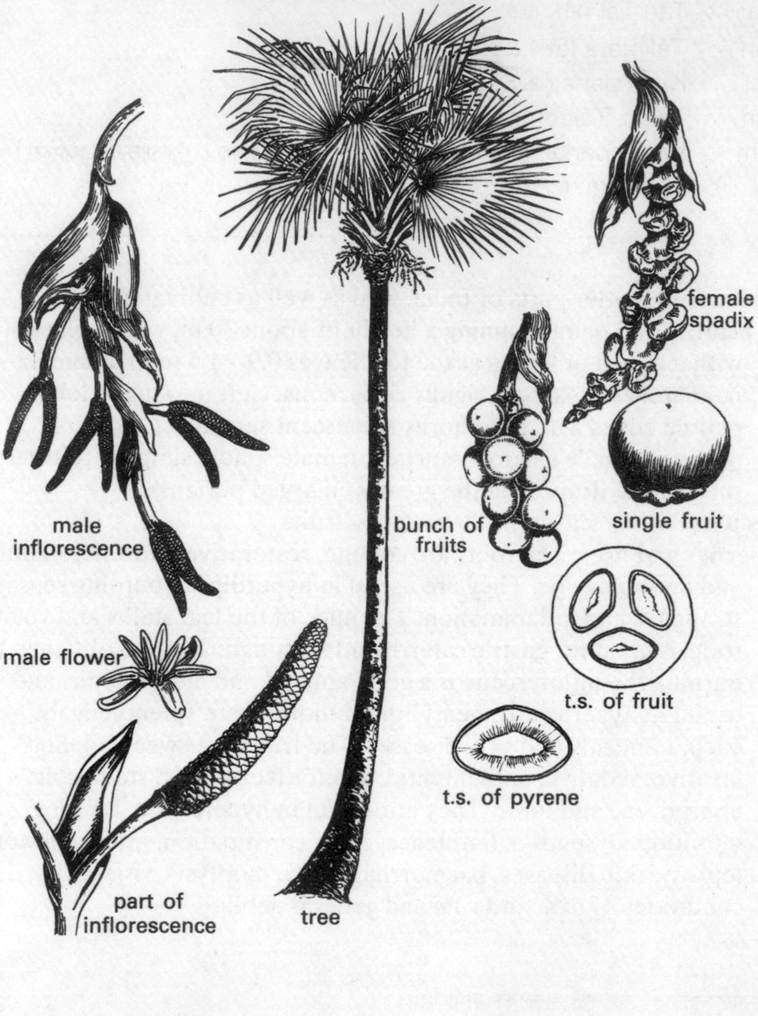

["Uktastālastu tālō mahātṛṇaḥ sallakī śamōvyāsaḥ
Dīrghatarustṛṇarājō drumēśvarō lēkhyapatraśca
Dhvajavṛkṣō'sitakāyō durāruhō dīrghavaryaśca
Cirapākyaḥ pitṛbījō dīrghaskandhaśca paryāyaiḥ" (A.ma.)]

"तालस्तु लेखपत्रः स्यात्तृणराजो महोन्नतः ।" (भा.प्र.)
["Tālastu lēkhapatraḥ syāttṛṇarājō mahōnnataḥ" (Bhā. pra.)]

"तालस्तालद्रुमः पत्री दीर्घस्कन्धो ध्वजद्रुमः ।
तृणराजो मधुरसो मदाढ्यो दीर्घपादपः ॥
चिरायुस्तरुराजश्च गजभक्षो दृढच्छदः ।
दीर्घपत्रो गुच्छपत्रोऽप्यासवद्रुश्च षोडश ।" (रा.नि.)
["Tālastāladrumaḥ patrī dīrghaskandhō dhvajadrumaḥ
Tṛṇarājō madhurasō madāḍhyō dīrghapādapaḥ
Cirāyustarurājaśca gajabhakṣō dṛḍhacchadaḥ
Dīrghapatrō gucchapatrō'pyāsavadruśca ṣōḍaśa" (Rā.ni.)]

"पक्वं तालफलं पित्तरक्तश्ळेष्मविवर्धनम् ।
दुर्जरं बहुमूत्रं च तन्द्राभिष्यन्दशुक्ळदम् ॥
तालमज्जा तु तरुणा किञ्चिन्मदकरी लघुः ।
श्ळेष्मळो वातपित्तघ्नः सस्नेहो मधुरः सरः ॥
तालजं तरुणं तोयमतीव मदकृन्मतम् ।
अम्ळीभूतं यदा तु स्यात्पित्तकृद्वातदोषहृत् ॥" (भा.प्र.)
["Pakvaṃ tālaphalaṃ pittaraktaśḷēṣmavivardhanaṃ
Durjaraṃ bahumūtraṃ ca tandrābhiṣyandaśukḷadaṃ
Tālamajjā tu taruṇā kiñcinmadakarī laghuḥ
Śḷēṣmaḷō vātapittaghnaḥ sasnēhō madhuraḥ saraḥ
Tālajaṃ taruṇaṃ tōyamatīva madakṛnmataṃ
Amḷībhūtaṃ yadā tu syātpittakṛdvatadōṣahṛt" (Bhā. pra.)]

"फलं स्वादु रसे पाके तालजं गुरुपित्ताजित् ।
तद्बीजं स्वादुपाकं तु मूलं स्याद्रक्तपित्तजित् ॥" (ध.नि.)
["Phalaṃ svādu rasē pākē tālajaṃ gurupittajit
Tadbījaṃ svādupākaṃ tu mūlaṃ syādraktapittajit" (Dha.ni.)]

"तालाङ्गुली स्वादुरसं गुल्मप्लीहान्त्ररोगजित् ।" (रा.नि.)
["Tālāṅgulī svādurasaṃ gulmapḷīhāntrarōgajit" (Rā.ni.)]

"तालाम्बु पित्तजित् शुक्ळस्तन्यवृद्धिकरं गुरु ।" (रा.व.)
["Tālāmbu pittajit śukḷastanyavṛddhikaraṃ guru" (Rā.va.)]

"तालवृक्षस्तु मधुरः शीतळो मदकृद्गुरुः ।
पुष्टिकृद् शुक्ळकफकृन्मेदकृद् बलकारकः ॥
वृष्यश्च सारकः पित्तदाहशोषविषश्रमान् ।
विषकुष्ठकृमीरक्तदोषवातांश्च नाशयेत् ॥" (नि.र.)
["Tālavṛkṣastu madhuraḥ śītaḷō madakṛdguruḥ

Puṣṭikṛd śukḷakaphakṛnmēdakṛd balakārakaḥ
Vṛṣyaśca sārakaḥ pittadahāśōṣaviṣaśṛamān
Viṣakuṣṭhakṛmīraktadōṣavātāṁśca nāśayēt" (Ni.ra.)]

"तालस्तु मधुरः शीतो मेदःश्ळेष्मबलप्रदः ।
शुक्ळळो बृंहणो हन्ति वातपित्तव्रणकृमीन् ॥
फलं तस्य गुरु स्निग्धं स्वादु बल्यं हिमं सरम् ।
विष्टंभि बृंहणं वृष्यं तर्पणं कफमांसकृत् ॥
रक्तपित्तानिलश्वास क्षयदाह क्षतव्रणान् ।
बीजं स्वादु रसे पाके मूत्रळं वातपित्तजित् ॥
पक्वं तालफलं पित्तश्ळेष्मरक्तविवर्धनम् ।
दुर्जरं बहुमूत्रं च तन्द्राभिष्यन्दि शुक्ळळम् ॥
तालमज्जा तु तरुणः किञ्चित् मदकरो लघुः ।
श्ळेष्मळो वातपित्तघ्नः सस्नेहो मधुरः सरः ॥
तालजं तरुणतोयमतीव
प्राणिनां मदविकारकरं तत् ।
अम्ळभावमुपयाति यदा तत्
पित्तकृत् पवनदोषहरं च ॥
श्ळेष्मापहं स्याद् विष्टंभि पित्तकृत् शुक्ळळं गुरु ।
तालस्य मस्तकं ज्ञेयं वस्तिशुद्धिकरं परम् ॥ " (कै.नि.)

["Tālastu madhuraḥ śītō mēdaḥśḷēṣmabalapradaḥ
Śukḷaḷō bṛṁhaṇō hanti vātapittavṛaṇakṛmīn
Phalaṃ tasya guru snigdhaṃ svādu balyaṃ himaṃ saraṃ
Viṣṭambhi bṛmhaṇaṃ vṛṣyaṃ tarpaṇaṃ kaphamāṁsakṛt
Raktapittānilaśvāsakṣayadāhakṣatavṛaṇān
Bījaṃ svādu rasē pākē mūtraḷaṃ vātapittajit
Pakvaṃ tālaphalaṃ pittaśḷēṣmaraktavivaṛdhanaṃ
Durjaraṃ bahumūtraṃ ca tandrābhiṣyandi śukḷaḷaṃ
Tālamajjā tu taruṇaḥ kiñcit madakarō laghuḥ
Śḷēṣmaḷō vātapittaghnaḥ sasnēhō madhuraḥ saraḥ
Tālajaṃ taruṇatōyamatīva
prāṇināṃ madavikārakaraṃ tat
Amḷabhāvamupayāti yadā tat
pittakṛt pavanadōṣaharaṃ ca
Śḷēṣmāpahaṃ syād viṣṭaṁbhi pittakṛt śukḷaḷaṃ guru
Tālasya mastakaṃ jñēyaṃ vastiśuddhikāraṃ paraṃ "(Kai.ni.)]

Remarks: The inflorescence of this plant, called *panaviral* in Malayalam and *tālāṅgulī* in Sanskrit, is one of the constituents in a widely used Ayurvedic formulation of Kerala, *Panaviralādibhasmaṃ*

Coll. No. AVS 2541

Boswellia serrata **Roxb. ex Colebr.**

Burseraceae : (गुग्गुलु–कुलम्)

Eng	:	Indian Olibanum tree
Hin	:	Sālai, Kundur (सालै, कुन्दुर)
Kan	:	Guggula, Madi (ಗುಗ್ಗುಲ, ಮಡಿ)
Mal	:	Kunturukkaṃ, Sāmpṛāṇi (കുന്തുരുക്കം, സാമ്പ്രാണി)
San	:	Sallakī, Kunduruṣkaḥ (सल्लकी, कुन्दुरुष्कः)
Tam	:	Paraṅkisāmpirāṇi (பறங்கிசாம்பிராணி)
Tel	:	Sāmbrāṇi (సాంబ్రాణి)

Distribution: Throughout central and northern India on dry hills

The plant: A medium sized deciduous tree with ash coloured papery bark peeling off in thin flakes, young shoots pubescent; leaves alternate, imparipinnate, crowded at the ends of branches, leaflets opposite, pubescent, crenate-serrate; flowers small, white in axillary racemes; fruits trigonus drupes, three-valved; seeds compressed, pendulous.

The commercially used olibanum is the solidified oliogum-resin exuded from the tree. A good quality is of golden colour and is transparent. The colour varies from golden yellow to dark brown or to dark greenish brown.

Parts used: bark, gum-resin

Properties and uses: The bark is sweet, acrid, cooling and tonic. It is good for vitiated conditions of *pitta,* asthma, dysentery, ulcers, haemorrhoids and skin diseases. The gum-resin is sweet, bitter, astringent, antipyretic, antidysenteric, expectorant, diaphoretic, diuretic, stomachic and emmenagogue. It is useful in fevers, diaphoresis, convulsions, dysentery, urethrorrhea, orchiopathy, bronchitis, asthma, cough, stomatitis, syphilitic diseases, chronic laryngitis, jaundice and arthritis.

"सल्लकी निम्बपत्रा स्यात् गजभक्ष्या महातरुः ।
पीता त्र्यस्रफला पिच्छा निर्यासोऽस्यास्तु कुन्दुरुः ॥ " (शिवदासः)

["Sallakī nimbapaṭrā syāt gajabhakṣyā mahātaruḥ
Pīta tṛyasṛaphalā picchā niryāsoऽsyāstu kunduruḥ" (Śivadāsaḥ)]

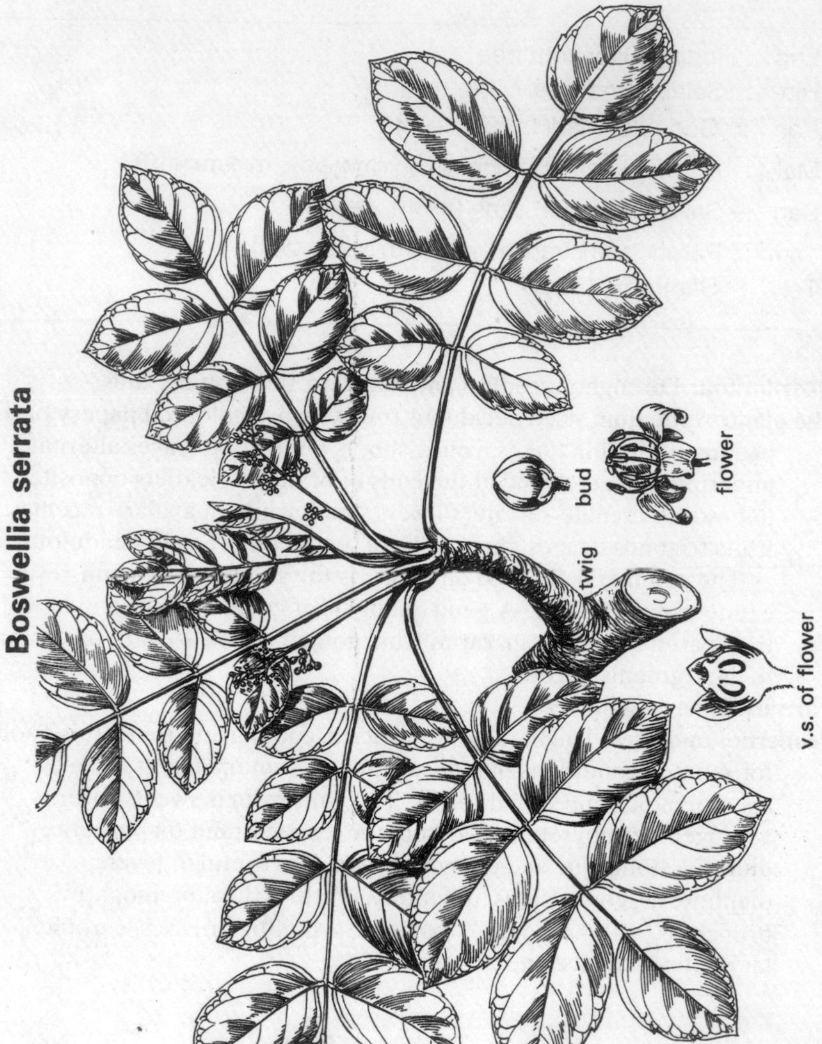
Boswellia serrata
bud
flower
twig
v.s. of flower

"शल्लकी गजभक्षा च सुवहा सुरभी रसा ।
महेरुणा कुन्दुरुकी वल्लकी च बहुस्रवा ॥" (भा.प्र.)
["Sallakī gajabhakṣā ca suvahā surabhī rasā
Mahēruṇā kundurukī vallakī ca bahusṛavā" (Bhā.pṛa.)]

"सल्लकः सल्लकी सल्ली सुगन्धा सुरभिस्रवा ।
सुरभिर्गजभक्षा च सुवहा गजवल्लभा ॥
गन्धमूला मुखामोदा सुश्रीका जलविक्रमा ।
हृद्या कुण्टरिका चैव प्रोक्ता त्र्यस्रफला च सा ॥
छिन्नरुहा गन्धफला ज्ञेया चाष्टादशाह्वया ।" (रा.नि.)
["Sallakaḥ sallakī sallī sugandhā surabhisṛavā
Surabhiṛgajabhakaṣā ca suvahā gajavallabhā
Gandhamūlā mukhāmōdā suśṛīkā jalavikṛamā
Hṛdyā kuṇṭarikā caiva pṛōktā tṛyasṛaphalā ca sā
Chinnaruhā gandhaphalā jñēyā cāṣṭādaśāhvayā" (Rā.ni.)]

"सल्लकी तुवरा शीता श्ळेष्मपित्तातिसारजित् ।
रक्तपित्तव्रणहरी पुष्टिकृत्समुदीरिता ॥
तत्फलं कफवातार्शःकुष्ठारोचकनाशनम् ।
पुष्पञ्चास्य कफं वातमर्शःकुष्ठारुचिर्जयेत् ॥" (ग.नि.)
["Sallakī tuvarā śītā śḷēṣmapittātisārajit
Raktapittavṛaṇaharī puṣṭikṛtsamudīritā
Tatphalaṃ kaphavātāṛśaḥkuṣṭhārōcakanāśanaṃ
Puṣpañcāsya kaphaṃ vātamaṛśaḥkuṣṭhārucirjayēt" (Ga.ni.)]

"वृक्षस्तु सल्लकीसंज्ञः पुष्टिकारी कषायकः ।
शीतवीर्यश्च मधुरस्तिक्तो ग्राह्यस्रदोषनुत् ॥
व्रणदोषं कफं वातं पित्तञ्चार्शञ्च नाशयेत् ।
पक्वातिसारं कुष्ठं च रक्तपित्तं विनाशयेत् ॥
निर्यासोऽस्य मतो नाम्ना कुन्दुरुः सुज्ञभाषितः ।
कुन्दुरुर्मधुरस्तीक्ष्णो तिक्तो रुच्यः कटुः स्मृतः ॥
स्निग्धश्चोष्णस्तथा त्वच्यो ज्वरस्वेदकफापहः ।
रक्तरुक् प्रदरं वातमलक्ष्मीं ग्रहपीडनम् ॥
रक्तातिसारं यूकाञ्च नाशयेदिति कीर्त्तितः ।" (नि.र.)
["Vṛkṣastu sallakīsaṃjñaḥ puṣṭikārī kaṣāyakaḥ
Sītavīryaśca madhurastiktō grāhyasṛadōṣanut
Vṛaṇadōṣaṃ kaphaṃ vātaṃ pittañcāṛśañca nāśayēt
Pakvātisāraṃ kuṣṭhaṃ ca raktapitaṃ vināśayēt
Niryāsōʃsya matō nāmnā kunduruḥ sujñabhāṣitaḥ
Kundurumadhurastīkṣṇō tiktō rucyaḥ kaṭuḥ smṛtaḥ
Snighdhaścōṣṇastathā tvacyō jvarasvēdakaphāpahaḥ
Raktaruk pṛadaraṃ vātamalakṣmīṃ grahapīḍanaṃ
Raktātisāraṃ yūkāñca nāśayēditi kīṛttitaḥ" (Ni.ra.)]

"सल्लकी तुवरा शीता पित्तश्ळेष्मातिसारजित् ।
रक्तापित्तव्रणहरी पुष्टिकृत्समुदीरिता ॥ " (भा.प्र.)
["Sallakī tuvarī śītā pittaśḷēṣmātisārajit
Raktapittavṛaṇaharī puṣṭikṛtsamudīritā" (Bhā.pra.)]

"सल्लकी स्यात् कषायाा्तिशीता वीर्ये प्रकीर्त्तिता ।
वलासं हन्ति पित्तस्य प्रकोपशमनी मता ॥ " (ध.नि.)
["Sallakī syāt kaṣāyāḷtiśītā vīryē pṛakīṛttitā
Valāsaṃ hanti pittasya pṛakōpaśamanī matā" (Dha.ni.)]

"सल्लकी तिक्तमधुरा कषाया ग्राहिणी परा ।
कुष्ठास्रकफवातार्शोव्रणदोषार्त्तिनाशिनी ॥ " (रा.नि.)
["Sallakī tiktamadhurā kaṣāyā grāhiṇī parā
Kuṣṭhāsṛakaphavātāṛśōvṛaṇadōṣāṛttināśinī" (Rā.ni.)]

"सल्लकी तुवरा शीता क्रमेण रसवीर्ययोः ।
वलासपित्तपक्वातिसारव्रणविनाशिनी ॥
तत्पुष्पं कफवातास्रकुष्ठारोचकनाशनम् । " (कै.नि.)
["Sallakī tuvarā śītā kṛamēṇa rasavīryayōḥ
Valāsapittapakvātisāravṛaṇavināśinī
Tatpuṣpaṃ kaphavātāsṛakuṣṭhārōcakanāśanaṃ" (Kai.ni.)]

കച്ചെരിച്ചുഷ്ണമായുള്ളു കുന്തിരിക്കമതേറ്റവും
സ്നിഗ്ദ്ധമായിട്ടിരിപ്പോന്നു വാതശോണിതനാശനം
ത്വഗ്ദോഷഘ്നം ചൊറിക്കും നന്നേറ്റവും കുഷ്ഠനാശകൃത്
സൗരഭ്യഗുണമുണ്ടാകകൊണ്ടതീശ്വരനും പ്രിയം. (ഗു.പാ.)
["Kaccericcuṣṇamāyuḷḷu kuntirikkamatēṟṟavuṃ
Snigddhamayiṭṭirippōnnu vātaśōṇitanāśanaṃ
Tvagdōṣaghnaṃ coṛikkuṃ nannēṟṟavuṃ kuṣṭhanāśakṛt
Saurabhyaguṇamuṇṭākakoṇṭatīśvaranuṃ pṛiyaṃ" (Gu.pā.)]

Coll. No. AVS 1055

Brassica juncea **Czern. & Coss.**

Brassicaceae : (राजिका–कुलम्)

Eng	:	Indian mustard
Hin	:	Rāyī (राई)
Kan	:	Sāsive (ಸಾಸಿವೆ)
Mal	:	Kaṭukụ, Ceṛukaṭukụ (കടുക്, ചെറുകടുക്)
San	:	Sarṣapaḥ, Rājikā (सर्षपः, राजिका)
Tam	:	Kaṭugu (கடுகு)
Tel	:	Āvālu (ఆవాలు)

Distribution: Cultivated throughout India

The plant: A glabrous annual with a few bristles at the base upto 1.5 m in height; basal leaves long, broadly ovate, coarsely dentate, persistent middle leaves oblong, 8-dentate, upper leaves broadly linear, entire; flowers yellow in racemes; fruits siliqua, breaking away from below upwards; seeds attached to the replum.

Parts used: seeds, oil

Properties and uses: The seeds are acrid, bitter, thermogenic, anodyne, anti-inflammatory, carminative, digestive, anthelmintic, aperient, sudorific and tonic. They are useful in vitiated conditions of *vāta* and *kapha,* dengue fever, abdominal colic, anorexia, dyspepsia, intestinal worms, flatulence, inflammations, morbid state of the cerebrospinal system, skin diseases, splenomegaly and persistent vomiting. Mustard is used in larger doses as an emetic in cases of poisoning and it will causc hyperdipsia, burning sensation, and other disorders due to the vitiation of *pitta.*

"राजी तु राजिका तीक्ष्णगन्धा क्षुज्जनकासुरी ।
क्षवः क्षुधाभिजनकः कृष्णिका कृष्णसर्षपः ॥
सर्षपः कटुकः स्नेहस्तन्तुभश्च कदंबकः ।
गौरस्तु सर्षपः प्राज्ञैः सिद्धार्थ इति कथ्यते ॥ "(भा.प्र.)
["Rājī tu rājikā tīkṣṇagandhā kṣujjanakāsurī
Kṣavaḥ kṣudhābhijanakaḥ kṛṣṇikā kṛṣṇasarṣapaḥ
Sarṣapaḥ kaṭukaḥ snēhastantubhaśca kadambakaḥ
Gaurastu sarṣapaḥ prājñaiḥ siddhārtha iti kathyatē" (Bhā.pra.)]

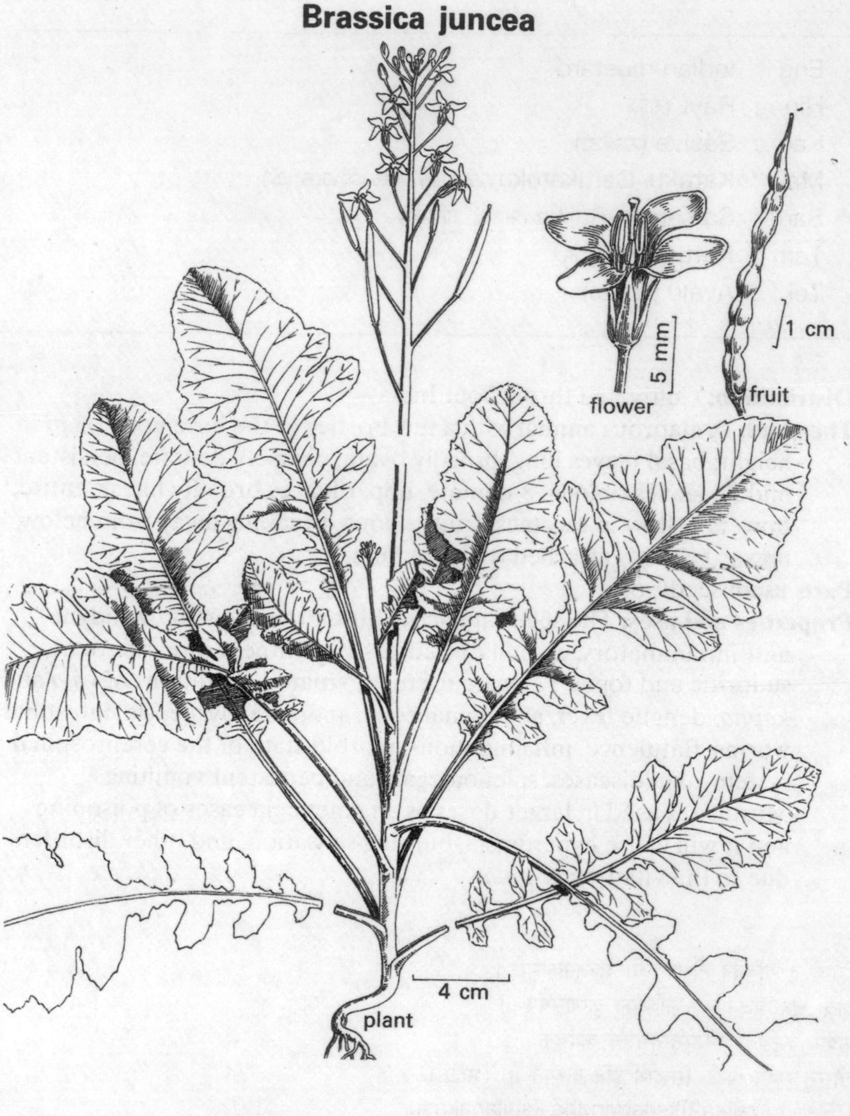
Brassica juncea
flower
5 mm
fruit
1 cm
4 cm
plant

"आसुरी राजिका राजी रक्तिका रक्तसर्षपः ।
तीक्ष्णगन्धा मधुरिका क्षवकः क्षुवकः क्षवः ॥
राजक्षवकः कृष्णतीक्ष्णफला राजराजिका राज्ञी ।
सा कृष्णसर्षपाख्या विज्ञेया राजसर्षपाख्या च ॥
तीक्ष्णकश्च दुराधर्षो रक्षोघ्नः कुष्ठनाशनः ।
सिद्धप्रयोजनः सिद्धसाधनः सितसर्षपः ॥" (रा.नि.)
["Asurī rājikā rājī raktikā raktasarṣapaḥ
Tīkṣṇagandhā madhurikā kṣavakaḥ kṣuvakaḥ kṣavaḥ
Rājakṣavakaḥ kṛṣṇatīkṣṇaphalā rājarājaikā rājñī
Sā kṛṣṇasarṣapākhyā vijñēyā rajasarṣapākhyā ca
Tīkṣṇakaśca duradharṣō rakṣōghnaḥ kuṣṭhanāśanaḥ
Siddhaprayōjanaḥ siddhasādhanaḥ sitasarṣapaḥ" (Rā.ni.)]

सर्षपस्तु रसे पाके कटुः स्निग्धः सतिक्तकः ।
तीक्ष्णोष्णः कफवातघ्नो रक्तपित्ताग्निवर्धनः ॥
रक्षोहरो जयेत् कण्डूकुष्ठकोठकृमिग्रहान् ।
यथा रक्तस्तथा गौरः किन्तु गौरो वरो मतः ॥
राजिका कफवातघ्नी तीक्ष्णोष्णा रक्तपित्तकृत् ।
किञ्चिद्रूक्षाग्निदा कण्डूकुष्ठकोष्ठकृमीन् हरेत् ॥
अतितीक्ष्णा विशेषेण तद्वत्कृष्णाऽपि राजिका ।
सरा हिमा गुरुर्ग्राही तत्पुष्पं प्रदरास्रजित् ॥
दीपनं सर्षपं तैलं कटुपाकरसं लघुः ।
लेखनं स्पर्शवीर्योष्णं तीक्ष्णं पित्तास्रदूषकम् ॥
कफमेदोऽनिलार्शघ्नं शिरकर्णामयापहम् ।
कण्डूकुष्ठकृमिश्वित्रकोठदुष्टकृमिप्रणुत् ॥
तद्वद्राजिकयोस्तैलं विशेषान्मूत्रकृच्छ्रकृत् । (भा.प्र.)
["Sarṣapastu rasē pākē kaṭuḥ snigdhaḥ satiktakaḥ
Tīkṣṇōṣṇaḥ kaphavātaghnō raktapittāgnivardhanaḥ
Rakṣōharō jayēt kaṇḍūkuṣṭhakōṭhakṛmigrahān
Yathā raktastathā gauraḥ kintu gaurō varō mataḥ
Rājikā kaphavātaghnī tīksnōsnā raktapittakrt
Kiñcidrūkṣāgnidā kaṇḍūkuṣṭhakōṣṭhakṛmīn harēt
Atitīkṣṇā viśēṣēṇa tadvatkṛṣṇā'pi rājikā
Sarā himā gururgrāhī tatpuṣpaṃ pradarāsrajit
Dīpanaṃ sarṣapaṃ tailaṃ kaṭupākarasaṃ laghuḥ
Lēkhanaṃ sparśavīryōṣṇaṃ tīkṣṇaṃ pittāsradūṣakaṃ
Kaphamēdō'nilārśaghnaṃ śirakarṇāmayāpahaṃ
Kaṇḍūkuṣṭhakṛmiśvitrakōṭhaduṣṭakṛmipraṇut
Tadvadrājikayōstailaṃ viśēṣānmūtrakṛcchrakṛt" (Bhā.pra.)]

"गौरसर्षपकोऽत्युष्णो रक्षोघ्नः कफवातजित् ।
कृम्यामकण्डूकुष्ठघ्नः श्रुतिशीर्षानिलार्त्तिजित् ॥
तद्वद्रक्तस्तु सिद्धार्थः तिक्तः स्निग्धोष्णकः कटुः ॥

आसुरी कटुतिक्तोष्णा कुष्ठघ्नी कफगुल्मजित् ॥
निद्राकरी शोफहरी ग्रहकारी च सा स्मृता । " (ध.नि.)
["Gaurasarṣapakōṣṭyuṣṇō rakṣōghnaḥ kaphavātajit
Kṛmyāmakaṇḍūkuṣṭhaghnaḥ śrutiśīrṣānilārttijit
Tadvadraktastu siddhārthaḥ tiktaḥ snighdhōṣṇakaḥ kaṭuḥ
Āsurī kaṭutiktōṣṇā kuṣṭhaghnī kaphagulmajit
Nidrākarī śōphaharī grahakārī ca sā smṛtā" (Dha.ni.)]

"आसुरा कटुतिक्तोष्णा वातप्लीहार्त्तिशूलनुत् ।
दाहपित्तदा हन्ति कफगुल्मकृमिव्रणान् ॥
राजसर्षपकस्तिक्तः कटूष्णो वातशूलनुत् ।
पित्तदाहप्रदो गुल्मकण्डूकुष्ठव्रणापहः ॥
सिद्धार्थः कटुतिक्तोष्णो वातरक्तग्रहापहः ।
त्वग्दोषशमनो रुच्यो विषभूतव्रणापहः ॥
तीक्ष्णं तु राजिकातैलं ज्ञेयं वातादिदोषनुत् ।
शिशिरं कटु पुंस्त्वघ्नं केश्यं त्वग्दोषनाशनम् ॥ " (रा.नि.)
["Āsurā kaṭutiktōṣṇā vātaplīhārttiśūlanut
Dāhapittadā hanti kaphagulmakṛmivraṇān
Rājasarṣapakastiktaḥ kaṭūṣṇō vātaśūlanut
Pittadāhapradō gulmakaṇḍūkuṣthavraṇāpahaḥ
Siddhārthaḥ kaṭutiktōṣṇō vātaraktagrahāpahaḥ
Tvagdōṣaśamanō rucyō viṣabhūtavraṇāpahaḥ
Tīkṣṇaṃ tu rājikātailaṃ jñēyaṃ vatādidōṣanut
Śiśraṃ kaṭu puṃstvaghnaṃ kēśyaṃ tvagdōṣanāśanaṃ " (Rā.ni.)]

"सर्षपं कटुकं रूक्षं गुरूष्णं बद्धमूत्रविद् ।
सक्षारं लवणं स्वादु दोषत्रयकरं परम् ॥
तद्वच्च राजिकाशाकं रक्तपित्तविदाहकृत् ।
तीक्ष्णं रूक्षमचक्षुष्यं भृशोष्णं कृमिहृत् गुरु ॥ " (कै.नि.)
["Sarṣapaṃ kaṭukaṃ rūkṣaṃ gurūṣṇaṃ baddhamūtravit
Sakṣāraṃ lavaṇaṃ svādu dōṣatrayakaraṃ paraṃ
Tadvaca rājikāśākaṃ raktapittavidāhakṛt
Tīkṣṇaṃ rūkṣamacakṣuṣyaṃ bhṛśōṣṇaṃ kṛmihṛt guru" (Kai.ni.)]

കടുകിൻെറ രസം പാരം പാകത്തിങ്കലെരിച്ചതു
തീക്ഷ്ണമായുള്ളതായേറ്റം മലമൂത്രവിരോധകൃത്
കഫവാതങ്ങളെത്തീർക്കും രക്തപിത്തവിവർദ്ധനം.
കറുത്തകടുകിൻെറയും ഗുണമീവണ്ണമായ്വരും
ഉഷ്ണമായിട്ടെരിച്ചുള്ള കടുകെണ്ണകഫാപഹം
കൃമികുഷ്ഠങ്ങൾ ദുർന്നാമവാതങ്ങൾക്കും വിനാശകൃത്. (ഗു. പാ.)
["Kaṭukinte rasaṃ pāraṃ pākattinkalericcatu
Tīkṣṇamāyuḷḷatāyēttaṃ malamūtravirōdhakṛt
Kaphavātannaḷettīrkkuṃ raktapittavivarddhanaṃ

Karutta kaṭukinṟeyuṃ guṇamīvaṇṇamāyvaruṃ
Uṣṇamāyiṭṭericcuḷḷa kaṭukeṇṇa kaphāpahaṃ
Kṛmikuṣṭhannaḷ durṇnāmavātannaḷkkuṃ vināśakṛt" (Gu.pā.)]

Remarks: The four kinds of mustard described in the above quotations are white mustard (*Brassica alba;* Sanskrit *Sitasarṣapā;* Malayalam *Veṇkaṭukụ*)brown mustard (*B.campestris,* Sanskrit *Raktasarṣapā,* Malayalam *Ceṅkaṭukụ*), Indian mustard (*B. juncea,* Sanskrit *Sarṣapā,* Malayalam *Ceṛukaṭukụ*) and black mustard (*B. nigra,* Sanskrit, *Kṛṣṇasarṣapā,* Malayalam *Kariṅkaṭukụ*).

Coll. No. AVS 2545

***Brassica oleracea* Linn. var. *capitata* Linn.**

Brassicaceae : (राजिका–कुलम्)

Eng	:	Cabbage
Hin	:	Bantgōpī (बन्तगोपी)
Kan	:	Kōbi-gaḍḍi (ಕೋಬಿ-ಗಡ್ಡೆ)
Mal	:	Moṭṭakkūsu, Kyābēj (മൊട്ടക്കൂസ്, ക്യാബേജ്)
San	:	Kēmbukaḥ, Kēmukḥ (केम्बुकः केमुकः)
Tam	:	Muttaikkōs (முட்டைக்கோஸ்)
Tel	:	Kōsugaḍḍa (కోసుగడ్డ)

Distribution: Cultivated on hill-tops

The plant: A suffruticose biennial 0.5 m in height, stems quite glabrous, branching in the upper part; leaves basal and lower cauline, large, stalked, nerves stout, white, especially prominent below, margins crenulate and undulate, the middle cauline leaves amplexicaul, oblong-obovate, obtuse, the upper leaves oblong-linear, almost entire, all leaves fleshy, glabrous; flowers large, pale yellow, 20–40 in racemes; fruits irregularly spreading or ascending linear pods, tetragonous, often serpentine-flexuose with a beak, mostly one-seeded, seeds globose, obscurely brown, pendulous.

Parts used: leaves

Properties and uses: Leaves are sweet, cooling, stomachic, antiscorbutic, emollient, constipating, diuretic, anthelmintic and cardiotonic. They are useful in abdominal disorders, pruritus, skin diseases, diarrhoea, strangury, intestinal worms, cough, bronchial asthma, fever, warts, urorrhea, haemorrhoids, gout and vitiated conditions of *pitta* and *vāta*.

केबुका केमुकः केम्बू सुपत्रा दळमालिनी ।
केलूटः स्वल्पविटपः स्वादुकन्दश्च पोलिनी ॥ (भा.प्र.)

["Kēbukā kēmukaḥ kēmbū supatṛā daḷamālinī
Kēlūṭaḥ svalpaviṭapaḥ svādukandaśca pōlinī" (Bhā.pṛa.)]

"केमुकं कटुकं पाके तिक्तं ग्राहि हिमं लघु ।
दीपनं पाचनं हृद्यं कफपित्तज्वरापहम् ॥

Brassica oleracea var. capitata

plant with head

v.s. of head

कुष्ठकासप्रमेहास्रनाशनं वातळं कटुः । " (भा.प्र.)
["Kēmukaṃ kaṭukaṃ pākē tiktaṃ grāhi himaṃ laghu
Dīpanaṃ pācanaṃ hṛdyaṃ kaphapittajvarāpahaṃ
Kuṣṭhakāsapṛamēhāsṛanāśanaṃ vātaḷaṃ kaṭuḥ" (Bhā.pṛa.)]

"केम्बुको मारुतं हन्ति पित्तं तिक्तः सुशीतळः । " (सो.नि.)
["Kēmbukō mārutaṃ hanti pittaṃ tiktaḥ suśītaḷaḥ" (Sō.ni.)]

"केयूरं शीतळं ग्राहि पित्तळं कफवातजित् । " (म.पा.नि.)
["Kēyūraṃ śītaḷaṃ grāhi pittaḷaṃ kaphavātajit" (Ma.pā.ni)]

"केमुकं कटुकं पाके तिक्तं ग्राहि हिमं लघु ।
दीपनं रोचनं हृद्यं कफपित्तज्वरापहम् ॥
कुष्ठकासप्रमेहासृक् हरते कुरुतेऽनिलम् । " (कै.नि.)
[Kēmukaṃ kaṭukaṃ pākē tiktaṃ grāhi himaṃ laghu
Dīpanaṃ rōcanaṃ hṛdyaṃ kaphapittajvarāpahaṃ
Kuṣṭhakāsapṛamēhāsṛk haratē kurutē∫nilaṃ" (Kai.ni.)]

Coll. No. B.S.I. (C.N.H.)-1458

Buchanania lanzan **Spreng.**

(B. latifolia *Roxb.*)

Anacardiaceae : (आम्र–कुलम्)

Hin	:	Piyār, Ciraumcī (पियार, चिरौंची)
Kan	:	Nurkala (ನುರ್ಕಲ)
Mal	:	Muraḷ, Mūnnāpēḷu, Pṛiyāḷaṃ (മുരൾ, മൂങ്ങാപേഴ്, പ്രിയാളം)
San	:	Pṛiyāḷaḥ (प्रियाळः)
Tam	:	Muṛāḷā (முறாளா)
Tel	:	Sara (సర)

Distribution: Throughout India,in deciduous forests in areas upto 900 m elevation

The plant: A medium sized tree about 18 m in height with dark grey or nearly black rough fissured bark and young branches clothed with silky hairs; leaves simple, broadly oblong, obtuse, base rounded, thickly coriaceous, main nerves 10–20 pairs, straight and parallel; flowers small, greenish white, in terminal and axillary panicles which are shorter than the leaves; carpels 5, only one perfect, other four reduced to cylindrical filaments, fruits black, lenticular drupes.

Parts used: roots, leaves, fruits

Properties and uses: The roots are acrid, astringent, cooling, depurative and constipating, and are useful in vitiated conditions of *pitta* and *kapha,* leprosy, skin diseases and diarrhoea.

The leaves are cooling, digestive, expectorant, purgative, depurative and aphrodisiac, and are useful in hyperdipsia, burning sensation, cough, bronchitis, dyspepsia, flatulence, constipation, leprosy, skin diseases and seminal weakness.

The fruits are sweet, sour, cooling, emollient, depurative, anti-inflammatory, nervine tonic, cardiotonic, stomachic, laxative, diuretic, expectorant, aphrodisiac, rejuvenating, febrifuge and tonic. They are useful in vitiated conditions of *pitta* and *vāta,* leprosy, skin diseases, gleet, inflammations, nervous debility, hyperdipsia, burning sensation, cardiac debility, abdominal disorders, constipation, strangury, urinary calculus, cough, asthma, seminal weakness, fever, emaciation, ulcers and general debility.

Buchanania lanzan

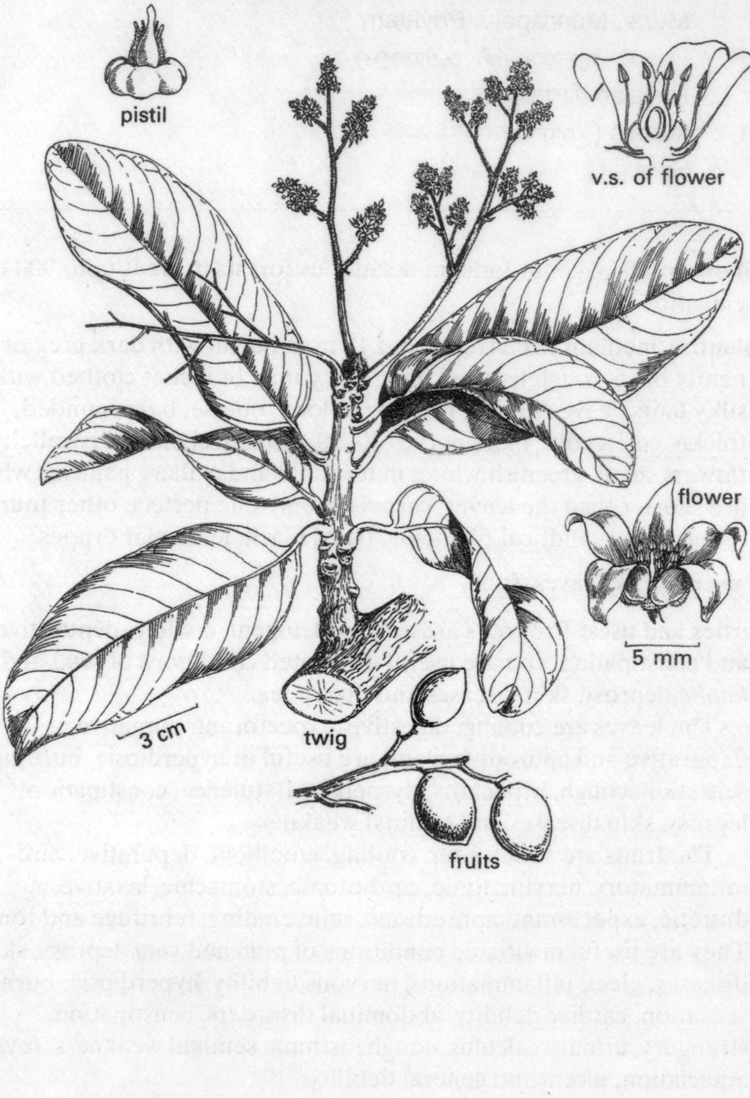

"प्रियाळस्तु खरस्कन्धश्चारारो बहुवल्कलः ।
राजादनं तापसेष्टः सन्नकर्दुर्धनुः पटः ॥ " (भा.प्र.)
["Pṛiyāḷastu kharaskandhascārārō bahuvalkalaḥ
Rājādanaṃ tāpasēṣṭaḥ sannakaṛduṛdhanuḥ paṭaḥ" (Bhā.pṛa.)]

"प्रियाळोऽथ खरस्कन्धश्चारो बहुळवल्कलः ।
स्नेहबीजश्चावपुटो ललनस्तापसप्रियः ॥ " (ध.नि.)
["Pṛiyāḷōऽtha kharaskandhaścārō bahuḷavaḷkalaḥ
Snēhabījaścāvapuṭō lalanastāpasapṛiyaḥ" (Dha.ṇi.)]

"धनुष्पुटः खरस्कन्धश्चारो द्राक्षाफलः परः ।
प्रियाळोऽम्ळफलस्त्वक्कः सन्नकद्रुर्मुनिप्रियः ॥
शालः शाखामृगश्चाधः पुटोऽथ ललनो वरः । (कै.नि.)
["Dhanuṣpuṭaḥ kharaskandhaścārō drākṣāphalaḥ paraḥ
Pṛiyāḷōऽmḷaphalastvakkaḥ sannakadruṛmunipṛiyaḥ
Śālaḥ śākhāmṛgaścādhaḥ puṭōऽtha lalanō varaḥ" (Kai.ni.)]

"चारस्तु पित्तकासघ्नस्तत्फलं मधुरं गुरु ।
स्निग्धं सरं मरुत्पित्तदाहज्वरतृषापहम् ॥
प्रियाळमज्जा मधुरा वृष्या पित्तानिलापहा ।
हृद्योऽतिदुर्जरः स्निग्धो विष्टंभी चामवर्धनः ॥" (भा.प्र.)
["Cārastu pittakāsaghnastatphalaṃ madhuraṃ guru
Snigdhaṃ saraṃ marutpittadāhajvaratṛṣāpahaṃ
Pṛiyāḷamjjā madhurā vṛṣyā pittānilāpahā
Hṛdyōऽtiduṛjaraḥ snigdhō viṣṭaṁbhī cāmvaṛdhanaḥ" (Bhā.pṛa.)]

प्रियाळः कफपित्तघ्नः कषायोऽस्य फलं गुरु ।
स्वाद्वम्ळं मधुरं पाके सुस्निग्धं शीतळं सरम् ॥
विष्टंभि बृंहणं वृष्यं बल्यं श्ळेष्मविवर्धनम् ।
जयेन्मारुतपित्तास्रदाहतृष्णाक्षतक्षयान् ॥
तन्मज्जा मधुरः स्निग्धो वृष्यः पित्तानिलापहः ।
हृद्योऽतिदुर्जरो बल्यो विष्टंभी कफवर्धनः ॥
प्रियाळतैलं मधुरं गुरु श्ळेष्मविवर्धनम् ।
हितमिच्छन्ति नात्युष्णं संयोगे वातपित्तयोः ॥ (कै.नि.)
["Pṛiyāḷaḥ kaphapittaghnaḥ kaṣāyōऽsya phalaṃ guru
Svādvamḷaṃ madhuraṃ pākē susnigdhaṃ śītaḷaṃ saraṃ
Viṣṭaṁbhi bṛṁhaṇaṃ vṛṣyaṃ balyaṃ śḷēṣmavivaṛdhanaṃ
Jayēnmārutapittāsṛadāhatṛṣṇākṣatakṣayān
Tanmajjā madhuraḥ snigdhō vṛṣyaḥ pittānilāpahaḥ
Hṛdyōऽtiduṛjarō balyō viṣṭaṁbhī kaphavaṛdhanaḥ
Pṛiyāḷatailaṃ madhuraṃ guru śḷēṣmavivaṛdhanaṃ
Hitamicchanti nātyuṣṇaṃ saṃyōgē vātapittayōḥ" (Kai.ni.)]

"............... प्रियाळं च बृंहणं गुरु शीतळम् ।

दाहक्षतक्षयहरं रक्तपित्तप्रसादनम् ॥
स्वादुपाकरसं स्निग्धं विष्टंभि कफशुक्ळकृत् ।
परं वातहरं स्निग्धमनुष्णं तु प्रियाळजम् ॥ (फलं)
प्रियाळमज्जा मधुरो वृष्यः पित्तानिलापहः । " (अ.हृ.सू.६.)

["........... pṛiyāḷaṃ ca bṛṁhaṇaṃ guru śītaḷaṃ
Dāhakṣatakṣayaharaṃ raktapittapṛasādanaṃ
Svādupākarasaṃ snigdhaṃ viṣṭambhi kaphaśukḷakṛt
Paraṃ vātaharaṃ snigdhamanuṣṇaṃ tu pṛiyāḷajaṃ (phalaṃ)
Pṛiyāḷamajjā madhurō vṛṣyaḥ pittānilāpahaḥ" (A.hṛ.Sū.6)]

"वातपित्तहरं वृष्यं प्रियाळं गुरु शीतळम् ।
चारस्य तु फलं पक्वं स्वाद्वम्ळं दुर्जरं प्रियम् ॥
चारमज्जा समधुरा वृष्या पित्तानिलापहा । " (ध.नि.)

["Vātapittaharaṃ vṛṣyaṃ pṛiyāḷaṃ guru śītaḷaṃ
Cārasya tu phalaṃ pakvaṃ svādvamḷaṃ durjaraṃ pṛiyaṃ
Cāramajjā samadhurā vṛṣyā pittānilāpahā " (Dha.ni.)]

"चारस्य च फलं पक्वं वृष्यं गौल्याम्ळकं गुरु ।
तद्बीजं मधुरं वृष्यं पित्तदाहार्त्तिनाशनम् ॥ " (रा.नि.)

["Cārasya ca phalaṃ pakvaṃ vṛṣyaṃ gaulyāmḷakaṃ guru
Tadbījaṃ madhuraṃ vṛṣyaṃ pittadāhārttināśanaṃ" (Rā.ni.)]

"चारः पित्तकफास्रघ्नः तत्फलं मधुरं गुरु ।
स्निग्धं सरं मरुत्पित्तदाहतृष्णक्षतापहम् ॥
तन्मज्जा मधुरा वृष्या शुक्ळळा पित्तवातजित् । " (म.वि.)

["Cāraḥ pittakaphāsṛaghnaḥ tatphalaṃ madhuraṃ guru
Snighaṃ saraṃ marutpittadāhatṛṣṇakṣatāpahaṃ
Tanmajjā madhurā vṛṣyā śukḷaḷā pittavātajit (Ma.vi.)]

"चरोली मधुरा वृष्या चाम्ळा गुर्वी सरा मता ।
मलस्तंभकरी स्निग्धा शीतळा धातुवर्धिनी
कफकृद्दुर्जरा बल्या प्रिया वातविनाशिनी ।
पित्तदाहज्वरतृषाक्षतरुक्रक्तदोषनुत् ॥
क्षतक्षयं नाशयति तन्मज्जा मधुरा मता ।
वृष्या च दाहपित्तघ्नी तत्तैलं मधुरं गुरु ॥
किञ्चिदुष्णं कफकरं पित्तवातविनाशनम् ।
चारमूलं तु तुवरं रक्तरुक्कफपित्तहम् ॥
चारमज्जा तु मधुरा वृष्या स्निग्धा च शीतळा ।
मलस्तंभकरी चामवर्धका दुर्जरा मता ॥
हृद्या च शुक्ळळा वातपित्तनाशकरी मता ॥ "(नि.र.)

["Carōḷī madhurā vṛṣyā cāmḷā gurvī sarā matā
Malastambhakarī snighdhā śītaḷā dhātuvaṛdhinī
Kaphakṛddurjarā balyā pṛiyā vātavināśinī

Pittadāhajvaratṛṣākṣatarukraktadōṣanut
Kṣatakṣayaṃ nāśayati tanmajjā madhurā matā
Vṛṣyā ca dāhapittaghnī tattailaṃ madhuraṃ guru
Kiñciduṣṇaṃ kaphakaraṃ pittavātavināśanaṃ
Cāramūlaṃ tu tuvaraṃ raktarukkaphapittahaṃ
Cāramajjā tu madhurā vṛṣyā snigdhā ca śītaḷā
Malastaṃbhakarī cāmavardhakā durjarā matā
Hṛdyā ca śukḷaḷā vātapittanāśakarī matā"(Ni.ra.)]

"वातपित्तहरं वृष्यं प्रियाळं गुरु शीतळम् ।
प्रियाळमज्जा मधुरो वृष्यः पित्तानिलापहः ॥ " (सु.सू.४६)
["Vātapittaharaṃ vṛṣyaṃ priyāḷaṃ guru śītaḷaṃ
Priyāḷamajjā madhurō vṛṣyaḥ pittānilāpahaḥ" (Su.Sū. 46)]

"प्रियाळतैलं मधुरं गुरु श्ळेष्माभिवर्धनम् ।
हितमिच्छन्ति नात्यौष्ण्यात् संयोगे कफपित्तयोः ॥ " (च.सं.सू. २७)
["Priyāḷatailaṃ madhuraṃ guru śḷēṣmābhivardhanaṃ
Hitamicchanti nātyauṣṇyāt samyōgē kaphapittayōḥ" (Ca.sam.Sū.27)]

Coll. No. AVS 2444

Butea monosperma (Lam.) Taub.

(B. frondosa *Koenig ex Roxb.*)

Fabaceae : (अपराजिता–कुलम्)

Eng	:	Flame of the forest, Bastard teak
Hin	:	Ḍhāk, Palāś (ढाक, पलाश)
Kan	:	Muttagamara (ಮುತ್ತಗಮರ)
Mal	:	Pḷāśụ, Camata (പ്ലാശ്, ചമത)
San	:	Palāśaḥ (पलाशः)
Tam	:	Camatá (சமதா)
Tel	:	Mōduga (మోదుగ)

Distribution: Throughout India,in deciduous forests in areas upto 1,200 m elevation, also in open areas

The plant: A medium sized deciduous tree, very conspicuous when in flower, 12–15 m in height with gum-containing grey bark exfoliating in irregular pieces, and somewhat crooked trunk; leaves 3-foliate, leaflets coriaceous, obtuse, glabrous above when old, finely silky and conspicuously reticulately veined beneath; flowers bright orange red, large, in rigid racemes; fruits pods, thickened at the sutures, containing a single seed.

Parts used: bark, leaves, flowers, seeds, gum

Properties and uses: The bark is acrid, bitter, astringent, thermogenic, emollient, aphrodisiac, appetiser, digestive, constipating, anthelmintic and tonic. It is useful in vitiated conditions of *pitta* and *kapha,* anorexia, dyspepsia, diarrhoea, dysentery, haemorrhoids, intestinal worms, bone fractures, rectal diseases, dysmenorrhoea, gonorrhoea, hepatopathy, ulcers, tumours, hydrocele and diabetes. The leaves are astringent, anti-inflammatory, anodyne and aphrodisiac, and are useful in pimples, boils, flatulence, colic, worm infestations, inflammations, arthralgia and haemorrhoids. The flowers are astringent, sweet, cooling, constipating, aphrodisiac, haemostatic, diuretic, febrifuge, depurative and tonic. They are useful in vitiated conditions of *pitta* and *kapha,* diarrhoea, haemorrhoids, menorrhagia, strangury, fever, leprosy, skin diseases, swellings, hyperdipsia, haemoptysis, arthritis, burning sensation, bone fractures, and are very efficacious in birth control. The seeds are purgative, ophthalmic, anthelmintic, rubefacient, depurative and tonic. They are useful in herpes, skin diseases, ringworm, ophthalmopathy, epilepsy, round worm, arthritis, flatulence, constipation and diabetes. The gum known as Bengalkino

314

Butea monosperma

Plate 16

or Buteakino is astringent, constipating, haemostatic, aphrodisiac, depurative and tonic, and is useful in diarrhoea, haemorrhoids, haemoptysis, haematemesis, diabetes, leprosy, skin diseases, ulcer, pharyngodynia, general debility, hyperacidity, dyspepsia and fever. The ash of the tender branches is useful in abdominal disorders such as flatulence, colic, etc.

"पलाशपादपः सिद्धस्त्रिदळः शिशिरे क्षयः ।
कृष्णवृन्तो ज्वलद्रक्तपुष्पश्च तिक्तबीजकः ॥
एकबीजायता शिम्बी त्रिपर्णश्च समिद्धवान् ।
गुणैः सर्वे समा ज्ञेयाः सितो विज्ञानदः परः ॥" (शि.नि.)
["Palāśapādapaḥ siddhastridaḷaḥ śiśirē kṣayaḥ
Kṛṣṇavṛntō jvaladraktapuṣpaśca tiktabījakaḥ
Ekabījāyatā śimbī triparṇaśca samiddhavān
Guṇaiḥ sarvē samā jñēyāḥ sitō vijñānadaḥ paraḥ" (Śi.ni.)]

"पलाशः किंशुकः पर्णी याज्ञिको रक्तपुष्पकः ।
क्षारश्रेष्ठो वातहरो ब्रह्मवृक्षः समिद्वरः ॥" (भा.प्र.)
["Palāśaḥ kiṃśukaḥ parṇī yājñikō raktapuṣpakaḥ
Kṣāraśrēṣṭhō vātaharō brahmavṛkṣaḥ samidvaraḥ" (Bhā.pra.)]

"किंशुको वातपोथश्च रक्तपुष्पोऽथ याज्ञिकः ।
त्रिपर्णो रक्तपुष्पश्च पूतदुर्ब्रह्मवृक्षकः ॥
क्षारश्रेष्ठः पलाशश्च बीजस्नेहः समिद्वरः ।" (ध.नि.)
["Kiṃśukō vātapōthaśca raktapuṣpō'tha yājñikaḥ
Triparṇō raktapuṣpaśca pūtadrurbrahmavṛkṣakaḥ
Kṣāraśrēṣṭhaḥ palāśaśca bījasnēhaḥ samidvaraḥ" (Dha.ni.)]

"पलाशो दीपनो वृष्यः सरोष्णो व्रणगुल्मजित् ।
कषायः कटुकस्तिक्तः स्निग्धो गुदजरोगजित् ॥
भग्नसन्धानकृद् दोषग्रहण्यर्शःकृमीन् हरेत् ।
तत्पुष्पं स्वादुपाके तु कटुतिक्तं कषायकम् ॥
वातळं कफपित्तास्रकृच्छ्रजिद्ग्राहि शीतळम् ।
तृड्दाहशामकं वातरक्तकुष्ठहरं परम् ॥
फलं लघूष्णं मेहार्शःकृमिवातकफापहम् ।
विपाके कटुकं रूक्षं कुष्ठगुल्मोदरप्रणुत् ॥" (भा.प्र.)
["Palāśō dīpanō vṛṣyaḥ sarōṣṇō vraṇagulmajit
Kaṣāyaḥ kaṭukastiktaḥ snigdhō gudajarōgajit
Bhagnasandhānakṛd dōṣagrahaṇyarśaḥkṛmīn harēt
Tatpuṣpaṃ svādupākē tu kaṭutiktaṃ kaṣāyakaṃ
Vātaḷaṃ kaphapittāsṛakṛcchrajidgrāhi śītaḷaṃ

Tṛḍḍāhaśāmakaṃ vātaraktakuṣṭhaharaṃ paraṃ
Phalaṃ laghūṣṇaṃ mēhārṣaḥkṛmivātakaphāpahaṃ
Vipākē kaṭukaṃ rūkṣaṃ kuṣṭhagulmōdarapṛaṇut" (Bhā.pṛa.)]

"क्षारश्रेष्ठः कृमिघ्नश्च संग्राही दीपनः सरः ।
प्लीहगुल्मग्रहण्यर्शोवातश्ळेष्मविनाशनः ॥
किंशुकस्यापि कुसुमं सुगन्धि मधुरं च यत् ।
बीजं तु कटुकं स्निग्धमुष्णं कृमिवलासजित् ॥ (ध.नि.)
["Kṣāraśrēṣṭhaḥ kṛmighnaśca saṃgrāhī dīpanaḥ saraḥ
Plīhagulmagrahaṇyarṣōvātaśḷēṣmavināśanaḥ
Kimśukasyāpi kusumaṃ sugandhi madhuraṃ ca yat
Bījaṃ tu kaṭukaṃ snigdhamuṣṇaṃ kṛmivalāsajit" (Dha.ni.)]

"पलाशमूलस्वरसो नेत्रच्छायान्ध्यपुष्पजित् ।
तद्रक्तमपि तद्वच्च पुष्पं बकुळपुष्पवत् ॥
तद्बीजं कृमिविध्वंसि काण्डो रसायने हितः ।" (सो.नि.)
["Palāśamūlasvarasō nētracchāyāndhyapuṣpajit
Tadraktamapi tadvacca puṣpaṃ bakuḷapuṣpavat
Tadbījaṃ kṛmividhvamsī kāṇḍō rasāyanē hitaḥ" (Sō.ni.)]

"पलाशस्तु कषायोष्णः कृमिदोषविनाशनः ।
तद्बीजं पामकण्डूतिदद्रुत्वग्दोषनाशकृत् ॥
तस्य पुष्पं च सोष्णं च कण्डूकुष्ठार्त्तिनाशनम् ।
रक्तः पीतः सितो नीलः कुसुमैस्तु विभज्यते ॥
किंशुकैर्गुणसाम्येऽपि सितो विज्ञानदः स्मृतः ।" (रा.नि.)
["Palāśastu kaṣāyōṣṇaḥ kṛmidōṣavināśanaḥ
Tadbījaṃ pāmakaṇḍūtidadrutvagdōṣanāśakṛt
Tasya puṣpaṃ ca sōṣṇaṃ ca kaṇḍūkuṣṭhārttināśanaṃ
Raktah pītaḥ sitō nīlaḥ kusumaistu vibhajyatē
Kimśukairguṇasamyē'pi sitō vijñānadaḥ smṛtaḥ" (Rā.ni.)]

"पलाशस्तुवरस्तिक्तः स्निग्धोष्णो दीपनः कटुः ।
सरः सन्धानकृत् वृष्यो जयेद्दोषव्रणकृमीन् ॥
ग्रहणीगुल्मगुदजान् तत्पुष्पं स्वादु तिक्तकम् ।
तृड्दाहकफपित्तास्रकुष्ठहृत् फलमस्य च ॥
कषायं कटुकं पाके वातळं ग्राहि शीतळम् ।
रूक्षं विपाके कटुकं लघूष्णं कफवातजित् ॥
कुष्ठगुल्मोदरप्लीहमेहार्शःकृमिशूलनुत् ।
किंशुकस्य प्रवाळं तु कृमिवातहरं परम् ॥" (कै.नि.)
["Palāśastuvarastiktaḥ snigdhōṣṇō dīpanaḥ kaṭuḥ
Saraḥ sandhānakṛd vṛṣyō jayēddōṣavraṇakṛmīn
Grahaṇīgulmagudajān tatpuṣpaṃ svādu tiktakaṃ
Tṛḍḍāhakaphapittāsṛakuṣṭhahṛt phalamasya ca
Kaṣāyaṃ kaṭukaṃ pākē vātaḷaṃ grāhi śītaḷaṃ

Rūkṣaṃ vipākē kaṭukaṃ laghūṣṇaṃ kaphavātajit
Kuṣṭhagulmōdarapḷīhamēhāṛśaḥkṛmiśūlanut
Kimśukasya pṛavāḷaṃ tu kṛmivātaharaṃ paraṃ" (Kai.ni.)]

"उष्णः पलाशस्तुवरो वृष्यो दीप्तिकरः सरः ।
तिक्तः स्निग्धो ग्राहकश्च भग्नसन्धानकारकः ॥
व्रणगुल्मकृमिप्ळीहासंग्रहण्यर्शःवातहा ।
कफं योनिरुजं पित्तं नाशयेदिति कीर्त्तितम् ॥
पुष्पभेदादयं रक्तपीतशुभ्रकनीलकाः ।
पुष्पाणि स्वादु तिक्तानि उष्णानि तुवराणि च ।
वातळानि ग्राहकाणि शीतळान्यूषणानि च ॥
तृषादाहपित्तकफाद् रक्तदोषं च कुष्ठकम् ।
मूत्रकृच्छ्रं घातयन्ति फलं रूक्षं लघु स्मृतम् ॥
उष्णं च कटुकं पाके कफवातोदरकृमीन् ।
कुष्ठगुल्मप्रमेहार्शःशूलानां चैव नाशकम् ॥
फलबीजं च स्निग्धोष्णं कटु कृमिकफान् जयेत् ।
नूतनाः पल्लवाश्चास्य कृमिवातविनाशकाः ॥ (नि.र.)
["Uṣṇaḥ palāśastuvarō vṛṣyō dīptikaraḥ saraḥ
Tiktaḥ snigdhō grāhakaśca bhagnasandhānakārakaḥ
Vṛaṇagulmakṛmipḷīhāsaṃgrahaṇyaṛśaḥvātahā
Kaphaṃ yōnirujaṃ pittaṃ nāśayēditi kīṛttitaṃ
Puṣpabhēdādayaṃ raktapītaśubhṛakanīlakāḥ
Puṣpāṇi svādu tiktāni uṣṇāni tuvarāṇi ca
Vātaḷāni grāhakāṇi śītaḷānyūṣaṇāni ca
Tṛṣādāhapittakaphād raktadōṣaṃ ca kuṣṭhakaṃ
Mūtrakṛcchṛaṃ ghātayanti phalaṃ rūkṣaṃ laghu smṛtaṃ
Uṣṇaṃ ca kaṭukaṃ pākē kaphavātōdarakṛmīn
Kuṣṭhagulmapṛamēhāṛśaḥśūlānāṃ caiva nāśakaṃ
Phalabījaṃ ca snigdhōṣṇaṃ kaṭu kṛmikaphān jayēt
Nūtanāḥ pallavāścāsya kṛmivātavināśakāḥ" (Ni.ra.)]

Coll. No. AVS 1739

***Caesalpinia bonduc* (Linn.) Roxb.**

(C. cristata *Linn.*)

Caesalpiniaceae : (कण्टकीकरञ्ज-कुलम्)

Eng :	Fever nut, Bonduc nut
Hin :	Kanṭkarēj, Kāntikarañjā (कण्टकरेज, कान्तिकरञ्जा)
Kan :	Gajikekāyi (ಗಜಿಕಾಯಿ)
Mal :	Kāḻañci (കഴഞ്ചി)
San :	Latākarañjaḥ, Kubērākṣī, Kanṭakīkarañjaḥ (लताकरञ्जः, कुबेराक्षी, कण्टकीकरञ्जः)
Tam :	Kaḻiccikkāi (கழிச்சிக்காய்)
Tel :	Gaccakāya (గచ్చకాయ)

Distribution: Throughout India,in the plains on waste lands and coastal areas

The plant: A large straggling,very thorny shrub, branches armed with hooks and straight hard yellow prickles; leaves bipinnate, large, stipules foliaceous, pinnae 7 pairs, leaflets 3–8 pairs with 1–2 small recurved prickles between them on the underside; flowers yellow, in dense long peduncled supra-axillary racemes at the top; fruits inflated pods, covered with wiry prickles, seeds 1–2 per pod, oblong or globular, hard, grey with a smooth shiny surface.

Parts used: root bark, leaves, seeds

Properties and uses: The root bark is emmenagogue, febrifuge, expectorant, anthelmintic and stomachic. It is useful in amenorrhoea, dysmenorrhoea, fevers, cough, asthma, intestinal worms, colic, flatulence and dyspepsia. The leaves are anthelmintic, emmenagogue and febrifuge, and are useful in elephantiasis, intestinal worms, splenomegaly, hepatomegaly,amenorrhoea, dysmenorrhoea, fevers and pharyngodynia. The seeds are bitter, astringent, acrid, thermogenic, anodyne, anti-inflammatory, anthelmintic, digestive, stomachic, liver tonic, depurative, expectorant, contraceptive, antipyretic, aphrodisiac and tonic. They are useful in vitiated conditions of *tridōṣa,* arthralgia, inflammations, hydrocele, cough, asthma, leucoderma, leprosy, skin diseases, dyspepsia, dysentery, colic, haemorrhoids, intestinal worms, hepatopathy, splenopathy, diabetes and intermittent fevers.

Caesalpinia bonduc

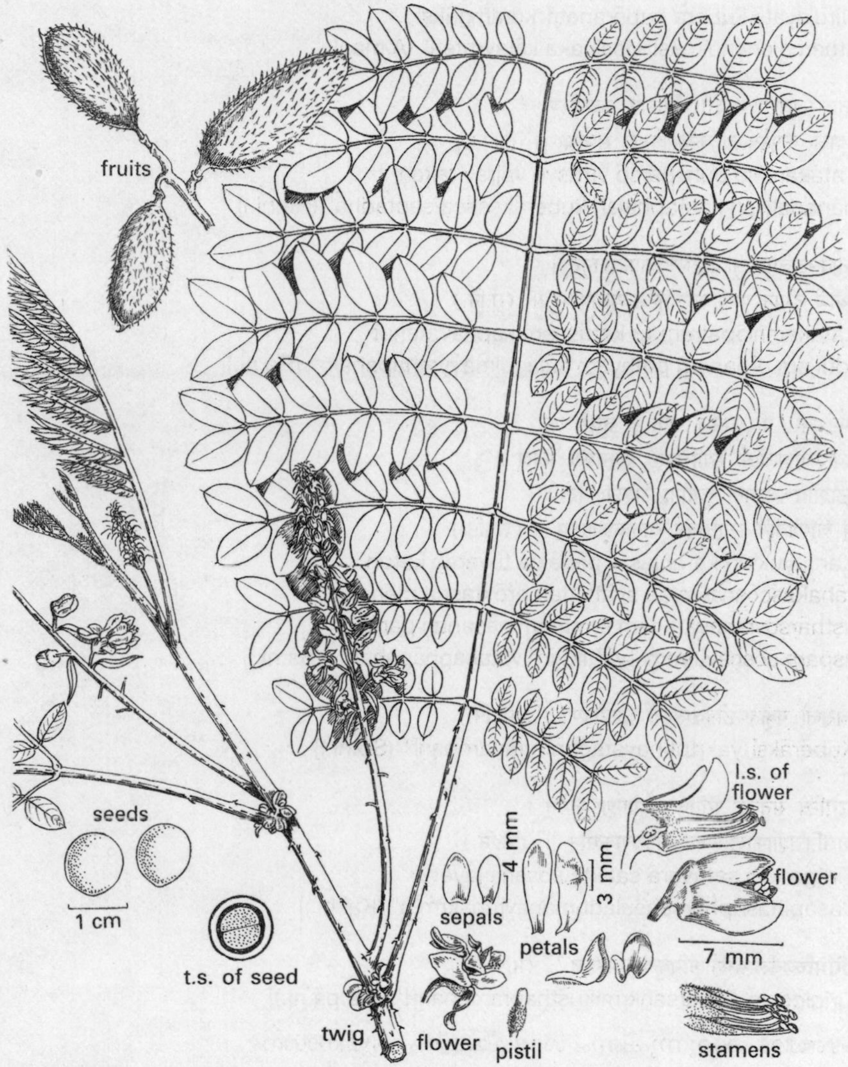

"कण्टकरञ्जजा वल्लीकण्टाढ्या सर्वतिक्तकः ।
द्वित्रिबीजा सर्वतिक्ता त्रिपुटा कृमिनाशिनी ॥" (शिवदासः)
["Kaṇṭakarañjajā vallīkaṇṭāḍhyā saṛvatiktakaḥ
Dvitṛibījā saṛvatiktā tṛipuṭā kṛmināśinī" (Śivadāsaḥ)]

"निर्दिश्यते कुबेरा कुबेरनेत्री कुरंगाक्षी ।
पाठा च धेनुकाक्षी विशल्यका काळवृन्तेति ॥" (अ.म.)
["Niṛdiśyatē kubērā kubēranētṛī kuraṃgākṣī
Pāṭhā ca dhēnukākṣī viśalyakā kāḷavṛntēti" (A.ma.)]

"लताकरञ्जो दुःस्पर्शो वीरास्यो वज्रवीरकः ।
धनदाक्षः कण्टफलः कुबेराक्षश्च सप्तधा ॥" (रा.नि.)
["Latākarañjo duḥspaṛśō vīrāsyō vajṛavīrakaḥ
Dhanadākṣaḥ kaṇṭaphalaḥ kubērākṣaśca saptadhā" (Rā.ni.)]

"लताकरञ्जपत्रं तु कटूष्णं कफवातनुत् ।
तद्बीजं दीपनं पथ्यं शूलगुल्मव्यथापहम् ॥" (रा.नि.)
["Latākarañjapatṛaṃ tu kaṭūṣṇaṃ kaphavātanut
Tadbījaṃ dīpanaṃ pathyaṃ śūlagulmavyathāpahaṃ" (Rā.ni.)]

"कण्टयुक्तः करञ्जस्तु पाके च तुवरः कटुः ।
ग्राहकश्चोष्णवीर्यः स्यात्तिक्तः प्रोक्तश्च मेहहा ॥
कुष्ठार्शोव्रणवातानां कृमीनां नाशनः परः ।
पुष्पं चोष्णवीर्यं स्यात्तिक्तं वातकफापहम् ॥ (शा.नि.)
["Kaṇṭayuktaḥ karañjastu pākē ca tuvaraḥ kaṭuḥ
Grāhakaścōṣṇavīryaḥ syāttiktaḥ pṛōktaśca mēhahā
Kuṣṭhāṛśōvṛaṇavātānāṃ kṛmīnāṃ nāśanaḥ paraḥ
Puṣpaṃ cōṣṇavīryaṃ syāttiktaṃ vātakaphāpahaṃ" (Śā.ni.)]

"कुबेराक्षी यकृत्प्लीहवातघ्नी व्रणरोपणी ।" (सो.नि.)
["Kubērākṣī yakṛtpḷīhavātaghnī vṛaṇarōpaṇī" (Sō.ni.)]

"तिरगन्धि सतुवरा सतिक्ता सोषणा जयेत् ।
वलासपित्तशोफार्शःशूलाध्मानव्रणकृमीन् ।" (कै.नि.)
["Tiragandhi satuvarā satiktā sōṣaṇā jayēt
Valāsapittaśōphāṛśaḥśūlādhmānavṛaṇakṛmīn" (Kai.ni.)]

"तिरिगिच्छिर्वलासार्शःकृमिकुष्ठप्रमेहहृत् ।" (म.पा.नि.)
["Tirigicchiṛvalāsāṛśaḥkṛmikuṣṭhapṛamēhahṛt" (Ma.pā.ni.)]

"കഴഞ്ചീടെ കുരുന്നുഷ്ണം ശ്ലേഷ്മഘ്നം കൃമിനാശനം
വാതന്ത്രശൂലാപഹരം കുരുവിന്നും ഗുണം തഥാ" (ഗു.പാ.)
["Kaḷañcīṭe kurunnuṣṇaṃ śḷēṣmaghnaṃ kṛmināśanaṃ
Vātāntṛaśūlāpaharaṃ kuruvinnuṃ guṇaṃ tatha" (Gu.pā.)]

Coll. No. AVS 1714

Caesalpinia sappan **Linn.**

Caesalpiniaceae : (कण्टकीकरञ्ज–कुलम्)

Eng	:	Sappan wood, Brazil wood
Hin	:	Patamg, Bakaṃ (पतंग, बकं)
Kan	:	Sappange (ಸಪ್ಪಂಗೆ)
Mal	:	Cappannaṃ, Sappannaṃ (ചപ്പങ്ങം, സപ്പങ്ങം)
San	:	Patrāngaḥ, Patangaḥ, Paṭṭarañjakaḥ (पत्राङ्गः पतङ्गः, पट्टरञ्जकः)
Tam	:	Śappamgu, Patamgaṃ (சப்பங்கு, பதங்கம்)
Tel	:	Bakarucakka (బకరుచక్క)

Distribution: Cultivated in south India and Bengal

The plant: A small thorny tree, 6–9 m in height and 15–25 cm in diameter with a few prickly branches; leaves compound, with 8–12 pairs of oblong leaflets and small prickles, leaflets vary, inequilateral and rounded at the apex; flowers yellow in terminal and axillary panicles; stamens waxy-white, filaments densely woolly at the base, fruits woody pods, subcompressed with a hard recurved short beak, seeds 3–4. The heartwood which is used in medicine is light yellow when freshly cut, but it quickly changes to red. The colour diffuses out easily in hot water. In about 7–10 hours the extract becomes deep orange in colour.

Parts used: heartwood

Properties and uses: The heartwood is bitter, astringent, sweet, acrid, refrigerant, vulnerary, depurative, constipating, sedative and haemostatic. It is useful in vitiated conditions of *pitta,* burning sensation, wounds, ulcers, leprosy, skin diseases, diarrhoea, dysentery, epilepsy, convulsions, menorrhagia, leucorrhoea, diabetes, haemoptysis, haemorrhages, stomatopathy and odontopathy.

"पटरञ्जनं चतुर्थं कुचन्दनं पत्तरं च पत्तङ्गम् ।
कथितं हि रक्तकाष्ठं कुगन्धकं पाण्डुरागमिति ॥" (अ.म.)
["Paṭarañjanaṃ caturthaṃ kucadanaṃ pattaraṃ ca pattangaṃ
Kathitaṃ hi raktakāṣṭhaṃ kugandhakaṃ pāṇḍurāgamiti" (A.ma.)]

"कुचन्दनं पतङ्गं च रक्तकाष्ठं सुरङ्गकम् ।
पत्राङ्गं पट्टरागं च पट्टरञ्जकमेव च ॥" (ध.नि.)

Caesalpinia sappan

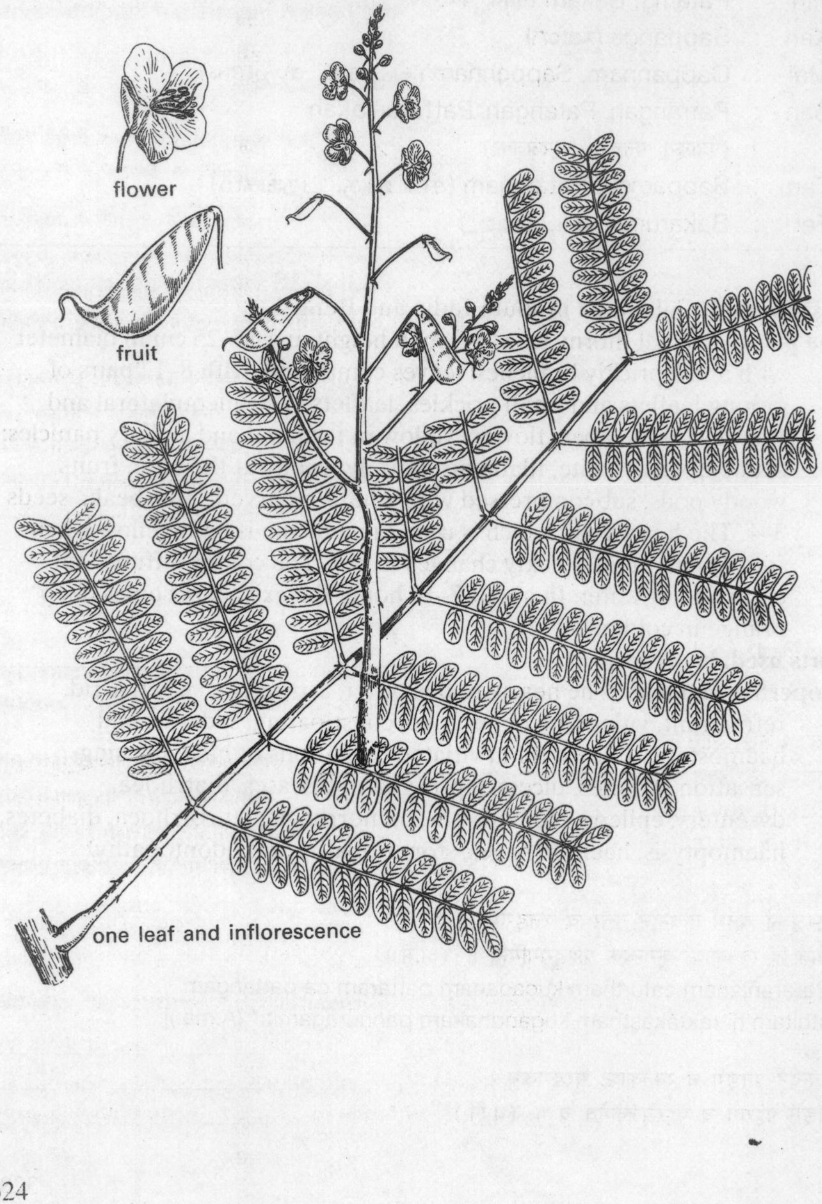

["Kucandanaṃ patangaṃ ca raktakāṣṭhaṃ surangakaṃ
Patṛāngaṃ paṭṭarāgaṃ ca paṭṭarañjakamēva ca" (Dha.ni.)]

"पतङ्गं रक्तसारं च सुरङ्गं रञ्जनं तथा ।
पटरञ्जकमाख्यातं धत्तूरं च कुचन्दनम् ॥" (भा.प्र.)
["Patangaṃ raktasāraṃ ca surangaṃ rañjanaṃ tathā
Paṭarañjakamākhyātaṃ dhattūraṃ ca kucadanaṃ" (Bhā.pṛa.)]

"पत्तङ्गं चैव पत्राङ्गं रक्तकाष्ठं सुरंगदम् ।
पत्राढ्यं पट्टरागं च भार्यावृक्षश्च रक्तकः ॥
लोहितं रङ्गकाष्ठं च रागकाष्ठं कुचन्दनम् ।
पट्टरञ्जनकं चैव सुरङ्गं च चतुर्दश ॥" (रा.नि.)
["Pattangaṃ caiva patṛāngaṃ raktakāṣṭaṃ surangadaṃ
Patṛādhyaṃ paṭṭarāgaṃ ca bhāryāvṛkṣaśca raktakaḥ
Lōhitaṃ rangakāṣṭ haṃ ca rāgakāṣṭhaṃ kucadanaṃ
Paṭṭarañjanakaṃ caiva surangaṃ ca caturdaśa" (Rā.ni.)]

"पतङ्गं मधुरं शीतं पित्तश्ळेष्मव्रणास्रनुत् ।
हरिचन्दनवद्वेद्यं विशेषात् दाहनाशनम् ॥" (भा.प्र.)
["Patangaṃ madhuraṃ śītaṃ pittaśḷēṣmavraṇāsṛanut
Haricandanavadvēdyaṃ viśēṣāt dāhanāśanaṃ" (Bhā.pṛa.)]

"पत्राङ्गस्तिक्तकः शीतो रूक्षोऽम्ळो मधुरः कटुः ।
व्रणशुद्धिकरो वर्ण्यः सुगन्धिर्वातपित्तहृत् ॥
उन्मादज्वरविस्फोटमूत्रकृच्छ्रव्रणान् जयेत् ।
कफाश्मरीरक्तदोषभूतबाधानिवारणः ॥" (नि.र.)
["Patṛāngastiktakaḥ śītō rūkṣōḷmḷō madhuraḥ kaṭuḥ
Vṛaṇaśuddhikarō vaṛṇyaḥ sugadhiṛvātapittahṛt
Unmādajvaravisphōṭamūtṛakṛcchravṛaṇān jayēt
Kaphāśmarīraktadōṣabhūtabādhānivāraṇaḥ" (Ni.ra.)]

स्वादुपाकरसं शीतं श्ळेष्मळं नातिपित्तळम् ।
कुचन्दनं तु तिक्तं स्यात् सुगन्धि व्रणरोपणम् ॥" (ध.नि.)
["Svādupākarasaṃ śītaṃ śḷēṣmaḷaṃ nātipittaḷaṃ
Kucandanaṃ tu tiktaṃ syāt sugandhi vṛaṇarōpaṇaṃ" (Dha.ni.)]

"पत्राङ्गं कटुकं रूक्षमम्ळं शीतं तु गौल्यकम् ।
वातपित्तज्वरघ्नं च विस्फोटोन्मादभूतहृत् ॥" (रा.नि.)
["Patṛāngaṃ kaṭukaṃ rūkṣamamḷaṃ śītaṃ tu gaulyakaṃ
Vātapittajvaraghnaṃ ca visphōṭōnmādabhūtahṛt" (Rā.ni.)]

Coll. No. AVS 1342

***Cajanus cajan* (Linn.) Millsp.**

(C. indicus *Spreng.*)

Fabaceae : (अपराजिता–कुलम्)

Eng	:	Red gram, Pigeon pea, Congo pea
Hin	:	Tuvar (तुवर)
Kan	:	Togari (ತೊಗರಿ)
Mal	:	Tuvara, Tuvarapparippu̥ (തുവര, തുവരപ്പരിപ്പ്)
San	:	Āḍhakī, Tuvarī (आढकी, तुवरी)
Tam	:	Tuvarai (துவரை)
Tel	:	Kandipappu (కందిపప్పు)

Distribution: Throughout India, cultivated

The plant: An erect shrub, 1.5–3 m in height with many branches provided with silky hair; leaves compound, pulvinate, leaflets oblong-lanceolate, entire, densely silky beneath; flowers yellow in terminal panicles or corymbose racemes; fruits pods, tipped with the persistent lower half of the style, seeds vary in colour from yellow and red to brown or black.

Parts used: leaves, seeds

Properties and uses: The leaves are astringent, sweet, diuretic, laxative, cooling, anti-inflammatory and anodyne, and are useful in oral ulcers, odontalgia, gingivitis, strangury and inflammations. The seeds are astringent, acrid, sweet, cooling, anthelmintic, resolvent, pectoral, constipating, alexeteric, febrifuge and expectorant. They are useful in vitiated conditions of *pitta,* intestinal worms, oral ulcers, tumours, bronchitis, cough, vomiting, haemorrhoids, fever and cardiac diseases.

The leaves and seeds when applied as a poultice over the breast may induce lactation.

"आढकी तुवरी प्रोक्ता नृत्यत्कोण्डक उच्चिटः ।
रेभुजः करभी चेति दर्दुस्तु पठितो बुधैः ॥" (अ.म.)
["Āḍhakī tuvarī prōktā nr̥tyatkōṇḍaka ucciṭaḥ
Rēbhujaḥ karabhī cēti dar̥dustu paṭhitō budhaiḥ (A.ma.)]

"आढकी तुवरी चाथ कालवृन्ता कुलत्थका ।
कुलत्थाश्चक्रका ज्ञेयास्ताम्रवर्णाश्चलापहाः ॥" (कै.नि.)

Cajanus cajan

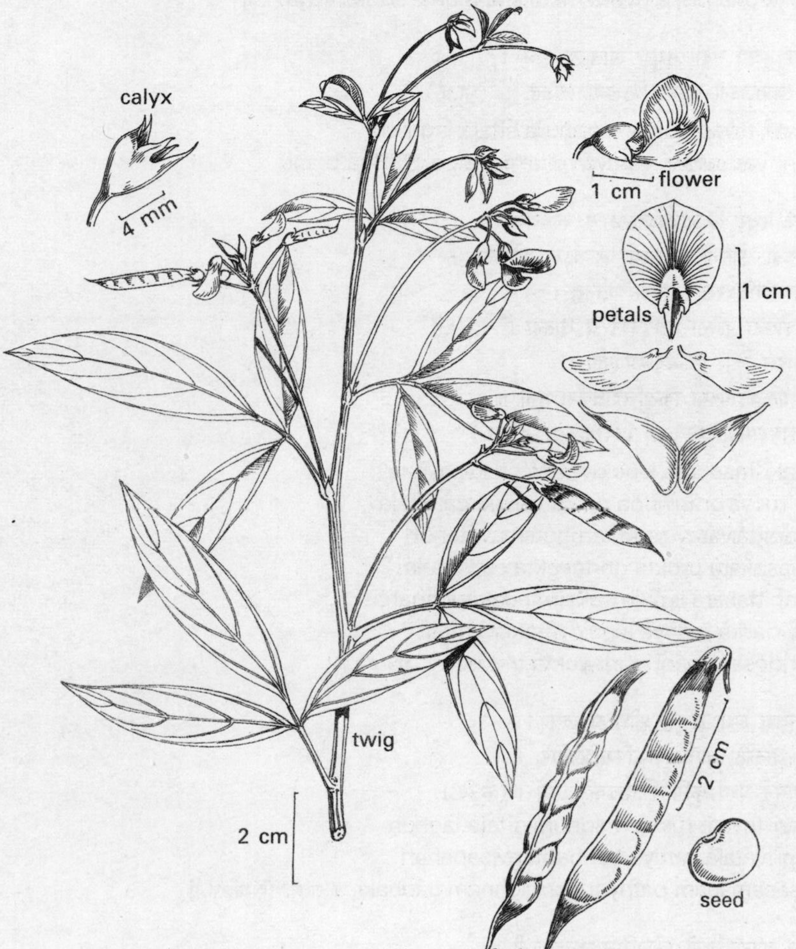

["Āḍhakī tuvarī cātha kālavṛntā kulatthakā
Kulatthāścakṛakā jñēyāstāmṛavaṛṇāścalāpahāḥ" (Kai.ni.)]

"आढकी तुवरी चापि सा प्रोक्ता शणपुष्पिका ।" (भा.प्र.)
["Āḍhakī tuvarī cāpi sā pṛōktā śaṇapuṣpikā" (Bhā.pṛa.)]

"आढकी तुवरी वर्या करवीरभुजा तथा ।
वृत्तबीजा पीतपुष्पा श्वेता रक्ताऽसिता त्रिधा ॥" (ध.नि., रा.नि.)
["Āḍhakī tuvarī varyā karavīrabhujā tathā
Vṛttabījā pītapuṣpā śvētā raktāऽsitā tṛidhā" (Dha.ni.,Rā.ni.)]

"आढकी तुवरा रूक्षा मधुरा शीतळा लघुः ।
ग्राहिणी वातजननी वर्ण्या पित्तकफास्रजित् ॥" (भा.प्र.)
["Āḍhakī tuvarā rūkṣā madhurā śītaḷā laghuḥ
Grāhiṇī vātajananī vaṛṇyā pittakaphāsṛajit" (Bhā.pṛa.)]

"आढकी मधुरा किञ्चिद्वातळा च कषायका ।
गुर्वी रुच्या ग्राहिणी च रूक्षा वर्ण्या च शीतळा ॥
कफपित्तज्वरविषरक्तरुग्गुल्मवातनुत् ।
अर्शोनाशकरा प्रोक्ता घृतयुक्ता च वातहा ॥
कफपित्तहरा लेपैः सेकैर्मेदकफापहा ।
तुवरी दालिका पथ्या किञ्चिद्वातकरा मता ॥
कृमित्रिदोषशमनी घृतयुक्ता त्रिदोषहा ॥" (नि.र.)
["Āḍhakī madhurā kiñcidvātaḷā ca kaṣāyakā
Guṛvī rucyā grāhiṇī ca rūkṣa vaṛṇyā ca śītaḷā
Kaphapittajvaraviṣaraktaruggulmavātanut
Aṛśōnāśakarā pṛōktā ghṛtayuktā ca vātahā
Kaphapittaharā lēpaiḥ sēkaiṛmēdakaphāpahā
Tuvarī dālikā pathyā kiñcidvātakarā matā
Kṛmitṛidōṣaśamanī ghṛtayuktā tṛidōṣahā" (Ni.ra.)]

तुवरी तुवरा रूक्षा मधुरा शीतळा लघुः ।
ग्राहिणी वातळा वर्ण्या कफपित्तविषापहः ॥
त्रिदोषशमनं पथ्यं कृमिघ्नं चाढकीदळम् । (कै.नि.)
["Tuvarī tuvarā rūkṣā madhurā śītaḷā laghuḥ
Grāhiṇī vātaḷā vaṛṇyā kaphapittaviṣāpahaḥ
Tṛidōṣaśamanaṃ pathyaṃ kṛmighnaṃ cāḍhakīdaḷaṃ" (Kai.ni.)]

"आढकी कफपित्तघ्नी किञ्चिन्मारुतकोपनी ।
कषाया स्वादु संग्राही कटुपाका हिमा लघुः ॥
मेदःश्ळेष्मास्रपित्तेषु हिता लेपोपसेकयोः ।" (ध.नि.)
["Āḍhakī kaphapittaghnī kiñcimārutakōpanī
Kaṣāyā svādu saṃgrāhī kaṭupākā himā laghuḥ
Mēdaḥśḷēṣmāsṛapittēṣu hitā lēpōpasēkayōḥ" (Dha.ni.)]

"तुवर्यतिकषाया च मेदःश्ळेष्मास्रपित्तजित् ।
विबन्धाघ्मानकृत्स्वादुः स्वादुपाकाल्पवातळा ॥
शीतळा बद्धविण्मूत्रा लघ्वी रूक्षा प्रकीर्तिता ।" (सो.नि.)
["Tuvaryatikaṣāyā ca mēdaḥśḷēṣmāsṛapittajit
Vibandhādhmanakṛtsvāduḥ svādupākālpavātaḷā
Śītaḷā baddhaviṇmūtrā laghvī rūkṣā pṛakīṛtitā" (Sō.ni.)]

"आढकी तु कषाया च मधुरा कफपित्तजित् ।
ईषद् वातकरा रुच्या विदळा गुरु ग्राहिका ॥
सा च श्वेता दोषधात्री तु रक्ता
रुच्या बल्या पित्ततापादि हन्त्री ।
सा श्यामा चेद्दीपनी पित्तदाह-
ध्वंसा बल्यञ्चाढकीयूषमुक्तम् ॥" (रा.नि.)
["Āḍhakī tu kaṣāyā ca madhurā kaphapittajit
Īṣad vātakarā rucyā vidaḷā guru grāhikā
Sā ca śvētā dōṣadhātṛī tu raktā
rucyā balyā pittatāpādihantṛī
Sā śyāmā cēddīpanī pittadāha-
dhvaṁsā balyañcāḍhakīyūṣamuktaṃ" (Rā.ni.)]

തുവരേടെ ഗുണം ഗ്രാഹി കഷായമധുരം രസം
അതീയായിത്തണുത്തുള്ളു ഗുരുവാകയുമുണ്ടതു
അതിസാരം കഫം പിത്തം ജ്വരാഞ്ചാശു വിനാശയേത്.
തുവരേടെ പരിപ്പിൻെറ ഗുണം വാതഹരം പരം
തൂനിപ്രതിതൂനീ ഗുന്മം പ്രമേഹം ശർക്കരാശ്മരീ
കാസമെന്നാദിയായുള്ള ദണ്ഡങ്ങൾക്കൊക്കെ നന്നിതു (ഗു.പാ.)
["Tuvarēṭe guṇaṃ grāhi kaṣāyamadhuraṃ rasaṃ
Atiyāyittaṇuttuḷḷu guruvākayumuṇṭatu
Atisāraṃ kaphaṃ pittaṃ jvarañcāśu vināśayēt.
Tuvarēṭe parippinṟe guṇaṃ vātaharaṃ paraṃ
Tūnipṛatitūnī gulmaṃ pṛamēhaṃ śaṛkkarāśmarī
Kāsamennādiyāyuḷḷa daṇḍannaḷkkokke nannitu" (Gu.pā.)]

Remarks: The authors of 'Abhidhānamañjarī' and 'Bhāvapṛakāśaṃ' have not listed different varieties of *āḍhakī*. 'Dhanvantarinighaṇṭu', 'Rājanighaṇṭu' and the Kerala works 'Ōṣadhinighaṇṭu' and 'Āyuṛvēdaviśvakōśaṃ' have described three different varieties of this plant according to the colour of the seeds, namely, white, red or black. The author of 'Śāligrāmanighaṇṭubhūṣaṇaṃ however, has differentiated four varieties of this plant viz. yellow, white, red and black according to the colour of the seeds.

The variety commonly used in Kerala is the one with yellow seeds.

Coll. No. AVS 2457

Calamus rotang **Linn.**

Arecaceae : (पूग–कुलम्)

Eng	:	Common rattan, Rattan
Hin	:	Bēt, Bēṁt (बेत, बेंत)
Kan	:	Beṭasu (ಬೆಟಸು)
Mal	:	Cūral (ചൂരൽ)
San	:	Vētraḥ (वेत्रः)
Tam	:	Pirampu (பிரம்பு)
Tel	:	Jaṭayūrkuli (జటయూర్కులి)

Distribution: Central and south India in dry tracts in areas upto 450 m elevation

The plant: A scandent slender shrub with cylindrical uniformly thick yellowish white stems armed with short flat spines on leaf sheaths, leaf sheaths glabrous, hollowed below, ochrea short, truncate, margined with small straight or recurved spines having laterally compressed bases, rachis near the base flat and smooth above, channelled at the sides to receive the leaflets, trigonous upwards, armed below along the middle, leaflets very numerous, equidistant, 1–ribbed, the rib bearing scattered bristles; flowers unisexual, male spadix very long, flagelliferous, spathes elongate tubular, female flowers scattered along the slender branches of the spadix; fruits seated on the minute perianth, subglobose, mucronate, scales many, pale yellow in vertical series.

Parts used: whole plant

Properties and uses: The roots are astringent, acrid, bitter, cooling, expectorant, alexeteric, antidysenteric, hypotensive, depurative, anti-inflammatory, diuretic, febrifuge and tonic. They are useful in vitiated conditions of *pitta,* burning sensation, hyperdipsia, cough, bronchitis, dysentery, leprosy, skin diseases, erysipelas, inflammations, strangury, vesical calculi, chronic fever and general debility. The leaves are acrid, bitter, cooling, astringent and laxative, and are useful in vitiated conditions of *pitta,* skin diseases, leprosy and pruritus. The seeds are astringent, acrid, sour, depurative and expectorant, and are useful in vitiated conditions of *kapha,* cough, skin diseases and pruritus. The sprouts are acrid, sweet and thermogenic, and are useful in vitiated conditions of *vāta* and *kapha.*

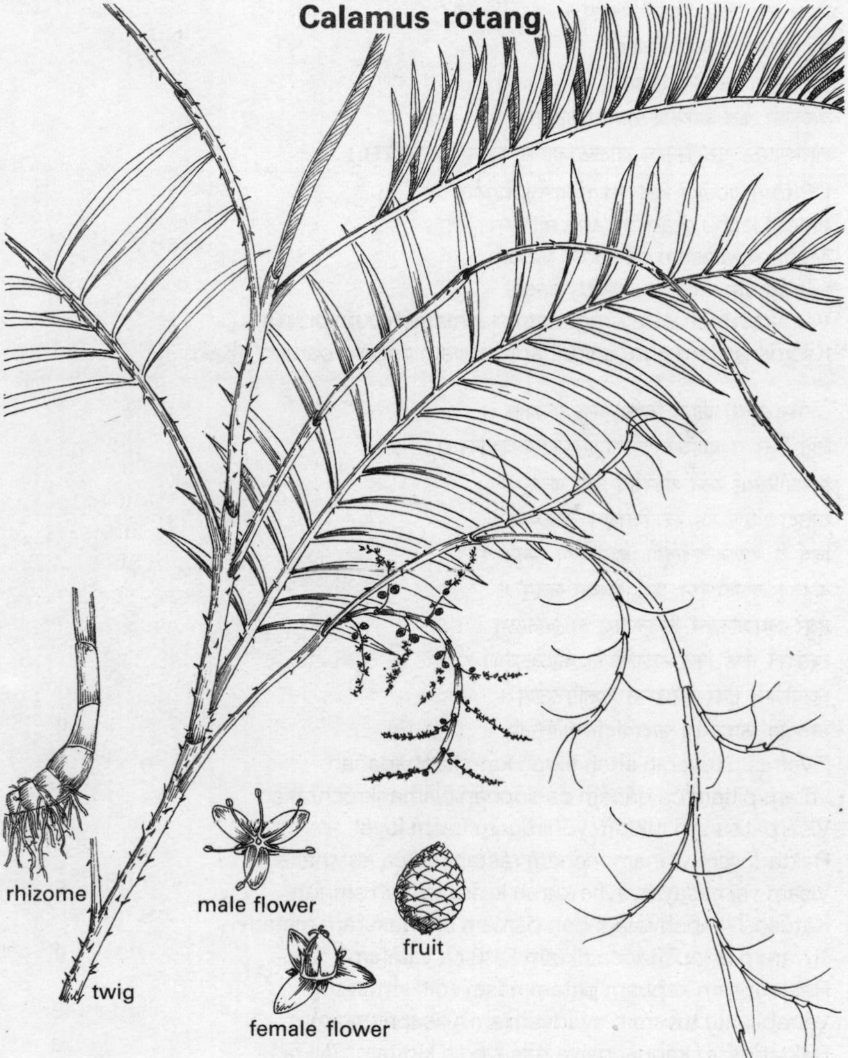
Calamus rotang
rhizome
twig
male flower
female flower
fruit

"वेत्रो वेतो योगिदण्डः सुदण्डो मृदुपर्वकः ।" (रा.नि.)
["Vēṭrō vētō yōgidaṇḍaḥ sudaṇḍō mṛduparvakaḥ" (Rā.ni.)

"इक्ष्वालिको रोमशरस्तेजनो वेत्रकः स्मृतः ।" (कै.नि.)
["Ikṣvālikō rōmaśarastējanō vēṭrakaḥ smṛtaḥ" (Kai.ni.)]

"शीतं विपाके कटुकं कृमिघ्नं
तिक्तं लघु ग्राहि निहन्ति पित्तम् ।
मेहं वलासं च करोति वातं
वेत्राग्रमुक्तं रुचिकृद्विशेषात् ॥
वेत्रकस्य फलं दृग्घ्नं श्ळेष्ममेहकृमिप्रणुत् ।
क्षारोष्णाम्ळं गुरु स्निग्धं वातळं चाग्नि दीपनम् ॥" (कै.नि.)
["Sītaṃ vipākē kaṭukaṃ kṛmighnaṃ
tiktaṃ laghu grāhi nihanti pittaṃ
Mēhaṃ valāsaṃ ca karōti vātaṃ
vēṭrāgramuktaṃ rucikṛdviśēṣāt
Vēṭrakasya phalaṃ dṛgghnaṃ śḷēṣmamēhakṛmipraṇut
Kṣārōṣṇāmḷaṃ guru snigdhaṃ vātaḷaṃ cāgnidīpanaṃ" (Kai.ni.)]

"वेत्रस्तु तुवरः शीतः तिक्तः कटु कफापहः ।
वातं पित्तं च दाहञ्च शोफार्शोऽश्मरिकृच्छ्रकान् ॥
विसर्पातिसारं रक्तं योनिरोगं तृषां जयेत् ।
रक्तदोषं व्रणं मेहं रक्तपित्तञ्च कुष्ठकम् ॥
विषं वै नाशयत्येवांकुराः क्षारो लघुः स्मृतः ।
कटूष्णः कफवातघ्नः पर्णं भेदकरं मतम् ॥
तुवरं लघुशीतञ्च तिक्तं कटु च वातळम् ।
रक्तदोषं कफं पित्तं नाशयेदिति कीर्त्तितम् ॥
वेत्रबीजन्तु तुवरं स्वाद्वम्ळं रूक्षपित्तळम् ।
रक्तदोषं कफञ्चैव नाशयेदिति कीर्त्तितम् ॥" (नि.र.)
["Vēṭrastu tuvaraḥ śītaḥ tiktaḥ kaṭu kaphāpahaḥ
Vātaṃ pittaṃ ca dāhaṃ ca śōphāṛśōऽśmarikṛcchṛakān
Visaṛpātisāraṃ raktaṃ yōnirōgaṃ tṛṣāṃ jayēt
Raktadōṣaṃ vraṇaṃ mēhaṃ raktapittañca kuṣṭhakaṃ
Viṣaṃ vai nāśayatyēvāmkuraḥ kṣārō laghuḥ smṛtaḥ
Kaṭūṣṇaḥ kapahvātaghnaḥ paṛṇaṃ bhēdakaraṃ mataṃ
Tuvaraṃ laghuśītañca tiktaṃ kaṭu ca vātaḷaṃ
Raktadōṣaṃ kaphaṃ pittaṃ nāśayēditi kīrttitaṃ
Vēṭrabījantu tuvaraṃ svādvamḷaṃ rūkṣapaittaḷaṃ
Raktadōṣaṃ kaphañcaiva nāśayēditi kīrtitaṃ" (Ni.ra.)]

"പിരമ്പിൻതലകച്ചുള്ളു രൂക്ഷമാകയുമുണ്ടത്
വിരേചനകരം രുച്യം കൃമിദോഷഹരം പരം
വാതത്തിനെ വരുത്തീടും കഫപിത്തവിനാശനം (ഗു. പാ.)

["Pirampintala kacuḷḷu rūkṣamākayumuṇṭatụ
Virēcanakaraṃ rucyaṃ kṛmidōṣaharaṃ paraṃ
Vātattine varuttīṭuṃ kaphapittavināśanaṃ" (Gu.pā)]

Callicarpa macrophylla Vahl

Verbenaceae : (निर्गुण्डी–कुलम्)

Hin	:	Priyamgu, Ḍaiyā (प्रियंगु, डइया)
Kan	:	Priyangu (ಪ್ರಿಯಂಗು)
Mal	:	Ñāḻal (ഞാഴൽ)
San	:	Pṛiyaṅgu, Phalinī (प्रियङ्गु, फलिनी)
Tam	:	Ñāḻal (ஞாழல்)
Tel	:	Priyangu (ప్రియంగు)

Distribution : Bengal, Assam and sub-Himalayan tracts upto 1,800m elevation

The plant : An erect shrub, 1.2–2.4m in height with branches having tomentose tips; leaves simple, opposite, ovate or ovate-lanceolate, acuminate, base cuneate or rounded, white tomentose beneath, main lateral nerves 12–16 pairs; flowers rose-coloured, crowded in axillary peduncled globose cymes; fruits white drupes.

Parts used : flowers, fruits

Properties and uses : The flowers and fruits are bitter, sweet, astringent, acrid, cooling, anodyne, deodorant, digestive, constipating, depurative, styptic, alexeteric and febrifuge. They are useful in vitiated conditions of *pitta* and *vāta,* rheumatoid arthritis, burning sensation, cephalalgia, diaphoresis, foul ulcers, dyspepsia, flatulence, colic, diarrhoea, dysentery, haemorrhages, haemoptysis, poisonous bites, skin diseases, diabetes, vomiting, fever and general weakness. The leaves are useful in gout and arthralgia.

"प्रियङ्गौ प्रियवल्ली च फलिनी कङ्गुनी प्रिया ।
वृत्ता गोचन्दनी श्यामा करंभा व्रणभेदिनी ॥
गौरी पुष्करपर्णी च वनिता नारिवल्लभा ।
स्वयंबला बलावल्ली क्षुद्राख्या पुष्यशोभना ॥
प्रियाङ्गवल्लभा प्रोक्ता पीतसर्षपसन्निभा ।
कोला गिरिस्वरा श्वेता तथा गन्धफला स्मृता ॥
विष्वक्सेना तु संवृता वल्लरी व्रततिस्तथा ।" (सो.नि.)

["Pṛiyangau pṛiyavallī ca phalinī kanguni pṛiyā
Vṛttā gōcandanī śyāmā karambhā vṛaṇabhēdinī

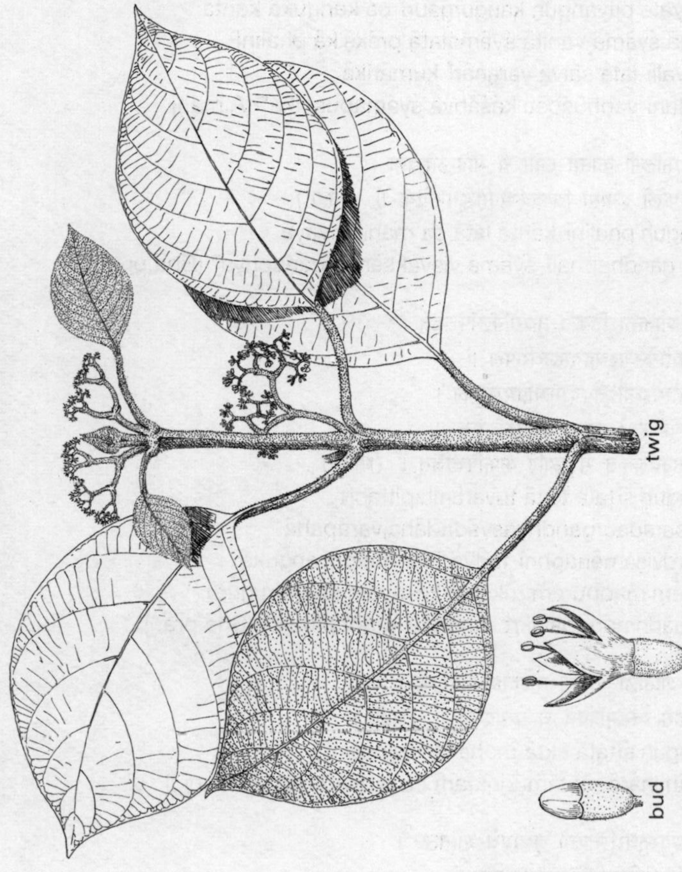

Callicarpa macrophylla

Gaurī puṣkaraparṇī ca vanitā nārivallabhā
Svayaṃbalā balāvallī kṣudrākhyā puṣyaśōbhanā
Pṛiyāngavallabhā prōktā pītasarṣapasannibhā
Kōla girisvarā śvētā tathā gandhaphalā smṛtā
Viṣvaksēnā tu saṃvṛtā vallarī vratatistathā'' (Sō.ni.)]

"निर्दिश्यते प्रियङ्गुः कङ्गुर्गौरी च कङ्गुका कान्ता ।
सुभगा श्यामा वनिता श्यामलता प्रेक्षिका फलिनी ॥
सिद्धवल्ली लता सैव वरनारी कुमारिका ।
गोवन्दनी वधूश्चेति काशाह्वा श्यामपुष्पिका ॥" (अ.म.)
["Nirdiśyatē priyanguḥ kangurgaurī ca kangukā kāntā
Subhagā śyāmā vanitā śyāmalatā prēkṣikā phalinī
Siddhavallī latā saiva varanārī kumārikā
Gōvandanī vadhūścēti kāśāhvā śyāmapuṣpikā" (A.ma.)]

"प्रियङ्गुः फलिनी कान्ता लता च महिळाह्वया ।
गुन्द्रा गन्धफली श्यामा विष्वक्सेनाऽङ्गनप्रिया ॥" (भा.प्र.)
["Priyanguḥ phalinī kāntā latā ca mahiḷāhvayā
Gundrā gandhaphalī śyāmā viṣvaksēnāṅganapriyā" (Bhā.pra.)]

"प्रियङ्गुः शीतळा तिक्ता तुवरानिलपित्तहृत् ।
रक्तातिसारदौर्गन्ध्यस्वेददाहज्वरापहा ॥
गुल्मतृड्विषमेहघ्नी तद्वद्गन्धप्रियङ्गुका ।
तत्फलं मधुरं रूक्षं कषायं शीतळं गुरु ॥
विबन्धाध्मानबलकृत् सङ्ग्राहि कफपित्तजित् ।" (भा.प्र.)
["Priyanguḥ śītaḷā tiktā tuvarānilapittahṛt
Raktātisāradaurgandhyasvēdadāhajvarāpahā
Gulmatṛḍviṣamēhaghnī tadvadgandhapriyangukā
Tatphalaṃ madhuraṃ rūkṣaṃ kaṣāyaṃ śītaḷaṃ guru
Vibandhādhmānabalakṛt sangrāhi kaphapittajit" (Bhā.pra.)]

"प्रियङ्गुः शीतळा तिक्ता मोहदाहविनाशिनी ।
ज्वरवान्तिहरा रक्तमुद्रिक्तं च प्रसादयेत् ॥" (ध.नि.)
["Priyanguḥ śītaḷā tiktā mōhadāhavināśinī
Jvaravāntiharā raktamudriktaṃ ca prasādayēt" (Dha.ni.)]

"गन्धप्रियङ्गुस्तुवरस्तिक्तो वृष्यश्च शीतळः ।
केश्यो वान्तिभ्रान्तिदाहपित्तरक्तरुजस्तथा ॥
ज्वरमोहस्वेदकुष्ठमुखजाड्यतृषा हरेत् ।
वातगुल्मं विषं मेहं मेदं चैव विनाशयेत् ॥
रक्तपित्तं नाशयति बीजमस्य कषायकम् ।
मधुरं शीतळं रूक्षं तुवरं ग्राहकं गुरु ॥
मलस्तंभकरं बल्यं पित्तघ्नं कफनाशनम् ।
आध्मानकारकञ्चैव मुनिभिः परिकीर्त्तितम् ॥" (नि.र.)

["Gandhapṛiyangustuvarastiktō vṛṣyaśca śītaḷaḥ
Kēśyō vāntibhṛāntidāhapittaraktarujastathā
Jvaramōhasvēdakuṣṭhamukhajāḍyatṛṣā harēt
Vātagulmaṃ viṣaṃ mēhaṃ mēdaṃ caiva vināśayēt
Raktapittaṃ nāśayati bījamasya kaṣāyakaṃ
Madhuraṃ śītaḷaṃ rūkṣaṃ tuvaraṃ grāhakaṃ guru
Malastambhakaraṃ balyaṃ pittaghnaṃ kaphanāśanaṃ
Ādhmānakārakañcaiva munibhiḥ parikīṛttitaṃ" (Ni.ra.)]

"रक्तसंग्राहणी शीता सुगन्धा पित्तनाशनी ।
वश्योपयोगिनी वृष्या प्रियङ्गु गुह्यरोगजित् ॥" (म.नि.)
["Raktasamgrāhaṇī śītā sugandhā pittanāśanī
Vaśyōpayōginī vṛṣyā pṛiyangu guhyarōgajit" (Ma.ni.)]

"प्रियङ्गु शीतळा तिक्ता दाहपित्तास्रदोषजित् ।
वान्तिभ्रान्तिज्वरहरा वक्त्रजाड्यविनाशनी ॥" (रा.नि.)
["Pṛiyangu śītaḷā ṭiktā dāhapittāsṛadōṣajit
Vāntibhṛāntijvaraharā vaktrajāḍyavināśanī" (Rā.ni.)]

"फलिनी शीतळा तिक्ता तुवरानिलपित्तहा ।
रक्तातियोगदौर्गन्ध्यस्वेददाहज्वरापहा ॥
गुल्मतृड्विषमोहघ्नी तद्वद् गन्धप्रियङ्गुका ॥
तत्फलं मधुरं रूक्षं कषायं शीतळं गुरु ।
विबन्धाध्मानबलकृत् संग्राहि कफपित्तजित् ॥" (कै.नि.)
["Phalinī śītaḷā tiktā tuvarānilapttahā
Raktātiyōgadauṛgandhyasvēdadāhajvarāpahā
Gulmatṛḍviṣamōhaghnī tadvad gandhapṛiyangukā
Tatphalaṃ madhuraṃ rūkṣaṃ kaṣāyaṃ śītaḷaṃ guru
Vibandhādhmānabalakṛt samgrāhi kaphapittajit" (Kai.ni.)]

"प्रियङ्गुः शीतळा वान्तिदाहपित्तज्वरास्रजित् ।
सुखकान्तिप्रजननी गात्रदौर्गन्ध्यनाशिनी ॥" (म.पा.नि.)
["Pṛiyanguḥ śītaḷā vāntidāhapittajvārasṛajit
Sukhakāntipṛajananī gātradauṛgandhyanāśinī" (Ma.pā.ni.)]

Remarks: In the Commentary on 'Bhāvapṛakāśanighaṇṭu' and 'Indian Medicinal Plants' *pṛiyaṅgu* has been given the botanical name *Aglaia odoratissima* Bl. But in the 'Ayurvedic Formulary of India', Commentaries on 'Kaiyadēvanighaṇṭu' and 'Dhanvantarinighaṇṭu', 'Glossary of Vegetable Drugs in Bṛhattṛayī' and 'Dravyaguṇavijñān', this has been identified as *Callicarpa macrophylla* Vahl.

In Kerala what is sold in the market as *pṛiyaṅgu* is the dried male flower of *Myristica fragrans (jātīvṛkṣa).* This cannot be justified.

Coll. No. AVS 2445

***Calophyllum inophyllum* Linn.**

Clusiaceae : (नागकेसर–कुलम्)

Eng	:	Alexandrian laurel
Hin	:	Sultān campā, Sultānā campak (सुलतान चंपा, सुलताना चंपक)
Kan	:	Umā (ಉಮಾ)
Mal	:	Punna (പുന്ന)
San	:	Punnāgaḥ (पुन्नागः)
Tam	:	Punnai, Punnagaṃ (புன்னை, புன்னகம்)
Tel	:	Ponnaviṭtulu (పొన్నవిత్తులు)

Distribution : East and west coasts, along river banks in certain localities

The plant : A medium sized evergreen glabrous tree, 15–18m in height with brownish black bark having irregular fissures; leaves simple, opposite, 5–7.5cm broad, broadly elliptic, rounded at the apex or emarginate with very close numerous parallel nerves at right angles with the mid-rib; flowers pure white, fragrant, in lax few-flowered racemes, stamens many, filaments united into 4–6 bundles; fruits globose, smooth, yellowish drupes, pulp scanty; seeds ovoid.

Parts used : bark, leaves, seeds

Properties and uses : The bark is astringent, sweet, cooling, anodyne, vulnerary, diuretic, emollient, emetic, purgative, resolvant and demulcent. It is useful in vitiated conditions of *pitta* and *vāta.*, wounds, strangury, skin diseases, pruritus, ophthalmitis, internal haemorrhages, orchitis and for improving the complexion. The leaves are useful in migraine, vertigo and ophthalmia. The seed oil is anodyne, diuretic and demulcent, and is useful in vitiated conditions of *vāta,* gout, intramuscular pain in leprosy, gonorrhoea, skin diseases, scabies and strangury.

"पुन्नागः पुरुषस्तुङ्गः पुन्नामाः पाटलीच्छदः ।
पाटली दीर्घमूला च सुगन्धी खचरः प्रियः ॥" (म.नि.)
["Punnāgaḥ puruṣastuṅgaḥ punnāma pāṭalīcchadaḥ
Pāṭalī dīrghamūlā ca sugandhī khacaraḥ priyaḥ" (Ma.ni.)]

"पुन्नागः पुरुषस्तुङ्गः पुन्नामा पाटलः पुमान् ॥

Calophyllum inophyllum

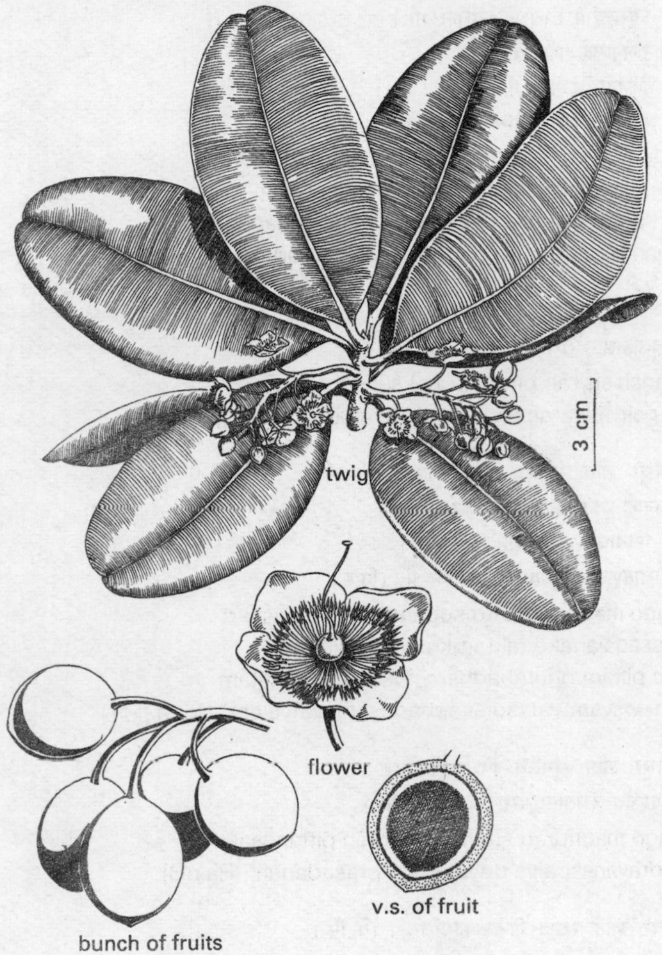

रक्तपुष्पो रक्तरेणुररुणोऽयं नवाह्वयः ॥" (रा.नि.)
["Punnāgaḥ puruṣastungaḥ punnāmā pāṭalaḥ pumān
Rakatapuṣpō raktarēṇuraruṇōʃyaṃ navāhvayaḥ" (Rā.ni.)]

"पुनर्नागः पुन्नामा चाम्पेयो देववल्लभो विबुधा ।
सुरकर्णिका सुरभिकः पीताख्यः पीतकेसरः प्रोक्तः ॥" (अ.म.)
["Punaṛnāgaḥ punnāmā cāmpēyō dēvallabhō vibudhā
Surakaṛṇikā surabhikaḥ pītākhyaḥ pītakēsaraḥ prōktaḥ" (A.ma.)]

"पुन्नागः पुरुषस्तुङ्गो विबुधो देववल्लभः ।
पुन्नामा पाटलीपुष्पकेशरो रक्तकेसरः ॥
पांशुर्नागो महानागः केशवः पाटलीच्छदः ।
काञ्चनः सुरपर्णी स्यात् सुगन्धः षट्पदालयः ॥" (कै.नि.)
["Punnāgaḥ puruṣastuṅgō vibudhō dēvavallabhaḥ
Puṇnnāmā pāṭalīpuṣpakēśarō raktakēsaraḥ
Pāṃśuṛnāgō mahānāgaḥ kēśavaḥ pāṭalīcchadaḥ
Kāñcanaḥ surapaṛṇī syāt sugandhaḥ ṣaṭpadālayaḥ" (Kai.ni.)]

"पुन्नागः शिशिरः पित्तहरी चक्षुःशिरोरुजम् ।
निहन्ति पक्वातिसारमरोचकविषव्रणान् ॥" (म.नि.)
["Punnāgaḥ śiśiraḥ pittaharī cakṣuḥśirōrujaṃ
Nihanti pakvātisāramarōcakaviṣavṛaṇān " (Ma.ni.)]

"पुन्नागो मधुरः शीतो सुगन्धिः पित्तनाशकृत् ।
देवप्रसादजनको रक्तरुक्रक्तपित्तजित् ॥
कफं पित्तं भूतबाधां नाशयेदिति कीर्तितम् ।
पुष्पं वृष्यं वातशूलकफदोषाञ्जयंत्यलम् ॥" (नि.र.)
["Punnāgō madhuraḥ śītō sugandhiḥ pittanāśakṛt
Dēvaprasādajanakō raktarukraktapittajit
Kaphaṃ pittaṃ bhūtabādhāṃ nāśayēditi kīṛttitaṃ
Puṣpaṃ vṛṣyaṃ vātaśūlakaphadōṣāñjayatyalaṃ" (Ni.ra.)]

"पुन्नागो मधुरः शीतः सुगन्धिः पित्तनाशकृत् ।
भूतविद्रावणश्चैव देवतानां प्रसादनः ॥" (रा.नि.)
["Punnāgō madhuraḥ śītaḥ sugandhiḥ pittanāśakṛt
Bhūtavidrāvaṇaścaiva dēvatānāṃ pṛasādanaḥ" (Rā.ni.)]

"पुन्नागस्तुवरः शीतो स्वादु पित्तकफास्रजित् । (कै.नि.)
["Punnāgastuvaraḥ śītō svādu pittakaphāsrajit"(Kai.ni.)]

"पुन्नागो मधुरः शीतो रक्तपित्तकफापहः ।" (म.पा.नि.)
["Punnāgō madhuraḥ śītō raktapittakaphāpahaḥ" (Ma.pā.ni.)]

Coll. No. AVS 2124

Calotropis gigantea (Linn.) R.Br.

Asclepiadaceae : (अर्क–कुलम्)

Eng	:	Gigantic swallow wort, Mudar
Hin	:	Madār (मदार)
Kan	:	Ekkamēli (ಎಕ್ಕಮೇಲಿ)
Mal	:	Erukkụ (എരുക്ക്)
San	:	Aṛkaḥ (अर्कः)
Tam	:	Erukku (எருக்கு)
Tel	:	Jillēḍu (జిల్లేడు)

Distribution : Throughout India,in dry waste places

The plant : A large hard much-branched milky shrub, very pale in colour, the branches, leaves and inflorescence covered with loose soft white wool; leaves opposite, subsessile, ovate, cordate at base; flowers beautiful lilac, rosy or purple tinted in umbellate lateral cymes; fruits fleshy follicles, green, seeds with abundant white coma.

Parts used : whole plant

Properties and uses : The dried whole plant is a good tonic, expectorant, depurative and anthelmintic. The dried root bark is a substitute for ipecacuanha. The root bark is febrifuge, anthelmintic, depurative, expectorant and laxative, and is useful in cutaneous diseases, intestinal worms, cough, ascites and anasarca. The powdered root promotes gastric secretions and is useful in asthma, bronchitis and dyspepsia. The leaves are useful in the treatment of paralysis, arthralgia, swellings and intermittent fevers. The flowers are bitter, digestive, astringent, stomachic, anthelmintic and tonic. They are useful in asthma, catarrh, anorexia, inflammations and tumours. In large doses it is purgative and emetic.

"अर्कः क्षीरदळः पुच्छी प्रतापः क्षीरकाण्डकः ।
विक्षीरो भास्करः क्षीरी खर्जूघ्नः शिवपुष्पकः ॥
भञ्जनः क्षीरपर्णी स्यात् सविता च विकीरणः ।
सूर्याह्वश्च सदापुष्पो रविरास्फोटकस्तथा ।
तूलफलः शुकफलो विंशतिश्च समाह्वयः ॥
शुक्ळार्कस्तपनः श्वेतः प्रतापश्च सितार्ककः ।

Calotropis gigantea

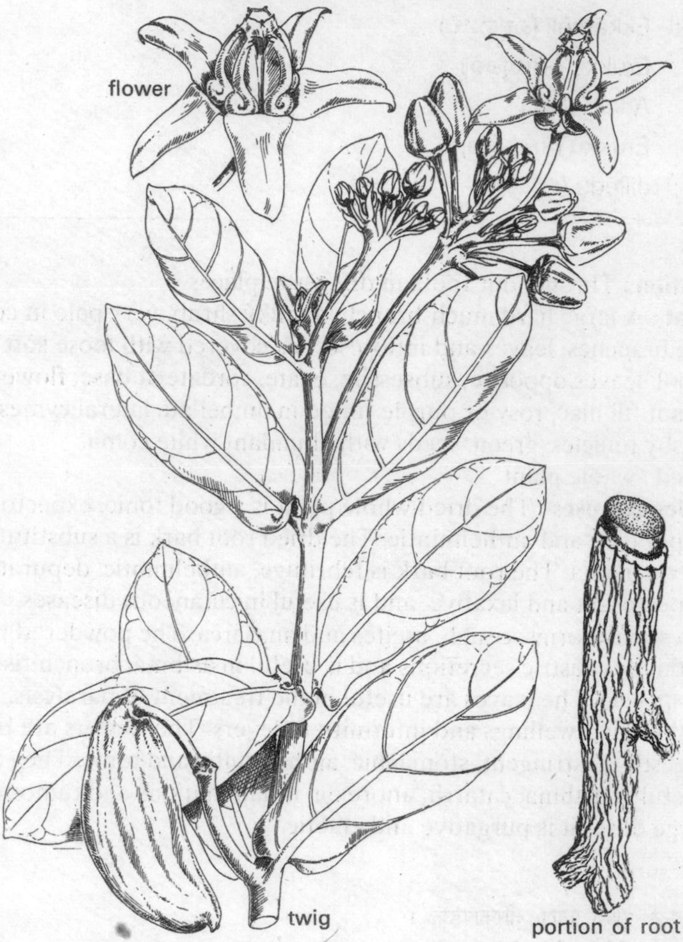

सुपुष्पः शङ्करादिः स्यादत्यर्को वृत्तमल्लिका ॥
राजार्को वसुकोऽळर्को मन्दारो गणरूपकः ।
काष्ठीलश्च सदापुष्पो ज्ञेयोऽत्र सप्तसम्मितः ॥" (रा.नि.)
["Aṛkaḥ kṣīradaḷaḥ pucchī pratāpaḥ kṣīrakāṇḍakaḥ
Vikṣīrō bhāskaraḥ kṣīrī kharjūghnaḥ śivapuṣpakaḥ
Bhañjanaḥ kṣīrapaṛṇī syāt savitā ca vikīraṇaḥ
Sūryāhvaśca sadāpuṣpō ravirasphōṭakastathā
Tūlaphalaḥ śukaphalō viṁśatiśca samāhvayaḥ
Śukḷāṛkastapanaḥ śvētaḥ pratāpaśca sitāṛkakaḥ
Supuṣpaḥ śankarādiḥ syādatyaṛkō vṛttamllikā
Rājāṛkō vasukōʃḷaṛkō mandārō gaṇarūpakaḥ
Kāṣṭhīlaśca sadāpuṣpō jñēyōʃtra saptasammitaḥ (Rā.ni.)]

अर्कः स्यादास्फोतो विकीरणो जां.... लोऽर्कपुष्पश्च ।
क्षीरिण्यादित्याह्वः सुरूपिणी दुग्धिनी शुकफलश्च ॥
स एव क्षीरवर्णश्च विक्षुरो दुग्धिका तथा ।
एकैषिकेति विज्ञेयः शब्दैः पर्यायवाचश्च ॥
अन्योऽळर्कोऽत्यर्को राजार्कः श्वेतपुष्पकः ।
श्वेतार्को मन्दारो वसुको गणरूपिकः सदापुष्पी ॥
शिवशेखरश्च वृक्षो वसुप्रदो दीर्घपुष्पश्च ॥
शिवमल्लिका शुकश्च प्रतापसाख्यो महापशुपतिः स्यात् ॥ (अ.म.)
["Aṛkaḥ syādāsphōtō vikīraṇō jaṁ.....lōʃrkapuṣpaśca
Kṣīriṇyādityāhvaḥ surūpiṇī dugdhinī śukaphalaśca
Sa ēva kṣīravaṛṇaśca vikṣurō dugdhikā tathā
Ekaiṣikēti vijñēyaḥ śabdaiḥ paryāyavācaśca
Aṇyōʃḷaṛkōʃtyaṛkō rājāṛkaḥ śvētapuṣpakaḥ
Śvētāṛkō mandārō vasukō gaṇarūpikaḥ sadāpuṣpī
Śivaśēkharaśca vṛkṣō vasupradō dīrghapuṣpaśca
Śivamallikā śukaśca pratāpasākhyō mahāpaśupatiḥ syāt" (A.ma.)]

"अर्कद्वयं सरं वातकुष्ठकण्डूतिषव्रणान् ।
निहन्ति प्लीहगुल्मार्शःश्लेष्मोदरशकृत्कृमीन् ॥
अळर्ककुसुमं वृष्यं लघु दीपनपाचनम् ।
अरोचकः प्रसेकार्शःकासश्वासनिवारणम् ॥
रक्तार्कपुष्पं मधुरं सतिक्तं
कुष्ठकृमिघ्नं कफनाशनञ्च ।
अर्शोविषं हन्ति च रक्तपित्तं
संग्राहि गुल्मे श्वयथौ हितं तत् ॥
क्षीरमर्कस्य तिक्तोष्णं स्निग्धं सलवणं लघु ।
कुष्ठगुल्मोदरहरं श्रेष्ठमेतद्विरेचनम् ॥" (भा.प्र.)
["Aṛkadvayaṃ saraṃ vātakuṣṭhakaṇḍūviṣavraṇān
Nihanti plīhagulmāṛśaḥśḷēṣmōdaraśakṛtkṛmīn
Aḷaṛkakusumaṃ vṛṣyaṃ laghu dīpanapācanaṃ

Arōcakaḥ prasēkārśaḥkāsaśvāsanivaraṇaṃ
Raktārkapuṣpaṃ madhruṃ satiktaṃ
kuṣṭhakṛmighnaṃ kaphanāśanañca
Arśōviṣaṃ hanti ca raktapittaṃ
saṃgrāhi gulmē śvayathau hitaṃ tat
Kṣīramarkasya tiktōṣṇaṃ snigdhaṃ salavaṇaṃ laghu
Kuṣṭhagulmōdaraharaṃ śrēṣṭhamētadvirēcanaṃ (Bhā.pra)]

"कफवातहरा तिक्ता कृमिकुष्ठनिवारिणी ।
दुष्टव्रणहरा तीक्ष्णा सदापुष्पी विषापहा ॥
तीक्ष्णो विषघ्नो भूतघ्नो मन्दारः कफवातहा ।
रूपिकाया गुणैस्तुल्यः प्लीहघ्नो रक्तगुल्मनुत् ॥" (म.नि.)
["Kaphavātaharā tiktā kṛmikuṣṭhanivāriṇī
Duṣṭavraṇaharā tīkṣṇā sadāpuṣpī viṣāpahā
Tīkṣṇō viṣaghnō bhūtaghnō mandāraḥ kaphavātahā
Rūpikāyā guṇaistulyaḥ plīhaghnō raktagulmanut" (Ma.ni.)]

"अर्कस्तु कटुरुष्णश्च वातजिद्दीपनीयकः ।
शोफव्रणहरः कण्डूकुष्ठकृमिविनाशनः ॥
श्वेतार्कः कटुतिक्तोष्णो मलशोधनकारकः ।
मूत्रकृच्छ्रास्रशोफार्त्तिव्रणदोषविनाशनः ॥
राजार्कः कटुतिक्तोष्णः कफमेदोविषापहः ।
वातकुष्ठव्रणान् हन्ति शोफकण्डूविसर्पनुत् ॥" (रा.नि.)
["Arkastu kaṭuruṣṇaśca vātajiddīpanīyakaḥ
Śōphavraṇaharaḥ kaṇḍūkuṣṭhakṛmivināśanaḥ
Svētārkaḥ kaṭutiktōṣṇō malaśōdhanakārakaḥ
Mūtrakṛcchrāsraśōphārttivraṇadōṣavināśanaḥ
Rājārkaḥ kaṭutiktōṣṇaḥ kaphamēdōviṣāpahaḥ
Vātakuṣṭhavraṇān hanti śōphakaṇḍūvisarpanut" (Rā.ni.)]

"अर्कस्य पुष्पं मधुरं सतिक्तं
कुष्ठं कृमिघ्नं कफनाशनञ्च ।
आखोर्विषं हन्ति च रक्तपित्तं
संग्राहि शोफे च हितं सगुल्मे ॥
अळर्ककुसुमं वृष्यं लघु पाचनदीपनम् ।
अरोचकप्रसेकार्शःकासश्वासनिबर्हणम् ।
अर्कक्षीरं स्नुहीक्षीरं स्निग्धं वा कटुकं लघु ।
गुल्मिनां कुष्ठिनां चापि तथैवोदररोगिणाम् ॥
श्रेष्ठमेतद्विरेकार्थे ये चान्ये दीर्घरोगिणः ।
क्षीरमर्कस्य तिक्तोष्णं स्निग्धं सलवणं लघु ।
कुष्ठगुल्मोदरहरं श्रेष्ठमेतद्विरेचनम् ॥" (कै.नि.)
["Arkasya puṣpaṃ madhuraṃ satiktaṃ
kuṣṭhaṃ kṛmighnaṃ kaphanāśanañca

Akhōrviṣaṃ hanti ca raktapittaṃ
saṃgrāhi śōphē ca hitaṃ sagulmē
Aḷaṛkakusumaṃ vṛṣyaṃ laghu pācanadīpanaṃ
Arōcakapṛasēkāṛśaḥkāsaśvāsanibaṛhaṇaṃ
Aṛkakṣīraṃ snuhīkṣīraṃ snigdhaṃ vā kaṭukaṃ laghu
Gulmināṃ kuṣṭhināṃ cāpi tathaivōdararōgiṇāṃ
Śṛēṣṭhamētadvirēkāṛthē yē cānyē dīṛgharōgiṇaḥ
Kṣīramaṛkasya tiktōṣṇaṃ snigdhaṃ saḷavaṇaṃ laghu
Kuṣṭhagulmōdaraharaṃ śṛēṣṭhamētadvirēcanaṃ" (Kai.ni.)]

"എരുക്കില ശമിപ്പിക്കും വാതത്തേയും കഫത്തേയും
നന്നേറ്റം കർണ്ണശൂലയ്ക്കും ദീപനത്തിനുമുത്തമം.
എരുക്കിൻപൂവെലിവിഷം കൃമികുഷ്ഠഞ്ച നാശയേത്". (ഗു. പാ.)
["Erukkila śamippikkuṃ vātattēyuṃ kaphattēyuṃ
Nannēṟṟaṃ kaṛṇaśūlaykkuṃ dīpanattinumuttamaṃ
Erukkinpūvelivisaṃ kṛmikuṣṭhañca nāśayēt. " (Gu.pā)]

Remarks : 'Abhidhānamañjarī, 'Madanādinighaṇṭu' and 'Dhanvantarinighaṇṭu' mention only two varieties of *aṛka,* namely, *aṛka* and *aḷaṛka (rājāṛka).* But 'Bhāvapṛakāsaṃ' after describing two kinds of *aṛka* says that there is another variety called *raktāṛka* and describes its properties separately. The author of `Rājanighaṇṭu' also enumerates three kinds of *aṛka* viz. *aṛka svētāṛka,* and *rājāṛka* and ascribes all of them properties separately.

However, only two varieties of *aṛka* are commonly met with, one with white flowers *(Calotropis procera)* and the other with lilac, rosy or purple tinted flowers *(C.gigantea).* In Ayurvedic texts the white-flowered varieties called *aḷaṛka* are said to be of superior quality, though all the commentators are of the opinon that either of these can be used with equal effect, as both have the same properties.

Irrational use of *C. gigantea* can cause poisoning. This can be treated by giving one of the following internally

1. Fresh leaf juice of *Indigofera tinctoria (nīlamari)*
2. Sugar solution
3. Castor oil
4. Diluted leaf juice of *Tamarindus indica (puḷimaraṃ)*

Coll. No. AVS 1528

Calycopteris floribunda Lam.

Combretaceae : (हरीतकी–कुलम्)

Hin	:	Kōkkarai (कोक्करै)
Kan	:	Marsadabaguli (ಮರ್ಸದಬಗುಲಿ)
Mal	:	Pullāni, Varavaḷḷi (പുല്ലാനി, വരവള്ളി)
San	:	Suṣavī (सुषवी)
Tam	:	Minnāṛkoṭi (மின்னார்கொடி)
Tel	:	Banḍimuruduḍu (బండిమురుదుడు)

Distribution: Throughout India in deciduous forests in areas upto 750 m elevation, as well as along water courses and in waste lands

The plant: A scandent woody shrub with slender brown streaked diffuse branches occasionally twining around supports and storing water abundantly; leaves simple, opposite, elliptic or ovate, acute or acuminate, surfaces tomentose, main nerves 5–8 pairs; flowers yellowish green, apetalous, in fulvous pubescent terminal panicles, ovary 1-chambered with pendulous ovules; fruits 5-ribbed, one seeded , crowned with strongly 3-nerved persistent calyx lobes.

Parts used: leaves, fruits

Properties and uses: The leaves are bitter, astringent, laxative, anthelmintic, depurative, diaphoretic and febrifuge. They are useful in intestinal worms, colic, leprosy, malarial fever, dysentery, ulcers and vomiting. The fruits are useful in jaundice, ulcers, pruritus and skin diseases.

"सुषवीति तोयवल्ली पार्वत्या कथ्यते रजतवल्ली ।
अबला च राजवल्ली बृहल्लता सा बृहद्वल्ली" ॥ (अ.म.)
["Suṣavīti tōyavallī pārvatyā kathyatē rajatavallī
Abalā ca rājavallī bṛhallatā sā bṛhadvallī (A.ma.)]

"पलाशिका बृहद्वल्ली तोयवल्यफलापि च ।
कारवल्ली वारिवल्ली सुषवी सुकुमारिका ॥" (कै.नि.)
["Palāśikā bṛhadvallī tōyavalyaphalāpi ca
Kāravallī vārivallī suṣavī sukumārikā" (Kai.ni.)]

Calycopteris floribunda

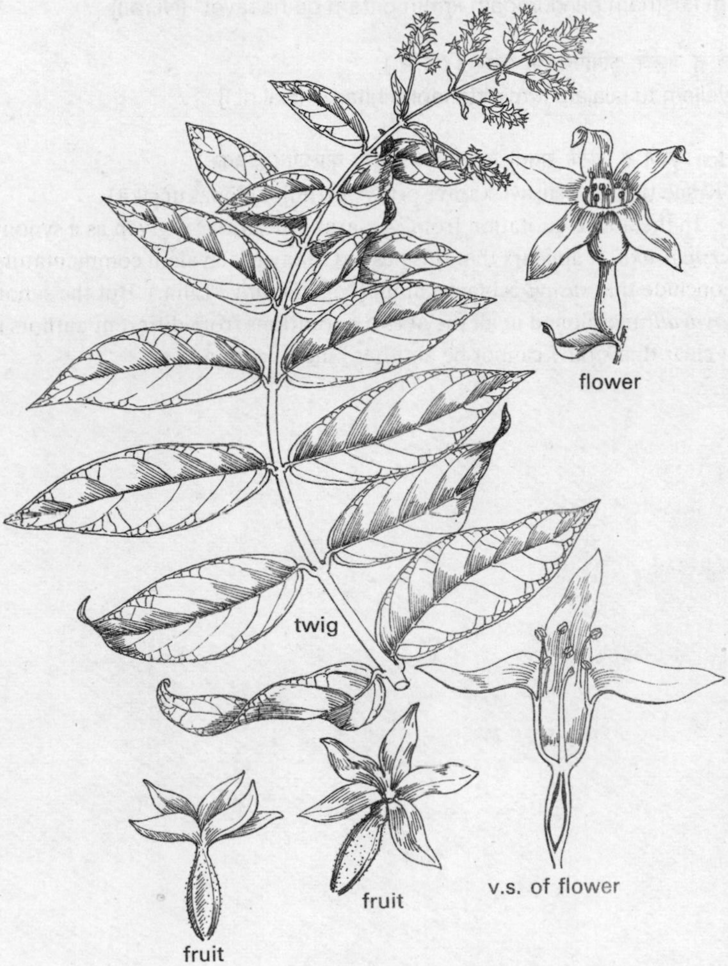

"कृमिपित्तहरा तिक्ता भेदिनी कफनाशिनी ।
पाण्डुकुष्ठविकारघ्नी कारवल्ली ज्वरापहा ॥" (म.नि.)
["Kṛmipittaharā tiktā bhēdinī kaphanāśinī
Pāṇḍukuṣṭhavikāraghnī kāravallī jvarāpahā (Ma.ni.)]

"जलजं कारवेल्लं स्यात् तिक्तं भेदकरं मतम् ।
कफं कुष्ठं पाण्डुरोगं कृमीन् पित्तं च नाशयेत् ॥" (नि.र.)
["Jalajaṃ kāravēllaṃ syāt tiktaṃ bhēdakaraṃ mataṃ
Kaphaṃ kuṣṭhaṃ pāṇḍurōgaṃ kṛmīn pittaṃ ca nāśayēt" (Ni.ra.)]

"कारवेल्लं तु जलजं कृमिपित्तकफे हितम् ।"(कै.नि.)
["Kāravēllaṃ tu jalajaṃ kṛmipittakaphē hitaṃ" (Kai.ni.)]

Remarks: "कृष्णे तु जीरके सुषवी कारवी पृथ्वी पृथुः कालोपकुञ्चिका ।
(Kṛṣṇē tu jīrakē suṣavī kāravī pṛthvī pṛthuḥ kālōpakuñcikā)

In the above quotation from 'Amarakosa' *suṣavī* is given as a synonym of *kṛṣṇajīrakā.* It appears that this has led many Malayalam commentators to conclude that *suṣavī* is black cumin (*Nigella sativa* Linn.). But the synonym *tōyavallī* mentioned in all the above quotations from different authors make it clear that *suṣavī* cannot be another kind of cumin.

Coll. No. AVS 2539

***Camellia sinensis* (Linn.) O.Kuntze**

(C.theifera *Griff.*)

Theaceae : (श्यामपर्णी–कुलम्)

Eng	:	Tea plant
Hin	:	Cāy (चाय)
Kan	:	Tēyāku (ತೇಯಾಕು)
Mal	:	Tēyila (തേയില)
San	:	Śyāmaparṇī, Cāhā (श्यामपर्णी, चाहा)
Tam	:	Tēyilai (தேயிலை)
Tel	:	Tēyāku (తేయాకు)

Distribution: Throughout India, cultivated at high altitudes

The plant: An evergreen shrub or tree, 9–15 m in height (60–150 cm in height owing to pruning in cultivation); leaves simple, alternate, elliptic-ovate or lanceolate with serrate margins, usually glabrous, leathery; flowers white, fragrant, solitary or 2–4 together; fruits depressed capsules, 3–cornered, 3–seeded.

Parts used: leaves

Properties and uses: The leaves are astringent, bitter, thermogenic, appetiser, digestive, carminative, diuretic, diaphoretic, detergent, resolvent and nervine tonic. They are useful in hyperdipsia, hemicrania, cardiodynia, ophthalmia, haemorrhoids, inflammations, abdominal disorders, strangury, fever and fatigue.

"चाहं तु चविका चाह" (शा.नि.)
["Cāhaṃ tu cavikā cāha" (Śā.ni.)]

"श्यामपर्णी श्यामका च श्यामा धात्रेयिका स्मृता ।
तौवरी मादकी चैव शीतहा प्रियमोदिका ॥"(स्व.)
["Śyāmaparṇī śyāmakā ca śyāmā dhāṭrēyikā smṛtā
Tauvarī mādakī caiva śītahā priyamōdikā" (Sva.)]

"तीक्ष्णोष्णा तुवरा चाहा दीपनी पाचनी लघुः ।
कफपित्तहरी चैव किञ्चिद्वातप्रकोपनी ॥"(शा.नि.)
["Tīkṣṇōṣṇā tuvarā cāhā dīpanī pācanī laghuḥ
Kaphapittaharī caiva kiñcidvātaprakōpanī" (Śā.ni.)]

Camellia sinensis

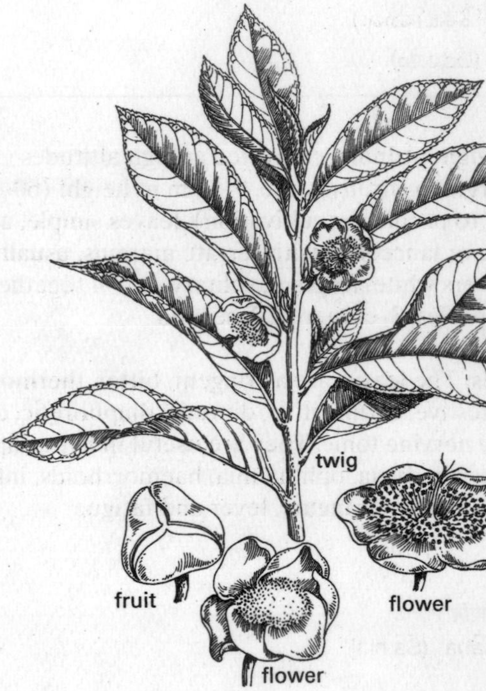

"श्यामपर्णी कषायोष्णा कटुका मूत्रळा लघुः ।
निद्राश्रमक्ळमहरा रुच्या दीपनपाचनी ।
तृष्णाहरा, चातियोगात् मदमोहादिकारिणी ॥"(स्व.)

["Śyāmaparṇī kaṣāyōṣṇā kaṭukā mūtraḷā laghuḥ
Nidrāśramakḷamaharā rucyā dīpanapācanī
Tṛṣṇāharā, cātiyōgāt madamōhādikāriṇī" (Sva.)]

Coll. No. AVS 1294

***Canavalia gladiata* (Jacq.)DC.**

(C.ensiformis *sensu Baker, non DC.*)

Fabaceae : (अपराजिता–कुलम्)

Eng	:	Sword bean, Broad bean, Patagonian bean
Hin	:	Lālkuḍusumpāl, Khaḍsampāl (लालकुडुसुम्पाल, खड़सम्पाल)
Kan	:	Tumbekonti, Sembi, Avare (ತುಂಬೆಕೊಂಟಿ, ಸೆಂಬಿ, ಅವರೆ)
Mal	:	Vāḷvara, Vāḷpayar, Vāḷamara (വാളവര, വാൾപയർ, വാളമര)
San	:	Asiśimbī, Mahāśimbī (असिशिम्बी, महाशिम्बी)
Tam	:	Śegapputampāṭṭai (செகப்புதம்பாட்டை)
Tel	:	Tamma, Karocikaḍu (తమ్మ, కరోచికడు)

Distribution: Throughout India, cultivated

The plant: A stout perennial twiner with glabrous stems and branches; leaves compound, leaflets membranous, acute or shortly acuminate, apiculate, base rounded, nearly glabrous on both surfaces; flowers large, white or lilac, in lax few-flowered curved axillary racemes; fruits large, sword shaped flattened pods, seeds reddish brown or white, strongly compressed.

Parts used: fruits

Properties and uses: The fruits are sweet, astringent, cooling, appetiser, digestive and vulnerary. They are useful in burning sensation, hyperdipsia, anorexia, dyspepsia, wounds, ulcers and vitiated conditions of *kapha* and *pitta.*

"असिशिम्बी खड्गशिम्बी शिम्बी निस्त्रिंशशिम्बिका ।
स्थूलशिम्बी महाशिम्बी बृहच्छिम्बी सुशिम्बिका ॥" (रा.नि.)
["Asiśimbī khaḍgaśimbī śimbī nistriṃśaśimbikā
Sthūlaśimbī mahāśimbī bṛhacchimbī suśimbikā" (Rā.ni.)]

"असिशिम्बी खड्गशिम्बी बृहच्छिम्बी च खड्गिनी ।
स्थूनशिम्बी महाशिम्बी दीर्घनिष्पाविका स्मृता ॥
रक्तबीजा श्वेतबीजा द्विधा साऽपि प्रकीर्तिता ।" (स्व.)
["Asiśmbī khaḍgaśimbī bṛhacchimbī ca khaḍginī
Sthūlaśimbī mahāśimbī dīrghaniṣpāvikā smṛtā
Raktabījā śvētabījā dvidhā sāʃpi prakīrttitā" (Sva.)]

Canavalia gladiata

Plate 17

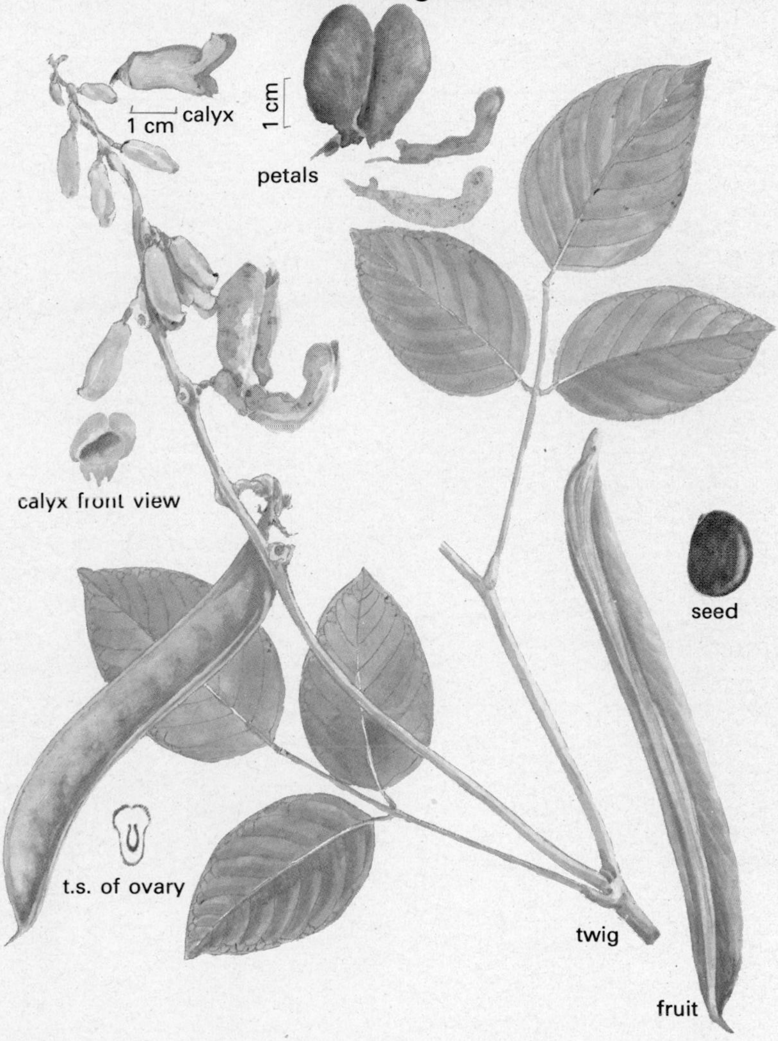

"असिशिम्बी तु मधुरा कषाया श्ळेष्मपित्तजित् ।
व्रर्णदोषापहन्त्री च शीतळा रुचिदीपनी ॥" (रा.नि.)
["Asiśimbī tu madhurā kaṣāyā śḷēṣmapittajit
Vṛaṇadōṣāpahantrī ca śītaḷā rucidīpanī "(Rā.ni.)]

"रुच्या सा शाकमुख्या च ,निष्पावसदृशा गुणैः ॥ " (स्व.)
["Rucyā sā śākamukhyā ca niṣpāvasadṛśā guṇaiḥ" (Sva.)]

Coll. No. AVS 2168

***Cannabis sativa* Linn.**

Cannabinaceae : (भङ्गा–कुलम्)

Eng	:	True hemp, Soft hemp, Indian hemp
Hin	:	Bhang, Gañjā, Caras (भङ्ग, गञ्जा, चरस)
Kan	:	Bhangi (ಭಂಗಿ)
Mal	:	Kañcāvu̥, Śivamūli (കഞ്ചാവ്, ശിവമൂലി)
San	:	Bhangā (भङ्गा)
Tam	:	Gañcā, Bhāmgī (கஞ்சா, பாம்கீ)
Tel	:	Ganjāyi (గంజాయి)

Distribution: Throughout India, wild (North west Himalayas) as well as cultivated

The plant: A large aromatic resinous annual herb 1.2–4.8 m in height with erect angular stem, the female plant usually taller than the male; leaves palmately divided, lower 3–8 foliate with long petioles, upper 3–1 foliate passing into bracts; male flowers in short drooping panicles, females in short axillary crowded spikes; fruits achenes seeds black, flattened.

Parts used: dried leaves and flowering shoots

Properties and uses: Leaves are bitter, astringent, tonic, aphrodisiac, antidiarrhoeic, intoxicating, stomachic, analgesic and abortifacient. They are used in convulsions, otalgia, abdominal disorders, diarrhoea, somatalgia and haematorrhoea. Its excessive use causes dyspepsia, cough, impotence, melancholy, dropsy, hyperpraxia and insanity. The bark is tonic, and is useful in inflammations, haemorrhoids and hydrocele. Seeds are carminative, astringent, aphrodisiac, antiemetic and anti-inflammatory.

"भङ्गा गञ्जा मातुलानी मादनी विजया जया।" (भा.प्र.)
["Bhangā gañjā mātulāni mādanī vijayā jayā" (Bhā.pra.)]

"विजया रञ्जिका भङ्गा तन्द्राकृद् बहुवादिनी ।
मादिनी मादिका मातुः प्रोक्ता गञ्चाकिनिस्तथा ॥" (ध.नि.)
["Vijayā rañjikā bhangā tandrākr̥d bahuvādinī
Mādinī mādikā mātuḥ pr̥ōktā gañcākinistathā" (Dha.ni.)]

Cannabis sativa

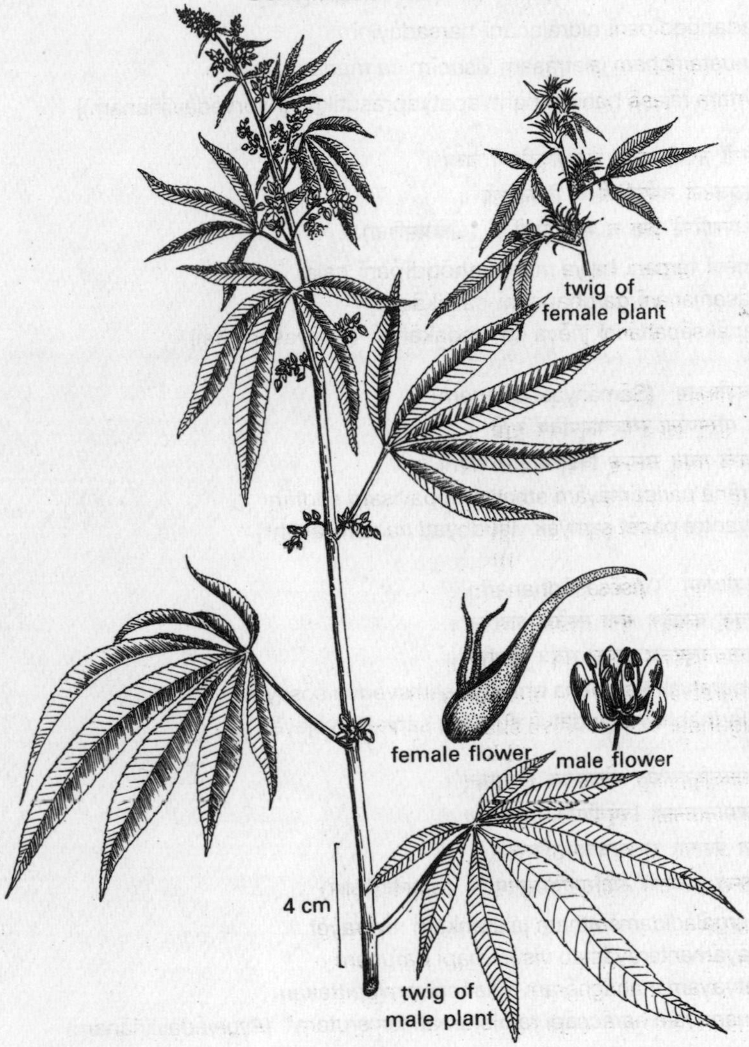

"भङ्गा कफहरी तिक्ता ग्राहिणी पाचनी लघुः ।
तीक्ष्णोष्णा पित्तळा मोदमदवाग्वह्निवर्धनी ॥" (भा.प्र., घ.नि.)
["Bhangā kaphaharī tiktā grāhiṇī pācanī laghuḥ
Tīkṣṇōṣṇā pittaḷā mōdamadavāgvahnivaṛdhanī" (Bhā.pṛa.,Dha.ni.)]

"मदनोद्दीपनी निद्राजननी हर्षदायिनी ।
धनुस्तंभं जलत्रासं विषूचीं च मदात्ययम् ॥
प्रवृत्तिं राजसो बह्विं हन्त्यपत्यप्रसूतिकृत् ।" (आयुर्वेदविज्ञानम्)
["Madanōddīpanī nidrājananī haṛṣadāyinī
Dhanustambhaṃ jalatṛāsaṃ viṣūcīṃ ca madātyayaṃ
Pṛavṛttiṃ rājasō bahviṃ hantyapatyapṛasūtikṛt" (Āyuṛvēdavijñānaṃ)]

"आग्नेयी तर्पणी बल्या मन्मथोद्दीपनी चला ।
निद्रासञ्जननी गर्भपातिनी च विकाषिणी ॥
वेदनाक्षेपहारिणी ज्ञेया च मदकारिणी ।" (आत्रेयसंहिता)
["Āgnēyī taṛpaṇī balyā manmathōddīpanī calā
Nidrāsañjananī gaṛbhapātinī ca vikāṣiṇī
Vēdanākṣēpahāriṇī jñēyā ca madakāriṇī" (Ātṛēyasamhitā)]

सामान्यशोधनम् (Sāmānyaśōdhanaṃ)
क्षीरेण परिपूर्णायां स्थाल्यामुपविषं सुधीः ।
डोळायन्त्रे पचेत् सम्यक् विशुध्यति न संशयः ॥
["Kṣīrēṇa paripūṛṇāyāṃ sthālyāmupaviṣaṃ sudhīḥ
Ḍōḷāyantṛē pacēt samyak viśudhyati na samśayaḥ"]

विशेषशोधनम् (Viśēṣaśōdhanaṃ)
"बर्बरत्वक् कषायेण भंगा संस्वेद्य शोषयेत् ।
गोदुग्धभावनाद्दत्वा शुष्कां सर्वत्र योजयेत् ॥"
["Baṛbaratvak kaṣāyēṇa bhamgā samsvēdya śōṣayēt
Gōdugdhabhāvanāddatvā śuṣkaṃ saṛvatṛa yōjayēt]

"श्वशृगालादिदंशोत्थं जलातङ्कं निवारयेत् ।
बाह्यायामान्तरायामौ विषूचीमपि दारुणम् ॥
मदात्ययं महाघोरं शूलञ्चैवाम्ळपित्तकम् ।
अग्निमान्द्यं हरेच्चापि रजोऽस्रमतिसंस्रुतम् ॥" (आयुर्वेदविज्ञानं)
["Śvaśṛgālādidamśōtthaṃ jalātankaṃ nivārayēt
Bāhyāyāmāntarāyāmau viṣūcīmapi dāruṇaṃ
Madātyayaṃ mahāghōraṃ śūlañcaivāmḷapittakaṃ
Agnimāndyaṃ harēccāpi rajōऽsṛamatisamsṛutaṃ" (Āyuṛvēdavijñānaṃ)

"भङ्गा क्षुद्दीपनी चैव ध्वजभङ्गहरा परम् ।
स्वप्नमेहहरा चैव शुक्ळस्तंभनकारिणी ॥
निद्राप्रदायिनी कामं कामोद्दीपनकारिणी ।
प्रलापनाशिका चैव घनुःस्तंभहरा तथा ॥

अन्नशूलहरा चैव वृक्कशूलप्रणाशिनी ।
पित्तदोषजशूलघ्नी त्वामाशयबलप्रदा ॥
अजीर्णजातिसारघ्नी तथाजीर्णनिवारिणी ।
उन्मादनाशिनी चैव वृक्कशोफव्यथाहरा ॥
मूत्रळा रक्तसंयुक्तमूत्रस्रावनिवारिका ।
विचित्रानन्दजननी स्वप्नसन्तानकारिका ॥
अर्शोव्यथाहरा चैव किञ्चिज्जरनिवारिका ।
व्रणमेहसमुद्भूतशिश्नशोफव्यथाहरा ॥
नाडीदौर्बल्यसंभूतं तथाक्षेपसमुत्थितम् ।
रजःशूलं निहन्त्याशु भास्करस्तिमिरं यथा ॥
आमाशयोत्थशूलघ्नी यक्ष्मकासहरा परम् ।
वस्त्याक्षेपहरा चैव साक्षेपतमकापहा ॥
दारुणाक्षेपसंयुक्तमतिकष्टप्रदायिनम् ।
परं सङ्क्रामकं कासं विनिहन्ति विशेषतः ॥ "(भा.प्र.नि.)

["Bhangā kṣuddīpanī caiva dhvajabhangaharā paraṃ
Svapnamēhaharā caiva śukḷastambhanakāriṇī
Nidrāpṛadāyinī kāmaṃ kāmōddīpanakāriṇī
Pṛalāpanāśikā caiva dhanuḥstambhaharā tathā
Annaśūlaharā caiva vṛkkaśūlapṛaṇāśinī
Pittadōṣajaśūlaghnī tvāmāśayabalapṛadā
Ajīṛṇajātisāraghnī tathājīṛṇanivāriṇī
Unmādanāśinī caiva vṛkkaśōphavyadhāharā
Mūtṛaḷā raktasamyuktamūtṛasṛāvanivarikā
Vicitṛanandajananī svapnasantanakārikā
Aṛśōvyathāharā caiva kiñcijjaranivārikā
Vṛaṇamēhasamudbhūtaśiśnaśōphavyathāharā
Nāḍīdaurbalyasambhūtaṃ tathākṣēpasamutthitaṃ
Rajaḥśūlaṃ nihantyāśu bhāskarastimiraṃ yathā
Amāśayōtthaśūlaghnī yakṣmakāsaharā paraṃ
Vastyākṣēpaharā caiva sākṣēpatamakāpahā
Dāruṇākṣēpasamyuktamatikaṣṭapṛadāyinaṃ
Paraṃ sankṛāmakaṃ kāsaṃ vinihanti viśēṣataḥ" (Bhā.pṛa.ni.)]

भङ्गसेवनविधिः–(Bhangasēvanavidhiḥ)
"विजयाबीजचूर्णस्य भक्षणं विधिना प्रिये।
सर्वोपकारकं तत्तु सर्वरोगापहारकम् ॥
परिपक्वानि बीजानि वृक्षादानीय यत्नतः ।
छायायां पातयेद्रक्षेद्भक्षयेत् कर्षमात्रकम् ॥
कपिलापयसा सार्धं मासमात्रं वरानने ।
धातुवृद्धिर्भवेत्तस्य चान्त्रवृद्धिर्विनश्यति ॥
मांसदार्ढ्यं वसादार्ढ्यं देहदार्ढ्यं भवेत् प्रिये ॥
अग्निदीप्तिर्मनोदीप्तिः कामदीप्तिस्तथैव च।
प्रज्ञादीप्तिर्दृष्टिदीप्तिर्दीप्तीनां पञ्चकं भवेत् ॥ (भा.प्र.नि)

["Vijayābījacūrṇasya bhakṣaṇaṃ vidhinā priyē
Saṛvōpakārakaṃ tattu saṛvarōgāpahārakaṃ
Paripakvāni bījāni vṛkṣādānīya yatnataḥ
Chāyāyāṃ pātayēdrakṣēdbhakṣayēt kaṛṣamātṛakaṃ
Kapilāpayasā sāṛdhaṃ māsamātṛaṃ varānanē
Dhātuvṛddhiṛbhavēttasya cāntṛavṛddhiṛvinaśyati
Māṃsadāṛḍhyaṃ vasādāṛḍhyaṃ dēhadāṛḍhyaṃ bhavēt priyē
Agnidīptiṛmanōdīptiḥ kāmadīptistathaiva ca
Pṛajñādīptiṛdṛṣṭidiptiṛdīptīnāṃ pañcakaṃ bhavēt" (Bhā.pṛa.ni.)]

Remarks: The narcotic drugs Bhang or Hasish, Ganja and Charas are the dried flowering and fruiting tops of the pistillate plants of *Cannabis sativa* from which no resin has been removed. Bhang, Siddhi, Sabji or Patti are the other names of this product.

The use of hemp resin for narcotic and sedative purposes affects the cerebrum of a person and can make him lose his self-control. In larger doses, they produce coma and death from cardiac failure.

Canscora decussata (Roxb.)Schult.

Gentianaceae : (त्रायमाणा–कुलम्)

Eng	:	Canscora
Hin	:	Śaṁkhaphūli (शंखफूलि)
Kan	:	Śankinisoppu (ಶಂಕಿನಿಸೊಪ್ಪು)
Mal	:	Śaṁkhapuṣpī, Kañcankora (ശംഖപുഷ്പി, കഞ്ചൻകൊാര)
San	:	Śaṅkhinī, Śaṅkhapuṣpī (शङ्खिनी, शङखपुष्पी)
Tel	:	Kancakūra (కచకూర)

Distribution: Throughout India,in moist areas upto 1,500 m elevation

The plant: An erect dichotomously branched annual upto 60 cm in height with 4-winged stems and decussate branches; leaves simple, ovate or lanceolate, acute, sessile, upto 5 cm long, prominently 3-nerved; flowers white, those in the forks, long pedicelled lax terminal dichasial cymes; fruits cylindric membranous septicidal capsules; seeds very small, brown, reticulate.

Parts used: whole plant

Properties and uses: The plant is bitter, acrid, astringent, thermogenic, laxative, vulnerary, emollient, alexeteric, anthelmintic, appetiser, intellect promoting, aphrodisiac, depurative, rejuvenating and tonic. It is useful in vitiated conditions of *kapha,* inflammation, ascites, abdominal disorders, intestinal worms, insanity, epilepsy, nervous debility, forgetfulness, leucoderma, leprosy, skin diseases, tuberculosis, ulcers and general debility.

"शङ्खपुष्पी कम्बुपुष्पी शङ्खाह्वा कम्बुमालिनी ।
तिलकी शङ्खकुसुमा मेध्या वनविलासिनी ॥" (ध.नि.)
["Śaṅkhapuṣpī kaṁbupuṣpī śaṅkhāhvā kaṁbumālinī
Tilakī śaṅkhakusumā mēdhyā vanavilāsinī" (Dha.ni.)]

"शङ्खपुष्पी क्षीरपुष्पी कम्बुपुष्पी मनोरमा ॥
शिवब्राह्मी भूतिलता किरीटी कम्बुमालिका ।
माङ्गल्यपूष्पी शङ्खाह्वा मेध्या वनविलासिनी ॥" (कै.नि.)

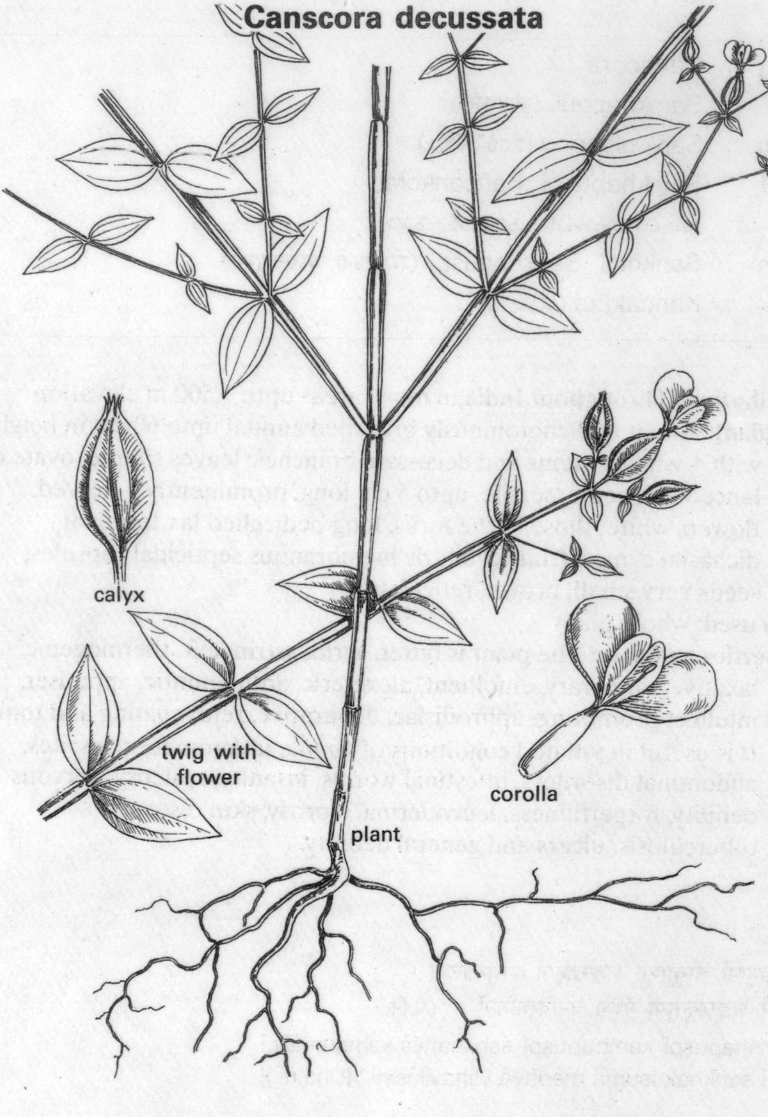
Canscora decussata
calyx
twig with flower
corolla
plant

["Śaṅkhapuṣpī kṣīrapuṣpī kaṁbupuṣpī manōramā
Śivabrāhmī bhūtilatā kirītī kaṁbumālikā
Māṅgalyapuṣpī śaṅkhāhvā mēdhyā vanavilāsinī" (Kai.ni.)]

"शङ्खपुष्पी तु शङ्खाह्वा माङ्गल्यकुसुमापि च।" (भा.प्र.)
["Śaṅkhapuṣpī tu śaṅkhāhvā māṅgalyakusumāpi ca" (Bhā.pra.)]

"शङ्खपुष्पी सुपुष्पी च शङ्खाह्वा कम्बुमालिनी ।
सितपुष्पी कम्बुपुष्पी मेध्या वनविलासिनी ॥
चिरिण्टी शङ्खकुसुमा भूलग्ना शङ्खमालिनी ।
इत्येषा शङ्खपुष्पी स्यादुक्ता द्वादशनामभिः ॥" (रा.नि.)
["Śaṅkhapuṣpī supuṣpī ca śaṅkhāvā kaṁbumālinī
Sitapuṣpī kaṁbupuṣpī mēdhyā vanavilāsinī
Ciriṇṭī śaṅkhakusumā bhūlagnā śaṅkhamālinī
Ityēṣā śaṅkhapuṣpī syāduktā dvādaśanāmabhiḥ (Rā.ni.)]

शङ्खपुष्पी सरा मेध्या वृष्या मानसरागहृत् ॥
रसायनी कषायोष्णा स्मृतिकान्तिबलाग्निदा ।
दोषापस्मारभूताश्रीकुष्ठकृमिविषप्रणुत् ॥ (भा.प्र.)
["Śaṅkhapuṣpī sarā mēdhyā vṛṣyā mānasarōgahṛt
Rasāyanī kaṣāyōṣṇā smṛtikāntibalāgnidā
Dōṣāpasmārabhūtāśrīkuṣṭhakṛmiviṣapraṇut" (Bhā.pra.)]

"शङ्खपुष्पी कषायोष्णा कफकुष्ठविनाशिनी ।
रसायनी सरा दिव्या लालाहृल्लासजूर्त्तिहा ।
लक्ष्मी मेधा बलाग्नीनां वर्धिनी कथिता बुधैः ॥
शुभ्रा च शङ्खिनी मेध्या शीतळा वश्यसिद्धिदा ।
रसायनी सरा स्वर्या किञ्चिदुष्णा च तूवरा ॥
स्मृतिकान्तिबलाग्नीनां वर्धिनी कटुका मता ।
पाचकायुःस्थिरकरी मङ्गल्या पित्तनाशिनी ॥
विषदोषमपस्मारं कफं कृमि विषं हरेत् ।
कुष्ठलूतात्रिदोषघ्नी ग्रहदोषस्य नाशिनी ॥" (नि.र.)
["Śaṅkhapuṣpī kaṣāyōṣṇā kaphakuṣṭhavināśinī
Rasāyanī sarā divyā lālāhṛllāsajūrttihā
Lakṣmī mēdhā balāgnīnāṃ vardhinī kathitā budhaiḥ
Subhrā ca śaṅkhinī mēdhyā śītaḷā vaśyasiddhidā
Rasāyanī sarā svaryā kiñciduṣṇā ca tūvarā
Smṛtikāntibalāgnīnāṃ vardhinī kaṭukā matā
Pācakāyuḥsthirakarī mangalyā pittanāśinī
Viṣadōṣamapasmāraṃ kaphaṃ kṛmi viṣaṃ harēt
Kuṣṭhalūtātridōṣaghnī grahadōṣasya nāśinī" (Ni.ra.)]

"शङ्खिनी कटुतिक्तोष्णा कासपित्तवलासजित् ।

विषापस्मारभूतादीन् हन्ति मेध्या रसायनी ॥" (ध.नि.)
["Śaṅkhinī kaṭutiktōṣṇā kāsapittavalāsajit
Viṣāpasmārabhūtādīn hanti mēdhyā rasāyanī" (Dha.ni.)]

"शङ्खपुष्पी हिमा तिक्ता मेधाकृत् स्वरकारिणी ।
ग्रहभूतादिदोषघ्नी वशीकरणसिद्धदा ॥" (रा.नि.)
["Śaṅkhapuṣpī himā tiktā mēdhākṛt svarakāriṇī
Grahabhūtādidōṣaghnī vaśīkaraṇasiddhidā" (Rā.ni.)]

"शङ्खपुष्पी सरा स्वर्या कटुतिक्ता रसायनी ।
अनुष्णा वर्णमेधाग्नि वलायुः कान्तिदा हरेत् ॥
दोषापस्मारलूता स्त्री कुष्ठभूतविष कृमीन् ।" (कै.नि.)
["Śaṅkhapuṣpī sarā svaryā kaṭutiktā rasāyanī
Anuṣṇā varṇamēdhagnibalāyuḥ kāntidā harēt ||
Dōṣāpasmāralūtāstrīkuṣṭhabhūtaviṣakṛmīn" (Kai.ni.)]

"शङ्खपुष्पी सरा मेध्योन्मादच्छर्दि विषापहा ।
कासमर्दस्त्रिदोषघ्नः स्वादुः कण्ढयोऽन्नपाचनः ॥
सतिक्तः कासविध्वंसी रेचनः कृमिनाशनः ।" (सो.नि.)
["Śaṅkhapuṣpī sarā mēdhyōnmādacchaṛddiviṣāpahā
Kạsamaṛdastṛidōṣaghnaḥ svāduḥ kaṇḍhayōऽ nnapācanaḥ
Satiktaḥ kāsavidhvaṁsī rēcanaḥ kṛmināśanaḥ" (Sō.ni.)]

"शङ्खपुष्पी सराऽऽयुष्या मेध्या मानसरोगहृत् ।
रसायनी कषायोष्णा स्मृतिकान्ति बलाग्निदा ॥
कटुका शीतळा स्वर्या कुष्ठकृमिविषप्रणुत् ।
पाचकायुः स्थिरकरी माङ्गल्या पित्तनाशिनी ॥
लूतापस्मारदोषघ्नी ग्रहदोषस्य नाशिनी ।
सर्वोपद्रवहा प्रोक्ता पुष्पैर्भेदा गुणैः समाः॥" (शा.नि.)
["Śaṅkhapuṣpī saraऽऽyuṣyā mēdhyā mānasarōgahṛt
Rasāyanī kaṣāyōṣṇā smṛtikantibalāgnidā
Kaṭukā śītaḷā svaryā kuṣṭhakṛmiviṣapraṇut
Pāckāyuḥsthirakarī māṅgalyā pittanāśinī
Lūtāpasmāradōṣaghnī grahadōṣasyanāśinī
Saṛvōpadravahā pṛōktā puṣpaiṛbhēdā guṇaiḥ samāḥ" (Śā.ni.)]

Remarks: In Ayurvedic dictionaries the botanical name given for *śaṅkhapuṣpī* is *Convolvulus pluricaulis.* 'The Ayurvedic Formulary of India' also identifies this plant as the same, and also adds that *Evolvulus alsinoides* and *Clitoria ternatea* can be used as substitutes. Also, except for the commentary on 'Rājanighaṇṭu', all other publications do not mention *Canscora decussata.*

However, *Convolvulus pluricaulis* does not find a mention as a medicinal plant in the 'Indian Medicinal Plants' or 'Glossary of Indian Medicinal Plants' or 'Wealth of India'. Therefore, it seems that it is unwise to use *Convolvulus pluricaulis* for the drug *śaṅkhapuṣpī.*

Clitoria ternatea is the drug commonly used in Kerala in all medical preparations wherever the names *śaṅkhinī* and *śaṅkhapuṣpī* occur (refer *Clitoria ternatea*).

Coll. No. AVS 2394

***Canthium parviflorum* Lam.**

Rubiaceae : (मञ्जिष्ठा–कुलम्)

Eng	:	Carray cheddie
Hin	:	Kirmā, Kadbar (किरमा, कदबर)
Kan	:	Kākegida (ಕಾಕೆಗಿಡ)
Mal	:	Ceṛukāra, Kaṇṭaṅkāra, Kāramuḷḷu, Kāra (ചെറുകാര, കണ്ടങ്കാര, കാരമുള്ള്, കാര)
San	:	Gāṅgērukī, Chāyātiniśaḥ (गाङ्गेरुकी, छायातिनिशः)
Tam	:	Kāraicceṭi (காரைச்செடி)
Tel	:	Balusu (బలుసు)

Distribution: Throughout India,in scrub forests and dry plains

The plant: A thorny subscandent shrub with spreading branches; leaves simple, small, opposite with interpetiolar stipules and axillary spines; flowers yellowish white, 4-merous, small, in axillary cymes, corolla tube short; fruits oblong-ellipsoid or compressed drupes, yellow when ripe.

Parts used: roots, leaves

Properties and uses: The roots and leaves are astringent, sweet, thermogenic, diuretic, febrifuge, constipating, anthelmintic and tonic. They are useful in vitiated conditions of *kapha,* diarrhoea, strangury, fever, leucorrhoea, intestinal worms and general debility.

"गाङ्गेरुकी कर्णवेधी दीर्घकण्टा च मोदका ।
कोरण्टकी कीटमारी छायातिनिश इत्यपि ॥" (स्व.)
["Gāṅgērukī karṇavēdhī dīrghakaṇṭā ca mōdakā
Kōraṇṭakī kīṭamārī chāyātiniśa ityapi" (Sva.)]

"गाङ्गेरुकी कषायोष्णा मधुरा ग्रहि मूत्रळा
कफातिसारशमनी कृमिकृच्छ्रज्वरापहम् ॥ " (स्व.)
["Gāṅgērukī kaṣāyōṣṇā madhurā grāhi mūtraḷā
Kaphātisāraśamanī kṛmikṛcchrajvarāpahaṃ" (Sva.)]

Canthium parviflorum

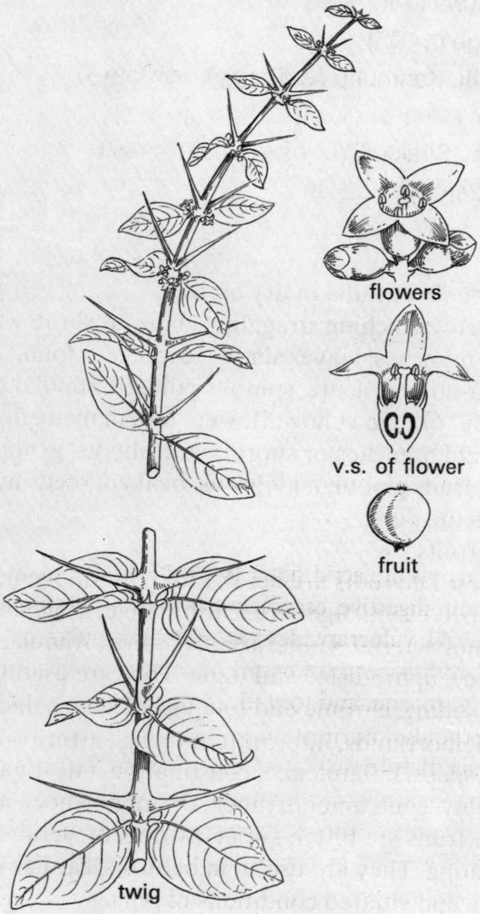

Capparis decidua (Forsk.) Edgew.

(C. aphylla *Roth.*)

Capparaceae : (करीर–कुलम्)

Eng	:	Caper plant
Hin	:	Karīl, Kurēl (करील, कुरेल)
Kan	:	Nispaṭīge (ನಿಸ್ಪಟಿಗೆ)
Mal	:	Karimuḷḷi, Karimuḷḷụ (കരിമുള്ളി, കരിമുള്ള്)
San	:	Karīraḥ (करीरः)
Tam	:	Śeṅkaṃ, Śirakkali (செங்கம், சிரக்கலி)
Tel	:	Ēnugadanta (ఏనుగదంత)

Distribution: Throughout India,in dry areas

The plant: A densely branching straggling glabrous shrub with smooth terete green branches; leaves simple, caducous, found only on young shoots, linear-oblong, acute, spinous pointed, stipular thorns long, sharp, straight, orange yellow; flowers red, in many flowered corymbs on old branches or short lateral shoots, gynophore about 12 mm long; fruits globular, glabrous, beaked; seeds numerous embedded in the pulp.

Parts used: roots, fruits

Properties and uses: The roots are acrid, bitter, thermogenic, anodyne, sudorific, expectorant, digestive, carminative, anthelmintic, purgative, antibacterial, vulnerary, alexeteric, stimulant, emmenagogue, aphrodisiac and tonic. They are useful in boils, eruptions, swelling, chronic and foul ulcers, cough, hiccough, asthma, vomiting, haemorrhoids, intermittent fevers, arthritis, odontalgia, lumbago, dyspepsia, flatulence, constipation, intestinal worms, cardiac debility, gout, amenorrhoea, dysmenorrhoea and general debility. The fruits are bitter, sweet, astringent, acrid, thermogenic and constipating. They are useful in halitosis, cardiac disorders, urethrorrhea and vitiated conditions of *pitta.*

"करीरो गूढपत्रश्च शाकपुष्पो मृदुफलः ।
ग्रन्थिलस्तीक्ष्णसारश्च क्रकचस्तीक्ष्णकण्टकः ॥" (ध.नि.)
["Karīrō gūḍhapatraśca śākapuṣpō mṛduphalaḥ
Granthilastīkṣṇasāraśca krakacastīkṣṇakaṇṭakaḥ" (Dha.ni.)]

Capparis decidua

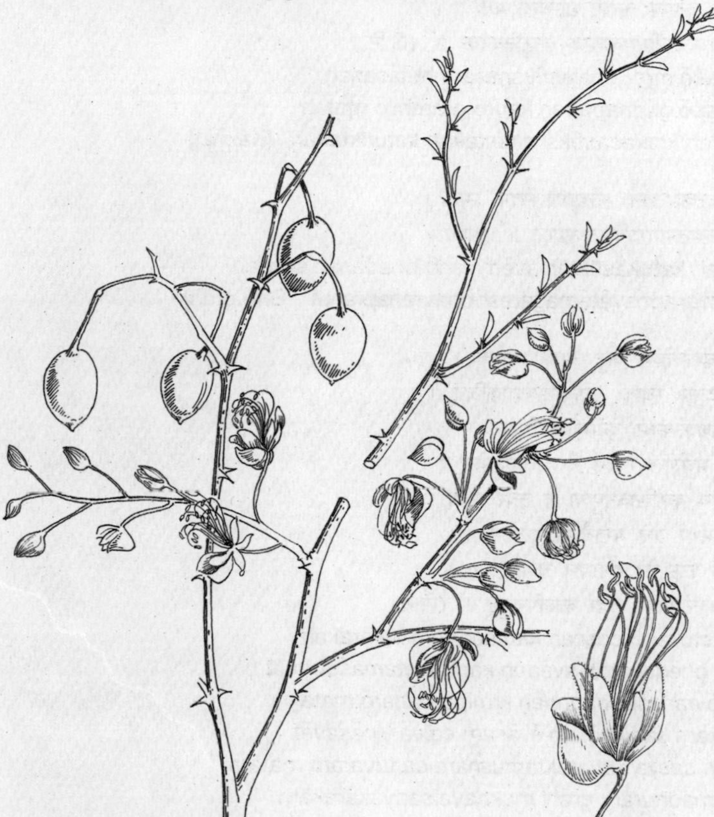

"निष्पत्रकः करीरश्च करीरः ग्रन्थिलस्तथा ।
क्रकरो गूढपत्रश्च करकस्तीक्ष्णकण्टकः ॥" (रा.नि.)
["Niṣpatṛakaḥ karīraśca karīraḥ granthilastathā
Kṛakarō gūḍhapatṛaśca karakastīkṣṇakaṇṭakaḥ" (Rā.ni.)]

"करीरः क्रकरीपत्रो ग्रन्थिलो मरुभूरुहः ।" (भा.प्र.)
["Karīraḥ kṛakarīpatṛō granthilō marubhūruhaḥ" (Bhā.pṛa.)]

"करीरको मृदुफलस्तीक्ष्णसारो हुताशनः ।
शाकपुष्पो गूढपत्रः करीरो ग्रन्थिलो मतः ॥
सुफलः क्रकचस्तीक्ष्णकण्टकः कटुतिक्तकः ॥" (कै.नि.)
["Karīrakō mṛduphalastīkṣṇasārō hutāśanaḥ
Sākpuṣpō gūḍhapatṛaḥ karīrō granthilō mataḥ
Suphalaḥ kṛakacastīkṣṇakaṇṭakaḥ kaṭutiktakaḥ" (Kai.ni.)]

"करीरः कटुकस्तिक्तः स्वेद्युष्णो भेदनः स्मृतः ।
दुर्नामकफवातामगरशोफव्रणप्रणुत् ॥" (भा.प्र.)
["Karīraḥ kaṭukastiktaḥ svēdyuṣṇō bhēdanaḥ smṛtaḥ
Duṛnāmakaphavātāmagaraśōphavṛaṇapṛaṇut" (Bhā.pṛa.)]

"करीरस्तुवरश्चोष्णः कटुश्चाध्मानकारकः ।
रुच्यो भेदकरः स्वादुः कफवातामशोफजित् ॥
विषार्शोव्रणशोफघ्नः कृमिपामाहरो मतः ।
अरोचकं सर्वशूलं श्वासं चैव विनाशयेत् ॥
फलं चास्य कटुस्तिक्तमुष्णं च तुवरं मतम् ।
विकाषि मधुरं ग्रहि मुखवैशद्यकारकम् ॥
हृद्यं रूक्षं कफं मेहं दुर्नामानं च नाशयेत् ॥
पुष्पं वातकरं प्रोक्तं तुवरं कफपित्तनुत् ॥" (नि.र.)
[Karīrastuvaraścōṣṇaḥ kaṭuścādhmānkārakaḥ
Rucyō bhēdakaraḥ svāduḥ kaphavātāmaśōphajit
Viṣāṛśōvṛaṇaśōphaghnaḥ kṛmipāmāharō mataḥ
Arōcakaṃ saṛvaśūlaṃ śvāsaṃ caiva vināśayēt
Phalaṃ cāsya kaṭustiktamuṣṇaṃ ca tuvaraṃ mataṃ
Vikāṣi madhuraṃ grāhi mukhavaiśadyakārakaṃ
Hṛdyaṃ rūkṣaṃ kaphaṃ mēhaṃ duṛnāmānaṃ ca nāśayēt
Puṣpaṃ vātakaraṃ pṛōktaṃ tuvaraṃ kaphapittanut" (Ni.ra.)]

"वातश्ळेष्महरं रुच्यं कटूष्णं गुदकीलजित् ।
करीरमाध्मानकरं रुचिकृत् स्वादुतिक्तकम् ॥" (ध.नि.)
["Vātaśḷēṣmaharaṃ rucyaṃ kaṭūṣnaṃ gudakīlajit
Karīramadhmānakaraṃ rucikṛt svādutiktakaṃ" (Dha.ni.)]

"करीरमाध्मानकरं कषायं
कटूष्णमेतत् कफहारि भूरि ।

श्वासानिलाऽरोचक सर्वशूल–
विच्छर्दिखर्जूव्रणदोषहारी ॥" (रा.नि.)
[Karīramādhmānakaraṃ kaṣāyaṃ
kaṭūṣṇamētat kaphahāri bhūri
Śvāsānilāऽrōckasarvaśūla -
vicchardikharjūvraṇadoṣahārī" (Rā.ni.)]

"करीरः कटुकस्तिक्तः स्वेद्युष्णो भेदनो जयेत् ।
दुर्नामकफवातामगरशोफकृमिव्रणान् ॥
तस्य पुष्पं तु तुवरं वातकृत् कफपित्तजित् ॥
फलं तिक्तं कषायोष्णं कटुकं रसपाकयोः ॥
विकाषि मधुरं रूक्षं सङ्ग्राहि कफपित्तजित् ॥" (कै.नि.)
["Karīraḥ kaṭukastiktaḥ svēdyuṣṇō bhēdanō jayēt
Durṇāmakaphavātāmagaraśōphakṛmivraṇān
Taśya puṣpaṃ tu tuvaraṃ vātakṛt kaphapittajit
Phalaṃ tiktaṃ kaṣāyōṣṇaṃ kaṭukaṃ rasapākayōḥ
Vikāṣi madhuraṃ rūkṣaṃ sangrāhi kaphapittajit" (Kai.ni.)]

"करीरो व्रणशोफार्शोरक्तहृत् कफवातजित् ।
कटुपाकरसोऽत्युष्णो यकृत्प्लीहापहोऽग्निकृत् ॥
तत्पुष्पं कफवातघ्नं कटुपाकरसं लघु ।
सृष्टमूत्रपुरीषं च सदा पथ्यं रुचिप्रदम् ॥
करीरं कटुकं पाके श्ळेष्मजित् सृष्टमूत्रविट् ।
कषायं वातळं तिक्तं तत्पक्वं कफपित्तजित् ॥" (सो.नि.)
["Karīrō vraṇaśōphārśōraktahṛt kaphavātajit
Kaṭupākarasōऽtyuṣṇō yakṛtplīhāpahōऽgnikṛt
Tatpuṣpaṃ kaphavātaghnaṃ kaṭupākarasaṃ laghu
Sṛṣṭamūtrapurīṣaṃ ca sadā pathyaṃ rucipradaṃ
Karīraṃ kaṭukaṃ pākē ślēṣmajit sṛṣṭamūtraviṭ
Kaṣāyaṃ vātaḷaṃ tiktaṃ tatpakvaṃ kaphapittajit" (Sō.ni.)]

Remarks: The word *karīra* is mentioned in `*Śākavarga*' of 'Aṣṭāṅgahṛdayaṃ Sūtrasthānaṃ ' Sri Vasudevan Moosad in his `Leelaplavam' Commentary gives the Malayalam as *agasti* for this *karīra.* But usually *karīra* is known in Malayalam as *āṇṭānmuḷa, muḷaṁukūṁpu,* and *karimuḷḷi* (*karimuḷḷu*).

"वंशाङ्कुरे करीरोऽस्त्री वृक्षभिद्घटयो पुमान् ।" (मेदिनीकोशं)
["Vaṁśāṅkurē karīrōऽstrī vṛkṣabhidghaṭayō pumān" (Mēdinīkōśaṃ)]

"वंशाङ्कुरे करीरोऽस्त्री तरुभेदे घटे च ना ।" (अमरकोशं)
["Vaṁśāṅkurē karīrōऽstrī tarubhēdē ghaṭē ca nā" (Amarakōśaṃ)]

From the above it is clear that *karīra* in neuter gender means *vaṁsaṅkura (muḷaṁkūṁpu)* and in the male gender it means *vṛkṣabhēda* or *ghaṭa* (pot). From Vāgbhata's statement" "करीरमाध्मानकरं कषायं स्वादुतिक्तकम्"
("Karīramadhmānakaraṃ kaṣāyaṃ svādutiktakaṃ ") as the word *karīra* is of the neuter gender, we learn that its meaning is *muḷaṁkūṁpu*.
Thus it can be concluded that when *karīra* is used in male gender it means *karimuḷḷi* and when used as *karīraṃ* in neuter gender it means *vaṁśāṁkuraṃ* or *vaṁśāgraṃ*

Capsicum annuum

Plate 18

Coll. No. AVS 2447

***Capsicum annuum* Linn.**

Solanaceae : (कण्टकारी–कुलम्)

Eng	:	Chillies, Long chillies, Red chillies
Hin	:	Lālmircā (लालमिर्चा)
Kan	:	Kempumeṇasu (ಕೆಂಪುಮೆಣಸು)
Mal	:	Muḷakụ, Kappaḷmuḷakụ, Paccamuḷakụ, Cuvannamuḷakụ (മുളക്, കപ്പൽമുളക്, പച്ചമുളക്, ചുവന്നമുളക്)
San	:	Kaṭuvīraḥ, Raktamaricaḥ (कटुवीरः, रक्तमरिचः)
Tam	:	Miḷagāi (மிளகாய்)
Tel	:	Mirapakāya (మిరపకాయ)

Distribution: Throughout India, cultivated

The plant: A suffrutescent annual shrub, 0.75–1.8 m in height with many angular branches; leaves simple, of varying shapes, entire, acuminate, usually wrinkled; flowers white or violet, in clusters of two or more; fruits long, cylindric, ovoid, obtuse or oblong, red when ripe with smooth shiny surface; seeds many, yellow, smooth, round, discoid with a spinescent protuberance on the edge.

Parts used: fruits

Properties and uses: The fruits are acrid, bitter, thermogenic, digestive, carminative, laxative, expectorant, sialagogue, stimulant, cardiotonic, antipyretic, antiperiodic, sudorific and rubefacient. They are useful in cephalalgia, gout, arthritis, sciatica, hoarseness, anorexia, dyspepsia, flatulence, cough, cardiac debility, malarial and intermittent fevers, dropsy, cholera, indolent ulcers and vitiated conditions of *kapha*.

"कटुवीरोज्वलस्तीक्ष्णो तीव्रशक्तिर्विदेशजः ।
रक्ताख्यमरिचश्चैव प्रोक्तो दीर्घफलस्तथा ॥" (स्व.)
["Kaṭurvīrōjvalastīkṣṇō tīvṛaśaktiṛvidēśajaḥ
Raktākhyamaricaścaiva pṛōktō dīṛghaphalastathā"(Sva.)]

"कटुवीरोज्जला तीक्ष्णा तीव्रशक्त्यजडे तथा ।" (आ.वि.)
["Kaṭurvīrōjjalā tīkṣṇā tīvṛaśaktyajaḍē tathā" (Ā.vi.)]

"कटुवीरो कटुस्तीक्ष्णो गुरूष्णः कफनाशनः ।
दीपनो रोचनो रुच्यः तृष्णादाहकरस्तथा ॥
रोगिणां नैव पथ्योऽसौ, सेवितस्त्वतियोगतः ।
कुर्यात् स्वस्थनरस्यापि मूत्रकृच्छ्रदिकान् गदान् ॥" (स्व.)
["Kaṭuvīrō kaṭustīkṣṇō gurūṣṇaḥ kaphanāśanaḥ
Dīpanō rōcanō rucyaḥ tṛṣṇādāhakarastathā
Rōgiṇāṃ naiva pathyō∫sau, sēvitastvatiyōgataḥ
Kuryāt svasthanarasyāpi mūtrakṛcchṛādikān gadān" (Sva.)]

"कटुवीराग्निजननी वलासघ्नी च दाहिनी ॥
हन्त्यजीर्णं विषूचीञ्च व्रणं क्लिन्नं सुदारुणम् ।
तन्द्रां मोहं प्रलापञ्च स्वरभेदमरोचकम् ॥
नरं लुप्तधरं क्षीणं सन्निपातनिपीडितम् ।
नष्ठेन्द्रियगणं तीक्ष्णा मृत्योराकृष्य जीवयेत् ॥" (आ.वि.)
["Kaṭuvīrāgnijananī valāsaghnī ca dāhinī
Hantyajīṛṇaṃ viṣūcīñca vṛaṇaṃ klinnaṃ sudāruṇaṃ
Tandrāṃ mōhaṃ pṛalāpañca svarabhēdamarōcakaṃ
Naraṃ luptadharaṃ kṣīṇaṃ sannipātanipīḍitaṃ
Naṣṭēndriyagaṇaṃ tīkṣṇā mṛtyōrākṛṣya jīvayēt" (Ā.vi.)]

"अरोचरेतः कफवातहारिणी
विपाचिनी शोणितिपित्तकारिणी ।
मेदोऽक्षिनिद्रानलमान्द्यकारिणी
विषूचिकां कृन्तति पित्तकारिणी ॥" (सि.भे.म.)
["Arōcarētaḥ kaphavātahāriṇī
vipācinī śōṇitapittakāriṇī
Mēdō∫kṣinidrānalamāndyakāriṇī
viṣūcikāṃ kṛntati pittakāriṇī" (Si.bhē.ma.)]

"പച്ചയായുള്ള മുളക് ഗുരുശ്ളേഷ്മപ്രസേകകൃത്
പാകത്തിങ്കലതിന്നുള്ള രസം മധുരമായ് വരും" (ഗു. പാ.)
["Paccayāyuḷḷa muḷakụ guruśḷēṣmapṛasēkakṛt
Pākattiṅkalatinnuḷḷa rasaṃ madhuramāy varuṃ" (Gu.pā.)]

Remarks: According to the shape, colour and size of fruits, *Capsicum annuum* Linn. is classified into different categories. Besides this, there is another kind of chilli used in Kerala under the names *cīnamuḷakụ, kāntārimuḷakụ* and *sūcimuḷakụ*'. All these belong to the species known as *C. frutescens* Linn.

Coll. No. AVS 1233

Cardiospermum halicacabum Linn.

Sapindaceae : (फेनिल–कुलम्)

Eng	:	Ballon vine, Heart's pea
Hin	:	Kānphuṭī, Kapālphōṭī (कानफुटी, कपालफोटी)
Kan	:	Kanakayya (ಕನಕಯ್ಯ)
Mal	:	Uḷiñña (ഉഴിഞ്ഞ)
San	:	Sakṛalatā, Indravallī (शक्रलता, इन्द्रवल्ली)
Tam	:	Mudukkoṭṭan, Mōdikkoṭṭan (முதுக்கொட்டன், மோதிக்கொட்டன்)
Tel	:	Vekkuḍutīga (వెక్కుడుతీగ)

Distribution: Throughout India,in the plains

The plant: A pubescent or nearly glabrous annual or perennial with slender branches climbing by means of tendrillar hooks; leaves ternately bicompound, leaflets acuminate at the apex; flowers white, small; fruits membranous, depressed, pyriform capsule winged at the angles; seeds black with a large white heart-shaped aril.

Parts used: roots, leaves, seeds

Properties and uses: Thc roots are diuretic, diaphoretic, emetic, mucilaginous, laxative and emmenagogue. They are useful in strangury, fever, arthritis, amenorrhoea, lumbago and neuropathy. But Koman (1919) reports that the roots are ineffective for chronic rheumatism. The leaves are rubefacient and are good for arthritis, otalgia and ophthalmodynia. The seeds are tonic and diaphoretic, and are good for arthritis and fever. The plant has sedative action on the central nervous system.

"इन्द्राह्वैन्द्री चेन्द्रवल्ली कथितेन्द्राणिकेति च ।
इन्द्राभिधानपूर्वन्तु वल्लीनामा च तां वदेत् ॥" (अ.म.)
["Indrāhvaindrī cēndravallī kathitēndrāṇikēti ca
Indrābhidhānapūṛvantu vallīnāmā ca tāṃ vadēt (A.ma.)]

"इन्द्रवल्ली शक्रलता कर्णास्फोता च कारवी ।
पारावताङ्गी शक्राह्वा प्रोक्ता तेजस्विनीति च ॥" (स्व.)
["Indravallī śakṛalatā kaṛṇāsphōtā ca kāravī
Pāravatāngī śakṛahvā pṛōktā tējasvinīti ca" (Sva.)]

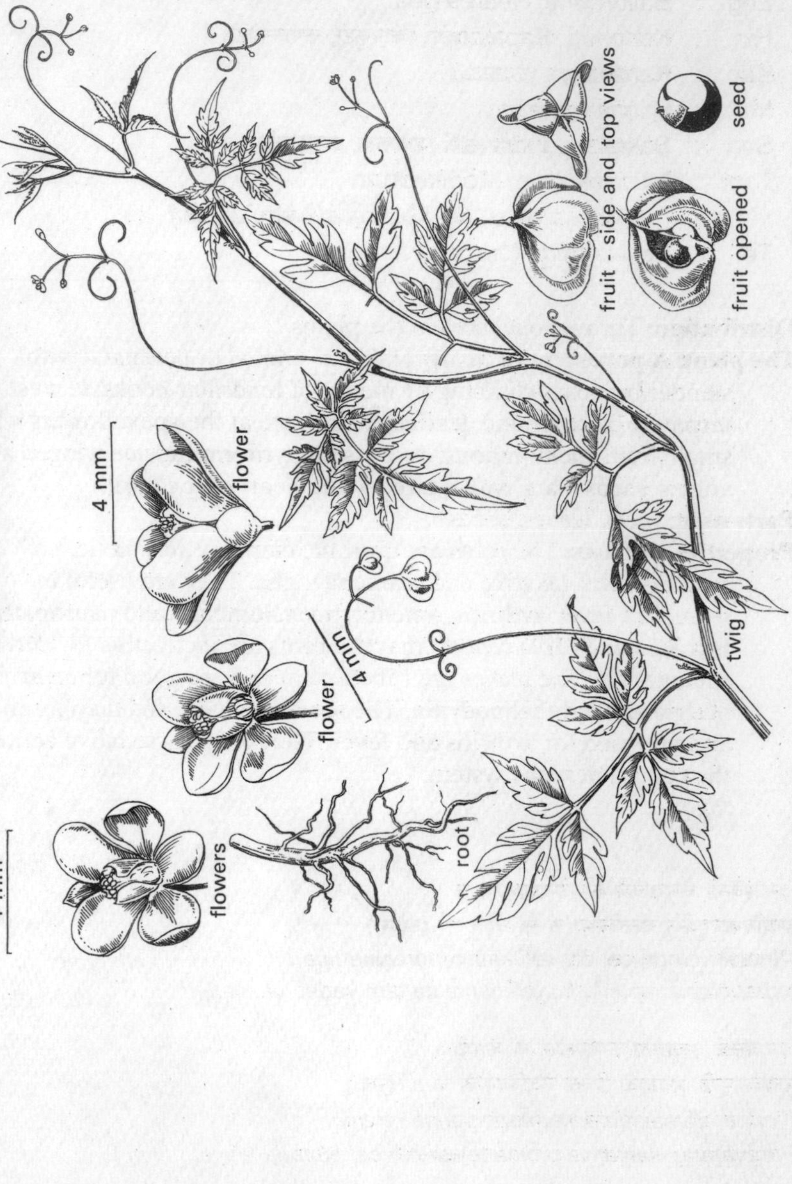

Cardiospermum halicacabum

"इन्द्रवल्ली ज्वरहरा वातघ्नी वृद्धिनाशिनी ।" (हृ.प्रि.)
["Indravallī jvaraharā vātaghnī vṛddhināśinī" (Hṛ.pri.)]

"इन्द्रवल्ली ज्वरहरा शोफपाण्डुहरा स्मृता ।
वातघ्नी मूत्रळा केश्या वृद्धिशूलापहारिणी ॥" (स्व.)
["Indravallī jvaraharā śophapāṇḍuharā smṛtā
Vātaghnī mūtraḷā keśyā vṛddhiśūlāpahāriṇī" (Sva.)]

Coll. No. AVS 2431

Careya arborea Roxb.

Barringtoniaceae : (सुमुद्रफल–कुलम्)

Eng	:	Kumbi
Hin	:	Kuṁbī (कुम्बी)
Kan	:	Daḍḍāla, Guḍḍa, Daḍḍippe (ದಡ್ಡಾಲ, ಗುಡ್ಡ, ದಡ್ಡಿಪ್ಪೆ)
Mal	:	Pēḷu, Ālaṃ, Pēru, Pēḷu (പേഴ്, ആലം, പേര്, പേള്)
San	:	Kuṁbhī, Kaṭabhī (कुम्भी, कटभी)
Tam	:	Kuṁbī, Aimā (கும்பீ, ஐமா)
Tel	:	Duḍippi (దుడిప్పి)

Distribution : Throughout India in deciduous forests and grasslands

The plant: A small to medium sized deciduous tree upto 15m in height with thick dark grey bark having shallow cracks and exfoliating in narrow flakes; leaves simple, alternate, broadly obovate or obovate-oblong, rounded or shortly acuminate, membranous, crowded at the ends of branches, lateral nerves 10–12 pairs; flowers yellowish white, large, showy, foul-smelling, in thick swollen hard terminal spikes, sepals 4, petals 4, stamens many, epigynous; fruits large, globose, green, glabrous, berries, crowned with persistent calyx and style.

Parts used: bark, leaves, flowers, fruits

Properties and uses: The bark is acrid, astringent, bitter, thermogenic, alexeteric, expectorant, anthelmintic, antipyretic and antipruritic, and is useful in tumours, cough, bronchitis, catarrh, dyspepsia, colic, haemorrhoids, intestinal worms, dysentery, urorrhea, leucoderma, epileptic fits and eruptive fevers particularly smallpox. The leaves are useful in ulcers. The flowers are useful in healing vaginal ruptures caused by childbirth. The fruits are acrid, astringent, aromatic and anaphrodisiac, and are useful in dyspepsia and vitiated conditions of *kapha*.

"कटभी नाभिका शौण्डी पाटली किणिही तथा ।
मधुरेणुः क्षुद्रशामा कैटर्या श्यामळा नव ॥" (रा.नि.)
["Kaṭabhī nābhikā śauṇḍī pāṭalī kiṇihī tathā
Madhurēṇuḥ kṣudraśāmā kaiḍaryā śyāmaḷā nava" (Rā.ni.)]

Careya arborea

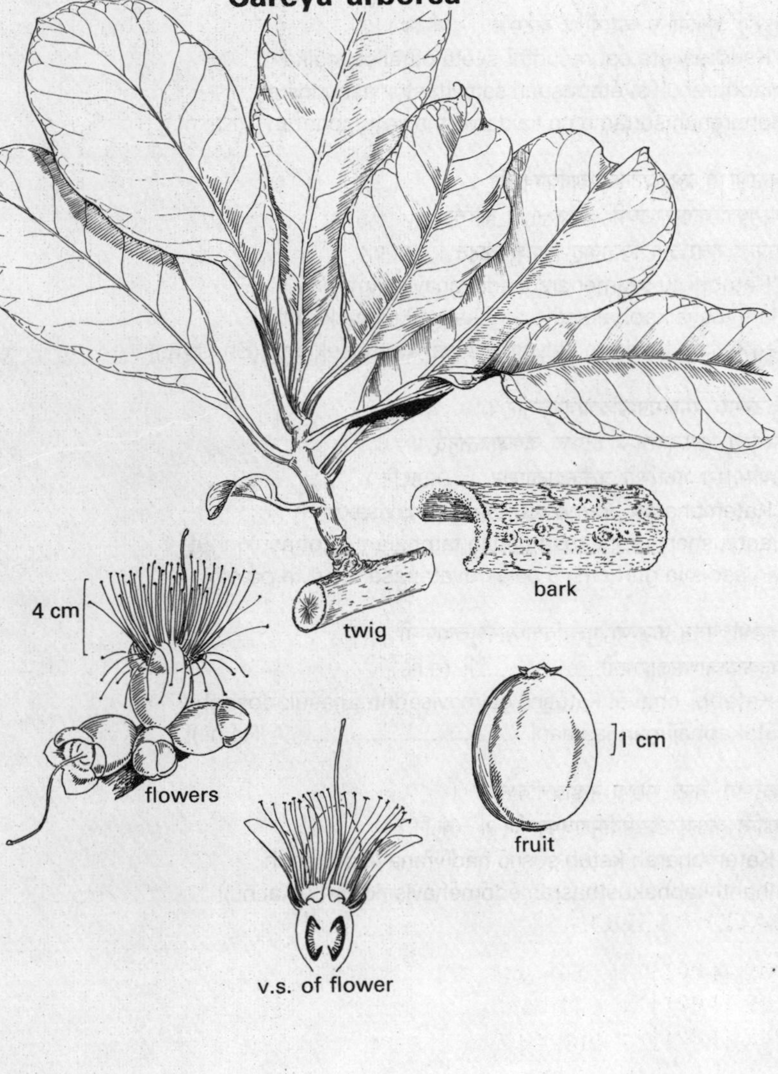

"कटम्भरश्चारुशृङ्गी कटभी तृणशौण्डकः ।" (म.पा.नि.)
[Kaṭaṁbharaśc̣āruśṛṅgī kaṭabhī tṛṇaśauṇḍakaḥ" (Ma.pā.ni.)]

"कटभी स्वादुपुष्पश्च मधुरेणुः कटम्भरः ।" (भा.प्र.)
[Kaṭabhī svādupuṣpaśca madhurēṇuḥ kaṭaṁbharaḥ" (Bhā.pṛa.)]

"क्षुद्रश्वेता चौरशुण्ठी श्वेता पाटलिशौण्डिका ।
मधुरेणुः श्वेतपुष्पः संवीतस्तृष्णशौण्डिकः ॥
बहुरेणुः सुनामा च कैडर्योऽथ कटम्भरः ।" (कै.नि.)
["Kṣudraśvētā cauraśuṇṭhī śvētā pāṭaliśauṇḍikā
Madhurēṇuḥ śvētapuṣpaḥ saṁvītastṛṣṇaśauṇḍikaḥ
Bahurēṇuḥ sunāmā ca kaiḍaryōऽtha kaṭaṁbharaḥ'' (Kai.ni.)]

"कटभी तु प्रमेहार्शोनाडीव्रणविषकृमीन् ।
हन्त्युष्णा कफकुष्ठघ्नीः कटुरूक्षा च कीर्त्तिता ॥
तत्फलं तुवरं ज्ञेयं विशेषात् कफशुक्ळहृत् ।" (भा.प्र.)
["Kaṭabhī tu pṛamēhāṛśōnāḍīvṛaṇaviṣakṛmīn
Hantyuṣṇā kaphakuṣṭhaghnī kaṭurūkṣā ca kīṛttitā
Tatphalaṃ tuvaraṃ jñeyaṃ viśēṣāt kaphaśukḷahṛt (Bhā.pṛa.)]

"कटम्भरः प्रमेहास्रनाडीव्रणविषकृमीन् ।
हन्त्युष्णः कफकुष्ठघ्नः तत्फलं कफशुक्ळनुत् ॥
निर्यासोऽस्य गुरुर्वृष्यो बलकृद्वातनाशनः ।" (म.पा.नि.)
["Kaṭaṁbharaḥ pṛamēhāsṛanāḍīvṛaṇaviṣakṛmīn
Hantyuṣṇah kaphakuṣṭhghnaḥ tatphalaṃ kaphaśukḷanut
Niryāsōऽsya guruṛvṛṣyā balakṛdvatanāśanaḥ (Ma.pā.ni.)]

"कटभी भवेत् कटूष्णा गुल्मविषाध्मानशूलदोषघ्नी ।
वातकफाजीर्णरुजाशमनी....................॥ (रा.नि.)
["Kaṭabhī bhavēt kaṭūṣṇā gulmaviṣādhmānaśūladōṣaghnī
Vātakaphājīṛṇarujāśmanī ...." (Rā.ni.)]

"कटम्भरः कटुः सोष्णो नाडीव्रणविशोधनः ।
निहन्ति कफकुष्ठास्रमेदोमेहविषकृमीन् ॥" (कै.नि.)
["Kaṭaṁbharaḥ kaṭuḥ sōṣṇō nāḍīvṛaṇaviśōdhanaḥ
Nihanti kaphakuṣṭhāsṛamēdōmēhaviṣakṛmīn" (Kai.ni.)]

Coll. No. AVS 2446

Carica papaya Linn.

Caricaceae : (ब्रह्मैरण्ड–कुलम्)

Eng	:	Papaw tree, Papaya
Hin	:	Pappāya, Pappīta (पप्पाय, पप्पीत)
Kan	:	Pappāya, Peragi, Piranji (ಪಪ್ಪಾಯ. ಪೆರಗಿ. ಪಿರಂಜಿ)
Mal	:	Pappāya, Kaṛmmūsu, Pappāḷi, Kaṛmmatti (പപ്പായ, കർമ്മൂസ്, പപ്പാളി, കർമ്മത്തി)
San	:	Brahmairaṇḍaḥ, Ēraṇḍakaṛkaṭī (ब्रह्मैरण्डः, एरण्डकर्कटी)
Tam	:	Pappāḷi, (பப்பாளி)
Tel	:	Bappāyi, Bobbāsi (బప్పాయి. బొబ్బాసి)

Distribution: Throughout India, cultivated

The plant: A small, soft-wooded, fast growing, short lived laticiferous tree upto 8.0m in height with a straight cylindric stem bearing characteristic leaf-scars throughout and with a tuft of leaves at the top; leaves deeply lobed, palm-like with characteristically long, hollow petiole; flowers unisexual, white or yellowish white, rarely bisexual, males in long drooping panicles, females in short clusters; fruits one-chambered, succulent, indehiscent, spherical or cylindrical; seeds many, yellowish brown, ash coloured or black.

Parts used: fruits , latex

Properties and uses: The fruits are bitter, acrid, thermogenic, anodyne, aphrodisiac, stomachic, appetiser, digestive, carminative, anthelmintic, styptic, anti-inflammatory, antifungal, demulcent and diuretic. They are useful in vitiated conditions of *vāta,* cough, bronchitis, stomachalgia, dyspepsia, anorexia, intestinal worms, haemoptysis, haemorrhoids, inflammations, splenomegaly, ringworm, skin diseases, psoriasis, urinary calculus and injures of the urinary tract. The latex is anthelmintic, anodyne, laxative, digestive, emmenagogue, galactagogue, depurative, sudorific, febrifuge and tonic. It is useful in round worm infestation, stomachalgia, dyspepsia, constipation, amenorrhoea, dysmenorrhoea, agalactia, skin diseases, leprosy, haemorrhoids, fever, strangury and general debility.

"एरण्डचिर्भिटो वृक्षः चिर्भिटा नळिकादळः ।
वातकुंभफलः प्रोक्तः स चैव मधुकर्कटी ॥"(शा.नि.)

["Ēraṇḍaciṛbhiṭō vṛkṣaḥ ciṛbhiṭā naḷikādaḷaḥ
Vātakumbhaphalaḥ pṛōktaḥ sa caiva madhukaṛkaṭī " (Śā.ni.)]

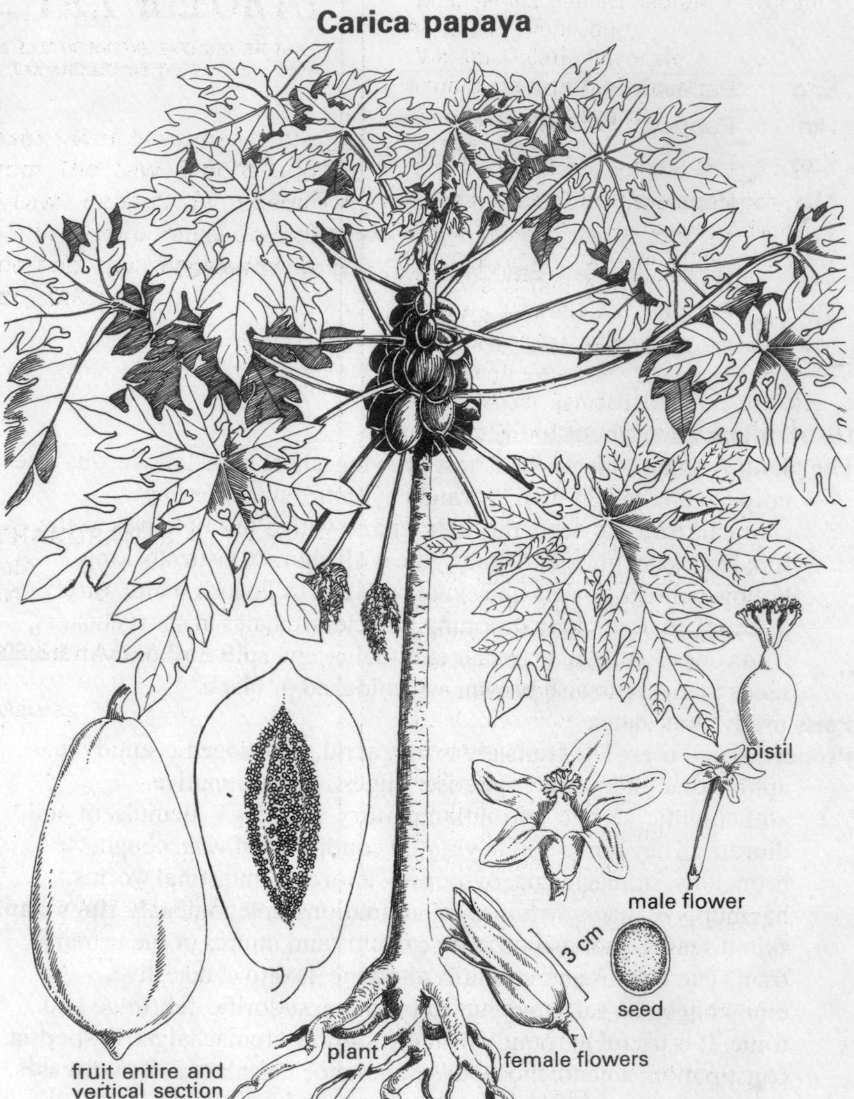
Carica papaya
pistil
male flower
3 cm
seed
plant
female flowers
fruit entire and
vertical section

"ब्रह्मैरण्डतरुः क्षीरी विशालच्छत्रपत्रकः ।
विसारनळिका काण्डः शीघ्रं भूरिफलावृतः ।।(स्व.)
["Brahmairaṇḍataruḥ kṣīrī viśālacchatṛaptṛakaḥ
Visāranaḷikā kāṇḍaḥ śīghṛaṃ bhūriphalāvṛtaḥ" (Sva.)]

"फलं कूश्माण्डवत् हृद्यं बृंहणं कृमिजित्परम् ।
दीपनं श्वासकासघ्नं प्रीतिदं पित्तवर्द्धनम् ॥
क्षीरं बीजं च कृमिहृत्, त्वङ्मूलादिकमस्य तु ।
त्वग्दोषवातरक्तादिरोगेष्वप्युपयुज्यते ॥" (स्व.)
["Phalaṃ kūśmāṇḍavat hṛdyaṃ bṛmhaṇaṃ kṛmijitparaṃ
Dīpnaṃ śvāsakāsaghnaṃ pṛītidaṃ pittavaṛdhanaṃ
Kṣīraṃ bījaṃ ca kṛmihṛt, tvaṅmūlādikamasya tu
Tvagdōṣavātaraktādirōgēṣvapyupayujyatē" (Sva.)]

Coll. No. C.U. (Cali) 11475

Carissa carandas Linn.

Apocynaceae : (कुटज–कुलम्)

Eng	:	Karaunda, Jasmine flowered carrisa
Hin	:	Karauṇṭā, Karōṇṭī (करौण्टा, करोण्टी)
Kan	:	Karikāyi (ಕರಿಕಾಯಿ)
Mal	:	Kḷāvu, Perumkḷāvu, Karaṇṭa (ക്ളാവ്, പെരുംക്ളാവ്, കരണ്ട)
San	:	Karamardaḥ, Avighnaḥ (करमर्दः, आविघ्नः)
Tam	:	Kaḷākkāi, Perumkḷā (களாக்காய், பெரும்களா)
Tel	:	Peddakalavi, Vaka (పెద్దకలివి, వక)

Distribution : Throughout India,in dry forests, also cultivated

The plant : A large dichotomously branched evergreen shrub with short stem and strong thorns in pairs, bark light grey, scaly; leaves simple, opposite, elliptic or obovate, shortly mucronate, glabrous, shining and coriaceous; flowers white, in pubescent terminal corymbose cymes; fruit ellipsoid or globose berry, purplish black when ripe enclosing two or more seeds.

Parts used : roots, fruits

Properties and uses: The roots are anthelmintic, stomachic and antiscorbutic, and are useful in stomach disorders, intestinal worms, scabies and pruritus. The unripe fruit is sour, astringent, bitter, thermogenic, constipating, anaphrodisiac, appetiser and antipyretic, and is useful in vitiated conditions of *pitta* and *kapha,* hyperdipsia, diarrhoea, anorexia, and intermittent fevers. The ripe fruit is sweet, cooling, appetiser and antiscorbutic, and is useful in anorexia, vitiated conditions of *pitta* and *vāta,* burning sensation, skin diseases, scabies and pruritus.

"करमर्दकमाविघ्नं सुषेणं पाणिमर्दकम् ।
कराम्ळं करमर्दं च कृष्णपाककफलं मतम् ॥" (ध.नि.)
["Karamardakamāvighnaṃ suṣeṇaṃ pāṇimardakaṃ
Karāmḷaṃ karamardaṃ ca krṣṇapākaphalaṃ mataṃ" (Dha.ni.)]

करमर्दः सुषेणश्च कराम्ळः करमर्दकः ।
आविघ्नः पाणिमर्दश्च कृष्णपाकफलो मुनिः ॥" (रा.नि.)

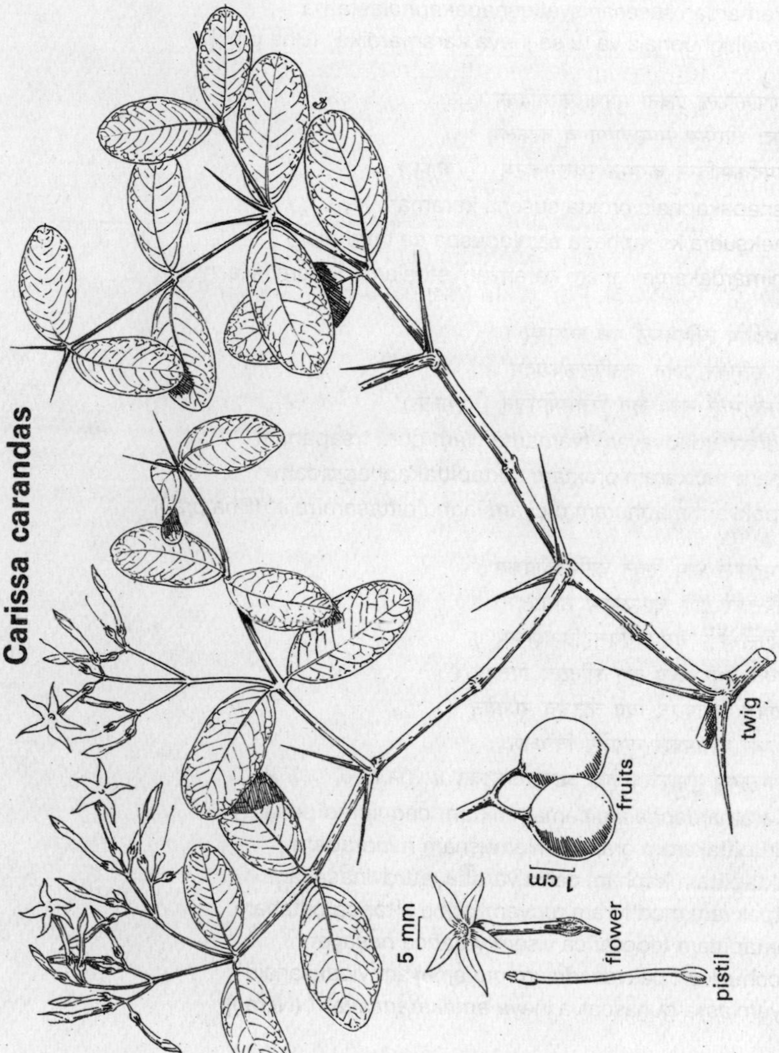

Carissa carandas

[Karamaṛdaḥ susēṇaśca karāmḷaḥ karamaṛdakaḥ
Āvignaḥ pāṇimaṛdaśca kṛṣṇapākaphalō muniḥ" (Rā.ni.)]

"करमर्दः सुषेणः स्यात्कृष्णपाकफलस्तथा ।
तस्माल्लघुफला या तु सा ज्ञेया करमर्दिका ॥" (भा.प्र.)
[Karamaṛdaḥ susēṇaḥ syātkṛṣṇapākaphalastathā
Tasmāllaghuphalā yā tu sā jñēyā karamaṛdikā" (Bhā.pṛa.)]

"कृष्णपाकफला प्रोक्ता सुषेणा करमर्दिका ।
वनेक्षुद्रा क्षीरफेना साम्ळपुष्पा च तत्फलम् ॥
पाणिमर्दकमाविग्नं कराम्ळं स्थलमर्कटम् ।" (कै.नि.)
[Kṛṣṇapākaphalā pṛōktā suṣēṇā karamaṛdikā
Vanēkṣudrā kṣīraphēnā sāmḷapuṣpā ca tatphalaṃ
Pāṇimaṛdakamāvignaṃ karāmḷaṃ sthalamaṛkataṃ" (Kai.ni.)]

"करमर्दद्वयं त्वाममम्ळं गुरु तृषापहम् ।
उष्णं रुचिकरं प्रोक्तं रक्तपित्तकफप्रदम् ॥
तत्पक्वं मधुरं रुच्यं लघु पित्तसमीरजित् ।" (भा.प्र.)
["Karamaṛdadvayaṃ tvāmamamḷaṃ guru tṛṣāpahaṃ
Uṣṇaṃ rucikaraṃ pṛōktaṃ raktapittakaphapṛadaṃ
Tatpakvaṃ madhuraṃ rucyaṃ laghu pittasamīrajit" (Bhā.pṛa.)]

"करमर्दफलं चामं तिक्तं चाग्निप्रदीपकम् ।
गुरुपित्तकरं ग्राहि चाम्ळमुष्णं रुचिप्रदम् ।
रक्तपित्तं कफं चैव वर्धयेत्तृड्विनाशकम् ॥
तत्पक्वं मधुरं रुच्यं लघु शीतञ्च पित्तहम् ।
रक्तपित्तं त्रिदोषञ्च विषं वातञ्च नाशयेत् ॥
तच्छुष्कं पक्वसदृशं गुणाज्ञेयं विचक्षणैः
अत्यम्ळस्य गुणाश्चैव ज्ञेया आमकराम्ळवत् ॥" (नि.र.)
["Karamaṛdaphalaṃ cāmaṃ tiktaṃ cāgnipṛadīpakaṃ
Gurupittakaraṃ grāhi cāmḷamuṣṇaṃ rucipṛadaṃ
Raktapittaṃ kaphaṃ caiva vaṛdhayēttṛḍvināśakaṃ
Tatpakvaṃ madhuraṃ rucyaṃ laghu śītañca pittahaṃ
Raktapittaṃ tṛidōṣañca viṣaṃ vātañca nāśayēt
Tacchuṣkaṃ pakvasadṛśaṃ guṇājñēyaṃ vicakṣaṇaiḥ
Atyamḷasya guṇāścaiva jñēyā āmakarāmḷavat " (Ni.ra.)]

"अम्ळं तृष्णापहं रुच्यं पित्तकृत्करमर्दकम् ।
पक्वं तु मधुरं शीतं रक्तपित्तहरं मतम् ॥" (ध.नि.)
["Amḷaṃ tṛṣṇāpahaṃ rucyaṃ pittakṛtkaramaṛdakaṃ
Pakvaṃ tu madhuraṃ śītaṃ raktapittaharaṃ mataṃ" (Dha.ni.)]

"करमर्दः सतिक्ताम्ळो बालो दीपनदाहकः ।
पक्वस्त्रिदोषशमनोरुचिघ्नो विषनाशनः ॥" (रा.नि.)

["Karamaṛdaḥ satiktāmḷō bālō dīpanadāhakaḥ
Pakvastṛidōsaśamanōʃrucighnō viṣanāśanaḥ" (Rā.ni.)]

"करमर्दं गुरूष्णाम्ळं रुच्यं पित्तकफास्रकृत् ।
तृड्वातजित् सरं पक्वं लघु स्वादु कफास्रजित् ॥
शुष्कं पक्ववदप्यामं पक्वमप्यार्द्रमामवत् ।" (कै.नि.)
["Karamaṛdaṃ gurūṣṇāmḷaṃ rucyaṃ pittakaphāsṛakṛt
Tṛḍvātajit saraṃ pakvaṃ laghu svādu kaphāsṛajit
Śuṣkaṃ pakvavadapyāmaṃ pakvamapyārdramāmavat" (Kai.ni.)]

"करमर्दफलं चार्द्रमम्ळं पित्तकफप्रदम् ।
भेदनं चोष्णवीर्यं च वातप्रशमनं गुरु ॥
पक्वशुष्केऽल्पपित्ते च तन्मूलं कृमिनुत्सरम् ।" (सो.नि.)
["Karamaṛdaphalaṃ cārdramamḷaṃ pittakaphapradaṃ
Bhēdanaṃ cōṣṇavīryaṃ ca vātapṛaśamanaṃ guru
Pakvaśuṣkēʃlpapittē ca tanmūlaṃ kṛminutsaraṃ" (Sō.ni.)]

Remarks : The *karamaṛdikā* described in 'Bhāvapṛakāśaṃ' under *karamaṛdadvayaṃ* (two varieties of *karamaṛda*) is *Carissa spinarum* Linn. and in Malayalam it is known as *ceṛukḷāvu*.

Carthamus tinctorius Linn.

Asteraceae : (भृङ्गराज–कुलम्)

Eng	:	Safflower, Bastard saffron
Hin	:	Kusuṃ, Kusuṃbā (कुसुम, कुसुंबा)
Kan	:	Kusubbi, Kasube (ಕುಸುಬಿ, ಕಸುಬೆ)
Mal	:	Kuyiṃpu̇, Centūrakaṃ (കുയിമ്പ്, ചെന്തൂരകം)
San	:	Kusuṃbaḥ (कुसुम्बः)
Tam	:	Sentūrakaṃ, Kusuṃbā (செந்தூரகம், குஸும்பா)
Tel	:	Agniśikha, Kusumbha (అగ్నిశిఖ, కుసుంభ)

Distribution : Cultivated in almost all the states of India

The plant : An erect branching annual herb 30–60 cm in height; leaves suberect, oblong, sessile, spinosely serrate; flowers yellowish or orange red in large terminal heads; fruits smooth, obovoid, 4-angled achenes.

Parts used : leaves, flowers, seeds

Properties and uses : The leaves are bitter sweet, laxative, appetiser and diuretic, and are useful in urorrhea and ophthalmopathy. The flowers are bitter, liver tonic, diuretic, laxative, expectorant, sedative and emmenagogue. They are useful in strangury, leprosy, inflammations, boils, ring worm, scabies, leucoderma, haemorrhoids and bronchitis. Seeds are bitter, purgative, carminative, aphrodisiac, diuretic and tonic. They are useful in leucoderma, scabies, catarrh, pectoralgia, pharyngodynia, arthritis and constipation.

The seed oil is used as a liniment in arthritis and as a dressing for foul ulcers. The oil is reported to cause pruritus and eye diseases and increases *tridōṣa.*

"कुसुम्भं पावकं पीतमलक्तं वस्त्ररञ्जनम् ।
कौसुंभं स्याद्वह्निशिखं वस्त्ररञ्जकसंज्ञितम् ॥
तद्बीजं कीलता लट्वा शुद्धा पद्मोत्तरा तथा ।" (ध.नि.)
["Kusuṃbhaṃ pāvakaṃ pītamalaktaṃ vastrarañjanaṃ
Kausumbhaṃ syādvahniśikhaṃ vastrarañjakasamjñitaṃ
Tadbījaṃ kīlatā laṭvā śuddhā padmōttarā tathā" (Dha.ni.)]

Carthamus tinctorius

Plate 19

flowering twigs

"कुसुंभबीज़ं वरटा स वै प्रोक्ता वराटिका ।" (भा.प्र.)
["Kusumbhabījaṃ varaṭā sa vai prōktā varāṭikā" (Bhā.pra.)]

"कुसुंभं वातळं रूक्षं रक्तपित्तकफापहम् ॥
कुसुंभतैलमुष्णं च विपाके कटुकं गुरु ।
विदाही च विशेषेण सर्वदोषप्रकोपणम् ॥" (ध.नि.)
["Kusumbhaṃ vātaḷaṃ rūkṣaṃ raktapittakaphāpahaṃ
Kusumbhatailamuṣṇaṃ ca vipākē kaṭukaṃ guru
Vidāhī ca viśēṣēṇa sarvadōṣaprakōpaṇaṃ" (Dha.ni.)]

"वराटा मधुरा स्निग्धा रक्तपित्तकफापहा ।
कषाया शीतळा गुर्वी स्याद्वृष्यानिलापहा ॥
कुसुंभतैलमम्ळं स्यादुष्णं गुरु विदाहि च ।
चक्षुष्यामहितं वृष्यं रक्तपित्तकफप्रदम् ॥" (भा.प्र.)
["Varāṭā madhurā snigdhā raktapittakaphāpahā
Kaṣāyā śītaḷā gurvī syādvṛṣyānilāpahā
Kusumbhatailamamḷaṃ syāduṣṇaṃ guru vidāhi ca
Cakṣuṣyamahitaṃ vṛṣyaṃ raktapittakaphapradaṃ" (Bhā.pra.)]

"कुसुंभो वातळो रूक्षो विदाही कटुकः स्मृतः ।
मूत्रकृच्छ्रं कफं रक्तपित्तञ्चैव विनाशयेत् ॥
कुसुंभपुष्पं सुस्वादुः त्रिदोषघ्नं च भेदकम् ।
रूक्षमुष्णं पित्तळञ्च केशरञ्जनकारकम् ॥
कफनाशकरञ्चैव लघु प्रोक्तं मनीषिभिः ।
कुसुभपत्रं मधुरं नेत्र्यमुष्णं कटु स्मृतम् ॥
अग्निदीप्तिकरञ्चापि रुच्यं रूक्षं गुरु स्मृतम् ।
सरं पित्तकरं चाम्ळं गुदरोगहरं मतम् ॥" (वैद्यकनिघण्डु)
[Kusumbhō vātaḷō rūkṣō vidāhī kaṭukaḥ smṛtaḥ
Mūtrakṛcchraṃ kaphaṃ raktapittaṃ caiva vināśayēt
Kusumbhapuṣpaṃ susvāduḥ tridōṣaghnaṃ ca bhēdakaṃ
Rūkṣamuṣṇaṃ pittaḷaṃ ca kēśarañjanakārakaṃ
Kaphanāśakaraṃ caiva laghu prōktaṃ manīṣibhiḥ
Kusumbhapatraṃ madhuraṃ nētryamuṣṇaṃ kaṭu smṛtaṃ
Agnidīptikaraṃ cāpi rucyaṃ rūkṣaṃ guru smṛtaṃ
Saraṃ pittakaraṃ cāmḷaṃ gudarōgaharaṃ mataṃ" (Vaidyakanighaṇṭu)]

Remarks : The safflowers are at times used as adulterants of saffron. They can be easily distinguished from real saffron by hot water treatment. In hot water the safflower will re-expand and regain its original shape and its corolla can be easily distinguished from the stylar tops of *Crocus sativus.*

APPENDIX A : GLOSSARY OF BOTANICAL TERMS

achene	a small dry one-seeded fruit developed from a superior ovary. Pericarp and testa are free from one another.
acicular	needle shaped
acuminate	tip drawn out into a narrow prolonged termination
acute	tip forming an acute angle, without a special tapering
adhesion	union of dissimilar parts
adnate anther	filament is attached to the back of the anther throughout
adnate stipule	stipules become concrescent during growth with the leafbase or petiole
amplexicaul	lobes clasping the stem
apetalous	when the corolla or inner whorl of perianth is not present
apocarpous	all carpels being free when the gynoecium consists of more than one carpel
aril	major or minor outgrowths of various kinds which develop from any part of the seed, funicle, integuments, chalaza or micropyle
auriculate	ear shaped; two lobes of a sessile leaf partially overlapping the stem
axile placentation	placentae on which the ovules are borne being on the axis in the centre of the ovary
basal	ovules attached to the base of the ovary
basifixed	the connective being less prominent and the filament attached to the base of the anther
berry	a fleshy fruit with usually a massive, soft and juicy pericarp which is differentiated into an outer epicarp and a massive fleshy mesocarp
bicarpellary	with two carpels
bifoliate	with two leaflets
bilabiate	with two projecting lips

bipinnate	rachis is once branched and bears secondary rachis on which the leaflets are borne
bracteate	flower with a bract
bracteolate	flower with bracteoles
bulbils	small axillary bulbs which become fleshy due to storage of food materials
caducous	falling away early
campanulate	bell shaped
capsule	a dry dehiscent fruit formed from a multicarpellary syncarpous gynoecium dehiscing in a variety of ways
caryopsis	an achene in which the fruit wall and seed coat are fused with one another
cauline	leaves arising on the stem
circinate	rolled up spirally like a watch spring from the apex to the base
cirrhose	tendrilled apex
cohesion	union of similar parts
conduplicate	leaves folded lengthwise along the midrib with the upper face within
connate	the lobes of two opposite sessile leaves united at the node
cordate	heart shaped. The base is rounded in forming a notch or sinus where the stalk is attached.
coriaceous	tough and rigid, leathery
corymb	a raceme relatively shorter and broader, the lower flowers bearing longer stalks relatively to the upper ones so that all the flowers reach the same level
cremocarp	a bicarpellary, bilocular capsule derived from an inferior ovary which splits into two indehiscent one-seeded parts or mericarps attached to the common axis, carpophore
crenate	teeth on the leaf margin rounded
crustaceous	hard and brittle

cuneate	wedge shaped, broad above and tapering by straight lines to an acute base
cuspidate	apex ends in a hard spine
cyathium	a special type of cymose inflorescence reduced to look like a single flower
cypsela	an achene that develops from a bicarpellary, inferior uniovulate ovary with the pericarp and testa free from one another
deciduous	lasting only for a single season
decompound	a general name applied to much or irregularly branched or dissected leaves
decurrent	leaf extending to a wing on the stem
decussate	the successive pairs of leaves stand at right angles to one another
dentate	margin with teeth directed outwards, not towards the apex of the blade
diadelphous	stamens united into two bundles
dichlamydeous	with two whorls of perianth or complete
didynamous	an androecium of four stamens in two pairs, a pair of short and a pair of long stamens
dioecious	unisexual flowers. The male and female flowers are present in different plants.
dorsifixed	tip of the filament attached to the back of the anther about the middle of it
drupe	a fleshy fruit having its pericarp differentiated into outer epicarp, middle mesocarp and inner endocarp
ebracteate	flower without a bract
ebracteolate	flower without bracteoles
elliptic	oblong but ends tapering towards both the ends
emarginate	with a terminal notch
epicalyx	a collection of bracteoles on the outside of the calyx

epigynous flower	The receptacle is cup shaped and the ovary of the gynaecium is sunk inside it and the ovary and the receptacle wall become fused. Calyx, corolla and androecium are inserted above the top of the ovary.
epipetalous	concrescent with the corolla
exstipulate	leaves without stipules
fascicle	a clustered form of an inflorescence in which the flowers are short and crowded
fistular	hollow
foliaceous	large green and leaf-like
foliaceous stipules	green and expanded leaf-like stipules that do the function of assimilation
follicle	a dry dehiscent fruit developed from a single carpel (superior ovary) which dehisces from the ventral suture only
free central	In a syncarpous unilocular ovary the ovules are borne on a mound or column in the centre, at the base of the common locule, free from the ovary walls
gamopetalous	petals united
gamosepalous	sepals united
glabrous	surface smooth without any hair
glaucous	covered with bluish waxy gloss
glumes	specialised bracts characteristic of the inflorescence of the grasses and the sedges
gynobasic	arising from the base of the ovary
gynophore	internode between the androecium and the gynaecium
hastate	with the two pointed lobes at the base stretching out horizontally
head (capitulum)	inflorescence with a common receptacle bearing sessile flowers in a dense mass with the youngest to the centre
helicoid	branching regularly to one side only

hesperidium	a fruit that develops from a superior multicarpellary syncarpous ovary. The fruit wall has outer glandular skin or epicarp, a middle fibrous mesocarp and an inner membranous endocarp and has juicy hairs or outgrowths from the placentae.
hispid	covered with rough bristly hair
hypanthodium	inflorescence axis hollowed into a cavity bearing a number of flowers and having a narrow opening at the top
hypogynous flower	calyx, corolla and androecium arranged in sequence below the gynaecium; the ovary is said to be superior.
imparipinnate	with an odd leaflet at the end
interpetiolar stipule	stipules lying between the petioles of opposite or whorled leaves so that they alternate with the latter
intrapetiolar stipule	stipules of the two sides of a leaf unite in the axil of a leaf and become axillary
involucre	a collection or cluster of bracts usually surrounding a condensed inflorescence
lanceolate	lance shaped
legume	a dry dehiscent fruit developed from a monocarpellary superior ovary which dehisces by both the sutures
lianes	large woody climbing or twining plants
ligule	a scale at the upper end of leaf sheath
linear	long and narrow
loculicidal	a capsule where the carpels split down along their dorsal sutures opening into their locules
lomentum	a pod oonstricted between the seeds breaking into one-seeded parts
lyrate	divided with a large terminal lobe
marginal	in single carpels, the ovules are arranged along the length of the margin
monadelphous	stamens form only a single bundle
monocarpellary	containing a single carpel

monochlamydeous:	with one whorl of perianth or incomplete—apetalous, if the corolla is not present
monoecious	flowers unisexual and both male and female flowers present in the same plant
mucronate	abruptly tipped with a small and short point on a nearly straight edge
multicarpellary	containing many carpels
multifoliate or digitate	with several leaflets
nut	a large dry indehiscent achene having woody hard pericarp
obcordate	heart shaped at the top
oblong	nearly elliptical, with sides more or less parallel, ends blunted, 2-4 times as long as broad
obovate	inversely ovate
obtuse	blunt tip ending in a blunt or roundish extremity forming an obtuse angle
offset	a stout and short runner-like branch which bends at the tip and gives rise to rosette of leaves above and roots below
orbicular	circular or round in outline
ovate	egg shaped; broad at the base and narrow at the tip
panicle	a compound raceme or any repeatedly branching inflorescence
papilionaceous	corolla consisting of vexillum (two laterals), alae (wings, two partially fused structures) and keel or carnia
pappus	reduced to bristles or hairs
parallel venation	veins and veinlets parallel
paripinnate	with an even number of leaflets
pendulous anther	filament flexible and hanging, carrying the anther at the top of it
pentacarpellary	containing five carpels

pepo	a baccate fruit developed from a tricarpellary syncarpous inferior ovary with parietal placentation. The epicarp is hard and the mesocarp fleshy.
parietal	ovules are borne on the inner walls of the ovary in unilocular syncarpous gynoecia
perfoliate	lobes of the sessile leaf fused together round the stem
perigynous flower	receptacle concave or cup shaped, gynoecium situated at the bottom of the cup, calyx, corolla and androecium arise from the rim of the cup of the receptacle
perisperm	persisting nucellus.
petaloid	brightly coloured and serves to attract insects
pilose	with soft scattered hair
pistillate	only gynoecium is present
polypetalous	petals free
polysepalous	sepals free
pome	a fleshy false fruit developed from a multicarpellary syncarpous inferior ovary in which the receptacle also develops along with the ovary to form fleshy edible part
pubescent	covered with fine, soft hair
pulvinate	swollen or cushion shaped
quadrifoliate	with four leaflets
radical	leaves all crowded together and springing from the level of the ground
raceme	a racemose inflorescence in which the main axis is unbranched and indefinite in growth, bearing pedicellate flowers
regular (actino-morphic)	a flower in which the members in each whorl are similar to one another, and can be divided in any plane into two equal halves
reniform	kidney shaped
repand	when the margin is wavy, slightly bending inward and outward

reticulate venation	ultimate branches of veins, forming a fine mesh or network
retuse	broad tip and slightly notched
rugose	ridged or wrinkled
sagittate	arrow-shaped where the ear-like parts are acute and turned downwards towards the stem, while the main body of the blade tapers upwards to a point
samara	a large winged achene
scabrous	surface rough
scarious	thin, dry, not green, stiff
scorpioid	branching alternately to either side
septicidal	a capsule that splits along the septa
septifragal	a capsule may split either in a loculicidal or septicidal manner but the septa break from the outer walls of the carpels and remain attached to the central axis with the seeds left in the centre of the fruit
serrate	small and sharp teeth directed forward like the teeth of a saw, pointing to the tip of the blade
serrulate	diminutive of serrate, and is equivalent to minutely serrate
sheathing	leaf base forming a sheath round the stem
siliqua	a dry dehiscent fruit developed from a bicarpellary syncarpous superior ovary divided vertically into two loculi by a false septum
simple pinnate	a once pinnate compound leaf possessing only a single unbranched rachis on which the leaflets are borne
sorosis	a multiple fruit that develops from a spicate inflorescence
spadix	a fleshy spike usually enclosed by a spathe
spathe	a large bract usually coloured and enclosing an inflorescence
spathulate	spoon shaped
spike	a raceme with sessile flowers

stipel	a stipule of a leaflet
stipulate	leaves with stipules
stolon	a prostrate or reclined branch which strikes root at its tip where it touches the ground and then develops an ascending growth
succulent	fleshy or spongy
sucker	a short branch which arises commonly from a subterranean stem from the axil of a scale leaf
superficial	ovary multilocular and placentae spread over the surface of the partition walls bearing the ovules
syncarpous	carpels united with one another
tomentose	covered with cottony felt
tricarpellary	containing three carpels
trifoliate	with three leaflets
tripinnate	secondary rachis of a pinnate compound leaf bearing tertiary rachii on which the leaflets are borne
truncate	tip as if cut off by a straight transverse line
umbel	a racemose inflorescence in which there is an extreme reduction of the inflorescence axis
unifoliate	a palmate compound leaf with a single leaflet joined to the petiole
variegated	multicoloured
versatile	top of the filament delicate and the anther free to swing in all directions
verticillaster	a special type of cymose inflorescence condensed and occurring in the axils of a pair of opposite leaves forming a false whorl at the node
whorled	more than two leaves arise at a node
zygomorphic	an irregular flower in which the members are so dissimilar to one another that the flower can be divided only into two equal halves in one plane only

APPENDIX B : GLOSSARY OF MEDICAL TERMS

abortifacient:	an agent that induces abortion
abscess	a localised collection of pus caused by suppuration in a tissue
absorbent	any agent which attracts and sucks up gases or secretions from a wound
acne	a term denoting an inflammatory disease occurring in or around the sebaceous glands
acrid	biting, pungent
agalactia	absence or failure of secretion of milk
ague	malaria
albuminuria	the presence of serum albumin and serum globulin in the urine
alexipharmic	antidote to poison
alexiteric	protective to infectious diseases
alopecia	loss of hair - a malady in which the hair falls from one or more circumscribed round or oval areas, leaving the skin smooth and white
alterative	causing a favourable change in the disordered functions of the body or metabolism
amenorrhoea	failure of menstruation
amentia	an arrest of the development of the mind from birth to early age
anaemia	lack of enough blood causing paleness
analgesic	an anodyne
anaphrodisiac	having the power to lessen or inhibit sexual feeling
anasarca	diffused dropsy in the skin and subcutaneous tissue
anodyne	a medicine that allays pain
anorexia	a condition of having lost the appetite for food
anthelmintic	destroying or expelling worms

antidote	an agent which neutralises or opposes the action of a poison
antiemetic	an agent that relieves vomiting
antilithic	an agent which prevents the formation of calculi or promotes their dilution
antiperiodic	preventing the regular recurrence of a disease
antiphlogistic	acting against heat or inflammation
antipruritic	preventing or relieving itching
antipyretic	counteracting fever
antiscorbutic	acting against scurvy
antiseptic	a chemical sterilising substance to kill or control pathogenic microbes
antispasmodic	opposing spasms or convulsions
anuria	complete cessation of the secretion and excretion of urine
aperient	a laxative or mild cathartic
aphrodisiac	a drug which stimulates sexual desire
aphthae	ulcer on the surface of a mucous membrane
apoplexy	a sudden loss of consciousness
arthralgia	pain in a joint
arthritis	inflammation of a joint
ascites	abnormal accumulation of fluid in the peritoneal cavity
asphyxia	inability to breathe
atrophy	wasting of a tissue or organ
balanitis	a condition of inflammation of the glans penis or of the glans of clitoris
bechic	anything which relieves or cures cough
beriberi	a deficiency disease caused by imbalance of carbohydrate and vitamin B

blennorrhagia	free discharge of mucus
bronchopathy	any disease of the bronchi
bubo	an inflammatory swelling of a lymph gland
cachexia	depressed habit of mind
calculus	a concretion formed in any part of the body usually compounds of salts of organic or inorganic acids
calefacient	a remedy which gives rise to a sensation of warmth
calmative	sedative
carbuncle	an infection of the skin and subcutaneous tissue by *Staphylococcus aureus*
carcinoma	a malignant epithelial tumour eventually becoming fatal
cardiodynia	pain in the region of the heart
cardiopalmus	palpitation of the heart
cardiopathy	a morbid condition of the heart
carminative	drug curing flatulence
cataplexy	a condition marked by abrupt attacks of muscular weakness
cataract	opacity in the crystalline lens of the eye which may be partial or complete
catarrh	inflammation of a mucous membrane, usually associated with an increase in the amount of normal secretion of mucus
cathartic	having the power of cleansing the bowels - purgative
cephalalgia	headache
cephalic	a remedy for disorders of the head
cephalopathy	any disease of the head
cerebropathy	any disorder of the brain
cholagogue	a drug which causes increased flow of bile into the intestine

cholera	a severe infectious epidemic disease due to *Vibrio cholerae*
cirrhosis	a general term meaning progressive fibrous tissue overgrowth in an organ
colic	a severe spasmodic griping pain
colitis	inflammation of the colon
collyrium	an eye-salve or eye-wash
colonalgia	pain in the colon
colonitis	inflammation of the colon
colonorrhagia	haemorrhage from the colon
colonorrhea	a mucous discharge from the colon
colpitis	inflammation of the vagina
colpoptosis	prolapse of the vagina
colporrhagia	haemorrhage from the vagina
coma	the state of complete loss of consciousness
conjunctivitis	inflammation of the conjunctiva
consumption	pulmonary tuberculosis
contraceptive	any agent or device used to prevent conception
convulsion	a violent involuntary contraction of the skeletal musculature
corn	a small circumscribed painful horny growth
coxalgia	pain in the hip
coxitis	inflammation of the hip joint
croup	any condition caused by respiratory obstruction
cystalgia	pain in the urinary bladder
cystitis	inflammation of a bladder, especially the urinary bladder
cystodynia	cystalgia
cystorrhea	mucous discharge from the bladder

dandruff	dead scarf-skin separating in small scales and entangled in the hair
demulcent	soothing
dental caries	decay of teeth
dentalgia	toothache
dentifrice	any liquid, paste or powder used for cleansing the teeth
deobstruent	relieving or removing obstruction
deodorant	removing the odour
depurative	an agent that purifies blood
dermatopathy	any skin disorder
dermatophytosis	a superficial infection of the skin caused by a fungus
desiccating	depriving of moisture
diaphoresis	sweating
diaphoretic	a drug which induces perspiration
diphtheria	a specific infectious disease caused by virulent strains of a bacillus
disinfectant	having a lethal effect upon germs
diuretic	promoting the flow of urine
dizziness	any sensation of imbalance of a stable relationship with the immediate environment
dropsy	an excessive accumulation of clear or watery fluid in any of the tissues or cavities of the body
dysmenorrhoea	difficult or painful menstruation
dysopia	defective vision
dyspnoea	difficulty in breathing
dyspepsia	indigestion
dysphonia	difficulty or pain in speaking
dystocia	difficult parturition

dysuria	difficulty or pain while passing urine
eclampsia	an attack of convulsion associated with hypertension in pregnancy
eczema	a noncontagious inflammatory disease of the skin with much itching and burning
elephantiasis	gross lymphatic oedema of the limbs leading to hypertrophy
elixir	a drug capable of prolonging life indefinitely
embrocate	to moisten and rub
emetic	causing vomiting
emmenagogue	medicine intended to restore the menses
emollient	softening
emphysema	inflation, swelling
empyema	accumulation of pus in a body cavity
encephalitis	inflammation of the brain and spinal cord due to infection
encephalopathy	any degenerative brain disease
enuresis	involuntary voiding of urine
epilepsy	an affection of the nervous system resulting from excessive or disordered discharge of cerebral neurons
epistaxis	bleeding from the nose
errhine	an agent causing increased nasal discharge
erysipelas	an inflammatory disease generally affecting the face marked by a bright redness of the skin
expectorant	aiding the secretion of the mucous membrane of the air passages and the removal of fluid by spitting
febrifuge	anything which reduces fever
filariasis	infection with filarial nematode worms
fistula in ano	an open channel from the anus or rectum to the skin near the anus
flatulence	presence of excessive gas in the stomach or intestine

frenzy	violent temporary mental derangement
galactagogue	medicine that promotes secretion of milk
galactorrhea	excessive or spontaneous flow of milk
gangrene	necrosis and putrefaction of tissue due to lack of blood supply
gastralgia	pain in the stomach
gastrodynia	gastralgia
gastroenteritis	inflammation of the mucous coat of the stomach and intestine due to bacterial infection
gastrohelcosis	ulceration of the stomach
gastromegaly	enlargement of the stomach
gastropathy	any disease of the stomach
germicidal	causing destruction of micro-organisms
gingivitis	inflammation of the gingival margins around the teeth accompanied by swelling and bleeding
glaucoma	a term signifying increased intraocular pressure and its consequences
gleet	chronic discharge of thin mucus from the vagina
glycosuria	excretion of sugar in the urine
goitre	enlargement of the thyroid gland
gonorrhoea	an inflammatory disease of the genitourinary passages characterised by pain and discharge
gout	a disease of purine metabolism characterised by attacks of arthritis with an associated raised level of serum uric acid
gripe	a sharp pain in the stomach
haematemesis	vomiting of blood
haematuria	the presence of blood in the urine
haemoptysis	spitting of blood
haemorrhoid	a bleeding pile

haemostatic	styptic
halitosis	offensive odour of the breath
helminthiasis	morbid state due to infestation with worms
hematorrhea	copious haemorrhage
hemicrania	headache confined to one side
hemiplegia	paralysis of one side of the body
hepatitis (viral)	inflammation of the liver; jaundice
hepatodynia	pain in the liver
hepatomegaly	enlargement of the liver
hepatopathy	any disease of the liver
hepatosis	downward displacement of the liver
hepatalgia	pain in the liver
hernia	the protrusion of an internal organ through a defect in the wall of the anatomical cavity in which it lies
herpes	inflammation of the skin or mucous membrane with clusters of deep seated vesicles
hydragogue	promoting expulsion of water or serum
hydrocele	a circumscribed collection of fluid in the tunica vaginalis testis
hydrophobia	exaggerated fear of water as in rabies
hyperadenosis	proliferation of glandular tissue
hyperdipsia	intense thirst of relatively brief duration
hyperdiuresis	excessive secretion of urine
hyperemesis	excessive vomiting
hyperhidrosis	excessive perspiration
hyperorexia	excessive appetite
hyperpraxia	abnormal activity; restlessness

hypertension	high arterial blood pressure
hyperthermia	a very high body temperature
hypochondriasis	a state of mind in which the sufferer is much preoccupied with his health
hypotension	a fall in blood pressure below the normal level
hypothermia	greatly decreased temperature
hysteria	a neurotic disorder with varying symptoms
impetigo	an inflammation of the skin associated with discrete vesicles due to streptococcal infection
impotence	inability to perform the sexual act due to failure of the reflex mechanism
insecticide	any agent which kills or destroys insects
insanity	mental disease of a grave kind
insomnia	the condition of being unable to sleep
intoxication	general condition which results following the absorption and diffusion in the body of a soluble poison
lactifuge	retarding or causing cessation of the secretion of milk
laryngitis	inflammation of the larynx
laxative	having the action of loosening the bowel
lentigo	a brownish or yellowish spot found on the skin, most often on the hands, arms or face often caused by exposure to sunlight
leucoderma	any white area on the skin
leucorrhoea	an abnormal mucous discharge from the vagina
leukaemia	blood cancer
lithiasis	the formation of calculus of any kind
linthontriptic	an agent that effects the dissolution of a calculus
lumbago	pain in mid or lower back
malignant	threatening life or tending to cause death

mammillitis	inflammation of the nipple
maturate	to bring to maturity
melalgia	pain in the limbs
melancholia	a mental illness in which the predominant symptom is melancholy, depression of spirits, unhappiness and misery
menolipsis	temporary cessation of menstruation
menorrhagia	excesive or prolonged menstruation
menostasis	amenorrhoea
metropathy	any uterine disease
metroptosis	prolapse of the uterus
metrorrhagia	uterine bleeding, usually of normal amount occurring at completely irregular intervals, the period of flow sometimes being prolonged
metrorrhea	abnormal uterine discharge
micturition	the act of passing urine
migraine	a periodic condition with localised headaches, frequently associated with vomiting and sensory disturbances
morbid	belonging or relating to disease
mumps	epidemic parotitis, an acute infectious disease caused by a virus
myalgia	muscular pain
mydriasis	dilatation of the pupil
mydriatic	a drug that dilates the pupil
myringitis	inflammation of the tympanic membrane
narcotic	a drug that induces sleep
nasitis	inflammation of the nose
nauseant	an agent that causes nausea
nephralgia	pain in the kidney

nephritis	inflammation of the kidneys
nephrolithiasis	presence of renal calculi
nephropathy	disease of the kidneys
neuralgia	a painful affection of the nerves due to functional disturbances or neuritis
neurasthenia	nervous debility
notalgia	pain in the back
nyctalopia	night blindness
obesity	an excessive accumulation of fat in the body
odontalgia	toothache
odontopathy	any disease of the teeth
oleaginous	oily, greasy
opacity	an opaque or non-transparent area
ophthalmia	a term usually applied to conjunctivitis
opthalmitis	inflammation of the eye ball
cphthalmodynia	pain in the eye
ophthalmopathy	any disease of the eye
orchialgia	pain in the testis
orchiopathy	any disorder of the testis
orchitis	inflammation of the testis characterised by hypertrophy and pain
ostalgia	pain in the bones
osteomalacia	softening of the bones, resulting from vitamin D deficiency
otalgia	pain in the ear
otopathy	any disease of the ear
otopyorrhea	purulent discharge from the ear
pancreatitis	inflammation of the pancreas

paraplegia	stroke affecting one side
parkinsonism	Parkinson's disease - a disease characterised by rigidity of muscles and tremor of the hands
pectoral	effective in diseases of the chest
pectoralgia	pain in the chest
pertussis	whooping cough
pharyngitis	inflammation of the mucous membrane and underlying part of the pharynx
pharyngodynia	pain in the pharynx
pharyngopathy	any disease of the pharynx
phthisis	any wasting disease in which the whole body or part of the body is involved
pneumonia	a general disease in which the essential lesion is an inflammation of the spongy tissue of the lung with consolidation of the alveolar exudate
pneumonitis	inflammation of lung tissue
pneumonopathy	any disease of the lungs
pneumonosis	any lung disorder
pneumorrhagia	a severe haemoptysis
poliomyelitis	an acute inflammation of the anterior horn cells of the spinal cord due to an enterovirus infection
poultice	a soft mush prepared by various substances with oily or watery fluids
procreant	the drug which begets
proctalgia	pain in the rectum
proctitis	inflammation of the rectum
proctoptosis	prolapse of the rectum
prophylactic	pertaining to the prevention of the development of a disease
prurigo	an eruption of the skin causing severe itching

pruritus	itching
psoriasis	a condition characterised by the eruption of circumscribed discrete and confluent reddish, silvery scaled lesions
psoriasis plantaris	psoriasis of the sole
psychopathy	any disease of the mind
ptyalism	excessive secretion of saliva
pyrexia	a condition characterised by the presence of pus
pyorrhoea	a discharge of pus
rachialgia	pain in the vertebral column
radiculalgia	neuralgia of the nerve roots
radiculitis	inflammation of spinal nerve roots
ramitis	inflammation of a nerve root
rectalgia	proctalgia
rectitis	proctitis
refrigerant	cooling
renal calculi	calculi relating to kidney
renopathy	any disease of the kidney
resolvent	causing resolution of a tumour or swelling
restorative	having the power to restore or renew health
resuscitative	the act of restoring to life
retinitis	inflammation of the retina
revulsive	causing revulsion in drawing away of blood from a pathological area to another area
rheumarthritis	rheumatoid arthritis
rheumatalgia	rheumatic pain
rhinalgia	pain in the nose
rhinitis	inflammation of the nasal mucous membrane

rhinodynia	pain in the nose
rhinopathy	any disease of the nose
rhinorrhagia	copious haemorrhage from the nose
rickets	a disturbance of the calcium/phosphorus metabolism which occurs in the growing child as a result of vitamin D deficiency
roborant	a strengthening agent
sarcocele	fleshy swelling or tumour of the testis
scabies	sarcoptic infestation of the human skin particularly a contagious skin disease caused by invasion of the epidermis
scald	the lesion caused by contact with a hot liquid or vapour
scalding of urine	severe burning sensation during micturition
scleritis	inflammation of the sclera
scrofula	tuberculous cervical adenitis with or without ulceration
scurvy	a deficiency disease due to lack of Vitamin C
sialogogue	an agent that increases the flow of saliva
sinovitis	inflammation of the synovial membrane of a joint
sinusitis	inflammation affecting the mural epithelium of a sinus
somatalgia	body pain
somnifacient	causing sleep
somnolence	sleepiness
soporific	inducing sleep
spanomenorrhea	scanty menstruation
splenalgia	pain in the spleen
splenitis	inflammation of the spleen
splenohepato-megaly	enlargement of spleen and liver

splenomegaly	enlargement of the spleen
splenopathy	any disease of the spleen
stomachalgia	pain in the stomach
stomatalgia	pain in the mouth
stomatitis	generalised inflammation of the oral mucosa
stomatopathy	any disorder of the mouth
stomatorrhagia	haemorrhage from the mouth
styptic	having the power to arrest bleeding
suppurative	pus forming
syphilis	a contagious venereal disease
tetanus	an infective disease due to the toxins of *Clostridium tetani*
thermoplegia	sun stroke
tonsilitis	inflammation of the tonsil
toxaemia	the condition of general poisoning caused by the entrance of soluble bacterial toxins into the blood
trauma	a pathological alteration of the supporting tissues of a tooth due to abnormal occlusion
trichogenous	stimulating the growth of hair
ulemorrhagia	bleeding from the gums
ulitis	inflammation of the gums
ulocace	ulceration of the gums
ulorrhagia	free haemorrhage from the gums
ulorrhea	bleeding from the gums
urelcosis	ulceration of the urinary tract
ureteralgia	pain in the ureter
ureteritis	inflammation of the ureter
urethritis	inflammation of the urethra

urethrorrhagia	flow of blood from the urethra
urethrorrhea	abnormal discharge from the urethra
urocyst	the urinary bladder
urocystitis	inflammation of the urinary bladder
urodynia	pain on urination
uro-oedema	oedema due to infiltration of urine
urolithiasis	urinary calculi
uropathy	any disease of the urinary tract
urorrhagia	excessive secretion of urine
urorrhea	involuntary flow of urine
uroschesis	retention of urine
urticaria	nettle rash
uteralgia	pain in the uterus
uteritis	inflammation of the uterus
vaginitis	inflammation of the vagina
vaginodynia	pain in the vagina
vaginopathy	any disease of the vagina
vermifuge	a drug that expels worms
verminosis	helminthiasis
vertigo	dizziness
vesical	referring to the urinary bladder
visceromegaly	abnormal enlargement of the viscera
wart	a circumscribed cutaneous excrescence

INDEX TO SANSKRIT TERMS

Ābhīru 218
Āḍhakī 326
Ādityabhaktā 239
Agragrāhī 140
Aguruḥ 171
Aindrī 239
Ākārakarabhaḥ 140
Alarkaḥ 345
Anādanā 115
Anaṁnāsaṁ 146
Aṅkōḍaḥ 77
Aṅkōlaḥ 77
Apāmārgaḥ 39
Arimēdaḥ 23
Arkaḥ 341
Asiśiṁbī 352
Aśmabhēdā 69
Ativiṣā 42
Āvighnaḥ 386

Bahulavalkalaḥ 268
Bahunētraphalaṁ 146
Bālavilvaṁ 66
Barburaḥ 26
Bastāntrī 191
Bhadrā 67
Bhadrailā 128
Bhaṇḍī 81
Bhaṅgā 356
Bhēṇḍā 1
Bhūcanakaḥ 176
Bhūchatrā 70
Bhūniṁbaḥ 149
Bhūriphēnaḥ 35
Bhūrjaḥ 268
Bhūśirīṣaḥ 85
Brahmadantī 187
Brahmairaṇḍaḥ 383

Brāhmī 235
Bṛhaddantī 243
Bṛhatkuraṇḍikā 127

Cāhā 349
Carmakaṣā 35
Carmasāhvā 33
Chagaḷāntṛī 194
Chatrakaḥ 70
Chāyātiniśaḥ 366

Damanaḥ 202
Damanakaḥ 202
Dantī 240
Dhavaḥ 163

Ēlāparṇī 109
Ēraṇḍakarkaṭī 383

Gandhanākulī 110
Gāṅgērukī 366
Garalaphalā 143
Garaḷikā 199
Ghṛtakuṁārī 103
Guñjā 10

Haimavatī 54,189
Haritamañjarī 36

Indravallī 377
Īśvarī 199

Jhullapuṣpaḥ 271

Kadaraḥ 30
Kākamārī 143
Kāḷamēghā 152
Kāñcanākṣīrī 189
Kāñcanāraḥ 256
Kaṇṭakīkarañjaḥ 320
Karamardaḥ 386

Karamardikā 389
Karīraḥ 368
Karmaraṅgaḥ 224
Kārukaḥ 224
Kaṭabhī 380
Kaṭuvīraḥ 375
Kēṁbukaḥ 306
Kēmukaḥ 306
Khadiraḥ 19
Khadirasāraḥ 22
Kirātatiktā 149
Kīṭamārī 196
Kōvidāraḥ 256
Kṛṣṇabōḷaḥ 105
Kṛṣṇāguruḥ 171
Kṛṣṇajīrakā 348
Kṛṣṇasarṣapaḥ 305
Kṣudrapanasaḥ 207
Kubērākṣī 320
Kucandanaḥ 58
Kukkuradruḥ 278
Kukundaraḥ 278
Kulañjanaḥ 109
Kumārī 103
Kumārīsāraḥ 105
Kuṁbhī 380
Kunduruṣkaḥ 297
Kuraṇḍikā 125
Kūśmāṇḍaḥ 261
Kusuṁbhaḥ 390

Laghubrāhmī 239
Laghudantī 243
Lakucaḥ 215
Laśunaḥ 93
Latākarañjaḥ 320
Latākastūrikā 4
Laṭvā 264

Mahādrōṇaḥ 157
Mahāśatāvarī 223
Mahāśiṁbī 352
Maṇḍapī 176
Maṇḍūkaparṇī 239
Maṇḍūkī 239
Matsyākṣī 118
Mayūraśikha 55
Mōcā 289
Mōcarasaḥ 292

Nākulī 110
Nēpāḷaniṁbaḥ 152
Nikuṁbhaḥ 243
Nikuñjikā 17
Niṁbaḥ 227

Pālakyā 265
Palāṇḍuḥ 88
Palāśaḥ 314
Panasaḥ 208
Pataṅgaḥ 323
Patrāṅgaḥ 323
Pattarañjakaḥ 323
Pattūraḥ 118
Phalinī 334
Pītakāñcanāraḥ 260
Prabhadraḥ 227
Priyāḷaḥ 309
Priyaṅgu 334
Pūgaḥ 180
Punarṇavā 281
Punnāgaḥ 338

Rājārkaḥ 345
Rājikā 301
Raktakōvidāraḥ 260
Raktamaricaḥ 375
Raktapuṣpakōvidāraḥ 260
Raktārkaḥ 345
Raktasarṣapaḥ 305
Rāsnā 106
Rasōnaḥ 93
Rōhītakaḥ 167

Ś akralatā 377
Sallakī 297
Śālmalī 289
Samudraphalaḥ 250
Śaṅkhapuṣpī 361
Śaṅkhinī 361
Saptacchadaḥ 111
Saptalā 33
Saptaparṇaḥ 111
Sarasvatī 235
Sarṣapaḥ 301
Sātalā 35
Śatapuṣpā 153
Śatāvarī 218
Sindūrī 274
Śirīṣaḥ 81
Sītāphalaṃ 160
Sitasarṣapaḥ 305
Śīvadrumaḥ 62
Sōmavalkaḥ 30
Śōphaghnī 281
Śrīphalaḥ 62
Sthūlailā 128
Sugandhamūlā 106
Sūraṇaḥ 132
Suṣavī 346
Svarṇakṣīrī 187
Śvētāguru 175
Śvētakāñcanāraḥ 260
Śvētapunarṇavā 285
Śvētārkaḥ 345
Śvētavacā 54
Śyāmaparṇī 349

Tāladrumaḥ 293
Tālaḥ 293
Tālāṇgulī 296
Tālīsaṃ 7
Tālīsapatraṃ 7
Tāmrakaḥ 58
Taṇḍulīyaḥ 121
Tōyavallī 348
Triputaḥ 99
Tuvarī 326

Ugragandhā 51
Upōdikā 253

Vacā 51
Vaikuṇṭhaḥ 157
Vaṁśaḥ 244
Vaṁśāṅguraṃ 372
Vaṁśarōcanā 248
Vaṁśayavaṃ 248
Vánasūraṇaḥ 136
Vatsanābhaḥ 47
Vāvarī 26
Vēnāṁraḥ 137
Vēṇuḥ 244
Vētraḥ 330
Vilvaḥ 62
Vilvakarkaṭī 66
Vilvamajjā 66
Vilvapēśikā 66
Vilvaśalāṭu 66
Vimalā 35
Viparītalajjālu 271
Viṣaghnī 115
Viṣamuṣṭiḥ 74
Vṛddhadārukaḥ 191
Vṛkkabījaḥ 137
Vṛkkaphalaḥ 137